THE
CHEMISTRY
OF
LIVING
CELLS

Second Edition

THE
CHEMISTRY
OF
LIVING
CELLS

Helen R. Downes

Professor Emeritus of Chemistry
Barnard College, Columbia University

Harper & Row, Publishers

New York and Evanston

Contents

Preface to the First Edition   ix

Preface to the Second Edition   xi

PART I. SOME PRELIMINARY CONSIDERATIONS

1. **Biochemical History and Literature**   3

   Athenian Science—The Hellenistic Era—Arabic Science—The Renaissance—The Age of Modern Science

2. **Some Selected Properties of Aqueous Solutions**   14

   Properties of Water—Solubility of Gases in Water—Membrane Phenomena—Light Absorption—Fluorescence—Hydrogen Ion Concentration—Free Energy—The Colloidal State

3. **The Structure of Living Forms**   89

   Nature and Activities of Living Cells—Plants and Animals—Multicellular Organisms—The Aims of Biochemistry

PART II. THE ORGANIC CONSTITUENTS OF CELLS

4. **The Chemistry of the Carbohydrates**   115

   The Monosaccharides—Compounds Related to the Monoses—The Oligosaccharides—The Polysaccharides

5.   The Compounds of Nitrogen   184

The Amino Acids and the Proteins—Nonprotein Compounds of Nitrogen

6.   The Lipids   256

Structure of the Simple Lipids—Structure of the Compound Lipids— The Steroids—Analysis and Characterization of the Lipids

7.   The Enzymes   283

Early Work on Enzymes—Isolation of Enzymes—Properties of Enzymes

PART III.   INTERMEDIARY METABOLISM

8.   The Methods Used in the Study of Intermediary Metabolism   321

Experiments with Whole Organisms—Experiments with Individual Organs—Tissue Slice Experiments—Experiments with Cellular Particles—Cell-Free Enzyme Systems—Use of Isotopes

9.   Transportation Systems   340

Blood—Transport in Plants

10.   Digestion and Absorption   369

The Digestive System—Digestion and Absorption of Proteins— Digestion and Absorption of Fats—Digestion and Absorption of Carbohydrates

11.   Biological Oxidations   387

Formation of Water—The Pyridinoprotein Enzymes—Respiratory Carriers—Miscellaneous Oxidizing Enzymes—Formation of Carbon Dioxide

12.   Biosynthetic Mechanisms   434

High Energy Compounds

13.   Metabolism of the Compounds of Nitrogen   456

Sources of Nitrogen—Relation Between Food and Body Proteins in Animals—Metabolism of Nitrogen Compounds—Excretion of Nitrogen—Biosynthesis of Nitrogen Compounds

14. **Metabolism of the Lipids** **535**

Occurrence of the Lipids—The Lipid Equilibrium—Degradation of the Lipids—Biosynthesis of the Lipids

15. **Carbohydrate Metabolism** **579**

Anaerobic Carbohydrate Metabolism—The Pentose Phosphate Pathway—The Glucuronic Acid Pathway—Biosynthesis of Carbohydrates—Photosynthesis

Index **625**

Preface to the First Edition

THIS BOOK is the outgrowth of a course in biochemistry which has been given at Barnard College for the past twenty years. The students have been senior majors in chemistry or in one of the biological sciences. The subject matter included in the book has been chosen not only to provide the material for a course in the fundamentals of biochemistry, but also to serve as a simple reference book for students whose primary interest is in zoology or botany or related fields. In practice it has always been found necessary to review the laws of solutions and the chemistry of the foodstuffs before attempting to deal with the complex transformations which take place in the cell.

The historical approach has been used where it seemed suitable in the belief that students should be introduced to the outstanding scientists in their field and encouraged to give them "a local habitation and a name." In this way students may begin to sense the nature of the great intellectual adventure which we call science, to understand how it progresses, and to appreciate the qualities which go toward the making of a scientist. Above all they may be led to meditate upon a truth which T. H. Huxley stated long ago: ". . . anyone who is practically acquainted with scientific work is aware that those who refuse to go beyond fact, rarely get as far as fact; and anyone who has studied the history of science knows that almost every great step therein has been made by . . . the invention of hypotheses, which, though verifiable, often had very little foundation to start with; and, not infrequently, in spite of a long career of usefulness, turned out to be wholly erroneous in the long run."

As far as possible, the subject matter has been presented in conjunction with specific experimental data, but since this is an introductory textbook, no attempt has been made to cite individual authorities for each statement. The references given at the ends of the chapters have been chosen with a view to helping the inexperienced student find his way into the subject. Recent review articles have been included not only for their full bibliographies, but also because a logical and coherent summary of a mass of experimental data is often of great assistance to a beginner. The references given to original papers have been chosen either to emphasize work which has been of special significance or to bring the bibliographies up to date with respect to the main topics discussed in the text. The majority of the papers cited are in English; when references are given to German or French sources, the titles have been given in translation.

I am, as the figures in the book bear witness, greatly indebted to a number of people who not only have allowed me to reproduce material from their books and papers, but have couched their permissions in terms of friendliness and encouragement that went far beyond the call of duty. To all of these and to their publishers in England, Switzerland, Germany, Sweden, and here at home I tender my grateful thanks.

To two colleagues on the Barnard College faculty I owe special debts of gratitude. Professor Victor Larsen of the Botany Department has done his best to save me from the consequences of my own ignorance of his science, and Professor Ingrith Deyrup of the Zoology Department, in the performance of a like service, not only has read and criticized portions of the manuscript but has taken time for many helpful discussions. The extent to which the book is sound zoologically and botanically is a result of the friendly efforts of my colleagues; its shortcomings, alas, are my own.

I count myself especially fortunate in having had during the writing of this book the encouragement and wise advice of my former teacher, Professor Emeritus Marie Reimer of the Barnard Chemistry Department. She has read a large part of the manuscript and has made many valuable suggestions as to its organization and presentation. This present occasion for expressing my gratitude to her is but one in a long series, dating back to my own student days when her contagious enthusiasm first inspired in me the desire to become a chemist.

In such a book as this I have inevitably attempted to simplify and summarize material which is far outside the field of my own major interest. I shall therefore be especially grateful if readers will point out mistakes of fact or of interpretation.

HELEN R. DOWNES

New York
September, 1954

Preface to the Second Edition

IN THE SEVEN YEARS SINCE THIS BOOK WAS PUBLISHED, so much new material has appeared that the text has had to be very nearly completely rewritten, with the exception of the purely historical and the purely structural parts. The plan is, in general, that followed in the first edition, except that the chapter on oxidation and the one which surveys broadly the field of biosynthesis now appear before instead of after the chapters concerned with metabolism. It is hoped that this change will make the development of the subject more unified and complete at each stage.

As in the earlier edition, references have been omitted from the body of the text. In compiling the references at the ends of the chapters an attempt has been made to include any papers of special historical interest, and beyond that to use summarizing articles wherever possible or to give only a late reference or two. Only in this way could the list be kept manageable, and both types of papers always carry adequate references for those who want more detail. In citing references I have reluctantly omitted all except one author's name if the joint authorship included more than two names. This is hard on both the young coauthors for whom the paper may be a unique claim to fame and the senior authors whose names often appear last. To both groups I offer my apologies and regrets, but the citing of every author when a paper may carry eight or ten names has become too unwieldy a job. It seemed more important from the point of view of the student to make room for the titles of articles, or for some indication of their subject matter. The latter has been done when the title was so general that a student might miss its significance.

I am happy to acknowledge my indebtedness to many colleagues and friends. Again Professor Ingrith Deyrup has contributed much to the accuracy of certain chapters, both through informal discussions and through critical reading of several sections of the book. The members of the Barnard College Chemistry Department have been incredibly patient about my raids upon their library, and both Professor Edward J. King and Professor Emma D. Stecher have been generous beyond the call of duty in putting at my disposal their special knowledge of physical and organic chemistry. A special word of thanks goes to Paul Stecher, editor of the *Merck Index*, who has provided me with several recent structural formulas. Thanks are also due the biochemists at Michigan State University for several very helpful critical discussions. I am especially indebted to Professor John C. Speck for suggestions in the field of carbohydrate chemistry and nomenclature and to Professor James L. Fairley who read and criticized three long chapters. Finally I offer sincere thanks to the many people who have permitted me to reproduce their tables and figures. I am especially indebted to Dr. George E. Palade and to Dr. A. E. Vatter for their beautiful electron micrographs and to Dr. M. F. H. Wilkins for the unpublished photograph of his nucleic acid model.

If it was pertinent to acknowledge six years ago that I had had to write about material well outside the field of my own special interests, it is doubly so today. I shall be most grateful if readers will point out errors of fact or interpretation.

HELEN R. DOWNES

Yorktown Heights, N. Y.
January, 1962

Abbreviations

Acta Chem. Scand.	Acta Chemica Scandinavica
Advances in Carbohydrate Chem.	Advances in Carbohydrate Chemistry
Advances in Enzymol.	Advances in Enzymology
Advances in Protein Chem.	Advances in Protein Chemistry
Am. J. Physiol.	American Journal of Physiology
Anal. Biochem.	Analytical Biochemistry
Anal. Chem.	Until 1947 Industrial and Engineering Chemistry, Analytical Edition
Ann.	Annalen der Chemie (Justus Liebig's)
Ann. chim. phys.	Annales de chimie et de physique
Ann. Rev. Biochem.	Annual Review of Biochemistry
Ann. Rev. Plant Physiol.	Annual Review of Plant Physiology
Arch. Biochem. Biophys.[1]	Archives of Biochemistry and Biophysics
Arch. ges. Physiol.	Archiv für gesamte Physiologie
Beitr. chem. Physiol. u. Pathol.	Beiträge zur chemischen Physiologie und Pathologie
Ber.	Berichte der deutschen chemischen Gesellschaft

[1] Up to 1955 was simply the Archives of Biochemistry.

Biochem. J.[2]	Biochemical Journal (London)
Biochem. Z.	Biochemische Zeitschrift
Biochim. et Biophys. Acta	Biochimica et Biophysica Acta
Bull. soc. chim. France	Bulletin de la société chimique de France
Chem. Eng. News	Chemical and Engineering News
Chem. Revs.	Chemical Reviews
Compt. rend.	Comptes rendus hebdomadaires des séances de l'académie des sciences, Paris
Federation Proc.	Proceedings of the Federation of American Societies for Experimental Biology
Helv. Chim. Acta	Helvetica Chimica Acta
J. Am. Chem. Soc.	Journal of the American Chemical Society
J. Biochem. (Tokyo)	Journal of Biochemistry (Tokyo)
J. Biol. Chem.[3]	Journal of Biological Chemistry
J. Chem. Soc.[4]	Journal of the Chemical Society (London)
J. Colloid Sci.	Journal of Colloid Science
J. Chromatog.	Journal of Chromatography
J. Gen. Physiol.	Journal of General Physiology
J. Lipid Research	Journal of Lipid Research
J. Physiol. (London)	Journal of Physiology (London)
Nature	Nature
Naturwiss.	Naturwissenschaften
Physiol. Revs.	Physiological Reviews
Proc. Natl. Acad. Sci. U. S.	Proceedings of the National Academy of Sciences of the United States of America
Proc. Roy. Soc. (London)	Proceedings of the Royal Society (London) Series A: Mathematical and Physical Series B: Biological
Proc. Soc. Exptl. Biol. Med.	Proceedings of the Society for Experimental Biology and Medicine

[2] Summaries of papers presented at meetings of the Society are printed together from time to time at the back of the Journal with independent paging, and the references carry the letter P before the page number.

[3] Preliminary communications are segregated in a special section at the back of some numbers and given independent paging. References carry the letters P.C. before the page numbers.

[4] Recent numbers carry no volume number. The year of publication is given in parentheses.

Trans. Faraday Soc.	Transactions of the Faraday Society
Z. physikal. Chem. (Leipzig)	Zeitschrift für physikalische Chemie (Leipzig)
Z. physiol. Chem.	Zeitschrift für physiologische Chemie (Hoppe-Seyler's)

Part I

SOME
PRELIMINARY
CONSIDERATIONS

Biochemical history and literature

1

B IOCHEMISTRY IS THAT BRANCH OF SCIENCE which is concerned with the chemical events which take place in living tissues. It has existed as a separate discipline for less than one hundred years, but it is rooted in that distant past, almost lost in the mists of prehistory, in which men first began to observe the world about them. Thus Babylonia contributed to science the beginnings of astronomy and of mensuration, and the Egyptians' skill in embalming bears witness to their knowledge of anatomy. Although these earliest-known civilizations have left few records of their own, it is clear from the writings of the early Greeks that the knowledge which they had accumulated was disseminated by traders and travelers throughout the eastern Mediterranean lands and became part of the Hellenic heritage. This heritage had been growing in a haphazard, empirical, and often accidental way for several millenia. But in the course of comparatively few years it was to be transmuted by the Greeks into a new way of living and thinking. It is not easy to define even superficially the Greek contribution. It was partly a sturdy independence and a respect for the rights of the individual which are not matched elsewhere until comparatively modern times. It was partly a rare clarity of mind, coupled with a wide ranging intellectual curiosity. It was partly the first stirrings of the experimental method. But chiefly it was an attitude toward life and a belief in the fundamental importance of truth and beauty which worked together in the social structure of that small nation to foster a freedom of the human mind and spirit which is unique.

3

ATHENIAN SCIENCE

The story of civilization in Greece and on the islands and mainland of Asia Minor can be traced back beyond 1500 B.C., but the earliest records of Greek biological science date from about the sixth century before Christ. By this time the great colonizing period was over, and people of the Greek race were established in city-states not only on the Greek mainland, but in southern France, in Italy and Sicily, around the Aegean and on its islands, and even on the shores of the Black Sea. Thus it happened that the two outstanding figures in Greek biological science although closely associated with Athens were neither of them born in Greece itself. The physician Hippocrates[1] was born on the island of Cos and Aristotle's home was the colonial city of Stagira on the shore of Thrace.

Hippocrates, who was born about 460 B.C., lived for nearly one hundred years, traveling about the regions bordering the Aegean, teaching and practicing medicine. His ideas were not only far in advance of his own time but also of any intervening time until very recent ones. He taught first-hand observation of disease and patient checking of facts, and expressed clearly for the first time the fundamental faith on which all progress in science still depends, namely belief in an orderly universe in which effects follow inevitably from natural causes. For example, in the Hippocratic work dealing with the plague we find, "As for this disease called divine, surely it has its nature and causes as have other diseases." This was a far cry from the attitude toward disease which is characteristic of primitive people, that it results from the anger of the gods and can be cured by magic and incantation. It is of course impossible at this distance in time to know how many of the writings of the so-called Hippocratic Collection are truly the work of the great physician himself. But what is certain is that the medical learning which he collected and systematized was treasured by generations of students in what were called schools of Greek medicine though many of them were founded long after the fall of Greece. And although the learning of these schools crystallized into a stifling dogma during the Dark Ages, yet the spirit of modern medicine can be traced back in almost unbroken continuity to that springtime of learning in which Hippocrates lived and taught.

Aristotle (384–322 B.C.) as a young man was sent from his provincial home to study under Plato in Athens. Some years later he acted for six years as tutor to the young Prince Alexander of Macedon, returning to Athens when his famous pupil set out on his brief career of conquest. There he founded the famous Peripatetic School, so-called because of Aristotle's habit of walking

---

[1] Not to be confused with the mathematician, Hippocrates of Chios, who was a contemporary of the physician.

back and forth as he taught. The doctrines which originated with the Peripatetics were destined to exert a great and lasting influence upon the development of both science and philosophy. That this influence proved to be partly bad arose from the fact that Aristotle's writings, which covered the whole field of learning, were of two sorts. His earliest studies were biological, and in this area he was a scientist of erudition and originality. He observed and recorded and classified a wide range of biological forms and phenomena, and when he was thus in immediate contact with his material he wrote in the true scientific vein.

But Aristotle had in full measure that "exuberant genius for speculation" which characterized his nation. Given a few observations he was impelled to build them into a coherent philosophical system, and his speculations soon outran his data. Indeed in his later writings he made statements which could easily have been put to the test of experiment, but which he never tested. Thus undeterred by inconvenient facts he outlined a system of terrestrial mechanics and fitted a small number of data into a richly imaginative astronomical system in which he assumed that celestial motion is regulated by quite different laws from those which are operative on the earth. In thus allowing free play to his fancy Aristotle was not only disobeying his own behests but also was all unwittingly forging chains which were to bind and inhibit western thought for hundreds of years.

THE HELLENISTIC ERA

Biological science came as a relatively late development in Greece. Hippocrates lived in that Age of Pericles when classical Greek learning centered in Athens had already reached its brilliant culmination. Before his death the long Peloponnesian War had been fought to its costly conclusion. Technically it was won by Sparta, but actually all the Greek city-states including Sparta were the losers. They were left at the end (404 B.C.) torn with dissension and jealousy and weakened by twenty-seven years of intermittent fighting during which not only armies but whole communities had been destroyed. Thus the survivors fell an easy prey when in 338 B.C. Alexander's father, Philip of Macedon, struck from the north. He quickly made himself master of Greece, and by the time Aristotle returned to Athens in 336 B.C. the day of the old independent city-states was past.

Although this conquest spelled the end of that first, unique expression of the Greek genius in its own homeland, it was also the beginning of a new period, known to history as the Hellenistic Age, in which the culture of Greece was preeminent throughout the ancient world. In the course of about nine years Philip's son Alexander swept triumphantly with his armies through Asia Minor, Egypt, Syria, Mesopotamia, and Persia, and even penetrated into India.

Wherever he went, Greek colonists followed and founded Greek towns. In this way Greek learning was carried to the people of the East, and in turn the civilizations of the East were made known to the Greeks and ultimately through them to the people of the Mediterranean world. Out of this cross-fertilization arose a new learning, predominantly Greek in expression, which was to constitute the cultural link with modern times.

Alexander died in 323 B.C. at the age of thirty-three, and his hastily forged empire fell apart. It was ultimately divided into several independent states, each governed by one of his more powerful generals. Egypt was seized by Ptolemy Lagus who established there a dynasty which lasted for three centuries. Under the Ptolemies Alexandria became the intellectual center of the Mediterranean world. The famous Museum, founded by the second Ptolemy, developed into a kind of university where during several centuries scholars from all over the world gathered to study and teach. The Library of Alexandria ultimately housed the largest collection of books in the ancient world and numbered among its curators some of the most eminent scholars. During the five hundred years of the Alexandrian period, roughly from 300 B.C. to A.D. 200, a form of Greek was the universal language of scholars, and classical Greek learning supplied the foundations on which the scholarly edifice was built.

During these years the political picture was radically changed by the emergence from obscurity of the city of Rome. It was about the time of Aristotle's birth that Rome sent out her first military expedition against a neighboring state. By 272 B.C., or roughly fifty years after Alexander's death, she had subjugated the entire Italian peninsula, including the Greek cities in the south and east. From that time until the establishment of the Roman Empire in 30 B.C. Rome went from one conquest to another until she was finally undisputed mistress of most of the known world. Then for about two hundred years the lands under Roman rule enjoyed the time of peace and consolidation and prosperity which is known as the Pax Romana. This period coincided with the last two centuries of the Alexandrian era, so that for two centuries after world government became centered in Rome Alexandria was still the acknowledged intellectual capital.

In science the Hellenistic period was most fertile in mathematics, astronomy, and physics. Euclid (ca. 330–ca. 260 B.C.), an outstanding figure in the early years, was among the first scholars to be called to Alexandria, and Archimedes (287–212 B.C.) of the Greek city of Syracuse in Sicily was probably the foremost mathematician of antiquity. Much later than these was Claudius Ptolemy,[2] a mathematician and geographer in whose writings was summarized the geographical and astronomical knowledge of his time. His most famous work is known as the *Almagest*. In this he outlined a cosmic system with the earth at

---

[2] This Ptolemy was not a member of the Egyptian royal family. He wrote in the first half of the second century A.D.

the center surrounded by rotating planets of which the sun was one. Perhaps the most formidable task faced by scientists in the fifteenth and sixteenth centuries was the overthrow of this concept, so pleasantly flattering to the human ego.

The early Alexandrian period saw also the beginnings of physiology and anatomy as independent disciplines. Dissection of the human body was introduced and attempts were made to explain respiration and the functions of veins, arteries, and nerves. But in medicine as in cosmology the contribution which most influenced later generations was not a specific bit of original research, but a compendium of existing knowledge. Galen of Pergamum in Asia Minor (A.D. 131–201) studied at Alexandria but spent most of his active life in Rome where he acted as physician to three Emperors. For his writings he depended to some extent upon his own dissections and observations, but he also drew very largely upon the medical works of the past. In the twenty-one volumes of his which survive we have not only a summary of contemporary medical and biological knowledge but a synthesis of these into a very ingenious physical system. So satisfactory was this synthesis to Galen's successors that they made it into a medical Bible, used it as their only medical text, and finally came to regard any divergent ideas as medical heresies.

Before leaving the subject of the Alexandrian contribution to learning it may not be irrelevant to note that the later years of this period were those in which the new Christian doctrine was slowly taking form under the combined influences, especially in Alexandria, of the Mystery religions of the East, the learning of Hebrew scholars, and the teachings of the Neoplatonist philosophers who drew their inspiration from Plato and Aristotle. Thus it need not surprise us as it did the men of the Renaissance that when Aristotle's work was rediscovered a thousand years later it was found to contain much that was compatible with Christian theology.

Although the Romans had come into contact with Greek civilization when they first overran the Greek colonies in Italy, and had studied under Greek philosophers and scientists for generations, they themselves made almost no contribution to pure science. Their interests were practical and administrative, and when they did write on scientific subjects, they relied for their facts on the observations of others. It is true that they drew upon contemporary medical knowledge in setting up hospitals. But the medical schools of the Roman Empire were Greek schools in which Hippocratic writings and traditions were cherished. Gradually, however, the spirit changed. The method of exact observation was superseded by a slavish study of the works of antiquity and, after the third century, by unquestioning acceptance of the Galenic dogma. Meantime the rise of Christianity, with its emphasis on the life hereafter, also tended to discourage studies of this world. "Go not out of doors," said St. Augustine, "in the inner man dwells truth." And for several hundred years the men of western Europe obediently turned their eyes inward. These were the years after the long peace had ended, when the Western Empire was disintegrating under the pressure of barbarians on her borders and dissension within. By the beginning of the fifth century this Empire and scientific inspiration had gone into eclipse together, and the Dark Ages had begun.

ARABIC SCIENCE

To understand how Greek learning was preserved and ultimately made available to western Europe, we must turn to the East. When Rome fell to the barbarians, there still remained the Eastern Empire with its capital at Constantinople. This Eastern or Byzantine Empire extended from Greece to the borders of Persia and continued to maintain its independence for a further eight centuries. Here the works of antiquity were treasured and classical learning was cultivated long after all interest in these things had failed in the West.

Thus it happened that when the heretical Nestorian Christians were driven from Constantinople in the fifth century they took with them some knowledge of Greek learning and traditions. They went first to Mesopotamia and later to Persia where they settled at Gondisapur or Jundi-Shapur. Here in the course of two centuries of scholarship they built up a rich collection of classical manuscripts and made their city a center of learning.

When in the seventh century the Arabs surged out of the desert their first conquests brought them into contact with the Nestorians and through the Nestorian scholars with Greek learning. They were particularly impressed with Greek medicine and gradually made Greek science and philosophy the focal points around which their Moslem civilization developed. It is true that the Arabs made few original contributions to biology or medicine, but their commentaries on and translations of the classical writings conserved and spread throughout their Empire the learning of antiquity and of the later Alexandrian scholars. As their crescent of conquest spread across northern Africa and into Spain the love of Greek learning accompanied them and led to the establishment in the Iberian peninsula of some of the most famous schools of the Middle Ages. Here were accumulated treasure troves of early manuscripts in translation and of Arabic commentaries on and summaries of these manuscripts. It was largely from these Spanish centers, partly Moslem and partly Jewish, that Greco-Arabic learning first filtered into France in the knapsacks of travelers, and made its way thence to Germany and England. The vitality of the Arabic-Jewish contribution to western science is attested by the survival in our own language of such Semitic words as *antimony* and *alembic*, of Persian roots in *alcohol* and *camphor* and of words derived from the Arabic of which *alizarin* and *algebra* are familiar examples.

The rediscovery of the classics which reached significant proportions in the twelfth and thirteenth centuries in western Europe had two quite different results. In the fields of art, architecture, and literature it fostered that great burst of artistic inspiration which is truly called the Renaissance. In the field of science, however, there followed no such freeing of the human spirit and genius. For about eight centuries scholars had been almost exclusively concerned with theology, and it was only natural that when the new learning appeared they chose to emphasize those phases of it which were compatible with their faith. Thus it was Aristotle's philosophy, which had already furnished one strand in the fabric of Christian theology, which captured their imaginations, while his scientific biological treatises were completely ignored. The *Almagest* of Ptolemy with its anthropocentric cosmology also exerted a wide influence without ever suggesting the need of corroboration. In the field of medicine, the one science which had survived precariously through the centuries of darkness, the "vast, windy, ill-arranged treatises of Galen," had for more than a thousand years been considered a sufficient summary of medical knowledge, and the discovery of Arabian science brought no change in this point of view. Some new writings, notably those of Rhazes (865–925) and of Avicenna of Bokhara (980–1037) took their places in the medical literature, but none of them became the inspiration for a new and experimental approach.

Meantime Aristotle's doctrines were slowly acquiring a prestige which ultimately made them sacrosanct. Surely one of the saddest ironies of intellectual history is the way in which that great scientist and scholar was made the excuse in medieval times for an obscurantism and an intolerance which were totally at variance with his own spirit of free inquiry. The Aristotelian dogma which proved most disastrous for chemistry was his doctrine of the four elements. According to this theory all matter is made up of the four elements, earth, air, fire, and water, in varying proportions. Obviously the word "element" as used by Aristotle has none of its modern connotations, but the years during which alchemy was gradually merging into the beginnings of chemistry were darkened and confused by attempts to attach some rational meaning to the word and to adjust the facts to fit his theory.

THE RENAISSANCE

It was not until the mid-sixteenth century that science in its modern form really began to take shape. By this time there was available a considerable body of empirical knowledge in the fields of astronomy, chemistry, physics, and medicine. Books were issuing from the new presses in ever increasing numbers and were even beginning to carry illustrations and diagrams made from woodcuts and copper plates. Scholars again were turning seriously after a lapse of nearly two thousand years to the study of nature at first hand and to a consideration of the implications of their findings. Already the Flemish anatomist

Vesalius (1514–1564) was moving toward a rational approach to medicine, carrying out dissections for his students and even daring in a second edition of his book to question the dicta of Galen. Before the mid-century Copernicus (1473–1543) had completed the astronomical observations which were to shatter the Ptolemaic cosmology, and Giordano Bruno (1547–1600), that strange and wayward genius, had been born in Nola near Naples. Though not himself an observer, he brought to bear upon the data of others a clear and a questioning mind. He concluded that the universe had not been "created" but was infinite both in time and space and that the earth, far from being the center of the cosmos, moved as a planet about the central sun. For these heretical doctrines Bruno met his death by fire at the hands of the Inquisition in 1600, but the three small books which he had published continued to spread his scientific philosophy in spite of repeated attempts to suppress them.

The intellectual revolution was given an enormous and crucial impetus by the work of another Italian whose long life was devoted entirely to experimental science. The studies of Galileo Galilei (1564–1642) in physics and astronomy, his improvement of the telescope and the compound microscope, his sponsoring of a rational interpretation of Copernicus' data, and rejection of the errors of Aristotelian mechanics constitute in themselves a truly formidable contribution to science. But their influence went far beyond a revision of our ideas about the laws of physics or the structure of the universe. His experimental approach to knowledge came like a fresh breeze blowing through a closed room into a world almost suffocated by tradition and authority, and spurred men to thinking for themselves as few had thought since the days of ancient Greece. Out of this new freedom to experiment and to reason came a great upsurge in scientific inspiration which led to new discoveries in all fields, including those which were much later to be known as biochemical.

THE AGE OF MODERN SCIENCE

One of the interesting evidences of this new intellectual climate was the sudden appearance in the seventeenth century of numerous small scientific societies, often sponsored by some interested prince or noble. The Roman *Academy of Lynxes* was founded in 1603 and a Florentine *Academy of Experimentation* in 1657, the latter under the sponsorship of the Medici. In Germany the famous *Leopoldine Academy* evolved from an association of physicians which met first in 1652 at Schweinfurt to "consider medical and physical wonders and curiosities." Louis XIV supported a *French Academy of Sciences* organized in 1666, while in England a group known as the "Invisible College," which had been carrying on secret experimental studies since about 1645, was given a Royal Charter by Charles II in 1660. The *Royal Society* thus initiated is of special interest because it has an unbroken history of over three hundred years and is still one of the most distinguished of scientific organizations. The publication of its *Transactions* began in 1665 and except for the years 1679–1682[3] has been continuous to the present.

From the beginning the Royal Society was concerned with science in all its branches, and published side by side papers on gunnery, on blood transfusions, on mathematics, and even one telling "of a Spiders not being inchanted by a Circle of *Unicorn's horn*, or *Irish Earth*, laid round about it." It is of interest, too, that from its inception the Royal Society of London was international in its scope. Its members began immediately the voluminous official correspondence which justified the title given to the early volumes: *Philosophical Transactions giving some Accompt of the Present Undertakings, Studies and Labours of the Ingenious in many considerable parts of the World.* In 1800 the *Transactions* gave way to the *Proceedings of the Royal Society*, later divided into Series A, concerned with mathematics and physics, and Series B, which publishes research of biological interest. This last is one of the small group of journals which publish the major part of the specifically biochemical research of the present day.

By the end of the eighteenth century, science—or "natural philosophy" as it was first called—had progressed to the point where some specialization had become inevitable. Chemistry had become a separate branch of inquiry and before the end of the century Chemical Societies were beginning to be formed. At their meetings there were reported results of chemical studies of living material as well as studies of the inorganic world.

It was early in the nineteenth century that Justus von Liebig (1803–1873), having helped to lay the foundations which gave to organic chemistry an independent existence, founded in 1832 the journal which is still called *Liebig's Annalen*. Although its first title was *Annalen der Pharmacie*, since it had been formed by the fusion of two older pharmaceutical journals, it was designed to serve as an outlet for the young science of organic chemistry. This was still very close to pharmacology and medicine from which it had originally derived, and indeed it is clear that Liebig always thought of his journal as contributing to the growth of agriculture and other biological sciences. But as a matter of fact the brilliant half century which was initiated by the synthesis of urea in 1828 saw organic chemistry moving temporarily farther and farther away from agricultural and biological interests as the new synthetic compounds proved to be better suited to the study of molecular constitution than were most of the naturally occurring organic substances. However, the *Annalen der Chemie* has always carried some articles of specifically biological import side by side with

---

[3] In the early years these publications seem to have been a private financial venture of the secretary of the Royal Society. A change in secretaries led to suspension of publication for a few years, though published summaries of the proceedings are available. Publication of the *Transactions* was resumed when the Society guaranteed that at least 30 copies would be purchased by members!

those of more obviously chemical emphasis. Twentieth century biological chemistry must always be enormously indebted to the great organic chemists of the previous century, especially to Liebig and to Emil Fischer.

It is hard to say just when and where biochemistry began to emerge as an independent discipline. It is to France that we owe the first thorough study of a substance of primary biological importance. Chevreul published in the *Annales de chimie et de physique* (founded in 1795) a series of papers entitled "Researches on Various Fatty Bodies," and this was felt to be so important that by 1818 we find it summarized at some length in an English journal. But it was in the University of German Strasbourg that the first Department of Physiological Chemistry was established, with Felix Hoppe-Seyler (1825–1895) as its head. In 1877 he founded the first biochemical journal, the *Zeitschrift für Physiologische Chemie*, more often referred to still as *Hoppe-Seyler's Zeitschrift* though the founder died more than half a century ago. In the introduction to the first volume Hoppe-Seyler wrote: "Die Biochemie ist hierdurch aus ihren ersten natürlichen und notwendigen analytischen Anfängen zu einer Wissenschaft erwachsen,"[4] so that if any year is to be chosen for the birth of biochemistry perhaps 1877 is the year, since it saw the publication of the first exclusively biochemical journal. By this time scientists in America were also concerned with biochemistry, and Yale had established in 1874 the first American laboratory for physiological chemistry under the directorship of Russell Chittenden.

From this point the story is too complex to be compressed into a few paragraphs. It can be read only in the journals. At the turn of the century it had become evident that the number of these must be increased to take care of the volume of research which was going forward in biochemistry. Within the space of about a year (1905–1906) the *Biochemical Journal* was founded in England, the *Biochemische Zeitschrift* in Germany, and the *Journal of Biological Chemistry* in the United States. With the publication of these three journals, biochemistry may be said to have come of age just twenty-eight years after Hoppe-Seyler chronicled its birth.

From the time when biochemical journals first began to be published it was obvious that they carried only a small part of the literature of interest to biochemists. The first number of the first volume of the *Zeitschrift für Physiologische Chemie* carried a list of titles of papers of biochemical importance in four other journals, three German and one French. It was only a few months later that the sixth number, the last of Volume I, listed papers from sixty-eight journals in eleven different languages, all of them having some bearing on biochemical problems. It is even more true today than it was in 1877 that "biochemical" papers may appear in any scientific journal. New analytical methods or refinements of old ones are rapidly adapted to biochemical ends.

---

[4] "Biochemistry has at this point grown from its first natural and necessary analytical beginnings to a science."

The instruments of physical chemistry and its special methods have been invaluable in the study of cell dynamics. Structural organic chemistry is obviously fundamental to any understanding of the chemical changes taking place in the cell. The task of keeping track of this vast literature is somewhat lightened by the many abstract journals in different languages, and more specifically by the indispensable *Annual Review of Biochemistry*. One volume of this publication has appeared yearly since 1932. A volume carries twenty to twenty-five articles, each written by an expert in a restricted field, and in this way there is available a reasonably up-to-date and critical summary of important papers published all over the world. From the very full bibliographies there given a thread can be found to lead to detailed studies of almost any problem in biochemistry.

SUGGESTIONS FOR FURTHER READING

Boyle, Robert, *The Skeptical Chymist*, 1661.
>   There is available a Modern Library edition of this book. It brings out clearly the tenacity with which men held to the Aristotelian dogmas.

Dampier, Sir William C., *A History of Science*, Cambridge, 1944.

Garrison, Fielding H., The medical and scientific periodicals of the 17th and 18th centuries, *Bulletin of the Institute of the History of Medicine*, July, 1934.
>   This has been reprinted and is available as a pamphlet.

Kitto, H. D. F., *The Greeks*, Penguin, 1951.
>   This book, written for the Penguin Series, is a charming introduction to the story of Greek contributions to intellectual history.

Needham, Joseph, and Walter Pagel (eds.), *Background to Modern Science*, Macmillan, New York, 1938.
>   The chapters of special interest in this volume are: F. M. Cornford, "Greek Natural Philosophy and Modern Science," and Sir William C. Dampier, "From Aristotle to Galileo."

Ornstein, Martha, *The Role of Scientific Societies in the Seventeenth Century*, University of Chicago Press, Chicago, 1928.

Singer, Charles, *A Short History of Science*, Oxford, New York, 1941.

Sprat, Thos., *History of the Royal Society*, first published in 1665.
>   Since the Society had had only a very short history when this book was written, Bishop Sprat has actually written a defense of science. The charges against which he defends it indicate the suspicion with which it was viewed.

Wightman, William P. D., *The Growth of Scientific Ideas*, Yale, New Haven, Conn., 1951.

Woodruff, L. L. (ed.), *The Development of the Sciences*, Yale, New Haven, Conn. 1923.
>   Of special interest is Chapter VI written by the editor.

Progress in biology at the molecular level is becoming increasingly dependent on physical and physicochemical techniques. . . .

G. B. B. M. SUTHERLAND (1959)

Some selected properties of aqueous solutions 2

THE LIVING CELL IS ESSENTIALLY A DILUTE AQUEOUS SOLUTION, of which the solutes, organic and inorganic, make up only a minor portion. The substance which makes up more than half of all tissues, and may account for 75–80 per cent of the weight of some, is that familiar but remarkable substance, water. Its solvent properties are unique and make it possible for it to hold, either in true solution or in colloidal suspension, a complex array of particles varying in size from the hydrated proton, H_3O^+, to enormous macromolecules such as the proteins and the polysaccharides. Life is supposed to have begun in the sea, and certainly it is hard to imagine any other medium with properties so well adapted to conserving life whether in a single-celled plant or in an organism as complex as a tree or a mammal.

PROPERTIES OF WATER

A water molecule consists of the highly electronegative oxygen atom holding two hydrogen atoms by covalent bonds which form an angle of approximately 105°. The oxygen attracts electrons away from the protons and leaves them deficient in electrons. Each oxygen carries, furthermore, two unshared electron pairs or "lone pairs," and this concentration of electrons around the oxygen, and consequent lack of electrons in the vicinity of the hydrogens, leads to formation of hydrogen bonds. Since each water molecule has two lone pairs and two protons, it can coordinate with four other molecules as indicated in

Fig. 2.1, in which the solid lines represent the covalent bonds and the dotted lines the relatively weaker hydrogen bonds. In ice this three-dimensional arrangement involves all the water molecules and gives rise to the beautifully symmetrical patterns seen in ice crystals. When ice melts only about 15 per cent of the intermolecular bonds are broken, so that liquid water still has a true "molecular weight" far larger than the formula H_2O would indicate. It is not

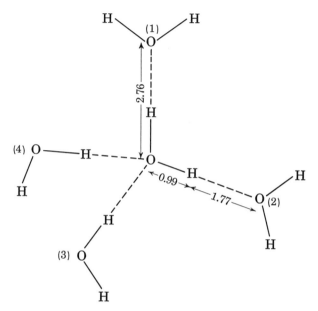

Fig. 2.1. Tetrahedral coordination of water molecules in ice. Molecules (1) and (2), as well as the central water molecule, lie entirely in the plane of the paper. Molecule (3) lies above this plane, molecule (4) below it, so that oxygens (1), (2), (3), and (4) lie at the corners of a regular tetrahedron. Distances in angstroms. [From J. T. Edsall and J. Wyman, *Biophysical Chemistry*, Academic, New York, 1958.]

known how large it is, and probably particle sizes vary from moment to moment as some hydrogen bonds break and others form. Since vaporization requires the escape of single water molecules and therefore the breaking of all the hydrogen bonds, water has a boiling point much higher than that of other compounds with similar basic structures. Hydrogen sulfide, for example, in which the central sulfur atom is less electronegative than oxygen, shows almost no tendency to form hydrogen bonds and boils at $-59.6°C$. Beyond the fact that its high boiling point makes it a liquid at ordinary temperatures, many of the other physical constants of water fit it peculiarly for the role it plays in living matter.

Heat Capacity of Water

The heat capacity of a system is defined as the number of calories required to raise its temperature one degree centigrade. If the weight of the system is 1 g, the heat capacity is called the *specific heat*. For water this quantity is by definition unity, since the standard calorie is defined as the amount of heat required to raise the temperature of 1 g of water from 15° to 16°. Actually the specific heat of water varies only slightly from unity between 0° and 100°. Only one other liquid, liquid ammonia, has a higher specific heat than water, and the

TABLE 2.1. Some Physical Constants of Water and Other Compounds

	Temperature, °C	Specific Heat, cal/g	Heat of Vaporization, cal/g	Latent Heat of Fusion, cal/g
Water	0	1.00738	595.9	79.7
	15	0.99976		
	65	1.00000		
	100	1.00697	540.0	
Methyl alcohol	−97			16
	20	0.60		
	64.7		262.8	
n-Propyl alcohol	25	0.586		
	97.2		164	
Acetic acid	0	0.468		
	16.6			45
	118		97	
Chloroform	20	0.234		
	61		59	
Benzene	5.40			30
	80		94	
	90	0.473		
Nitrobenzene	5.7			22
	30	0.339		
	151		79	
Methane	−159		138	
	15	0.528		
Hydrogen sulfide	−61.4		132	
	15	0.253		

Source: Most of these data from *Handbook of Chemistry and Physics*, 40th ed., Chemical Rubber Publishing Co., Cleveland, O., 1958–1959.

specific heats of solids are lower than those of liquids (see Table 2.1). This means that an aqueous system will have a smaller temperature rise per calorie of heat absorbed than any other type of solution which can exist at ordinary temperatures. This high heat capacity which makes us more comfortable in summer than we would otherwise be is, of course, referable to the fact that part of any heat energy absorbed by water must be used to break hydrogen bonds before the increased molecular motion which is called heat can be brought about.

Heat of Vaporization

When a beaker of cold water is heated, the temperature rises to 100° and then remains stationary, if superheating of the container is avoided, until nearly all the water has evaporated. The heat which is absorbed during the evaporation is the heat of vaporization, defined as the number of calories required to change 1 g of liquid at its boiling point to vapor at the same temperature. Again the figure for water is very much higher than those for other liquids, organic or inorganic, as is shown in Table 2.1. This means that evaporation of water will effectively cool the surroundings, and this is in fact an important part of the mechanism for controlling the temperature of living organisms. During combustion of the foodstuffs, as much as half of the energy set free may be dissipated as heat, and it is the evaporation of water from the organism which uses up much of this heat and prevents a disastrous temperature rise.

Heat of Fusion

The number of calories used in transforming 1 g of a solid at its melting point to the liquid state without change of temperature is called the heat of fusion. This constant for water is higher than for any comparable liquids, only liquid ammonia and certain fused salts having higher values. Since freezing of a liquid will set free the same amount of heat as was used to melt it, during the freezing of ponds and rivers in cold weather a certain amount of heat is given off and minimizes the abruptness of the temperature change. Conversely, in the spring the melting of ice uses up some of the heat from sun and warm winds and prevents the violent fluctuations of temperature which would be so difficult for living organisms to endure.

SOLUBILITY OF GASES IN WATER

The solubility of gases in water varies with the nature of the gas, with the temperature, and with the gas pressure. Of the gases of biological interest, oxygen, nitrogen, and carbon monoxide are relatively insoluble, whereas carbon dioxide is considerably more soluble in water.

The solubility of gases is not usually expressed in terms of molarity or normality. In biological work the *absorption coefficient* (α) is the unit most often encountered. This is defined as the volume of a gas, *reduced to standard temperature and pressure* (STP), which dissolves in unit volume of solvent at a specified temperature when the gas pressure is one atmosphere. For example, the absorption coefficient of oxygen at 15°C is 0.03415, and this means that at 15°, 1 ml of water in contact with oxygen at 760 mm pressure will dissolve an amount of gas which would occupy 0.03415 ml under standard conditions (see Table 2.2).

TABLE 2.2. Absorption Coefficients of Gases (α)

Temperature, °C	Oxygen	Nitrogen	Carbon Dioxide	Carbon Monoxide
0	0.0489	0.0235	1.713	0.0354
15	0.0342	0.0169	1.019	0.0254
25	0.0283	0.0143	0.759	0.0214
35	0.0244	0.0126	0.592	0.0188
40	0.0231	0.0118	0.530	0.0178

Effect of Temperature

A familiar example of the effect of temperature on solubility is the collection of air bubbles in a glass of tap water as it stands in a warm room. All gases are less soluble at higher temperatures and become insoluble at the temperature of boiling water.

Effect of Pressure

The relationship between the weight of a gas which dissolves and the pressure of that gas was discovered by the Scots physician, William Henry (1775–1836). Henry's law states that the weight of gas absorbed by a given volume of solvent at a fixed temperature is directly proportional to the gas pressure. Since the volume of a gas is inversely proportional to its pressure, the actual volume of gas absorbed under specific experimental conditions is independent of the pressure. The two relationships are shown graphically in Fig. 2.2 in which curve *A* plots the weights dissolved at various gas pressures, while curve *B* shows the volume of gas, measured under experimental conditions, which dissolves at the different pressures.

When gas mixtures are in contact with a solvent the solubility of each gas is proportional to its partial pressure. Suppose for example that 15 ml of water is to be shaken at 38°C with a gas mixture which is 95 per cent oxygen and 5 per cent carbon dioxide. Assuming atmospheric pressure to be 760 mm, the total

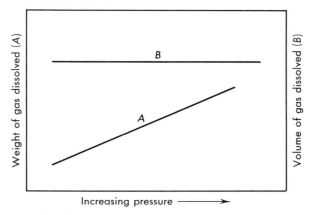

Fig. 2.2. Graphic representation of Henry's law.

gas pressure will be only 760–49.8, or approximately 710 mm since the gas must be saturated with water vapor. At $38°\alpha_{O_2} = 0.024$ and $\alpha_{CO_2} = 0.55$.

$$\text{Partial pressure of } O_2 = 710 \times 0.95 = 674 \text{ mm}$$

$$\text{Partial pressure of } CO_2 = 710 \times 0.05 = 36 \text{ mm}$$

The 15 ml of water will therefore dissolve

$$0.024 \times 15 \times \frac{674}{760} = 0.319 \text{ ml } O_2 \text{ at STP}$$

$$0.55 \times 15 \times \frac{36}{760} = 0.391 \text{ ml } CO_2 \text{ at STP}$$

It should be noted that Henry's law does not hold if the gas reacts with the solvent or with some other solute. Thus, for example, the ability of mammalian blood to transport oxygen depends in only very small part on its ability to dissolve the gas. By far the greater part of the oxygen present in blood is held there in loose molecular combination with the hemoglobin of the red blood cells. This is indicated graphically in Fig. 2.3, which shows for increasing pressures the amounts of oxygen that are carried in equal volumes of plasma and of whole blood with its hemoglobin. The oxygen absorbed by plasma forms a simple solution, but in whole blood there is added to the dissolved oxygen the amount of the gas which is in combination with hemoglobin at each pressure.

Use of the absorption coefficients is further limited by the fact that salts in solution lower the solubility of most gases. For example at 38°C the absorption coefficient of carbon dioxide in water is 0.55, but in the nutrient solution which contains bicarbonate ion as well as those of sodium, calcium, potassium, and

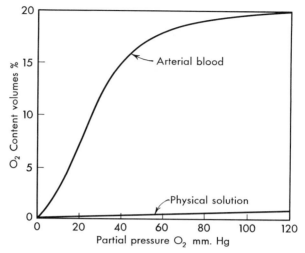

Fig. 2.3. Oxygen carried in solution in plasma and in whole blood at various oxygen pressures. [From J. F. Fulton (ed.), *Textbook of Physiology*, Saunders, Philadelphia, 1949. After Barcroft.]

chloride, it is 0.537. In experiments on the respiration of living tissue these differences are of moment. The effect of salts upon the solubility of gases is illustrated in Table 2.3.

TABLE 2.3. Influence of Salts on the Solubility of Gases

Gas	Solvent	Temperature, °C	Absorption Coefficient
Oxygen	Water	25	0.028
	0.5M NaCl	25	0.024
	1.0M NaCl	25	0.020
Carbon dioxide	Water	38	0.550
	Bicarbonate-Ringer soln.	38	0.537
	Serum	38	0.510

MEMBRANE PHENOMENA

A cell is not only a dilute aqueous solution but also an organism in which a complex series of chemical events take place in an orderly fashion. This presupposes organization and controlled movement of substances within the cell.

In recent years the electron microscope has shown clearly that certain areas of the cell are separated from others by what we call membranes. A membrane is not to be thought of as a kind of skin made up of substances quite different from those in the fluid enclosed by the membrane. Rather a membrane results whenever at the surface of a unit or particle of solution the concentration of solute molecules is different from that in the bulk of the solution. By admitting some molecules and excluding others, such membranes, enclosing various localities within a cell, control the flow of solutes into those areas. Because of their differential action these membranes are spoken of as semipermeable. The way in which natural membranes are constituted is imperfectly understood, but some of the principles involved have been studied in simpler systems.

Osmotic Pressure

Several different materials have served as experimental semipermeable membranes. The earliest experiments were done with cells enclosed in their own membranes as in de Vries' work with plant cells, cited below. Red blood cells have served the same purpose, and experiments on a larger scale have made use of animal bladders and parchment paper. An artificial membrane which was used in early quantitative experiments consisted of a gelatinous precipitate of cupric ferrocyanide deposited in the pores of an unglazed porcelain cup. Small collodion sacs are easily prepared, and many commercial materials of graded porosity are now available.

When a sac of collodion or other semipermeable material is partly filled with a solution of cane sugar and immersed in pure water, water flows into the sac. If a manometer is attached to the neck of the container, it is possible to measure the pressure which develops as the solvent pushes in. This pressure is the result of *osmosis*, or diffusion of water through a membrane. The equilibrium pressure, attained by allowing a solution to come to equilibrium with pure solvent through a membrane permeable only to the solvent, is known, therefore, as the osmotic pressure of the solution.

This is not the place to enter into the arguments about the nature of osmotic pressure, and whether it is due to the solute or to the solvent. Experimentally it is the "pressure difference that must be imposed by the analyst across a membrane . . . in order to establish equilibrium with respect to a substance which can cross the barrier," usually the pure solvent. When an external pressure is not applied and there are solutions of unequal concentrations on the two sides of the membrane, there results a flow of the solvent into the more concentrated solution. It is this flow which interests the biochemist and which must be guarded against in experiments with intact living cells.

Two investigators are especially associated with the development of the quantitative laws governing osmotic pressure. In 1877 the German botanist Wilhelm Pfeffer (1845–1920) determined the osmotic pressures of a series of sucrose solutions, using cupric ferrocyanide in an unglazed porcelain cup as the semipermeable membrane. From Pfeffer's figures, which had shown the osmotic pressure to be proportional to the concentration of the solution and to the absolute temperature, van't Hoff was led to his classical analogy between gas pressure and osmotic pressure. That is, in the ideal case of a membrane completely impermeable to the solute the pressure for dilute solutions is given by the equation

$$\pi v = nRT$$

in which π is the osmotic pressure in atmospheres, v is the volume of the solution in liters, n the number of moles of solute, R the gas constant in liter-atmospheres (0.083), and T the absolute temperature.

Osmotic pressure in living cells

The first attempt to measure the osmotic pressure of living cells was made in 1888 by the Dutch botanist Hugo de Vries (1848–1935), using epidermal cells of leaves. Under normal conditions the protoplasm of these cells, within a fine plasma membrane, fills completely the space within the heavy supporting walls of cellulose, as shown in Fig. 2.4(*a*). The cellulose shows no selective permeability; it is the plasma membrane which is semipermeable. It was found that

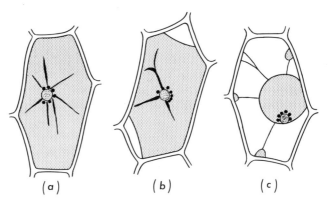

(a) (b) (c)

Fig. 2.4. Microscopic appearance of leaf cells: (*a*) normal cell; (*b*) cell after immersion in 0.22*M* sucrose; (*c*) cell after immersion in 1*M* KNO$_3$. [From H. de Vries, *Z. physikal. Chem.*, **2**, 415 (1888).]

when such cells were placed in 0.22*M* sucrose solutions water passed out of the cells and the plasma membrane contracted slightly as indicated in Fig. 2.4(*b*). This escape of water from a cell is known as *plasmolysis*, and indicates that the cell osmotic pressure is less than that of the solution surrounding it. When the leaf cells were immersed in strong salt solutions they lost large amounts of water and assumed the appearance shown in Fig. 2.4(*c*). But if the depleted cells were then transferred to pure water, the plasmolysis was reversed and the cell contents again filled the space within the cellulose walls. By bathing the cells with sucrose solutions of varying concentrations, de Vries showed that water neither entered nor left the cell when it was immersed in 0.21M cane sugar solution. Such a solution is said to be *isosmotic* or *isotonic* with the cell contents, that is, to have an equal osmotic pressure. On the basis of the van't Hoff equation this pressure in the cells used by de Vries is approximately 5 atmospheres. Later determinations of the osmotic pressures of plant saps indicate that the range is wide but that for most land plants it lies between 10 and 20 atmospheres.

Experiments with animal cells similar to those of de Vries with plant tissue have given the approximate osmotic pressures of various cells and emphasized the importance of maintaining appropriate osmotic conditions if cells are to survive. Red blood cells transferred to pure water absorb water until their membranes are so distended that the hemoglobin escapes to give the clear red solution of *hemolyzed* blood. In order to avoid damage to the blood cells, solutions which are to be injected into the circulation are made up to be isotonic with serum. If a drug is to be administered in so dilute a solution that its own osmotic effect may be neglected, it is dissolved in isotonic or "physiological" saline, that is in a solution of sodium chloride which contains approximately 0.85 g of the salt in 100 ml of solution. In ordinary biochemical parlance this solution is said to be an 0.85 per cent solution.

Permeability of cell membranes

Undoubtedly tissues and organisms differ greatly in the permeability of their membranes. Furthermore, many of the lower forms such as molds and bacteria possess great adaptability in this matter and can be trained over a period of time to survive in media which are far from the norm. It is therefore possible to speak of the permeability of living membranes only in most general terms.

The one substance to which all living membranes seem to be completely permeable is water. When we consider other small molecules and ions the evidence is conflicting. Many animal and plant cells lose water when placed in concentrated aqueous solutions of salts or of various soluble organic compounds. This would indicate that their membranes are impermeable to these solutes. Yet clearly these very substances must find their way into living cells, for it is only in this way that cells can obtain food or maintain the ionic ratios which are essential to them. One way in which this is brought about is by what is known as "active transport." This means that by using some of the energy at its disposal from oxidation of foodstuffs a cell can do osmotic work, that is, it can bring in some molecules and exclude others without reference to the concentration gradient at the cell membrane.

In contrast to their limited permeability for many ions and charged organic molecules, cell membranes are in general much more readily permeable to substances which resemble the fats in solubility. This has led to the belief that cell membranes "generally consist of lipid layers penetrated by aqueous pores."

Surface Equilibria

Some indication of the way in which cell membranes form may be obtained from a consideration of the energy relations which obtain at the surface.

Surface tension

When a drop of liquid falls freely it assumes a spherical form because of unbalanced forces of molecular attraction. A molecule in the center of the drop is attracted in all directions by surrounding molecules. But while molecules on the periphery are attracted inward, this attraction is not balanced by any comparable attraction between the surface molecules and the air. As a result there is at the surface an amount of free surface energy which depends in part on the surface area and for the rest on what is known as the surface tension of the liquid. This tension is a measure of the work required to form unit area of additional surface, and is expressed in units of force and length, usually dynes per centimeter. The actual free energy at a surface, F_s, is then expressed

$$F_s = \gamma A$$

in which A denotes the area of the surface and γ the surface tension. Thus when a drop assumes spherical form, it is reducing as far as possible the free surface energy, since a sphere presents the smallest possible surface area for a given volume. When the temperature of a liquid is increased, the surface tension decreases, since the increased molecular motion tends to overcome the forces holding the surface molecules in place.

The free energy of any system tends toward a minimum at constant temperature and pressure. As just indicated, a freely falling pure liquid exemplifies this tendency when it assumes spherical form. When instead of a pure liquid a solution is allowed to fall freely, a second resource for reducing the free surface energy is available. In general the surface tension of a solution differs from that of the pure solvent, being greater or less, depending upon the nature of the solute and upon its concentration. Many organic compounds in solution cause a significant lowering of surface tension, and these substances are said to be *surface active*. Such solutes, by collecting in greater concentration at the surface than in the bulk of a solution, reduce the surface tension and therefore the free energy of the system. Some solutes, among them strong electrolytes, cause slight increases in surface tension perhaps by binding to their ions so much of the available water that the effective structure of the solvent is altered. Such solutes are said to be *surface inactive*.

When a liquid surface is in contact with that of another liquid the boundary between the two is known as an *interface*, which consists essentially of two mutually saturated solutions of the two liquids. In general, as shown in Tables 2.4 and 2.5, interfacial energies are less than those which obtain at a liquid-gas interface. This would be expected since the surface molecules of one liquid

TABLE 2.4. Surface Tension of Selected Liquids in Contact with Air

Liquid	Concentration	Temperature, °C	Surface Tension, dynes/cm
Water		0	75.6
		20	72.75
		100	58.9
Acetic acid		20	27.6
		50	24.7
Benzene		20	28.9
Chloroform		20	27.1
Ethyl acetate		20	23.9
Ethyl alcohol		20	22.3
Ethyl ether		20	17.0
Aq. NaCl	$0.1M$	20	72.92
Aq. MgCl$_2$	$0.1M$	20	73.07
Aq. acetic acid	5.0%	25	55.45

SOURCE: Data from *Handbook of Chemistry and Physics*, 40th ed., Chemical Rubber Publishing Co., Cleveland, O., 1958–1959.

TABLE 2.5. Interfacial Tension Between Two Liquids

Liquids	Temperature, °C	Surface Tension, dynes/cm
Water/olive oil	23	17.0
Water/isoamyl alcohol	23	4.4
Water/benzene	20	35.0
9% Ox gall/olive oil		7.2
Soap soln./olive oil		3.65
Water/oleic acid	25	12.8

would be attracted more strongly to molecules of another liquid than to the widely dispersed molecules of a gas. When one or both of the liquids is a solution, surface active solutes collect at the interface as they do at any surface, thus reducing the interfacial tension.

Measurement of interfacial tensions between living cells and their environment has revealed very low values, as for example 1.3 dynes for frog leukocytes suspended in frog plasma. This points clearly to a high concentration of surface active material at the boundary, and has led to the suggestion that the cytoplasmic membrane is simply a heightened concentration of certain cell constituents at the surface of the cell. Among the compounds universally present in living cells are certain complex fatty substances known as phospholipids which depress the surface tension markedly. A concentration of these compounds at the cell surface would account for the permeability of the cell membrane to fat-soluble materials and would also satisfy that tendency of all systems to reduce their free surface energy.

Adsorption

The removal of toxic gases from air by finely divided charcoal is a familiar procedure, as is decolorization of solutions by certain forms of the same substance. These are both examples of adsorption, a substance in the gas or liquid phase forming a concentrated film on the solid surface. It has been shown that the amount of material adsorbed is proportional to the area of the interface, but depends also on the concentration of the material which is to be adsorbed and on the solvent employed. In general a substance is most completely adsorbed from the solvent in which it is least soluble. Analytical procedures which are based in part on adsorption are those known as *chromatographic analyses*. Several of the more important types are here described in general terms. Specific references to their use will be found in later chapters.

1. COLUMN CHROMATOGRAPHY. As the name indicates, chromatography was originally developed in work with colored substances. In recent years it has become one of the most versatile analytical methods available to chemists, and it is used for analysis of many mixtures which are themselves colorless and which form no colored derivatives.

The various chromatographic processes depend upon a few basic facts: (*a*) Substances differ in the readiness with which they are adsorbed upon a solid surface. When an organic compound is freed of colored impurities by boiling its solution with decolorizing charcoal, the success of the separation depends upon the fact that the colored molecules are adsorbed on the surface of the charcoal while most of the others remain in solution. (*b*) The relative ease and tenacity of adsorption depend also upon the solvent employed. This fact was used in early attempts to separate enzymes from other cellular contents. It was found that when a tissue extract was shaken with some colloidal material such as aluminum hydroxide, many enzymes would be adsorbed on the colloid. They could then be removed from the adsorbent or *eluted* by shaking with a different solvent or with the same solvent adjusted to a different pH.

These facts were used early in the century when an adsorption column was first elaborated for chlorophyll studies. But it was not until about 1931 that

Kuhn[1] and his co-workers made chromatographic analysis a common laboratory method. In its simplest form the method uses a long glass tube packed with an adsorbing material such as aluminum hydroxide or the clay known as "fuller's earth." If a solution containing a number of colored solutes is allowed to trickle down this column, the solutes are selectively adsorbed. The rate of migration of a given substance down the column is almost inversely proportional to what is known as its adsorption coefficient. The adsorption coefficient is defined as the ratio of the amount adsorbed per gram of dry column material to the concentration of the solute in the solution. If its adsorption coefficient is high, it is readily adsorbed, is difficult to elute, and will remain near the top of the column. If its adsorption coefficient is low, it will travel down the column rapidly. After the solution has passed through the tube, the chromatogram is "developed" by passing a large volume of the same or a different solvent slowly through the column. This results in innumerable elutions and readsorptions, with each substance moving down the column at its own rate. Each will after a time occupy a zone which appears as a colored band in the white column. In Fig. 2.5 is shown the separation of a crude cyclohexane extract of grass into three different colored components. The column was packed with magnesium oxide, and the position of the chlorophylls near the top shows that they were strongly adsorbed. From such a column the three components could be recovered by pushing out the magnesium oxide cylinder and cutting out the colored portions.

The type of separation just described has been adapted to resolve all sorts of colorless mixtures. This has been greatly facilitated by the appearance on the market of a variety of ion exchange resins which adsorb selectively, and of other synthetic adsorbing materials. Among the naturally occurring adsorbents in addition to aluminum hydroxide, starch, inulin, cellulose, silica gel, and various insoluble salts have been used to pack the columns. We shall see later how column chromatography has made possible the separation of minute amounts of very complex mixtures. Often the development with the second solvent is prolonged so that instead of remaining in layers in the column, the components of the mixture are washed out one after the other and are caught as the developing solvent drips from the bottom of the column. If the outflow is collected in small portions, a single chromatographic analysis may serve to isolate each of several substances occurring in small amounts in a complex mixture.

2. PAPER CHROMATOGRAPHY. The use of paper in a modified chromatographic procedure was developed by A. J. P. Martin and his colleagues in England, and this method is probably now the most widely used of all the

---

[1] Richard Kuhn was born in Vienna in 1900. For many years he published from Zürich, but he has been Director of the Kaiser-Wilhelm Institute for Medical Research in Heidelberg since 1929, and since 1950 Professor of Biochemistry at the University. He was awarded the Nobel Prize in Chemistry in 1938, but was not able to accept it.

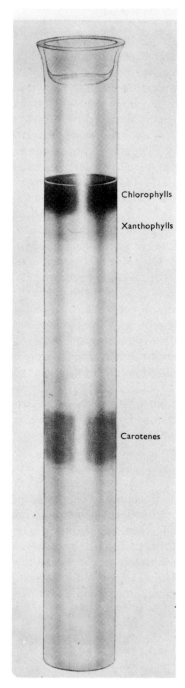

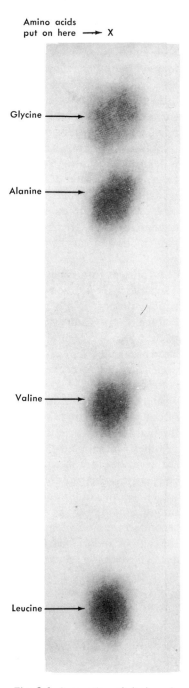

Fig. 2.5. Separation of a grass extract dissolved in cyclohexane into three fractions by passing it through a column of magnesium oxide. [From A. J. P. Martin, *Endeavour*, **6,** 21 (1947).]

Fig. 2.6. Separation of glycine, alanine, valine, and leucine by filter paper chromatography, using butanol as solvent. [From A. J. P. Martin, *Endeavour*, **6,** 25 (1947).]

chromatographic procedures. In this procedure, a strip of moist filter paper hangs in an atmosphere saturated with water. A very small sample (0.002–0.02 ml) of the mixture to be separated is applied near the top of the paper with a micropipet. The top of the paper dips into a trough containing an organic solvent saturated with water. As this solvent flows down the paper by gravity, the components of the mixture flow with it at different rates. The ratio of the velocity with which a component moves to that with which the solvent front moves is denoted by the symbol R_f. Actual values are, of course, always less than unity. The R_f value depends to some extent upon adsorption of the solute by the paper, but a far more important factor in the separation is the partition ratio of each component between the two solvents, water adsorbed on the paper and the moving organic solvent. After the lapse of a certain amount of time the components will be spread out along the strip as shown in Fig. 2.6. In this particular experiment the spots were made visible, since each of the components of the mixture reacted with ninhydrin (see p. 216) to form a blue derivative. For other types of mixtures other means of identifying the spots have to be used.

Paper chromatography becomes more discriminating if the spot containing the mixture is put in one corner of a square sheet of filter paper. After development of the chromatogram as just described, the components will be spread out in a column near one margin of the paper. The paper is then turned through 90^0 and, with a different solvent, the sheet is developed at right angles to the first procedure. Since R_f values are likely to differ in the two solvents, the second development may separate a single spot into two or more, substances which traveled together in the first solvent having different rates in the second. Figure 2.7 shows such a two-dimensional chromatogram, made with the mixture of 18 amino acids obtained by hydrolysis of gelatin. The five which were not identified were each present to the extent of 2 per cent or less. We shall have many occasions to realize how the technique of paper chromatography has been improved since 1947, and how widely it is now used.

3. GAS CHROMATOGRAPHY. Since about 1952 the chromatographic technique has been applied in a method known as gas chromatography to the separation of mixtures which can be volatilized. The mixture is applied to one end of a column containing an adsorbing liquid which is a stationary coating on some inert supporting material. The column is heated to whatever temperature is needed and a stream of inert gas carries the components of the mixture along the tube, where they distribute themselves between the gas phase and the stationary liquid. Because of differences in the affinity of the liquid for the various components, they move through the column at different rates and emerge with separate portions of the effluent inert gas carrier. By use of suitable detectors the arrival of a component may be noted, and is often recorded automatically.

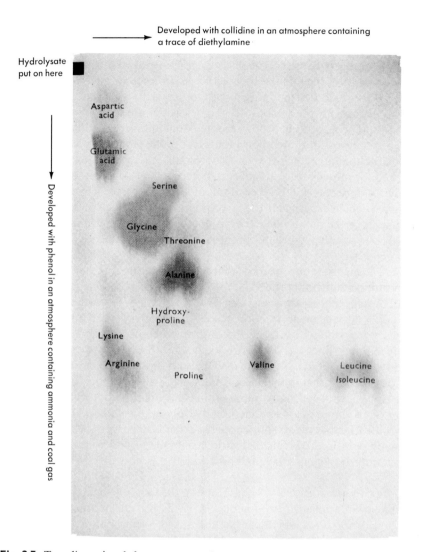

Developed with collidine in an atmosphere containing a trace of diethylamine

Hydrolysate put on here

Developed with phenol in an atmosphere containing ammonia and coal gas

Aspartic acid

Glutamic acid

Serine

Glycine

Threonine

Alanine

Hydroxy-proline

Lysine

Arginine

Proline

Valine

Leucine
Isoleucine

Fig. 2.7. Two-dimensional chromatogram of a gelatin hydrolysate. A drop of the solution was placed at the corner of the paper as shown. The chromatogram was developed with s-collidine, dried, and then developed at right angles to the first procedure with phenol. After drying a second time the paper was sprayed with ninhydrin and warmed to bring out the color wherever an amino acid had accumulated. [From A. J. P. Martin, *Endeavour*, **6**, 26 (1947).]

Columns for use in gas chromatography vary in length, in bore, and in supporting material. One commercial apparatus has a U-shaped column 6 ft long with a 4-mm bore. This is packed with an inert granular material coated with a liquid or soft gum. In another type of apparatus the column is a 200-ft-long capillary tube which carries no packing, but has a thin coating of the stationary phase on its own inner surface. These methods are proving useful

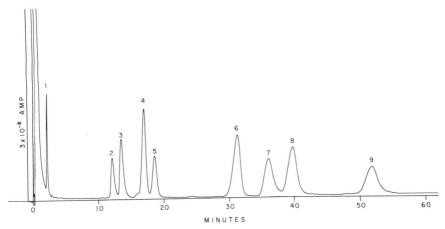

Fig. 2.8. Separation of 1, androstane; 2, pregnane-3,20-dione; 3, allopregnane-3,20-dione; 4, coprostane; 5, cholestane; 6, stigmastane; 7, cholesterol; 8, cholestan-3-one; 9, stigmasterol. Conditions: 3% SE-30 silicone gum on Chromosorb W (80–100 mesh); 6 ft × 4 mm column; 222°; argon inlet pressure, 10 psi. [From W. J. A. Vanden Heuvel *et al.*, *J. Am. Chem. Soc.*, **82**, 3481 (1960).]

in separation of substances which are very much alike chemically, for example, cis and trans isomers. A method of this type has very recently been used in separation of two different mixtures, one of which contained several different closely related steroids and the other eight or nine very similar alkaloids. Figure 2.8 records the separation of the steroids. The original mixture weighed only about 5 μg and was resolved in less than 60 min. The solvent in this separation was a recently developed methyl silicone polymer designated SE-30. The measuring device was, as the graph indicates, an electrical one.

The rates at which the gases travel through the column are compared as their "retention times," and one of the disadvantages of the early procedures was the long retention times encountered. It seems certain that the next few years will see this time greatly shortened by the use of new apparatus and different stationary phases, and that gas chromatography will prove invaluable in the separation not only of different substances but also of stereoisomers of the same substance. In recognition of its importance the *Annual Review of Biochemistry* for 1960 carries its first article devoted to gas chromatography.

LIGHT ABSORPTION

Among the most elegant analytical methods available to the biochemist are those which depend upon absorption of radiant energy. Colorimetry is used largely in routine analytical procedures to determine concentrations by comparing the light transmitted by a colored solution with that transmitted by a standard. When the comparison is made, not by matching two colors visually, but by measuring the energy of the transmitted light by means of such a device as the photoelectric cell, the process is known as *photometry*. Spectrophotometry is used to determine the absorption of radiant energy at a variety of wavelengths and is widely used in identification of compounds and in determination of structure.

The Spectrum

Light may be considered to be a corpuscular form of energy in which the particles are known as *photons* or *quanta*, or a wave of electromagnetic disturbance. In Fig. 2.9 the undulating line represents an advancing wave front.

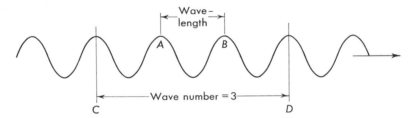

Fig. 2.9. Relation between wavelength and wave number.

The distance from *A* to *B*, from one wave crest to the next, is the *wavelength*. The number of complete waves in some unit length, as for example in the distance between *C* and *D*, is the *wave number*, while the *frequency* indicates the number of wave crests which pass a point in space in some unit time. Using λ (lambda) to stand for wavelength, σ (sigma) for wave number, ν (nu) for frequency, and c for the speed of light, the relations between these quantities may be expressed

$$\frac{1}{\lambda} = \sigma = \frac{\nu}{c}$$

When fundamental cgs units are used throughout, c has the value 3×10^{10} cm per sec.

The energy which is associated with light of any particular wavelength is proportional to its frequency as indicated by the equation

$$E = h\nu$$

The energy E is expressed in ergs, the frequency in waves per second, and h is Planck's constant with a value of 6.624×10^{-10} erg per sec. Thus light of high frequency (or short wavelength) has the higher energy or radiant power.

The wavelengths of various vibrating forms of energy range from approximately 10^8 meters for ultrasonic waves to 10^{-12} meter for the gamma radiation from radioactive elements. The wavelengths of cosmic rays are still shorter than this. Figure 2.10 shows the electromagnetic spectrum, in which the

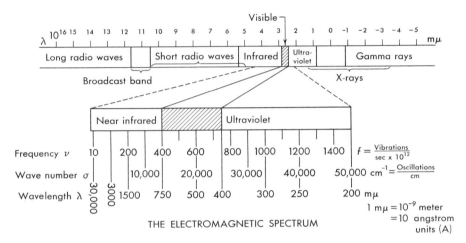

Fig. 2.10. The spectral distribution of radiant energy with the units in which it is measured.

narrow shaded band marks the portion which produces the sensation of visible light. In the lower part of the figure is represented the spectral region which is commonly used for spectroscopic measurements, with the three descriptive terms indicated in the appropriate units.

The wavelength of light is measured in different units, depending on the part of the spectrum which is involved. The longer waves are measured in meters. For wavelengths from those of the ultraviolet through the visible and the infrared the unit is sometimes the millimicron (mμ) which is 10^{-7} cm, and sometimes the angstrom unit, named for the Swedish physicist A. J. Ångstrom (1814–1874). This unit is now abbreviated in this country A and is 0.1 mμ or 10^{-8} cm. The conversion of wavelengths to wave numbers and frequencies must take account of the units in which the desired values are to be expressed.

The wave number is usually reported as the number of waves per centimeter (cm^{-1}). If a wavelength of 400 mμ (4000 A) is to be converted to wave number it must be expressed in centimeters.

$$400 \times 10^{-7} = \lambda \text{ in cm}$$

$$\frac{1}{400 \times 10^{-7}} = \frac{1}{400} \times 10^7 = 25,000 \text{ cm}^{-1} = \sigma$$

The frequency is occasionally expressed in waves per second, but since these numbers are very large the more usual unit is the fresnel (f) which gives the number of vibrations per 10^{-12} sec.

$$\sigma = \frac{\nu}{c}$$

$$25,000 = \frac{\nu}{3 \times 10^{10}}$$

$$\nu = 25,000 \times 3 \times 10^{10} = 7.5 \times 10^{14} \text{ vibrations/sec}$$

$$= \frac{25,000 \times 3 \times 10^{10}}{10^{12}} = 75,000 \times 10^{-2} = 750 \text{ f}$$

Colorimetry

When a beam of white light passes through a glass container holding a clear colored solution, the beam suffers a loss of radiant power. This loss is due in small part to reflections and refractions as the beam enters and leaves the container or cell, but it is largely the result of absorption of the radiant energy by the molecules of the colored solute. Thus the solution which appears blue has this appearance because it is absorbing the complementary yellow light with wavelengths of about 575–590 mμ. The quantitative methods which measure the extent of this absorption are applicable not only to substances which are themselves colored but also to a wide variety of colorless compounds which react to form colored products. The use of such measurements to estimate concentrations depends upon information summarized in the Lambert–Beer law.

Consider a beam of white light passing upward through a glass cell holding a column of colored liquid of depth b. Figure 2.11 indicates the changes in the energy of the beam, or its radiant power, symbolized by P. P_0 is slightly less than P_1 because of reflection and refraction at the glass-air interface and for the same reasons P_2 differs slightly from P. The large change, however, is the drop in energy from P_0 to P, due to light absorption by the molecules in the path of the beam. In the following discussion the small losses at the interfaces will be neglected both because they are quantitatively unimportant and because they are compensated for by using for comparison a standard solution which is subject to similar losses.

Lambert studied the relation between the original power or intensity of a parallel beam of monochromatic light and its intensity after passing through various *thicknesses* of a colored solution. He found that the power is reduced by some fractional amount in passing through equal thicknesses of absorbing solution. Thus if it is reduced by half in the first centimeter, it will be reduced

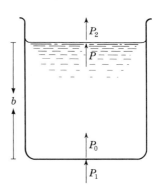

Fig. 2.11. Losses in radiant power of a beam of light in passing through a solution.

by half of the new intensity in traversing the next centimeter and so on. Allowing P_0 to stand for the original radiant power[2] which reaches the solution, and b for the depth of solution traversed, Lambert's results may be expressed

$$\log \frac{P_0}{P} \propto b$$

or, inserting the proportionality constant k_1

$$\log \frac{P_0}{P} = k_1 b$$

The value of k_1 depends on the solute and its concentration, upon the wavelength of the light and the temperature.

Beer investigated the relation between *concentration* of a colored solution and the amount of monochromatic light which it absorbed. He found that under suitable conditions the absorption is proportional to the number of solute molecules in unit volume. This may be expressed as

$$\log \frac{P_0}{P} \propto c(\text{conc.}) \quad \text{or} \quad \log \frac{P_0}{P} = k_2 c$$

---

[2] In recent years the letters and symbols customarily used to denote the various quantities have been revised, and those used in this book are the ones recommended in 1952 by the Joint Committee on Nomenclature in Applied Spectroscopy. See H. K. Hughes *et al.*, *Anal. Chem.*, **24**, 1349 (1952). Previously I_0 and I were used for the two intensities. Table 2.6 lists the revised symbols and some of the older synonyms, many of which are still used in European journals.

The constant k_2 is similar to k_1 above. By combining the two expressions, the relation between concentration, length of path, and absorption is given by the single equation

$$\log \frac{P_0}{P} = k_1 k_2 bc$$

When concentration is expressed in grams per liter, the product of the two constants is given the symbol *a* which stands for *absorptivity*. This is a specific physical property of the absorbing molecules. Its value, however, will depend also upon the nature of the solvent, on the wavelength of the light and upon the units chosen for *b* and *c*. The length of the path is usually given in centimeters. If the concentration is given in moles per liter the symbol for the constant is E (epsilon) which stands for *molar absorptivity*.

The quantity $\log P_0/P$ is of such fundamental importance that it has been given the special symbol *A*, and is called the *absorbance*. The relation between these various quantities may be shown as:

$$\log \frac{P_0}{P} = A = abc$$

Table 2.6 gives the presently accepted symbols for use with the Lambert–Beer law and indicates the other symbols which have been used in the past.

TABLE 2.6.   Units and Symbols for Use with the Lambert–Beer Law

Recommended Symbol	Definition	Recommended Name	Alternate Symbol	Alternate Name
T	P/P_0	Transmittance	—	Transmission[a]
A	$\log (P_0/P)$	Absorbance	D or O.D. E^b	Optical density Extinction
a	A/bc^c	Absorptivity	k	Extinction coefficient Specific extinction Absorbance index
E	A/bM^d	Molar absorptivity	a_M	Molar extinction coefficient
b		Length of path	l, d	

SOURCE: Information in this table is largely derived from report of H. K. Hughes *et al.*, *Anal. Chem.*, **24**, 1349 (1952).

[a] Often multiplied by 100 and reported as a per cent.

[b] This symbol occasionally appears as $E_{1cm}^{x\%}$. This may be defined as A/bc', where c' is the concentration in per cent by weight.

[c] c = concentration in grams per liter.

[d] M = concentration in moles per liter.

Absorption Spectra

Two types of spectra are used in the investigation of atoms and molecules. These are *emission* and *absorption* spectra. When a substance is exposed to some source of energy such as an electric spark or a flame, its electrons are pushed to outer or higher energy levels. As they fall back to lower levels, the energy which they have just acquired is released as radiant energy. If this emitted light is analyzed by a spectroscope there is obtained an emission spectrum consisting of a set of bright lines or bands against a dark background.

An absorption spectrum is the opposite of an emission spectrum. When radiation, visible or invisible, passes through an absorbing medium some wavelengths are absorbed and others are transmitted. Thus the spectrum obtained when the transmitted light is analyzed consists of a set of dark lines or bands, representing the absorbed light, against a bright background made up of the transmitted wavelengths. Whereas emission spectra are of special importance in the identification of elements, each of which gives out a highly characteristic set of radiations when suitably excited, absorption spectra are widely used in the study of molecules, especially those of organic compounds. These spectra may be obtained not only with visible light but with radiations in both the ultraviolet and the infrared ranges.

Theory of absorption

It was recognized by the early dye chemists that color is associated with the presence of certain groups in an organic molecule. These are known as chromophore groups, nearly all of which prove in practice to be unsaturated in some degree. According to modern theory all organic molecules absorb light energy, but the only compounds which absorb in the visible range are those which are capable of resonance, that is, of having more than one stable electronic configuration.

When energy is absorbed by a compound it may cause three different kinds of change in the molecule, the total energy change in any given case being the sum of the three. Electrons may be pushed to higher energy levels; the extent of vibration of atoms within the molecule may change and finally the rotation of the molecule as a whole about its center of mass may be altered. In order to induce one of these changes in a specific organic grouping the radiant energy provided must include the specific wavelengths which that group can absorb. Other wavelengths which may be present but are not absorbed by the compound in question are transmitted. In general, changes in the vibrational and rotational states involve small energy changes, and these are usually measured by infrared absorption spectra. Changes in the electronic state of a compound, on the other hand, involve much larger amounts of energy and are induced by absorption of light of shorter wavelength or higher frequency, usually in the ultraviolet but occasionally in the visible region.

Measurement of absorption

The simplest possible instrument for determining the absorption of visible light is the spectroscope. In such an instrument the entering white light is spread into a spectrum by means of a prism. When some colored substance is put in the path of the light beam, the absorbed wavelengths are indicated by dark bands on the bright solar spectrum.

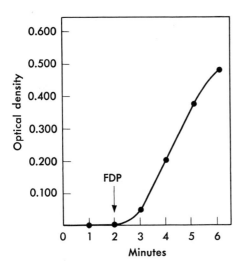

Fig. 2.12. Change in optical density with time in a solution in which an enzyme is changing "FDP" into a substance which absorbs light at 340 mμ. [From M. Losada, A. V. Trebst, and D. I. Arnon, *J. Biol. Chem.*, **235**, 835, (1960).]

For more exact work it is necessary to use a spectrophotometer, an instrument which measures light absorption electrically and in which the wavelength of the absorbed light can be determined precisely. In very general and greatly simplified terms a spectrophotometer works as follows. The incident beam of radiant energy is broken into a spectrum by a grating or prism. From this spectrum narrow bands, as nearly homogeneous as possible, are isolated and passed one at a time in sequence through the solution which is being examined. The intensity of the transmitted light is measured for each wavelength by means of a photoelectric cell.

Spectral data are reported in the form of curves in which the wavelength or wave number (cm^{-1}) or frequency (f) is often plotted on the abscissa and some value which indicates the extent of absorption is used as ordinate. Figures 2.12 to 2.15 illustrate some of the customary symbols and notations. In Fig. 2.12 an enzyme reaction is being followed which gives rise to a product with a high absorbance at 340 mμ. At the point indicated by the arrow a final essential reactant was added, and the rising optical density indicates the resultant formation of the absorbing compound. Figure 2.13(a) records the

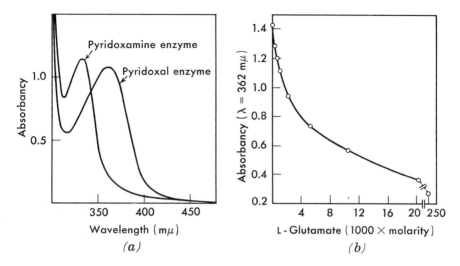

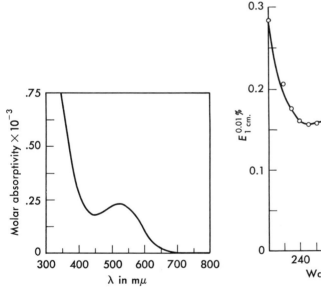

Fig. 2.13. (*a*) Absorbancy of two forms of an enzyme complex, one of which absorbs light of wavelength 340 mμ while the absorption maximum of the other is at 362 mμ. (*b*) Drop in absorbancy at 362 mμ as the pyridoxal form of the enzyme changes to the pyridoxamine form as a result of its interaction with increasing concentrations of glutamic acid. [From W. T. Jenkins and I. W. Sizer, *J. Biol. Chem.*, **235**, 621 (1960).]

Fig. 2.14. Molar absorptivity of the complex formed by the enzyme, carboxypeptidase, with cobalt. [From J. E. Coleman and B. L. Vallee, *J. Biol. Chem.*, **235**, 393 (1960).]

Fig. 2.15. Ultraviolet absorption spectrum of a bacterial lipopolysaccharide. [From A. P. MacLennan, *Biochem. J.*, **74**, 400 (1960).]

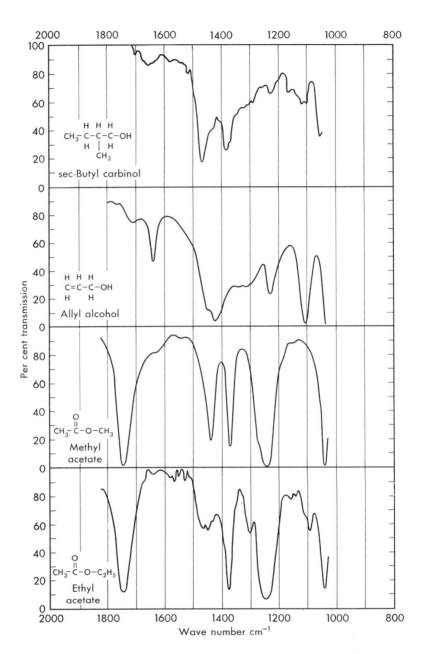

Fig. 2.16. Infrared absorption curves for four simple organic compounds. Note the absorption at 1640 cm⁻¹ in the allyl alcohol curve, referable to the double bond, and those at 1745 in the ester curves, referable to the ester carbonyl group. [From R. B. Barnes, U. Liddel, and V. Z. Williams, *Ind. Eng. Chem., Anal. Ed.*, **15**, 659 (1943). By permission of the American Chemical Society, copyright owner.]

light absorbances of two forms of the same enzyme. When this enzyme functions catalytically, the one form changes into the other. This is illustrated in Fig. 2.13(*b*). As noted on the previous curve, the pyridoxal form absorbs strongly at 362 mμ. When it reacts with L-glutamate it changes into the amine form which absorbs only slightly at this wavelength, and so the reaction is accompanied by a fall in absorbance to approximately 0.25 unit, which is characteristic of the amine form. In Fig. 2.14 the light absorption of a metallo-protein is plotted in terms of molar absorptivity, and Fig. 2.15, reporting absorption in the ultraviolet, illustrates the use of the extinction symbol with the concentration of the solution specified. In all these curves the peaks represent high absorption of light of the specified wavelength. In other graphs, particularly those which record absorption in the infrared, the ordinate unit is *transmittance* (P/P_0) or *percentage transmittance*, which is 100 times the transmittance. On such curves, since the value which is recorded is the fraction of the incident beam which is not absorbed, high absorbance is denoted by troughs in the curve. Such infrared absorption curves are illustrated in Fig. 2.16.

Infrared absorption

Infrared absorption, except that it involves radiant energy of low frequencies, is like absorption in the other spectral regions. But an infrared spectrum can be interpreted more specifically than those of the visible or ultraviolet ranges. It was noted earlier that the changes induced in a molecule when it absorbs infrared radiation are changes in molecular rotation or in atomic vibration. Actually most of the instruments now in use generate radiations in the near infrared (2–15μ) and these frequencies affect only the vibrational states. It has been found that, while part of the absorption in the near infrared is referable to the molecular structure as a whole, other frequencies absorbed are character-istic of small groups within the molecule. Whenever a given group is present, absorption of its particular frequency appears in the molecular spectrum, which is thus a summation of the bands due to the groups and those due to the gross molecular structure. Table 2.7 lists the wave numbers and wavelengths of the energy absorbed by a few of the common organic groupings. It should be noted that even the slight differences between carbonyl groups in ester, acidic, and ketonic linkages give rise to absorptions of different wavelengths. Because of this specificity the infrared spectrum of a compound has been called its "fingerprint."

As noted above, infrared absorption is reported in terms of transmittance plotted against wavelength or wave number. In such curves, of which Fig. 2.16 gives several examples, the largest absorbance is indicated by those portions of the curve nearest the base line.

Organic chemical analysis by means of infrared absorption is becoming increasingly important. This is particularly true in the biochemical field,

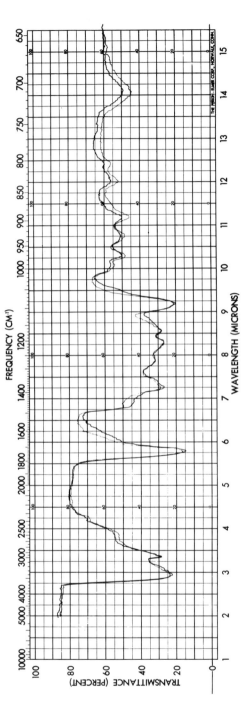

Fig. 2.17. Comparison of the infrared spectrum of synthetic α,β-dihydroxyisovaleric acid with that of a compound produced by enzyme action. The identical spectra prove that the enzymic product is also α,β-dihydroxyisovaleric acid [From M. Strassman *et al., J. Biol. Chem.,* **235**, 703 (1960).]

since many important compounds are colorless and also absorb very little in the ultraviolet, whereas nearly all show selective absorption in the infrared. Infrared spectra of such substances not only identify specific groups, but also

TABLE 2.7. Approximate Positions of Infrared Absorption Bands for Various Functional Groups

Group	Wavelength, μ	Wave Number, cm^{-1}
C—H (aliphatic)	3.3–3.7	2700–3000
C—H (aromatic)	3.2–3.3	3000–3100
C=O (anhydrides)	5.3–5.5	1800–1850[a] / 1750–1800
C=O (ester)	5.7–5.8	1725–1750
C=O (acid)	6.05	1650
C=O (aldehyde)	5.75–5.80	1720–1740
C—C	9.1–13.3	750–1100
C=C	5.98–6.17	1620–1670
C≡C	4.44–4.76	2100–2250
C≡N	4.44–4.76	2100–2250
N—H	2.96–3.33	3300–3370
S—H	3.85–3.90	2570–2600
O—H (phenolic)	2.7	3700

SOURCE: Data from H. H. Willard, L. Merritt, and J. A. Dean, *Instrumental Methods of Analysis*, 3rd ed. Copyright 1958, D. Van Nostrand Co., Inc., Princeton, N.J.

[a] Anhydrides usually show a double absorption band.

give an indication of the structure of the molecule as a whole. Figure 2.17 shows how comparison of two such curves will prove whether or not the substances from which they were obtained are identical.

FLUORESCENCE

It has long been known that certain substances will glow or fluoresce after exposure to light. Some substances respond in this way to visible light, but with others ultraviolet is needed. Within the last ten years, measurement of fluorescence has become increasingly important in biochemistry. Although the ability to fluoresce is on the whole rather rare, many of the compounds of most interest to biochemists do have this property or can be converted simply to derivatives which have it. For example, the chlorophylls, porphyrins, carotenes, and flavins are all fluorescent. Thiamine becomes fluorescent after oxidation.

When a molecule absorbs radiation, there is a small change in its potential energy due to increased vibration of the atoms, and a far larger change which results from the shifting of electrons to orbitals of greater energy, i.e., farther from the nucleus. With most molecules thus activated, the extra energy is lost through collisions which generate heat. Fluorescent substances, however, give off part of the energy which they lose when the electrons return to their original levels, in the form of light of longer wavelength than that of the

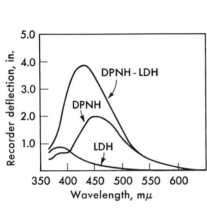

Fig. 2.18. Fluorescent spectra of an enzyme protein, lactic dehydrogenase (LDH), of reduced diphosphopyridine nucleotide (DPNH) and of the complex (DPNH-LDH) which they form when the enzyme is acting catalytically. [From A. D. Winer *et al.*, *J. Am. Chem. Soc.*, **79**, 6571 (1957).]

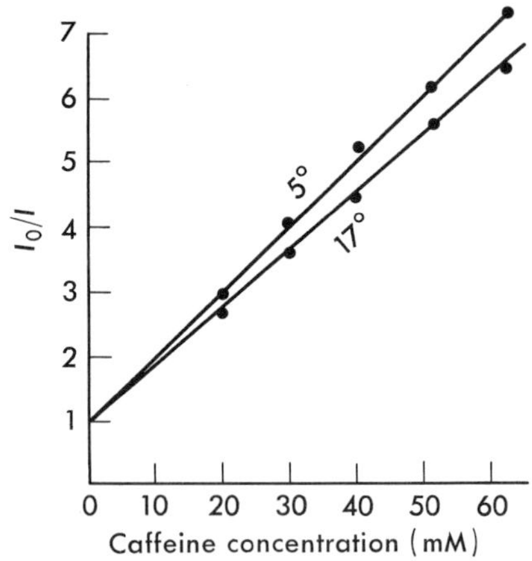

Fig. 2.19. Quenching of the fluorescence of riboflavin by caffeine. Riboflavin concentration, $7 \times 10^{-6} M$; I_0/I, ratio of the fluorescent intensities before and after addition of quencher. [From G. Weber, *Biochem. J.*, **47**, 116 (1950).]

activating radiation. By means of fluorophotometers the intensity of this fluorescent beam may be measured. Fluorimetry is far more sensitive than spectrophotometry, so that the lower limit of concentration suitable for the latter is the highest concentration suitable for fluorimetry. This makes it possible to measure fluorimetrically concentrations of about $10^{-8}M$, or even in favorable cases as low as $10^{-9}M$.

The intensity of fluorescence, F, is proportional to the radiation absorbed and is practically proportional to the concentration of the fluorescent compound if the concentrations are low enough so that $abc = 0.01$ (see Table 2.6 for definition of these symbols). Fluorescent intensities may be reported in arbitrary units or in terms of the particular measuring device used, such as inches of deflection of a galvanometer needle. In Fig. 2.18 fluorescent spectra are shown for a substance which is known in biochemistry as diphospho-pyridine nucleotide (DPNH), for a protein enzyme called lactic dehydrogenase

(LDH), and for a complex of the two which forms when they are mixed. The curves show that the protein alone shows only slight fluorescence at about 380 mμ and that complex formation results in a shift of the wavelength of the maximum fluorescent emission for DPNH from about 455 mμ to about 430 mμ. This shift to shorter wavelength when a complex forms is called the Boyer–Theorell effect. In this graph the emission is reported in terms of the actual galvanometer deflection which measured the intensity of the fluorescent beam.

Certain compounds which are themselves fluorescent lose this property in the presence of some other molecules or ions, or when they enter into combination. The fluorescence is then said to be *quenched*. Riboflavin, for example, is fluorescent, but loses about half of the fluorescence in the presence of silver ions. Figure 2.19 shows the effect of increasing concentrations of caffeine on the fluorescence of riboflavin, the effect being expressed as a ratio of the original fluorescence intensity (I_0) to that in the presence of the quenching agent (I). Thus in the presence of 30 millimoles of caffeine the fluorescence was only about one-quarter of the original.

HYDROGEN ION CONCENTRATION

The acidity of a living cell varies within very narrow limits, and work with biological systems is possible only in media in which a specified acidity can be maintained. For example, the cell catalysts or enzymes are extremely sensitive to variations in acidity, and may be completely inactivated by slight increases or decreases in the hydrogen ion concentration. Similarly the acidity of the soil determines the type of plant which can be grown on it, and optimum growth of bacteria is possible only if the medium is adjusted to maintain the correct acidity in the face of metabolic fluctuations in the actual acid content. Thus the measurement and control of hydrogen ion concentration are of fundamental importance in all types of biological work.

The units to be used in any quantitative discussion of ionic equilibria depend upon the concentrations of the solutions to be considered and upon the possible accuracy of the experimental procedures. The quantitative laws were originally worked out in terms of ion concentrations but it has long been known that, because of interionic attractions, the operative factor is not the actual concentration but something which has been called the "effective ion concentration" or the "activity." The activity of the ions in a solution of a specific concentration may be determined experimentally. The ratio of this activity to the actual concentration of a particular ion gives the "activity coefficient" of that ion, a quantity which is usually represented by the letter f.

$$\frac{a}{c} = f$$

When the activity coefficient is known the activity of an ion can be calculated as the product of its concentration by the coefficient.

$$a = fc$$

The activity coefficient is not constant for any one ion, but varies both with its own concentration and with the concentrations of other ions present in the solution. In very accurate formulations this factor must always be taken into account. But as it happens the solutions commonly used in biochemical work are relatively dilute, and at that concentration level the difference between concentration and activity is so small that it usually may be neglected. The following discussion is therefore couched in the simpler terms of concentrations, but it must be borne in mind that these terms are applicable to only a limited concentration range and that the results obtained are approximations.

The *p*H System

Although the range of hydrogen ion concentrations with which biochemists are concerned is relatively small, it may well include several hundred or even several thousand molar units. The difficulty in choosing a scale for a graph in which the hydrogen ion concentrations may range, for example, from 10^{-5} to 10^{-8} mole per liter, has led to the widespread adoption of Sørensen's[3] *p*H system. The *p* stood originally for the French *puissance* but has been generally adopted since it serves equally well for the German *Potenz* and the English "power" used in its mathematical sense. In this system then the acidity is expressed as a power of the reciprocal of the hydrogen ion concentration.

The *p*H is defined most simply as the *negative logarithm* of the hydrogen ion concentration. With values which are simple powers of ten the transformation is simple. The negative logarithm of a number is the logarithm of its reciprocal. Hence the *p*H corresponding to a hydrogen ion concentration of 10^{-3} is 3.

$$p\text{H} = \log \frac{1}{10^{-3}} = \log 10^3 = 3.00$$

For a hydrogen ion concentration of 1.3×10^{-3} the *p*H is obtained as follows:

$$p\text{H} = \log \frac{1}{1.3 \times 10^{-3}} = \log \frac{10^3}{1.3}$$

$$= \log 10^3 - \log 1.3 = 3.00 - 0.11 = 2.89$$

---

[3] S. P. L. Sørensen (1868–1939) was born in Denmark and spent the greater part of his life in Copenhagen. There in 1901 he succeeded Johann Kjeldahl as Director of the Chemistry Department of the Carlsberg Laboratory, and much of his work appeared in the *Comptes rendus* of that Laboratory. He is best known for research on the physical chemistry of the amino acids and the proteins.

By the use of the pH system the range of acidities from that of normal hydrochloric acid to that of normal sodium hydroxide may be expressed in 15 units from zero to 14, as shown in Table 2.8. This gives a convenient scale for plotting experimental results. For example, an acidity change from 10^{-5} to 10^{-7} would require hundreds of units, but in terms of pH it needs only three.

TABLE 2.8. Hydrogen Ion Concentrations and pH Values at 25°C

Hydrogen Ion Concentration	Hydroxyl Ion Concentration	Solution	pH
10^{0}	10^{-14}	$1N$ HCl	0
10^{-1}	10^{-13}	$0.1N$ HCl	1
10^{-2}	10^{-12}	$0.01N$ HCl	2
10^{-3}	10^{-11}	$0.001N$ HCl	3
10^{-12}	10^{-2}	$0.01N$ NaOH	12
10^{-13}	10^{-1}	$0.1N$ NaOH	13
10^{-14}	10^{0}	$1N$ NaOH	14

To convert pH values back to hydrogen ion concentrations, the process outlined above is reversed. Suppose that the pH is 5.9. Either of the two following procedures will give the corresponding hydrogen ion concentration.[4]

1.
$$5.9 = \log \frac{1}{[H^+]}$$

$$\text{antilog } 5.9 = 800,000 = \frac{1}{[H^+]}$$

$$[H^+] = \frac{1}{8 \times 10^5} = \frac{1}{8} \times 10^{-5}$$

$$= 0.125 \times 10^{-5} = 1.25 \times 10^{-6}$$

2. Since 5.9 is a negative logarithm, the logarithm is -5.9, the *entire number* being negative. But in logarithm tables the mantissa is always given as a positive number, hence this value must be rewritten with a negative characteristic and a positive mantissa.

$$-5.9 = -6 + 0.10 = \bar{6}.10$$
$$\text{antilog } -6 = 10^{-6}$$
$$\text{antilog } 0.10 = 1.25$$
$$[H^+] = 1.25 \times 10^{-6}$$

---

[4] In the equations that follow, brackets indicate, as usual, the concentration in moles per liter.

Weak Acids

An early definition of an acid referred to its sour taste and its effect on litmus. Later a substance was considered an acid if it gave rise in solution to hydrogen (or hydronium) ions, and in these terms a base was any substance which gave rise to hydroxyl ions in water. A modern and more generally applicable definition of an acid is that proposed by J. N. Brønsted, which classifies as an acid any ion or molecule that can furnish a proton to solution. The particle or unit which remains after removal of the proton, or hydrogen ion, is then the *conjugate base* of the original acid, and any molecule or ion which can accept a proton is defined as a base. Thus in the equation

$$HA + H_2O = H_3O^+ + A^-$$

which represents the ionization of acetic acid, HA, water is acting as a base and the acetate ion (A^-) is the conjugate base of acetic acid. In the Brønsted system, the many ions and molecules which can act under different conditions as proton donor or proton acceptor, are both acids and bases. Water is a familiar example. When it acts as a proton acceptor, forming the hydronium ion, it is acting as a base. When it ionizes, some of the molecules act as acids and others act as bases.

$$H_2O + H_2O = H_3O^+ + OH^-$$

Acid **Base** **Acid** **Conjugate base**

In order to act as a base, any ion or molecule must have at least one lone pair of electrons, though possession of such a pair does not guarantee that the substance will actually function as a base and accept a proton.[5]

Weak acids exist in solution in equilibrium with small amounts of their ions. The ionization of such an acid, HA, is most simply represented by the equation

$$HA \rightleftharpoons H^+ + A^-$$

it being understood that the ions are more or less hydrated and that water

---

[5] It should perhaps be noted here that some of the older biochemists and physiologists used the word base in a very special sense, meaning essentially cations. This arose from the mistaken belief that certain metal ions, especially sodium, potassium, calcium, and magnesium in the blood were available to "neutralize" carbonic acid, that is, to act as a base in the older sense. Thus when carbon dioxide was entering the blood stream its acidity would be lowered by interaction with a metal salt. Letting B stand for the metal, and BP for a protein or other salt, the reaction was represented as follows:

$$BP + H_2CO_3 = HP + BHCO_3$$

Thus the total "base" of the blood was the sum of the cations.

plays its usual essential part in the reaction. Application of the mass action law to this equilibrium gives

$$\frac{[H^+][A^-]}{[HA]} = K_i = \frac{[H^+][\text{base}]}{[\text{acid}]}$$

K_i is the ionization or dissociation constant and is a measure of the strength of the acid, being larger for more highly dissociated acids and very small for the weakest ones. Sometimes this constant is designated K_c, meaning that it is obtained by allowing the brackets to indicate as usual concentrations in moles per liter. In contrast, K_a is the more generally useful constant obtained by use of activities in place of concentrations. The relation between activity and the activity coefficient (f) was defined on page 45.

$$K_a = \frac{(a_{H^+})(a_{\text{base}})}{a_{\text{acid}}} = \frac{f[H^+] \times f[\text{base}]}{f[\text{acid}]}$$

Titration curves

1. MONOBASIC ACIDS. In Fig. 2.20 are shown the curves obtained when two different tenth molar acids are neutralized with tenth molar base. For comparison there are given also the *p*H values at which some of the common indicators change color. The curve for hydrochloric acid is typical of those given by strong acids. Since it is completely ionized in solution, its hydrogen ion concentration is nearly 10^{-1} or its *p*H is nearly unity before any base is added. When the acid is 99 per cent neutralized, the *p*H has increased only to about 3, but the drop of alkali which completes the neutralization changes the *p*H value suddenly from slightly more than 3 to 9 or 10. Thus for this neutralization any of the common titration indicators could be used, though neutral red which changes color at the equivalence point of the curve would be most suitable.

The curve is different with the weak acetic acid. Its original *p*H is higher (2.75), and as soon as base is added, the resulting salt suppresses the ionization of the remaining acid and raises the *p*H sharply. Thereafter the *p*H rises gradually while about three-quarters of the base is added, and again more sharply until the equivalence point is reached. The equivalence point on the curve for acetic acid comes at about *p*H 8.7, which is close to the *p*H at which phenolphthalein and cresol red change color. Either of these indicators may therefore be used to mark the end point in titration of acetic acid with a strong base.

2. POLYBASIC ACIDS. Polybasic acids ionize in steps, giving ionization constants of which the primary is always larger than the secondary, and the secondary larger than a tertiary.

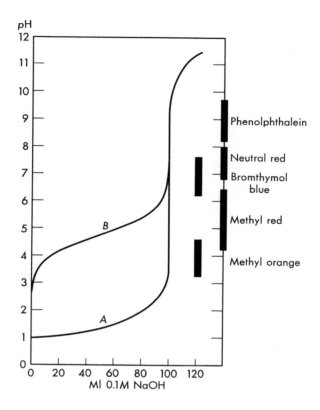

Fig. 2.20. Titration of 100 ml 0.1M hydrochloric acids (curve A) and of 100 ml 0.1M acetic acid (curve B) with 0.1M sodium hydroxide.

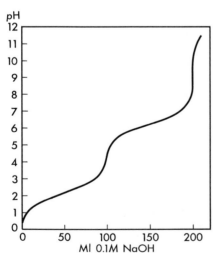

Fig. 2.2I. Titration of 100 ml of 0.1M orthophosphoric acid with 0.1M sodium hydroxide.

Figure 2.21 shows the curve obtained when $0.1 M$ phosphoric acid is titrated with $0.1 M$ sodium hydroxide. The equivalence point at about pH 4.4 results from the neutralization of the first hydrogen. This end point can be determined by the use of methyl orange as indicator. At the second equivalence point, when the second hydrogen has been neutralized, the pH is about 9.6 so that titration to a phenolphthalein end point marks the neutralization of the first two hydrogens. Table 2.9 gives the activity constants for a few of the compounds which would a few years ago have been classified as weak acids and

TABLE 2.9. Activity Constants of Selected Acids at 25°C

Acid	Conjugate Base	K_a	pK_a
CH_3COOH	CH_3COO^-	1.75×10^{-5}	4.76
H_2CO_3	HCO_3^-	4.47×10^{-7}	6.35
HCO_3^-	CO_3^{--}	4.68×10^{-11}	10.33
C_6H_5COOH	$C_6H_5COO^-$	6.86×10^{-5}	4.16
Lactic acid	Lactate ion		3.86
H_3PO_4	$H_2PO_4^-$	7×10^{-3}	2.15
$H_2PO_4^-$	HPO_4^{--}	7×10^{-8}	7.13
HPO_4^{--}	PO_4^{---}	4.8×10^{-13}	12.32
$^+H_3NCH_2COOH$	$^+H_3NCH_2COO^-$		2.35
$^+H_3NCH_2COO^-$	$H_2NCH_2COO^-$		9.78
NH_4^+	NH_3	5.6×10^{-10}	9.25
$^+NH_3C(CH_2OH)_3$	$NH_2C(CH_2OH)_3$	8.3×10^{-9}	8.08
Tris(hydroxymethyl)-aminomethane			

weak bases. It will be noted that even for such a typical "base" as ammonia an acid ionization constant is given. This refers to the equilibrium

$$NH_4^+ + H_2O \leftrightarrows NH_3 + H_3O^+$$

Acid   **Conjugate base**

$$K_a = \frac{a_{NH_3} \times a_{H_3O^+}}{a_{NH_4^+}}$$

Since for weak electrolytes the constants all involve a negative exponent, a value designated pK_a is frequently used instead. The pK_a is the negative logarithm of the activity constant, and consequently the smaller the pK_a the larger the K_a and the stronger the acid. The large pK_a for the ionization of the ammonium ion as an acid reflects the fact that ammonium ion is a very weak acid indeed. The relation between such a constant for a substance like ammonia, and the old basic ionization constant is expressed by the equations

$$K_a K_b = K_w \quad \text{or} \quad pK_a + pK_b = pK_w$$

These relations are simply obtained as follows, using concentrations to express the values of the constants.

$$K_a = \frac{[NH_3][H_3O^+]}{[NH_4^+]} \qquad K_b = \frac{[NH_4^+][OH^-]}{[NH_3]}$$

Multiplying these and cancelling gives

$$K_a K_b = \frac{[\cancel{NH_3}][H_3O^+][\cancel{NH_4^+}][OH^-]}{[\cancel{NH_4^+}][\cancel{NH_3}]} = [H_3O^+][OH^-] = K_w$$

Thus to get K_b for ammonia one need only divide K_w or 10^{-14} by K_a,

$$K_b = \frac{10^{-14}}{5.6 \times 10^{-10}} = \frac{10 \times 10^{-15}}{5.6 \times 10^{-10}} = 1.8 \times 10^{-5}$$

More simply, pK_b is obtained by subtracting pK_a from pK_w or 14.

$$pK_b = 14 - 9.3 = 4.7$$

Buffers

The long gradual slope in the titration curve for a weak acid indicates that the pH of a mixture of a weak acid and its salt changes only slightly as the ratio of the constituents varies. For example, a mixture of acetic acid and sodium acetate contains the conjugate base, or acetate ion, undissociated acetic acid, and a small amount of hydrogen ion. Addition of more hydrogen ion brings about the formation of additional undissociated acid, since there is a large reserve of conjugate base which can combine with nearly all the added hydrogen ion. There is thus no significant increase in the hydrogen ion concentration of the solution.

$$Ac^- + H^+ \rightleftarrows HAc$$

Similarly, although added hydroxyl ion neutralizes part of the free hydrogen ion in the solution this loss is immediately made good by further ionization of the undissociated acid, and again there is no appreciable change in the acidity of the solution.

$$HAc \rightleftharpoons H^+ + Ac^-$$
$$+$$
$$OH^-$$
$$\downarrow$$
$$H_2O$$

It is the presence of such *buffer mixtures* in living cells which maintains their nearly constant *p*H in the face of fluctuations in their acid content. The capacity of buffers to stabilize *p*H is also of the greatest importance in the laboratory. Experiments with living cells or with the catalysts extracted from living cells are feasible only because they can be conducted in a medium which is buffered against excessive changes in acidity.

The hydrogen ion concentration of a buffer mixture can be calculated from the expression for the dissociation of the weak acid concerned. For example, in a solution containing acetic acid and its sodium salt, the concentration of the conjugate base is essentially that of the salt, since the normally small dissociation of acetic acid is further repressed by the high concentration of acetate ion from the completely ionized salt. For the same reason the concentration of un-ionized acetic acid is essentially equal to the total concentration of acid present. As long as all concentrations are low, the expression for the dissociation of the weak acid in such a mixture may therefore be written

$$K_a = \frac{[\mathrm{H^+}][\mathrm{salt}]}{[\mathrm{acid}]}$$

The hydrogen ion concentration is thus seen to depend upon the size of the dissociation constant and upon the ratio of acid to salt (or base).

$$[\mathrm{H^+}] = K_a \frac{[\mathrm{acid}]}{[\mathrm{salt}]}$$

This is the standard buffer equation, often used in the form which is known as the Henderson-Hasselbalch equation:

$$p\mathrm{H} = pK_a + \log \frac{[\mathrm{salt}]}{[\mathrm{acid}]}$$

The activity constant of a weak electrolyte varies significantly with the total salt concentration. Thus the constant for aqueous acetic acid is 1.75×10^{-5}, but in $0.1M$ sodium chloride solution is 2.8×10^{-5}. It is therefore important when the salt concentration is at all high to use the proper dissociation constant in calculating the *p*H of a buffer mixture.

Preparation of buffers

The simplest way to prepare a buffer is to put into solution an acid and its salt. For example, suppose that a buffer of *p*H 5 is to be prepared by adding solid sodium acetate to $0.1M$ acetic acid. From the buffer equation it is obvious that equal concentrations of salt and acid give a *p*H equal to the *p*K, or a hydrogen ion concentration equal to the K_a. But 10^{-5} is not equal to the constant for acetic acid (2.8×10^{-5} when the salt concentration is approximately $0.1M$) but is roughly one-third of that value. This means that the salt concentration must be approximately 3 times the acid concentration to make the *p*H $= 5$. For a salt concentration of $0.3M$ the constant for acetic acid is 2.95×10^{-5}, and this is therefore the appropriate constant to use in calculating the weight of salt which is required.

$$10^{-5} = 2.95 \times 10^{-5} \frac{0.1}{x}$$

$$x = \frac{2.95 \times 10^{-6}}{10^{-5}} = 0.295 \text{ mole of sodium acetate}$$

which must be added to 1 liter of $0.1M$ acid to give the required buffer mixture.

For the preparation of a series of buffers of graded *p*H it is convenient to begin with a solution of the acid and to form the salt by adding varying amounts of hydroxide. A given acid may be used to prepare buffers with a range of *p*H values from slightly above to slightly below its own *pK_a*. Obviously the buffering capacity is greatest when the concentrations of salt and acid are equal, and the *p*H equals the *pK_a*. Under these conditions the buffer solution is as effective as it can be in preventing *p*H changes by either added hydrogen or hydroxyl ion. But for limited ranges on either side of this value satisfactory buffers may be prepared. Those in which the concentration of acid is greater than that of salt will be more effective against added base than against acid. When the salt concentration is relatively high this situation is reversed.

Phthalic acid, a dibasic organic acid, is widely used in the preparation of buffers. Since its primary ionization constant is 1.26×10^{-3}, appropriate mixtures of the acid and its monopotassium salt act as buffers with *p*H values which range from approximately 2.2 to 4.0. Its secondary constant is 3.91×10^{-6}, and this means that a series of different mixtures of the mono- and the dipotassium salts are buffers with *p*H values which lie between 4.2 and 5.8. In these latter mixtures the acid involved is the acid phthalate ion. A few examples will make clear how such solutions are prepared. In the calculations which follow, the solutions are assumed to be relatively dilute and so the salt effect is neglected.

Example I

To calculate the *p*H of two different phthalate buffer mixtures.

Suppose that a $0.1M$ solution of potassium hydrogen phthalate is available. To a liter of this solution 0.05 mole of hydrogen chloride is added. Interaction of the acid phthalate ion with the added hydrogen ion forms approximately 0.05 mole of the un-ionized phthalic acid. Strictly speaking, as in all buffer mixtures, the actual concentration of un-ionized acid is somewhat less than that of the added acid, since there is always a slight ionization. But accepting the approximations used in setting up the buffer equation, the solution now contains 0.05 mole of phthalic acid and 0.05 mole of the potassium salt. The hydrogen ion concentration is therefore equal to the primary dissociation constant, 1.26×10^{-3} or the $pH = 3 - 0.10 = 2.90$.

If instead of acid 0.025 mole of potassium hydroxide had been added to 1 liter of potassium acid phthalate solution, the resulting mixture would have contained 0.075 mole of hydrogen phthalate ion, and 0.025 mole of the simple phthalate ion. In this solution the acid of the buffer mixture is the acid phthalate ion, and it is therefore the secondary ionization constant which must be used to calculate the pH.

$$[H^+] = K_2 \frac{[\text{acid}]}{[\text{base}]}$$

$$= 3.91 \times 10^{-6} \times \frac{0.075}{0.025} = 1.17 \times 10^{-5}$$

$$pH = 5 - 0.07 = 4.93$$

Example 2

Directions for making up buffer mixtures are often given in the following form. To 50 ml of $0.2M$ acetic acid add 12.5 ml of $0.2M$ NaOH and make the solution to 200 ml. Since it is not the absolute concentrations but the concentration ratio which determines the pH, the calculation of the resulting pH may use moles per liter or moles per 200 ml, so long as both are in the same units.

There is 0.01 mole of acid in the 50 ml of solution used. Of this, one quarter is neutralized by NaOH giving 0.0025 mole of base and leaving 0.0075 mole of the original acid in the final 200 ml of solution. The pH is therefore:

$$pH = 4.76 + \log \frac{0.0025}{0.0075} = 4.76 + \log 1 - \log 3$$

$$= 4.76 - 0.48 = 4.28$$

Example 3

To prepare a phosphate buffer so that the total phosphate concentration will be $0.1M$ and the $pH = 7.5$.

Since the primary dissociation constant for phosphoric acid is 7.0×10^{-3}, the mixture cannot consist of the acid and its monopotassium salt, for this would give far too low a pH. But a mixture of mono- and dipotassium phosphate will have as its acid the $H_2PO_4^-$ ion with a dissociation constant of 7×10^{-8} and a $pK_a = 7.13$. These two should therefore be used to prepare a buffer of the desired pH.

Let the required concentration of base (HPO_4^{--} ion) $= x$. Since the total phosphate concentration is to be $0.1M$, the concentration of acid ($H_2PO_4^-$) will then be $0.1 - x$.

$$pH = pK_a + \log \frac{[base]}{[acid]}$$

$$7.5 = 7.13 + \log \frac{x}{0.1 - x}$$

$$\log \frac{x}{0.1 - x} = 0.37$$

$$\frac{x}{0.1 - x} = 2.34$$

$$x = 0.234 - 2.34x$$

$$3.34x = 0.234$$

$$x = 0.07 \text{ mole/liter of base} = \text{mole/liter } K_2HPO_4$$

$$0.1 - 0.07 = 0.03 \text{ mole/liter of acid } (KH_2PO_4)$$

To prepare 1 liter of this buffer requires

$$0.03 \times 136 = 4.08 \text{ g } KH_2PO_4$$

$$0.07 \times 174 = 12.2 \text{ g } K_2HPO_4$$

A buffer which is now widely used is made from tris(hydroxymethyl)amino-methane which as indicated in Table 2.9 has a pK_a of 8.08. It is therefore especially good for pH values in the physiological range, and the buffers are called simply tris buffers.

$$
\begin{array}{ccc}
NH_2 & & NH_3{}^+ \\
| & \xrightarrow{+H^+} & | \\
HOH_2C \cdot C \cdot CH_2OH & \underset{-H^+}{\rightleftarrows} & HOH_2C \cdot C \cdot CH_2OH \\
| & & | \\
CH_2OH & & CH_2OH \\
\textbf{Base} & & \textbf{Acid}
\end{array}
$$

Like ammonia, this compound in solution with varying amounts of acid would form a mixture of acid, or substituted ammonium ion, and its conjugate base, and thus a typical buffer mixture.

Measurement of pH

There are two general methods for the determination of pH, the one colori-metric, the other electrometric.

Colorimetric methods

The colorimetric estimation of pH is a simple procedure involving comparison of the color of an indicator in the unknown with the color of the same concentration of this indicator in a buffer of known pH.

The indicators are weak acids or bases, the molecules of which differ in color from the ions which they form in alkaline or acidic solution. A few indicators such as methyl red, methyl orange, and phenolphthalein have ionization constants which cause them to change color at such pH ranges that they can be used to determine the end point of a titration. The indicator

TABLE 2.10. Some Indicators, Their Ranges and Colors

Indicator	pH Range	Color at Lowest pH	Color at Highest pH	pK_{in}
Thymol blue (acid range)	1.2–2.8	Red	Orange	1.5
Bromphenol blue	3.0–4.6	Yellow	Blue	4.0
Methyl red	4.4–6.2	Red	Yellow	5.1
Bromcresol purple	5.2–6.8	Yellow	Purple	6.3
Bromthymol blue	6.0–7.6	Yellow	Blue	7.0
Phenol red	6.4–8.0	Yellow	Red	7.9
m-Cresol purple (alkaline range)	7.4–9.0	Yellow	Purple	8.2
Thymol blue (alkaline range)	8.0–9.6	Yellow	Blue	8.9
Thymolphthalein	9.3–10.5	Yellow	Blue	10.0

chosen for a particular titration must change color at the pH which is reached when an equimolar amount of acid or base has been added. If either the acid or base is a weak electrolyte, this pH will be higher or lower than 7, as was indicated on the titration curve for acetic acid.

But there are many more indicators which change color at pH values outside the usual titration ranges. These are suitable for use with a series of buffers to determine the pH value of an unknown solution. In Table 2.10 some of the common indicators are listed with their pH ranges. The dissociation constants of these indicator acids are also given as pK values. It should be noted that when an indicator is yellow, for example, at pH 3 and blue at pH 4.6, it will be yellow at all pH values below 3 and blue at those above 4.6. The chief exception is thymol blue which changes from red to yellow between pH 1.2 and 2.8, and from yellow to blue between pH 8.0 and 9.6.

A series of buffers differing by 0.2 pH unit may easily be prepared or purchased. To use these for colorimetric estimation of pH, nine series of buffers of graded pH, corresponding to the nine ranges of pH values given in Table 2.10 for the different indicators, are first set up in a series of tubes. To the tubes containing buffers at pH 1.2, 1.4, 1.6 . . . 2.8, a definite number of drops of thymol blue is added; bromphenol blue is added to the tubes covering the pH range 3.0 to 4.6; methyl red is put in the tubes of the next series, and so on. In each group of tubes there will result a graduated set of colors which can be matched against the color obtained when the same indicator is added to the same volume of an unknown solution. There are various laboratory techniques for matching colors as accurately as possible, but the essential operation consists of comparing the color given by the unknown with that given by solutions containing graded ratios of indicator acid and ion.

Electrometric method

Although for many purposes the colorimetric determination of pH is accurate enough, for experiments in which fine distinctions are important it is necessary to determine this value electrometrically. There are various instruments on the market for doing this, indeed many of them are so adjusted that the estimation of pH consists merely in putting a sample of the solution in the designated cup, turning a knob until the needle points to zero, and reading the pH from a scale. In order to understand why such a procedure gives the information desired, it will be necessary to review briefly some of the facts of electrochemistry.

ELECTRODE REACTIONS.   When a strip of zinc is immersed in a solution of cupric sulfate, metallic copper plates out on the zinc and zinc ions go into solution.

$$Zn^0 + Cu^{++} \rightarrow Zn^{++} + Cu^0$$

This oxidation-reduction is achieved by a direct transfer of electrons from zinc atom to cupric ion. The fact that such a transfer takes place indicates a tendency on the part of zinc to lose electrons and become an ion, and on the part of the cupric ions to acquire electrons and plate out as metallic copper.

In the galvanic cell these opposite tendencies are utilized to generate an electric current. In a cell the same type of oxidation-reduction reaction takes place, but under such conditions that the electrons must be transferred through an external wire. This stream of moving electrons constitutes an electric current.

A simple galvanic cell is represented diagrammatically in Fig. 2.22. One half cell consists of zinc metal dipping into zinc ion, the other of copper dipping into cupric ion. The two metals are connected through the voltmeter and the two solutions through the inverted U tube filled with sodium chloride solution. When zinc goes into solution as zinc ion the electrons which are left behind on the metal give this electrode a negative charge. When all connections have been made these extra electrons move through the wire and the voltmeter to the copper electrode. Here there is a deficiency of electrons, since the cupric ions tend to acquire them from the metallic copper, and the incoming stream makes good in some measure this loss. The two electrode reactions are

$$Zn \rightarrow Zn^{++} + 2e$$
$$Cu^{++} + 2e \rightarrow Cu$$

To complete the circuit negative ions move through the salt bridge toward the zinc solution to balance the charge on the newly formed zinc ions, and positive ions move in the other direction to make up in that half of the cell for

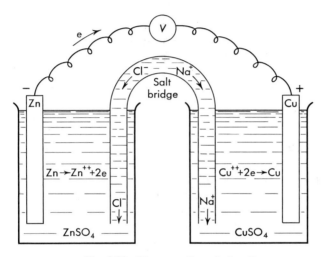

Fig. 2.22. Diagram of a voltaic cell.

the loss of the positive cupric ions. At the moment when the circuit is completed, a deflection of the needle of the voltmeter indicates a flow of current, or of electrons. The net chemical result is oxidation of the zinc electrode and reduction of the cupric ions. This is expressed as the sum of the two electrode reactions:

$$Zn + Cu^{++} \rightarrow Zn^{++} + Cu$$

The actual emf developed by such a cell as has just been described cannot be accurately measured by a voltmeter since in the process of measurement the voltage gradually changes as the current flows. If we consider the cell reaction above, it is obvious that a process which results in a gradual increase in the concentration of zinc ion and a decrease in the concentration of cupric ion will ultimately so change the relative concentrations that the reaction will cease. In order to measure the voltage of a galvanic cell it is necessary to use a potentiometer. In this instrument the emf of the cell being measured is exactly balanced by an opposing emf from an outside source, so arranged that it just prevents the flow of current. Under these experimental conditions it is found that a cell of the type described above, set up with molal solutions of zinc salt and of cupric salt, develops an emf of about 1.1 v.

Many different oxidation-reduction reactions can be utilized to generate larger or smaller potential differences. The accepted convention is to represent such cells with the element-ion pair which develops a negatively charged electrode on the left. This means that the pair written on the left is the

$$\text{Zn} \mid \text{Zn}^{++} \parallel \text{Cu}^{++} \mid \text{Cu}$$

one in which oxidation takes place. One of the pair on the right will be reduced. A series of possible cells is indicated below, with the emf which each develops if the solutions used are 1 molal.

$$\text{Mg} \mid \text{Mg}^{++} \parallel \text{Zn}^{++} \mid \text{Zn} \qquad 1.58 \text{ v}$$
$$\text{Zn} \mid \text{Zn}^{++} \parallel \text{Fe}^{++} \mid \text{Fe} \qquad 0.32 \text{ v}$$
$$\text{Fe} \mid \text{Fe}^{++} \parallel \text{Cu}^{++} \mid \text{Cu} \qquad 0.78 \text{ v}$$
$$\text{Cu} \mid \text{Cu}^{++} \parallel 2\text{Cl}^{-} \mid \text{Cl}_2(\text{Pt}) \qquad 1.02 \text{ v}$$

Such a representation of a cell tells us of the first pair, for example, that, when magnesium dips into a molal solution of magnesium ions and is connected through an external wire and a salt bridge (or other device) with zinc dipping into molal zinc ion, there will be a flow of electrons through the wire from the magnesium to the zinc. The magnesium will be oxidized to the ion, and the zinc ion will be reduced to metallic zinc. It should be noted that the voltage developed by the (Zn:Fe) pair plus that of the (Fe:Cu) pair equals that previously noted for the (Zn:Cu) cell.

$$\text{emf}\,(\text{Zn:Fe}) + \text{emf}\,(\text{Fe:Cu}) = \text{emf}\,(\text{Zn:Cu})$$
$$0.32 \quad + \quad 0.78 \quad = \quad 1.10 \text{ v}$$

As the last cell in the list would indicate, electrodes may be gaseous as well as metallic. One form of gas electrode is shown diagrammatically in Fig. 2.23. Hydrogen gas is bubbled through the cell solution in chamber A to saturate it with water. In chamber B a platinum electrode coated with platinum black dips into the same cell solution and is connected to the outside circuit C through the mercury which fills the tube E. On the catalytically active spongy platinum, equilibrium is rapidly established between the hydrogen ion in solution and the

$$\text{H}_2 \rightleftharpoons 2\text{H}^+ + 2e$$

gas, excess of which escapes at D. To use such an electrode as part of a galvanic cell the vessel *B* must be connected through a salt bridge or a liquid junction with the solution of another half cell, while the outside wire *C* is connected to the other electrode.

If such an arrangement were used to set up the (Cu:Cl) cell, it would be found that the copper furnishes electrons for the reduction of the chlorine, and

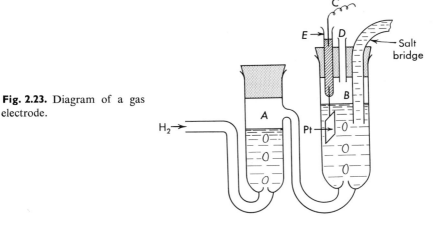

Fig. 2.23. Diagram of a gas electrode.

that it is itself oxidized to cupric ion. The electrode reactions for this combination are

$$Cu^0 \rightarrow Cu^{++} + 2e$$
$$Cl_2 + 2e \rightarrow 2Cl^-$$
$$\text{Sum:} \quad Cu^0 + Cl_2 \rightarrow Cu^{++} + 2Cl^-$$

Thus in this cell copper is oxidized although when this same copper half cell is combined with a zinc half cell, cupric ions are reduced. Evidently the "tendency" to be oxidized or reduced is not absolute, but relative, and the direction in which the oxidation-reduction will go depends on which of the two elements concerned has the greater electronegativity, or tendency to acquire electrons. In order to obtain a flow of electrons from one electrode to another there must be a difference in this tendency and the larger the difference, the larger the emf which the cell develops. For example, magnesium is strongly electropositive and chlorine strongly electronegative. A (Mg:Cl) cell registers this difference as a high emf. On the other hand, a cell made up of tin and copper and their ions has a much smaller emf, indicating that the tendency of tin to form stannous ions is not appreciably different from that of copper to form cupric ions. As a result the cupric ions do not draw any great number of electrons from the tin. We can measure with a potentiometer this *difference* in potential between two element-ion pairs, but there is no way to measure directly the individual "tendencies" on which the difference depends. However, by comparing all other elements with hydrogen it has been possible to construct a table of relative values, from which the difference between any two can be computed.

The reference electrode, to which all others are compared, is the standard hydrogen half cell consisting of hydrogen gas at 1 atmosphere pressure bubbling around a platinum electrode which dips into a solution in which the effective hydrogen ion concentration is 1 molal. The emf developed when this half cell is combined with a zinc electrode in a solution 1 molal in zinc ion is 0.761 volt, and the flow of electrons is from the zinc to hydrogen. For the purposes of constructing a scale, the electrode potential of the standard hydrogen half cell is arbitrarily set at zero, thus making the potential of the standard zinc electrode (zinc dipping into molal zinc ion) -0.761 v. The negative sign indicates that the zinc electrode is the negative one, that is, that in this particular cell zinc is oxidized and hydrogen ion reduced.

$$Zn^0 \rightarrow Zn^{++} + 2e$$
$$2H^+ + 2e \rightarrow H_2$$
$$\text{Sum:} \quad Zn^0 + 2H^+ \rightarrow Zn^{++} + H_2$$

When this same hydrogen half cell is combined with a standard copper half cell (copper metal and molal cupric ion), the emf of the cell proves to be 0.34 v. But in this cell oxidation takes place at the hydrogen electrode, which is therefore the negative electrode. The potential of the standard copper half cell is therefore $+0.34$ v.

TABLE 2.11.   Standard Reduction Potentials

Electrode Reaction	Half Cell	E_0, volts
$Na^+ + e = Na$	Na^+, Na	-2.71
$Mg^{++} + 2e = Mg$	Mg^{++}, Mg	-2.34
$Zn^{++} + 2e = Zn$	Zn^{++}, Zn	-0.76
$Fe^{++} + 2e = Fe$	Fe^{++}, Fe	-0.44
$Cr^{+++} + e = Cr^{++}$	Cr^{+++}, Cr^{++}(Pt)	-0.40
$Sn^{++} + 2e = Sn$	Sn^{++}, Sn	-0.14
$2H^+ + 2e = H_2$	H^+, H_2(Pt)	0.00
$Cu^{++} + 2e = Cu$	Cu^{++}, Cu	$+0.34$
$Fe^{+++} + e = Fe^{++}$	Fe^{+++}, Fe^{++}(Pt)	$+0.77$
$Ag^+ + e = Ag$	Ag^+, Ag	$+0.80$
$Cl_2 + 2e = 2Cl^-$	Cl_2, Cl^- (Pt)	$+1.36$
$Co^{+++} + e = Co^{++}$	Co^{+++}, Co^{++}(Pt)	$+1.82$

In Table 2.11 is given a list of a few standard electrode potentials (E_0) obtained in this way. Note that in a standard half cell the ion is always present in molal concentration and any gas involved is used at 1 atmosphere pressure.

When the potential given in the table carries a negative sign, it indicates that the electrode reaction which as written is a reduction, actually tends to go in the opposite direction and to result in an oxidation. Similarly a positive voltage means that the reaction tends to take place spontaneously as written. Thus when any two half cells are combined, the one with the more negative potential becomes the one in which oxidation takes place, while the one with the more positive potential undergoes a reduction.

The emf to be obtained from any combination of standard half cells depends upon the difference between their individual electrode potentials. These potentials as given in the table are reduction potentials, that is, they measure the tendency of the element in question to be reduced. Using this set of values the emf of the cell may be calculated by subtracting the reduction potential of the anode from that of the cathode. The anode is defined as the electrode at which oxidation takes place, and the cathode as the electrode at which reduction takes place. Thus in a voltaic cell the cathode is *positively* charged and the anode *negatively* charged. The opposite is true when the electrodes are being used for electrolysis.

$$E_{cell} = E_{0\ cathode} - E_{0\ anode}$$

For the (Zn:Cu) cell this means

$$E_{cell} = E_0(Cu^{++} \rightarrow Cu) - E_0(Zn^{++} \rightarrow Zn)$$

$$= +0.34 \qquad - (-0.76)$$

$$= 1.1 \text{ v}$$

In a cell made up of standard silver and copper half cells the copper will be oxidized since it has the lower reduction potential, and the silver ion will be reduced.

$$E_{cell} = E_0(Ag^+ \rightarrow Ag) - E_0(Cu^{++} \rightarrow Cu)$$

$$= +0.80 \qquad - (+0.34)$$

$$= 0.46 \text{ v}$$

Scattered through the table are certain electrode reactions involving two ions instead of an element-ion pair. It might be expected that if a cell were set up in which electrons could move through a wire to a platinum electrode dipping into a mixture of ferric and ferrous ions, the ferric ions would be reduced. The positive sign in the table for the reaction $Fe^{+++} + e \rightarrow Fe^{++}$ indicates that this is true, and that ferric ions do in fact take up electrons readily. Thus in a cell made up with the standard hydrogen half cell combined with an inert electrode dipping into a solution 1 molal in ferric and ferrous ions, the hydrogen is oxidized.

$$H_2(Pt) \quad | \quad H^+(1M) \quad \| \quad Fe^{+++}(1M), Fe^{++}(1M) \quad | \quad Pt$$

The reactions and voltages are computed as with other cells. The electrode reactions are

$$H_2 \rightarrow 2H^+ + 2e$$

$$2Fe^{+++} + 2e \rightarrow 2Fe^{++}$$

Sum: $\quad H_2 + 2Fe^{+++} \rightarrow 2H^+ + 2Fe^{++}$

$$E_{cell} = 0.77 - 0.00$$

$$= 0.77 \text{ v}$$

EFFECT OF CONCENTRATION. Since all the electrode reactions are reversible, it is obvious that the emf of a galvanic cell depends not only upon the element-ion pairs which are used but also upon the concentrations of the solutions.

The relation between the electrode potential of a standard half cell and that of the same element in a solution other than molal was developed theoretically by Walther Nernst (1864–1941) about 1889. It is expressed in the equation

$$E = E_0 \pm \frac{1.98 \times 10^{-4}T}{n} \log C$$

in which E denotes the new electrode potential in volts, E_0 is the standard electrode potential, T denotes the Kelvin temperature, n is the valence of the element, and C is the effective molal concentration of the ion. For the solutions with which we deal C may be taken as the molar concentration of the ion. In using the equation the positive sign is used when the ion concerned carries a positive charge, and the negative sign for a negative ion. At 30°C the equation becomes

$$E = E_0 \pm \frac{0.06}{n} \log C$$

Consider a half cell in which zinc is in contact with $0.001 M$ zinc sulfate solution. Here $n = 2$, the ion carries a positive charge, and the electrode potential becomes

$$E = -0.76 + \frac{0.06}{2} \log 10^{-3}$$

$$= -0.76 + (0.03)(-3)$$

$$= -0.76 - 0.09$$

$$= -0.85 \text{ v}$$

Thus decrease in the concentration of zinc ion, by making it easier for ions to form, has resulted in more rapid formation of new ions, which means a more negative potential for the electrode.

With a chlorine electrode and a solution $0.001 M$ in chloride ion, $n = 1$ and the Nernst equation is used with a negative sign.

$$E = +1.36 - \frac{0.06}{1} \log 10^{-3}$$

$$= +1.36 - (0.06)(-3)$$

$$= +1.36 + 0.18$$

$$= +1.54 \text{ v}$$

With the chlorine electrode a decrease in the concentration of the negative ion has made the electrode more positive since it makes it easier for the element to go into solution as a negative ion.

When the half cell consists of an oxidation-reduction pair and an inert electrode, the equation for calculating the potential for other than standard concentrations becomes

$$E = E_0 + \frac{0.06}{n} \log \frac{[\text{oxidized}]}{[\text{reduced}]}$$

where n stands for the number of electrons gained in the reduction. The final potential is thus seen to depend not on the absolute concentrations of the ions but on their ratio.

For the electrode reaction $Co^{+++} + e \rightarrow Co^{++}$, the standard electrode potential is $+1.82$ volts. If the concentration of the cobaltic ion is made 100 times that of the cobaltous, the electrode potential becomes

$$E = 1.82 + \frac{0.06}{1} \log 100$$

$$= 1.82 + (0.06)(2)$$

$$= 1.94 \text{ v}$$

CONCENTRATION CELLS.   Since there is a potential difference between electrodes of the same element dipping into solutions of different ionic strengths, it is possible to use two such element-ion pairs to make a cell. For example a zinc cell could be set up as follows:

$$Zn \mid Zn^{++} (10^{-3}M) \parallel Zn^{++} (1M) \mid Zn$$

Calculation of the voltage is carried out as before by subtracting the potential of the anode from that of the cathode.

$$E_{\text{cell}} = -0.76 - (-0.85)$$

$$= 0.09 \text{ v}$$

The emf of a concentration cell may be expressed in general terms as

$$E = (E \text{ for the cathode}) - (E \text{ for the anode})$$

$$= \left(E_0 + \frac{0.06}{n} \log C_2\right) - \left(E_0 + \frac{0.06}{n} \log C_1\right)$$

where C_1 is the concentration of the more dilute of the two solutions of a positive ion.

$$E = E_0 - E_0 + \frac{0.06}{n}(\log C_2 - \log C_1)$$

$$= \frac{0.06}{n} \log \frac{C_2}{C_1}$$

A simple hydrogen concentration cell is the basis for many pH meters. It may be represented as

$$(\text{Pt}) \tfrac{1}{2}H_2 \quad | \quad H^+ (xM) \quad || \quad H^+ (1M) \quad | \quad \tfrac{1}{2}H_2 \, (\text{Pt})$$

Since in this arrangement C_2 is molar, and n is also equal to 1, the expression for calculating the voltage of the cell reduces to

$$E = \frac{0.06}{1} \log \frac{1}{[H^+]}$$

where $[H^+]$ represents the hydrogen ion concentration of the unknown solution. But $\log \dfrac{1}{[H^+]}$ is the pH, hence

$$E = 0.06 \times pH$$

and the pH of an unknown solution measured in such a concentration cell as has been described would be numerically equal to the measured emf of the cell divided by 0.06.

In practice modern pH meters seldom use hydrogen electrodes, but whether the reference electrode is hydrogen or the glass electrode or the quinhydrone electrode, the operative principle is a variant of the one just outlined.

Potentials at physiological pH

For such pairs as the ferric-ferrous pair, or the two cobalt ions, the standard reduction potential is constant over a fairly wide pH range. This is not true, however, for those pairs in which the oxidation sets free hydrogen ion. This should be clear from a consideration of the dependence of the redox potential of the hydrogen half cell on the hydrogen ion concentration. In the standard hydrogen half cell the hydrogen ion is at unit activity, that is, the pH of the solution is zero. If a similar cell were set up with hydrogen gas at 1 atmosphere pressure, but with a pH of 7, the reduction potential of the half cell would become

$$E_0' = E_0 + 0.06 \times \log 10^{-7}$$
$$= 0 + 0.06 \times -7$$
$$= -0.42 \text{ v}$$

This variation of reduction potential with change in pH is of crucial importance in biological redox reactions. In the first place, these reactions usually begin with the removal of two hydrogen atoms, or of hydrogen ions and electrons, from a metabolite. Thus the first step in the oxidation of lactic acid transforms it into pyruvic acid.

$$CH_3CHOHCOOH \rightarrow CH_3COCOOH + 2H^+ + 2e$$

In the second place, the pH of the cell is carefully regulated, and for most cells is close to pH 7. Obviously then, the figure in which we are interested is the one which gives the reducing potential of the lactate-pyruvate pair at pH 7. The symbol used for reduction potentials at designated pH values is E_0' and many of these are now available for redox pairs which are of biological importance.

TABLE 2.12. Reduction Potentials at Physiological pH Values

Pairs	pH	$T, °C$	E_0', volts
Acetaldehyde/acetate	7		−0.468 (calc.)
Glucose/gluconate	7		−0.45
Glutamate/α-ketoglutarate	7		−0.03
Isopropyl alcohol/acetone	7	35	−0.251
Lactate/pyruvate	7	35	−0.180
Heme, ferro/ferri	8.18	30	−0.226
	9.50		−0.235
Cytochrome c, red./ox.	7		+0.254
Riboflavin, red./ox.	7	20	−0.186
Diphosphopyridine nucleotide, red./ox.	7	25	−0.32

Note: Heme is the oxygen-carrying pigment of the blood and cytochrome c and diphosphopyridine nucleotide are respiratory catalysts which undergo reversible oxidation and reduction.

The pH value must always be stated, since these figures are not always determined for pH 7. Table 2.12 lists a few selected values for pairs whose potentials change with pH. The figures should be considered approximations only as their determination is beset with pitfalls and they are continually being revised. This subject will be considered again in connection with biological oxidations, in the course of which two hydrogen ions and two electrons are passed along from one oxidizing agent to another until they finally unite with oxygen to form water. Obviously the order in which the various intermediate carriers will be reduced, one by the other, will depend on their relative redox potentials.

In this discussion, the courses of various oxidation-reductions have been predicted solely on the basis of the two redox potentials. It should be emphasized at this point that it is never possible to say, on this evidence alone, that a given reaction will take place. The only certainty is that if one pair has a potential more negative than another, it cannot possibly be reduced by that other. On the other hand, whether it will in fact be effectively oxidized by that other will depend not only on the respective potentials but also on the reaction rate. This in turn depends upon such factors as the availability of activation energy, and on the presence or absence of a catalyst. In biological material the last named factor is of special importance.

FREE ENERGY

It is a familiar fact that equilibrium constants provide a measure of the tendency of a reaction to proceed spontaneously, a large constant corresponding to a more or less complete reaction. For redox reactions the standard reduction potentials, or the modified potentials which are designated E_0' provide another means of predicting whether or not a given reaction can take place spontaneously. A third value which is also of use in making such predictions is the one which indicates the free energy change of the reaction and is designated by the symbol ΔF.

Consider the reversible reaction

$$A + B \rightleftharpoons C + D$$

For this reaction the concentration ratio,

$$\frac{[C][D]}{[A][B]}$$

equals the equilibrium constant K at equilibrium. For conditions other than those of equilibrium, this ratio is designated as Q. The relation of K to Q under specific conditions determines the direction in which a reaction will proceed. If Q is larger than K, that is, if the relative concentrations of the products are higher than the equilibrium ones, the reaction as written will be reversed. On the other hand, if K is larger than Q at a given moment, the reaction will proceed as written.

At equilibrium	$K = Q$
Reaction forward	$K > Q$
Reaction reversed	$K < Q$

If the relation of K to Q is expressed as a logarithm of their ratio, it is seen that for a reaction to proceed spontaneously the log (K/Q) must be a positive number, since under these circumstances (K/Q) is larger than unity.

According to the second law of thermodynamics, any system under constant conditions tends to approach its equilibrium state spontaneously, but can change away from equilibrium conditions only at the expense of some other system's approach to equilibrium. While the tendency of a system to change spontaneously at fixed temperature and pressure can be expressed by the value of log (K/Q), it is more convenient to use a quantity which is defined as proportional to log (K/Q), is designated ΔF, and known as free energy change.

$$\Delta F \propto - \log \frac{K}{Q}$$

From this it follows that at equilibrium $\Delta F = 0$, and that ΔF will be a negative number when the reaction proceeds as written, i.e., when log (K/Q) is positive.

A spontaneous reaction is then associated with a decrease in free energy. This is not the same as saying that a spontaneous reaction is exothermic; many such reactions are endothermic. The extent of reaction at fixed temperature and pressure is determined not only by evolution or absorption of heat but also by the degree to which the system acquires freedom from restraints. The ionization of a weak acid, for example, is exothermic at some temperatures and endothermic at others. Its extent is limited primarily by the fact that the attraction between the ions of the acid and polar water molecules reduces the freedom of action of the particles. The free energy change at fixed temperature and pressure is a composite of the two effects: the heat of reaction and the change in restraints upon the system.

The actual relation between ΔF, K, and Q for any reaction is expressed by the equation

$$\Delta F = -RT \ln K + RT \ln Q$$

in which ln stands as usual for the natural logarithms (to the base e, which is the number $2.7183 \cdots$), R is the gas constant (1.987 cal per degree per mole) and T is the Kelvin temperature. It should be noted that in most biochemical work K and Q are derived from concentrations rather than from activities. This is partly because the ordinary concentrations involved are so small that the activity coefficients may well be nearly unity, and partly because for many compounds of biochemical interest the activity coefficients are not known.

For the purposes of comparison there is a *standard free energy change*, just as there is a standard redox potential. This change, $\Delta F°$, is defined as the change in free energy when reactants and products are at unit activity and gases are at 1 atmosphere pressure. Under these conditions, the last term of the equation above becomes zero, and the standard free energy may be calculated from the equation

$$\Delta F^\circ = -RT \ln K$$

Converting to a common log (2.3 log ln) gives

$$\Delta F^\circ = -4.575T \log K$$

in which the relation between standard free energy change and the equilibrium constant is obvious.

In the chemistry of the cell many reactions take place which have a positive ΔF° and which therefore cannot take place spontaneously. These must take place at the expense of other reactions with negative ΔF values, and probably always come about through the mediation of a common intermediate or carrier. For example, consider the two reactions below, for which imaginary free energy changes have been assigned.

$$A \rightarrow B \qquad \Delta F = -5000 \text{ cal} \tag{1}$$

$$X \rightarrow Y \qquad \Delta F = +1000 \text{ cal} \tag{2}$$

At constant temperature the first reaction may take place spontaneously, but the second cannot. But by the use of a carrier molecule, C, which reacts with A to form the active intermediate C′, the free energy of reaction (1) can be harnessed to bring about reaction (2).

$$A + C \rightarrow B + C' \qquad \Delta F = -2000 \text{ cal} \tag{3}$$

$$C' + X \rightarrow Y + C'' \qquad \Delta F = -250 \text{ cal} \tag{4}$$

In reaction (3) part of the free energy of reaction (1) is built into the molecule of C′ which forms at the same time, hence although A is transformed to B in the course of (3), less energy is released than would be evolved in a simple A → B transformation. In reaction (4) part of the energy which was conserved in C′ is released, and the rest is used in formation of Y. It is by such balancing of energy gains and losses that the cell manages to carry on its many endergonic syntheses.

THE COLLOIDAL STATE

It has been estimated that about 90 per cent of the organic matter in many tissues occurs there in a special state of subdivision, the colloidal state, characterized by large surface areas. The word colloid (Greek *kolla* = glue) was coined by Thomas Graham (1805–1869) to distinguish those substances, such as starch and gelatin, which do not pass through a parchment paper membrane separating their solution from pure water, from those which do pass through. The latter he called crystalloids, since many of them crystallize readily.

Since Graham's time some substances apparently inherently colloidal in nature have been obtained in crystalline form, and most chemists have found to their sorrow that many which are normally crystalline do occasionally form colloidal solutions. Accordingly, it is now recognized that the unique properties associated with the colloidal state depend not upon the character of the solute but upon its specific state of subdivision. This is intermediate between the molecular or ionic dispersion which obtains in a true solution and the particle size which is found in fine suspensions and is visible under a microscope. Particles of colloidal size may consist of a single molecule with or without adsorbed ions or water molecules, or they may consist of aggregates of many small molecules. The proteins are examples of the first type of particle, and colloidal gold or antimony sulfide of the second.

A very precise definition of colloidal size is impossible, partly because the particles may vary widely in shape. It is sometimes said that particles with a radius between 0.001 μ and 0.01 μ are of colloidal dimensions. But this takes no account of the fact that while some particles are spherical, or nearly so, others may consist of long, slender threads, or of ovoids or disks. Figure 2.24 shows some of the shapes which have been found among purified proteins and indicates schematically other possible shapes of colloidal particles.

In a colloidal system one substance in a fine state of subdivision is evenly dispersed throughout a second. The first is known as the *dispersed* or *discontinuous phase*, the other as the *dispersion medium*, or the *continuous phase*. In biological systems the dispersion medium is usually water, although under some circumstances water may constitute the dispersed phase. (See later discussion of emulsions.)

The properties of colloidal systems depend very little on the chemical properties of the components, but they are chiefly referable to the large surface area between the two phases. If a cube 1 cm on a side were subdivided into cubes 10 mμ (10^{-6} cm) on a side, the resulting particles would be of colloidal dimensions and the surface area would have increased from 6 sq cm to 600 sq m. In the large interfacial area between these minute particles and a dispersion medium, surface equilibria are set up similar to those previously discussed in general terms. The molecules of the solvent form surface films around each particle similar to those at a water/air interface. Since the interfacial tension thus generated tends, as free energy always does, to be reduced, any surface active molecules in the dispersion medium become concentrated in the interfacial film. If there are electrolytes also in the solution the particles of the colloid may become charged through preferential adsorption of one ion at the interface.

Three major types of colloidal system are known as *sols*, *gels*, and *emulsions*. A sol consists of a solid phase dispersed in a liquid to yield a mobile, fluid colloidal system; when the resulting colloid has a firm, jelly-like texture it is known as a gel. An emulsion is a colloidal dispersion of one liquid in another.

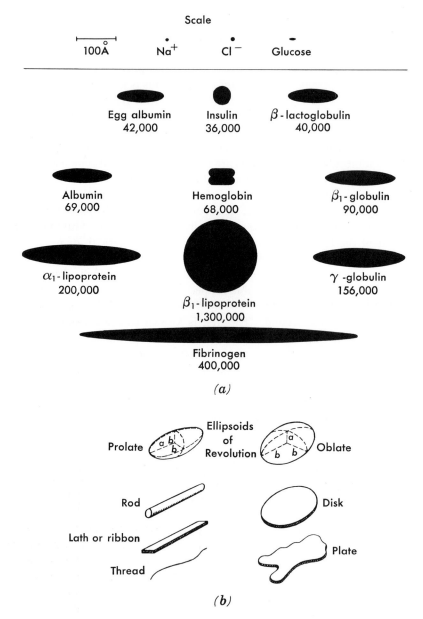

Scale

100Å   Na⁺   Cl⁻   Glucose

Egg albumin
42,000

Insulin
36,000

β-lactoglobulin
40,000

Albumin
69,000

Hemoglobin
68,000

β_1-globulin
90,000

α_1-lipoprotein
200,000

γ-globulin
156,000

β_1-lipoprotein
1,300,000

Fibrinogen
400,000

(a)

Prolate   Ellipsoids of Revolution   Oblate

Rod   Disk

Lath or ribbon

Thread   Plate

(b)

Fig. 2.24. (a) The probable shape and particle weight of some proteins. [Courtesy of Prof. J. L. Oncley, Harvard Medical School.] (b) Some schematic models for nonspherical particles and their relation. [From K. J. Mysels, *Introduction to Colloid Chemistry*, Interscience, New York, 1959.]

Sols

Colloidal particles are too small to be visible under an ordinary microscope. They are, however, visible in the ultramicroscope for the same reason that dust particles can be seen where a fine beam of light penetrates a darkened room. The particles of dust reflect and scatter the light waves, giving rise to a diffused light in which the dust is seen. In the ultramicroscope a beam of light is viewed at right angles through a microscope. When the light is directed upon a true solution the path of the beam is invisible since the particles are too small to scatter the light. The field of the microscope appears dark. But when the light shines into a colloidal solution a tiny point of light appears against the dark background wherever the beam impinges upon a particle large enough to diffract it. The points of light move about in a random fashion because the colloidal particles themselves are in a disordered kind of motion as a result of bombardment by the molecules of the dispersion medium. This motion, known as Brownian movement, was first noted by the Scots botanist Robert Brown as he examined suspensions of tiny pollen grains under the microscope.

The particles thus revealed in colloidal sols may belong to either of two classes, depending upon whether they have or have not an attraction for the dispersion medium. These classes are *lyophilic* or solvent-loving sols, and *lyophobic* or solvent-hating sols. Since in biological systems the dispersion medium is water, the groups are also referred to as hydrophilic and hydrophobic.

Hydrophobic sols

Many substances which have no attraction for water, and consequently no tendency to form true solutions, can be induced to form colloidal sols which are clear and transparent and often quite beautifully colored. Among these are the noble metals, silver, gold, and platinum, some metal sulfides including arsenic and antimony trisulfides, ferric and aluminum hydroxides, and a number of organic dyes. In these sols groups of atoms or molecules are held together in particles of colloidal dimensions stabilized by electric charges of the same sign. A typical hydrophobic sol exhibits the following properties:

1. In viscosity and surface tension it differs very little from pure water.
2. Its particles are electrically charged as shown by their migration in an electric field. The source of the charge varies from one sol to another. Colloidal ferric hydroxide may carry a positive charge because of dissociation of hydroxyl ions from the surface of the particle. Or it may, like many other colloidal particles, acquire a charge by capture of ions. A given colloid adsorbs preferentially either negative or positive ions, so that particles of ferric and aluminum hydroxides, for example, are

always positively charged, while the colloidal metals carry negative charges. The stability of hydrophobic sols depends largely upon these charges which prevent the particles from coalescing into large aggregates which would precipitate.

3. Hydrophobic sols are very sensitive to small amounts of added electrolyte, which induce flocculation of the colloid. This is apparently due to neutralization of the charge on the colloidal particles by the charge on ions of the opposite sign. Thus the negative arsenious sulfide is precipitated by much lower molar concentrations of trivalent cations than of monovalent ones, while the positive colloidal ferric hydroxide is coagulated much more effectively by trivalent anions than by monovalent.

4. Hydrophobic sols are *irreversible*, that is, once they have been precipitated it is not possible to redisperse them by removing the precipitating agent.

Hydrophilic sols

Most of the colloids which are important in biological systems are hydrophilic. These include the large group of proteins, the phospholipids, and many plant and animal polysaccharides. It is probable that the protein and polysaccharide particles consist of single giant molecules stabilized by hydration. In contrast with the hydrophobic colloids the water-loving sols exhibit the following properties:

1. Their solutions have greater viscosity and lower surface tension than pure water.

2. Although their particles are usually charged, it is not the charges alone which confer stability upon the sols. The colloidal particles are also heavily hydrated, and it is the presence of this protective layer of adsorbed solvent which prevents the particles from coalescing to form a precipitate.

3. The sign of the charge carried by a given colloid is not specific but may change with a change in pH. Thus the same protein may carry a net positive charge in neutral solution and a net negative charge in basic solution. Furthermore, it can undergo a change from one charge to the other without precipitating, though at the midpoint, when its net charge is zero, it is particularly easy to precipitate.

4. The hydrophilic sols are more stable than the hydrophobic to added *low* concentrations of electrolyte. This lack of sensitivity probably results from the fact that the stability of these sols depends more on the water envelope and less on the repulsion of like charges.

5. When certain electrolytes are added in *high* concentration even the hydrophilic sols precipitate. This process is known as *salting out* and is carried out by saturating or half saturating the colloid solution with such a salt as ammonium sulfate or sodium sulfate. It is believed that the added salt competes with the colloid for water and that the precipitation occurs

when the aqueous envelope around the colloidal particles has been removed.

6. A hydrophilic sol is a *reversible* colloid, since removal of the electrolyte which has been used to salt it out allows the precipitate to revert to colloidal form. This may be achieved by immersing the precipitate, enclosed in a semipermeable sac, in a large volume of water or in running water. The small electrolyte ions of the precipitant dialyze away, but the larger colloidal particles are retained and gradually go back into colloidal solution as the electrolyte concentration is reduced.

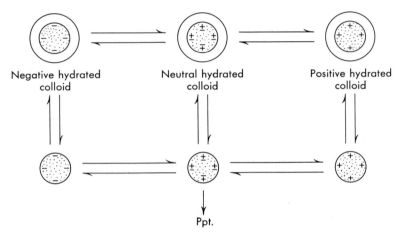

Negative hydrated   Neutral hydrated   Positive hydrated
colloid   colloid   colloid

Ppt.

Fig. 2.25. Diagrammatic representation of various types of colloidal particles. Those in the upper row are typical lyophilic particles; those below are lyophobic.

A conventional representation of various colloidal particles and their relationship to each other is given in Fig. 2.25.

Interaction of two colloidal sols

PROTECTIVE COLLOIDS.   The greater stability of hydrophilic sols may be used to confer stability on the more sensitive hydrophobic colloids. For example, small amounts of various plant gums added to inorganic sols reduce the likelihood of precipitation, probably through the formation of a thin protective coating. This property of hydrophilic colloids finds a diagnostic use in the clinical test known as the "gold number." The gold number is defined as the number of milligrams of hydrophilic colloid which just fails to prevent the change in color of a standard gold sol when 1 ml of 10 per cent sodium chloride is added to 10 ml of the sol. In certain diseases of the central nervous system the amount of protein (hydrophilic colloid) in the spinal fluid varies from the normal to give rise to abnormal gold numbers. Comparison of the gold number of the fluid from a patient with that of normal spinal fluid is often an aid in diagnosing the type of nervous disease.

SENSITIZATION.   While the presence of hydrophilic colloid may confer stability upon the more sensitive hydrophobic sols, this occurs only when the concentration of the protecting sol is above a certain critical level. Addition of a hydrophilic sol in lower concentration than this causes the hydrophobic sol to be less stable than usual and hastens its flocculation. This is believed to depend upon the ability of the few hydrophilic particles to catch

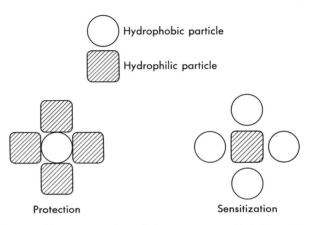

Fig. 2.26. Diagrammatic representation of the aggregates which form when hydrophilic colloids protect or sensitize a hydrophobic colloid.

and hold together a number of hydrophobic units. These relatively large aggregates are then very easily precipitated by electrolytes. The difference between protection and sensitization is indicated diagrammatically in Fig. 2.26.

COACERVATION.   When two hydrophilic colloids of opposite charge are mixed, it may happen that the dispersed phases unite to form a complex which first separates as small liquid drops. These then coalesce to form a viscous liquid layer, known as a *coacervate* (*acervus* = heap). That the oppositely charged particles retain their identity and their charges can be shown by placing the coacervate in an electric field. The oppositely charged particles are then found to move away from the viscous coacervate toward the appropriate electrodes. The stability of the coacervates is believed to result from a balance between the electrostatic attraction of the charged particles and the effect of the water envelope which prevents their approaching each other closely enough to achieve a neutralization of the opposite charges. It has been suggested that cell membranes may prove to be coacervate films, made from some of the oppositely charged colloids known to be present in the cell contents.

Gels

The name gel is given to a lyophilic colloid which is characterized by a somewhat elastic rigidity. The semisolid texture is believed to result from a tendency on the part of some colloidal particles to remain united when suitable groups come into contact and thus to form what is sometimes described as a "brush heap" structure. As this simile would suggest, the units in the aggregate are somewhat linear in nature and form interlacing masses. Such a structure is indicated diagrammatically in Fig. 2.27.

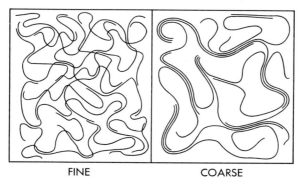

FINE   COARSE

Fig. 2.27. Schematic diagrams of gel structure. In the fine network the long macromolecules associate with others here and there for short distances; in the coarse network each aligns itself with a few others for long distances. [From J. D. Ferry, "Protein Gels," *Advances in Protein Chem.*, **4**, 1 (1948).]

Gelatin is a familiar example of a substance which forms a gel, and the ease with which its gel can be liquefied by heat illustrates the reversibility of the sol $\leftrightarrow$ gel transformation. Whether a gelatin solution will take the form of a sol or a gel depends upon the concentration of the gelatin, the temperature, and the pH.

The clotting of blood is a biological example of gel formation. In the plasma are a number of proteins in solution, including the one known as fibrinogen. At a point of injury this substance is somewhat changed to become fibrin, which then forms a local gel or clot.

One of the most striking properties of the gels is their ability to take up water. This *imbibition*, as it is called, is often accompanied by extreme examples of swelling. It is of biological interest that the extent of the swelling is dependent upon the ions which are present. With some colloids pH is the determining factor; with others there is evidence of ionic antagonisms, some ions promoting swelling, others preventing it. This is one of many examples of the antagonistic biological effects of different ions. Often the antagonism is between monovalent and divalent ions, but sometimes it is between two of the same valence. For example, when the blood of an experimental animal is entirely replaced by a solution of pure salts, the heart will continue to beat provided the solution is isosmotic with blood and provided further that it contains a suitable ratio of sodium, calcium, and potassium ions. But even with the correct osmotic pressure, if only one type of cation is used, the heart beat gradually diminishes and finally ceases entirely. In another type of experiment it has been found that raising the concentration of magnesium in the plasma from its normal value of 2–3 mg per 100 ml to about 20 mg results in unconsciousness. But if injection of a corresponding amount of calcium ion follows, this effect is entirely and rapidly reversed. There is at the moment no way of knowing how either of these biological effects is mediated, but it is at least suggestive that simple colloids are sensitive in much the same selective way to varying ionic ratios.

Some gels contract on standing and squeeze out part of the fluid caught in the network of colloidal particles. This process is known as *syneresis* and is responsible for the slow separation of serum from a blood clot.

Emulsions

At the surface of contact between two immiscible liquids there is set up an interfacial tension. When two such liquids are shaken together violently, one may form droplets in the other, but on standing the droplets coalesce and the liquids separate. This is to be expected, since droplet formation has greatly increased the surface and therefore the free surface energy of the system.

To convert such a temporary emulsion into a permanent one it is necessary to reduce the interfacial tension. This is usually done by adding something which acts as an emulsifier. The most familiar emulsifying agent is soap, which lowers the interfacial tension between water and insoluble fatty material and so promotes the emulsification of the fat.

When both phases of a colloidal system are liquid, either one may become the dispersed phase. Thus an oil:water emulsion may consist of oil droplets in a continuous aqueous medium, or the water may be dispersed as droplets in a continuous oily phase. The form taken by any particular pair depends upon the emulsifying agent used. Thus when this agent is sodium oleate it favors formation of oil-in-water emulsions, but calcium oleate stabilizes an emulsion of the water-in-oil type. This is usually explained by picturing the stabilizer, which concentrates in a film at the interface, as actually a third phase separating the two liquids. Then if the interfacial tension between water and the film is lower than that between oil and the film, the film reduces its area on the oily side by formation of oily droplets in the water. When the interfacial tension between water and the film is the greater of the two, the reverse occurs and water droplets are dispersed in the oil.

In this connection it is interesting to note that emulsifying agents of both sorts are almost universally distributed in living cells. This makes it easy to understand how a cell membrane could change its character from time to time and so be permeable first to one type of solute and then to another. If this membrane consists in part at least of fatty material this might be present at a given moment as an oil-in-water emulsion, stabilized both by adjacent sodium ions and by phospholipids of which the surface active lecithin is the most abundant. But cells also contain two substances which favor formation of a water-in-oil dispersion, namely calcium ions and a complex organic substance, cholesterol, which has many properties the opposite of those of lecithin. If calcium ion or cholesterol or both were to move to the cell surface, there would result a reversal of phase in the membrane, thus making the oil the continuous phase with watery droplets dispersed through it. During the time when the water was continuous throughout the film, water-soluble molecules and ions could pass the cell membrane by dissolving in one side and diffusing through. Later when the continuous phase had become oily, fat-soluble molecules would be admitted to the cell by a similar process. It should be noted that emulsification furnishes another example of ion antagonism, the monovalent ion predisposing to one type of organization and the divalent to the other. It seems that the plan of governing by a system of "checks and balances" was invented by living cells long before our lawmakers appropriated it.

The Donnan Equilibrium

Although particles of colloidal size cannot themselves diffuse through a semipermeable membrane, the presence of these large charged particles on one side of such a membrane does markedly influence the distribution of ions which are able to diffuse. This may at first sight seem surprising. Thus if a protein solution in a collodion sac were to be immersed in a solution of sodium chloride it might seem reasonable to expect that the sodium and chloride ions would ultimately distribute themselves evenly on both sides of the membrane, which is freely permeable to them and impermeable to the colloid. However this proves not to be the case. In the equilibrium which is actually established the ionic concentrations on the two sides of the membrane are unequal and the extent of the inequality depends on the relative concentrations of colloid and ions. This phenomenon was first studied quantitatively by F. G. Donnan of University College, London, about 1911, and has come to be known by his name. As an example of a Donnan equilibrium, consider two chambers separated by a semipermeable membrane. In the one is a solution of a protein which will be assumed for the sake of simplicity to give rise to one sodium ion and a singly charged protein anion. On the other side of the membrane is a solution of sodium chloride to which the membrane is freely permeable. Donnan showed that in such a system ions migrate into the colloid chamber until at equilibrium the ion concentrations satisfy the expression

$$[Na^+]_1[Cl^-]_1 = [Na^+]_2[Cl^-]_2$$

in which the subscripts refer to the two sides of the membrane. The initial and final states are shown in the diagram which is adapted from a similar chart in Donnan's original paper.

INITIAL STATE

Proteinate⁻	Na⁺		Na⁺	Cl⁻
C_1	C_1	‖	C_2	C_2

EQUILIBRIUM STATE

Proteinate⁻	Na⁺	Cl⁻	Na⁺	Cl⁻
C_1	$C_1 + X$	X	$C_2 - X$	$C_2 - X$

In order to maintain electrical neutrality, equal numbers of sodium and chloride ions must move across the membrane, thus causing the sodium ion concentration on the colloid side to be greater than that of the chloride ion. At equilibrium the Donnan equation reads

$$(C_1 + X)X = (C_2 - X)^2$$

This means that the concentration of sodium ion inside the colloid compartment must be larger than its concentration outside, and that the chloride concentration is correspondingly higher outside than in.

$$\frac{[Na^+]_1}{[Na^+]_2} = \frac{[Cl^-]_2}{[Cl^-]_1}$$

Thus when in the initial state the concentration of protein is, for example, ten times that of sodium chloride, the final concentration of sodium ion in the colloid compartment becomes approximately eleven times that of the sodium ion outside, with the chloride ion concentrations unequal in the reverse sense. The figures given in Table 2.13 show the relation between the initial and the final states for various concentration ratios.

The situation is similar when no common ion is involved. Table 2.14 gives the data from an experiment in which the dye Congo red (NaR) which furnishes sodium ion and a negative colloidal ion R^- was separated by a membrane from solutions of potassium chloride. In the final distribution both cation concentrations were higher in the colloid compartment, with a corresponding but opposite disparity in the anion concentrations.

Although the Donnan equilibrium explains how in the presence of colloidal particles ion concentrations may differ on two sides of a semipermeable membrane, it proved inadequate to explain such differences as are frequently encountered in living cells. For example, in the blood stream essentially all the potassium ion is found inside the red blood corpuscles, and a marine alga (*Valonia*) maintains in its protoplasm a far lower sodium ion and a far higher potassium ion concentration than obtains in the sea water which bathes it. In both these cells the preferential concentration of one ion inside a membrane depends upon a constant input of energy. This is furnished by

TABLE 2.13. Donnan Equilibria When One Ion Is Common to Both Chambers

Original Concentration, Protein	Original Concentration, NaCl	Equilibrium Conc. in Colloid Chamber		Equilibrium Conc. Outside Colloid Chamber	
		Na^+	Cl^-	Na^+	Cl^-
C_1	C_2	$C_1 + X$	X	$C_2 - X$	$C_2 - X$
0.1	1.0	0.576	0.476	0.524	0.524
1.0	1.0	1.33	0.33	0.66	0.66
1.0	0.1	1.008	0.0083	0.092	0.092

Source: Adapted from figures in F. G. Donnan, *Z. Elektrochem.*, *17*, 572 (1911).

TABLE 2.14. Donnan Equilibria with No Common Ion

Original Concentration, NaR	Original Concentration, KCl	Equilibrium Conc. Inside Chamber			Equilibrium Conc. Outside Chamber		
		Na^+	K^+	Cl^-	Na^+	K^+	Cl^-
C_1	C_2	$C_1 - Z$	X	Y	Z	$C_2 - X$	$C_2 - Y$
100	1.0	99	0.99	0.01	1.0	0.01	0.99
10	1.0	9.2	0.90	0.10	0.8	0.1	0.9
1	1.0	0.66	0.66	0.33	0.33	0.33	0.66

Source: Adapted from figures in F. G. Donnan, *Z. Elektrochem.*, *17*, 572 (1911).

oxidation of the metabolites, and its importance is shown by the fact that when oxidation is blocked these cells can no longer maintain their special ionic ratios. Thus osmotic work is one of several endergonic processes which must be carried out at the expense of the exergonic oxidations in the cell. The exact mechanism of this energy transfer is not known.

Analysis of Colloids

The large particles which have just been discussed present many analytical difficulties. They cannot usually be purified by recrystallization. Often a tissue extract or fluid contains many molecules which are almost indistinguishable chemically, such as the array of different proteins found in blood serum. Many colloids are sensitive to small changes in pH, and to other chemical manipulations. For the isolation of the different colloidal components in a mixture, two physical techniques are of enormous value, i.e., sedimentation in the ultracentrifuge and electrophoresis.

The ultracentrifuge

There are various sorts of high-speed centrifuges, all of which are modifications of the one originally developed by Theodor Svedberg at the University of Upsala. Recent models give centrifugal forces in excess of a million times that of gravity. Although any sort of high-speed centrifuge is frequently referred to as an ultracentrifuge, the name should strictly be reserved for those in which convection currents and vibration are carefully eliminated.

The rate of sedimentation of particles, whether under the influence of gravity or of a high-speed centrifuge depends upon (1) the size and shape of the particles, (2) the densities of the particles and of the dispersion medium, (3) the frictional forces which oppose particle movement, and (4) the magnitude of the sedimenting force. These various quantities can be so related in a mathematical statement that it becomes possible to calculate from ultracentrifugal data the weights of the particles and to estimate their shapes. The instrument is also widely used to determine whether a given sol is monodisperse (contains only one type of particle) or polydisperse (contains more than one type of particle). In recent years many supposedly pure proteins, for example, have been shown in the ultracentrifuge to contain particles which sediment at different rates and are presumably different substances.

When the particles in a homogeneous colloidal suspension have been spun for a time in a high-speed centrifuge, a boundary will have formed between the pure solvent at the top and the upper layer of solute particles. The position of this boundary may be determined by virtue of the fact that there is just there a sharp change in refractive index. If a beam of light is directed at right angles to the sedimenting column and moved along its length, it will show a sharp change in refraction whenever it passes across a boundary between regions of different density or concentration. Instruments in which concentration gradients are to be measured are set up with a series of lenses so that each boundary is recorded directly on a photographic plate. Figure 2.28 indicates diagrammatically the sedimentation of a mixture of two types of particles, with the right-hand diagrams giving the appearance of the graphs obtained when the optical system known as the Schlieren system is used to measure changes in refraction. The position of the horizontal "peak" shows where the change in refractive index was found, and its height indicates the rate of the change. The area under the peak is proportional to the concentration of solute. The peak in the upper diagram is obtained when the light beam moves from air to the meniscus of the solvent. Figure 2.29(a) reproduces actual sedimentation patterns obtained with a sample of a purified

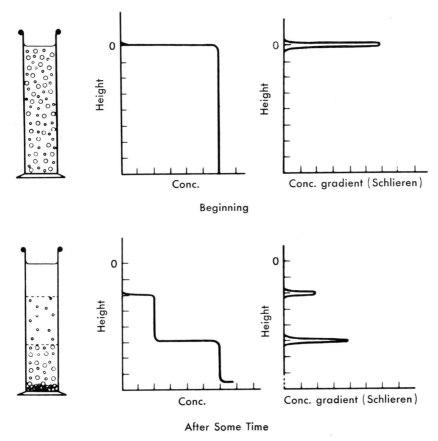

Fig. 2.28. Three representations of the sedimentation of a system formed by particles of two sizes. Note that below the boundaries the concentration is constant. [From K. J. Mysels, *Introduction to Colloid Chemistry*, Interscience, New York, 1959.]

protein suspended in a buffer. The meniscus is at the right, and the small peak nearer the meniscus indicates that the main protein is still contaminated with some slower moving component. Figure 2.29(b) represents a totally different kind of experiment. Ruptured bacteria have been centrifuged at about 56,740 rpm to separate the different small granules which are found inside the cells, and the several clear peaks indicate the presence of particles which sediment at different rates. In Fig. 2.29(b) the meniscus is at the left.

The rate at which the boundary moves for a given particle is indicated by its sedimentation constant or coefficient, s, given in svedberg units S. A sedimentation rate of 1×10^{-13} cm per sec per unit centrifugal field of force is called 1 svedberg. It has recently been found that an enzyme protein with an estimated molecular weight of 34,000 has a sedimentation coefficient of about 3.06S at *p*H 7, whereas another with a molecular weight approximately ten times as large has a coefficient of 12.82S. The particles in Fig. 2.29(*b*) are larger and have sedimentation coefficients which range from 20 to 100^+S as indicated on the diagram.

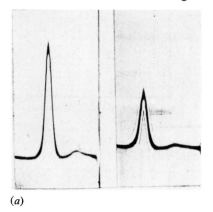 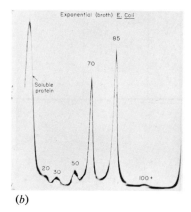

(*a*)   (*b*)

Fig. 2.29. (*a*) Sedimentation patterns of an enzyme protein, glutamic decarboxylase, after approximately 32 minutes sedimentation at 25° at 56,100 rpm. The two preparations differ in concentration of the enzyme and in the buffer used. The meniscus is at the right-hand edge of the photographs. [From R. Shukuya and G. W. Schwert, *J. Biol. Chem.*, **235**, 1650 (1960).] (*b*) Sedimentation pattern obtained when a total juice from growing *E. coli* was spun in the analytical ultracentrifuge at 56,740 rpm. The peaks indicate the presence of nucleoprotein particles known as *ribosomes*. Under the conditions of this particular experiment there are found particles which sediment at six different rates, indicated by the sedimentation constants $20S$ to 100^+S written over the peaks. [From E. T. Bolton *et al.*, in *Carnegie Institution of Washington Year Book 58*, p. 264, issued December 1959.]

Electrophoresis

It has been noted that most colloidal particles carry electric charges. These may be inherent in the colloidal particle in solution, as is true of the proteins in which free carboxyl and amino groups are centers of negative and positive charges. On the other hand, the charges may be due to adsorbed ions. However acquired, the net charge on the particle will determine the direction in which it will migrate in an electric field. Its rate of migration will depend on the size of the charge, on the weight of the particle and the magnitude of the potential difference imposed. Differences in migration rates are utilized in the process known as electrophoresis.

Electrophoresis was used in the early days as a preparative method. Solutions were put into relatively large vessels or cells which were divided in various ways into a horizontal series of compartments. The walls had to be porous enough so that the particles could pass through, but solid enough to discourage diffusion. Presently sintered glass serves the purpose, but leather has been used, and parchment and even cloth. A solution is put in the middle compartment of such a cell, and the other segments are filled with buffer solutions. When the whole is then subjected to an electric field, the various components will move toward the electrode of opposite charge at rates which will depend on the factors enumerated above. After a suitable interval, the material in the various compartments can be worked up separately. It has frequently happened that a significant purification of at least some of the components of the mixture has been achieved by this type of experiment.

Of late years the method of electrophoresis is chiefly used on a micro scale to determine whether or not a given substance is homogeneous. For this purpose the cell devised by the Swedish chemist, Arne Tiselius is used. Figure 2.30 shows diagrammatically how the cell is filled to establish the initial boundaries between the solution to be analyzed and the buffer. The three parts of the cell, numbered I, II, and III can each be displaced horizontally. In A, protein solution has been put into the bottom of the U-shaped channel before sections I and II were displaced to the right. After removal of excess protein from the left arm, buffer is poured into that arm and protein solution into the right one while the cell is still arranged as in A. Displacement of

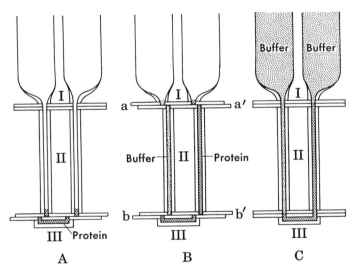

Fig. 2.30. Diagrams illustrating the initial formation of the boundaries in the Tiselius electrophoresis cell with the tall center section. [From L. G. Longsworth, *Chem. Rev.*, **30**, 323 (1942).]

section I to the left then isolates the columns of solution below the *a-a'* boundary and gives the arrangement shown in B. The extra protein is then washed out of the right-hand vessel of section I and both are filled with buffer. The channels are then aligned as in C, resulting in a buffer-protein boundary at a-a' on the right and a similar boundary at b-b' on the left. Figure 2.31 shows how this small U-shaped cell is attached to the rest of the apparatus which is used for electrophoresis. Application of a potential difference across the electrodes E and E' causes the boundary to rise on the left and to descend on the right. The movement of the boundaries may be followed by one of several optical methods. In Longsworth's scanning method, a photographic plate is moved past a narrow slit in such a way that a contour is obtained

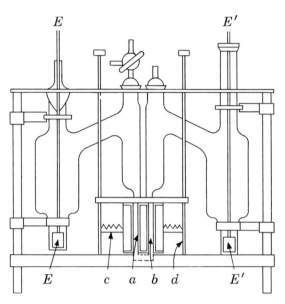

Fig. 2.31. The electrophoresis cell of Tiselius for quantitative study of the moving boundary and isolation of protein components. E and E' are silver-silver chloride electrodes. a and b are sections of the electrophoresis U tube. c and d are mechanical devices for moving sections a and b. [From J. B. Bull, *Physical Biochemistry*, 2nd ed., Wiley, New York, 1951.]

which is a graph of the refractive index gradient against the position in the cell column. Measurement of the areas under the peaks gives the concentration of solute at each level. In Fig. 2.32 such a descending electrophoresis pattern is shown for the same protein for which the ultracentrifugal pattern was given in Fig. 2.29(a). There is here as in the sedimentation pattern evidence of a small amount of an impurity which gives the low peak at the left. The arrow indicates the original boundary.

When a complex mixture is subjected to electrophoresis, the ascending and descending patterns should theoretically be exact mirror images of each other. This is never quite true in fact. There are a number of factors which contribute to the inequality, and they are considered in manuals which describe the workings of the apparatus. Figure 2.33 shows the pattern obtained several years ago when the complex mixture of proteins found in blood serum was subjected to electrophoresis. It is clear that the two patterns do coincide in large measure, though there are variations in the two arms.

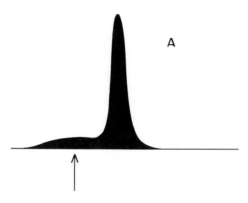

Fig. 2.32. Descending electrophoresis pattern of approximately 0.6 per cent protein in pyridine-pyridine hydro-chloride-HCl buffer, at pH 4.8, ionic strength 0.1. The pattern was recorded after passage of a 25 ma current for 350 minutes. [From R. Shukuya and G. W. Schwert, *J. Biol. Chem.*, **235**, 1651 (1960).]

Preparative electrophoresis has in recent years been carried out in the presence of some sort of supporting medium which facilitates the isolation of the different components. This has been done, for example, with such an arrangement that while the components of a mixture were being separated by

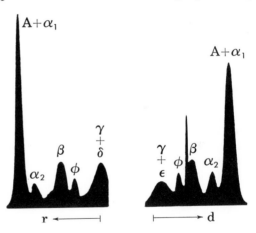

Fig. 2.33. Electrophoretic patterns of (r) the rising and (d) the descending boundaries of a human plasma, diluted 1 : 4, in a 0.025N LiCl-0.025N LiV-0.025N HV (V = diethylbarbiturate) buffer at pH 7.9 after electrolysis, at 0.5°C, for 5750 seconds at 7.76 volts per centimeter. The initial boundary positions are indicated by the ends of the arrows. [From L. G. Longsworth, *Chem. Rev.*, **30**, 323 (1942).]

paper chromatography they were also subjected to an electric field. The chromatography results in separation along a vertical line, and the electro-phoresis moves these moving components laterally. If provision is made for catching the solvent in small portions as the development of the chromatogram brings it to the bottom of the paper, there is obtained a series of solutions each taken from a thin vertical section of the paper above the collecting vessel. One such apparatus is described in the Durrum reference at the end of the chapter.

Many different types of supporting material are also used without any concomitant chromatography, in which case the procedure is known as *zone electrophoresis*. Starch, cellulose, silica gel and paper are among the materials commonly used. The components of a mixture move through a horizontally supported medium which can be sliced at the end of the experiment to isolate any number of different components from the zones to which they have migrated. It is found that zone electrophoresis is particularly effective in the separation of such complex mixtures as occur in blood serum, or are formed by hydrolysis of a protein. The value of the method lies not only in the ease of manipulation of the separate zones at the end of the experiment, but in the fact that it frequently gives a clear separation of several very similar substances.

SUGGESTIONS FOR FURTHER READING

Bier, M. (ed.), *Electrophoresis*, Academic, New York, 1959.

Boltz, D. F. (ed.), *Selected Topics in Modern Instrumental Analysis*, Prentice-Hall, Englewood Cliffs, N.J., 1952.

Chinard, F. P., and T. Enns, Osmotic pressure, *Science*, **124**, 472 (1956).

Delahay, P., *Instrumental Analysis*, Macmillan, New York, 1957.

Durrum, E. L., Electrophoresis on filter paper, *J. Am. Chem. Soc.*, **73**, 4875 (1951).

Edsall, J. T., and J. Wyman, *Biophysical Chemistry*, Academic, New York, 1958.

Ewing, G. W., *Instrumental Methods of Chemical Analysis*, McGraw-Hill, New York, 1960.

Lederer, M., *An Introduction to Paper Electrophoresis*, Elsevier, New York, 1955.

Mysels, K. J., *Introduction to Colloid Chemistry*, Interscience, New York, 1959.

Sutherland, G. B. B. M., Application of infrared spectroscopy to biological problems, in *Biophysical Science*, J. L. Oncley (ed.-in-chief), Wiley, New York, 1959.

Svedberg, T., and K. O. Pedersen, *The Ultracentrifuge*, Clarendon Press, Oxford, 1940.

Willard, H. H., *et al.*, *Instrumental Methods of Analysis*, 3rd ed., Van Nostrand, Princeton, N.J., 1958.

All the physiological activities of animals and plants—assimilation,
secretion, excretion, motion, generation—are expressions of the
activities of the cells considered as physiological units.

THOMAS HENRY HUXLEY (1887)

The structure of living forms 3

WHEN IT WAS ORIGINALLY DISCOVERED that all living material consists of cells, and that each cell arises from a previously existing one, no one could have predicted that the individual cells of diverse organs and organisms would prove to be as much alike chemically as they have proved to be. It is the main purpose of this book to consider those fundamental chemical processes which take place in nearly all cells. As a preliminary to this, the present chapter surveys briefly the various types of living things which have developed on earth and the organs and structures which they have evolved.

NATURE AND ACTIVITIES OF LIVING CELLS

At some time well over 350 million years ago life began, perhaps as a single cell, perhaps in a less organized form. From this beginning has arisen the whole complex variety of higher animals and modern vegetation. Numerous and different as are the present day offspring of that dimly imagined primordial organism, they are yet alike in this, that every living cell on earth must acquire and degrade foodstuffs in order to obtain building material and energy to maintain itself. The structural basis for these activities is to be found in the complex organization within the cell itself.

Cell Structure

Microscopic examination of plant and animal tissue reveals the fact that while cells differ markedly in shape and size and function, they still have certain fundamental characteristics in common. The existence of a nucleus in plant cells was first noted in 1831 by the Scots botanist Robert Brown, though he did not recognize its true importance. A few years later Felix Dujardin (1801–1860) described a semifluid, jelly-like substance in animal cells which he believed to be endowed with all the qualities of life and which he called *sarcode*. In 1846 a similar jelly-like material was found by Hugo von Mohl (1805–1872) in plant cells and was named *protoplasma*, meaning "first thing made." Eventually the word protoplasm came to be used to indicate the material within a cell membrane, whether plant or animal.

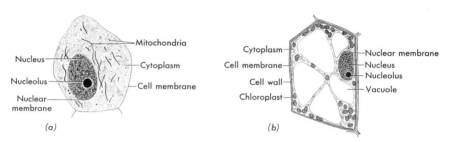

Fig. 3.1. The essential features of a typical animal cell (*a*) and a typical plant cell (*b*).

The appearance of typical plant and animal cells as revealed by an ordinary light microscope is shown diagrammatically in Fig. 3.1. There it is seen that each is bounded by a fine membrane. In plant cells this is supported by a heavier cell wall which consists largely of cellulose, but in animal cells the only boundary is so fine that it is sometimes invisible under the microscope. Its presence, however, must be inferred in order to explain the reactions of cells when immersed in solutions of varying concentrations. It has already been noted (page 22) that they swell when the external solution is dilute and shrink when it is more concentrated than the cell contents. This is, of course, the typical reaction of a solution enclosed in a semipermeable membrane. The cell membrane is believed to consist of proteins and various fatty, or *lipid*, substances arranged in a regular pattern to form lipoprotein macromolecules. If vacuoles are present in a cell, there is a similar membrane between them and the rest of the protoplasm, and each of the small particles shown inside the cell is enclosed in a membrane.

Within the cell membrane there appear several different structures of which the nucleus is the most conspicuous. It consists of an approximately spherical body which appears denser than the rest of the cell and is bounded by a membrane. Its general importance is attested by the fact that if a unicellular organism is cut in half, only the portion which contains the nucleus will regenerate. The nucleus serves a unique function in cell division and is the physical agency through which hereditary traits are transmitted.

The remainder of the cell contents outside the nucleus is called the *cytoplasm*, which is sometimes divided into the *ectoplasm*, or region nearest the cell membrane, and the *endoplasm* which lies within the outer layer. The cytoplasm appears granular under the microscope because of the presence of a great number of minute structures which are scattered about in it. In plant cells these structures include the small bodies known as *plastids*, some of which

TABLE 3.1.   Fractionation of Particulate Elements of Rat Liver

		Sedimentation	
Fraction	Diameter, μ	Time, min	Acceleration, g
Nuclei	50–100	10	600
Mitochondria	1–3	20	24,000
Microsomes	0.06–0.15	120	41,000

SOURCE: Adapted from E. L. Lehninger, in *Enzymes and Enzyme Systems*, John T. Edsall (ed.), Harvard University, Cambridge, Mass., 1951.

contain chlorophyll and are called *chloroplasts*. Those which are colorless are called *leukoplasts*. In all cells there are numerous tiny granules known as *mitochondria*, some of which are roughly spherical whereas others are more elongated.

For many years it was beyond the resolving power of even the best microscopes to show the fine structure of the mitochondria. This situation changed when the electron microscope made available enormously increased magnifications, which may be of the order of 100,000 or more. At about the same time biologists began using the ultracentrifuge to separate from the cytoplasm various particles which differed in their sedimentation rates. Table 3.1 gives the results of such a separation. The cell contents has been divided into three particulate fractions consisting of the relatively heavy nuclei, the lighter mitochondria, and the material known as *microsomes* which sedimented at the highest speed used. There remained as a supernatant the *cell sap* or fluid part of the cytoplasm with its varied solutes. In the years since this separation was recorded, the techniques for handling disrupted cells have been greatly improved so that the particles can now be separated largely undamaged. This has put at the disposal of the biologist and the chemist isolated fragments of the metabolic machinery of the cell, each of which can be studied separately. Such studies have revealed a complex organization within the tiny particles themselves, and are slowly leading to an understanding of the localization

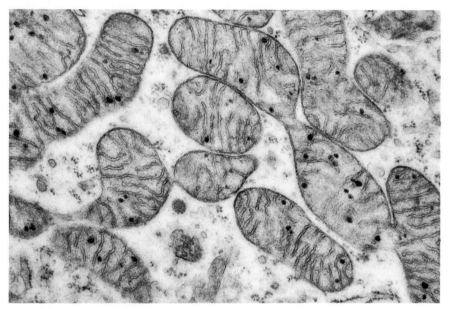

Fig. 3.2. Mitochondrial profiles in guinea pig pancreas (×36,000). (Courtesy of Dr. G. E. Palade.)

within the cell of various enzymes and, in consequence, of the chemical events which they catalyze.

The mitochondria are small bodies having a diameter of 0.2 to 0.5 μ, and a length of 0.3 to 5.0 μ. A mitochondrion is surrounded by a double membrane, the inner one of which penetrates the body of the particle with a series of infoldings which form shelflike projections, often roughly parallel to each other. Figure 3.2 is an electron micrograph of part of a cell of guinea pig pancreas. It shows several mitochondria, and in various places it is quite clear that the transverse striations are projections of the inner layer of the double limiting membrane. These projections are known as *cristae mitochondriales*, and are usually, though not always, disposed perpendicular to the long axis of the particle. Within the mitochondrial membrane the matrix appears to be largely homogeneous, though the fluid which is between the two layers of the membrane and which fills the tubular infoldings of the cristae is often less dense than that which fills the body of the organelle. The tiny dark dots which appear inside the mitochondria are as yet unexplained, though they are a constant feature.

Examination of the microsomal fraction in the electron microscope has revealed that it consists not of discrete particles but of a complex membranous system to which particles may or may not be attached. The whole body of the cytoplasm, which appears under the light microscope to be structureless, proves to contain a large number of vesicles and tubules enclosed in a membrane which connects them to form a continuous reticulum or network. Since in some cells the network is less concentrated in the ectoplasm it is known as the *endoplasmic reticulum.* It sometimes includes relatively large flat vesicles known as *cisternae*, without any apparent break in the continuity of the membrane system. Furthermore, its membrane is in some cells continuous with the outer layer of the double nuclear membrane, and in some with the limiting membrane of the cell itself. Since the various subcellular units are larger than the allowable thickness of the slices to be viewed in the

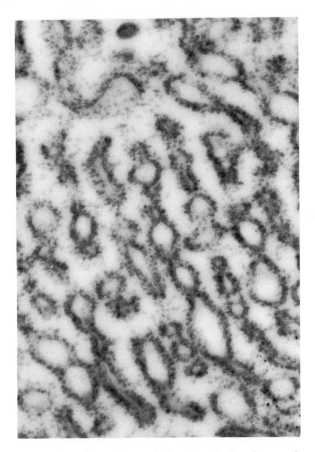

Fig. 3.3. Rough-surfaced profiles of the endoplasmic reticulum in an acinary cell of rat pancreas (×52,500). [From G. E. Palade, Electron microscopy of mitochondria and other cytoplasmic structures, in *Enzymes: Units of Biological Structure and Function*, O. H. Gaebler (ed.), Academic, New York, 1956.]

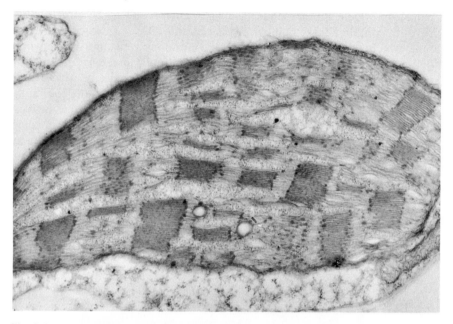

Fig. 3.4. Electron micrograph of maize chloroplast. The dense rectangular regions are the grana in which the chlorophyll is localized. When the plane of sectioning is at right angles to the one shown here, the grana appear circular, indicating that they are cylindrical in shape (×25,200). [Courtesy of Dr. A. E. Vatter.]

electron microscope, both mitochondria and the reticular system appear in micrographs as slices or profiles. Figure 3.3 shows a section of the endoplasmic reticulum in a cell of rat pancreas. It consists, as noted above, of a continuous lipoprotein membrane to which in some areas tiny, dense particles 100–150 A in diameter are attached. The discrete small particles are clearly visible in the micrograph, most of them attached to the membrane though a few are apparently free in the cytoplasmic matrix. Those portions of the endoplasmic reticulum which do not have the attached particles are spoken of as "smooth-surfaced" as opposed to the rough-surfaced region shown in the figure. The two types are simply local variations in a single continuous system.

Plant cells also include mitochondria. These are best isolated from colorless parts of plants since in cells which contain chlorophyll they are likely to be smaller than the chloroplasts and to be present in much smaller numbers.

The particles which are most interesting in plant cells are, of course, the chloroplasts which make possible their remarkable synthetic achievements. These, like the mitochondria, are discrete small particles in which is concentrated the chlorophyll of the cell. Figure 3.4 is an electron micrograph of a maize chloroplast. It shows a particle enclosed in a membrane and nearly filled with a membranous structure which folds back and forth. The dark areas are those in which the chlorophyll is concentrated, and consist of flat, laminated disks piled on top of each other to make the tiny units known as *grana*. The membrane is as usual a lipoprotein complex. The chlorophyll is believed to lie in monomolecular layers between the two parts of the membrane complex. The structure of chlorophyll itself is such that one part of the molecule is hydrophilic, while a long hydrocarbon side chain is lipophilic (fat-loving). Through the hydrophilic part of the molecule chlorophyll is bound to the aqueous protein part of the membrane, while its hydrocarbon side chain forms a link with the lipid part of the membrane. Figure 3.5 shows a section of maize chloroplast at higher magnification. This micrograph brings out clearly the continuity of the membrane and the laminated structure of the grana.

Since bacterial cells are themselves about the size of a mitochondrion, it is not strange that they contain no mitochondria. However, particles can

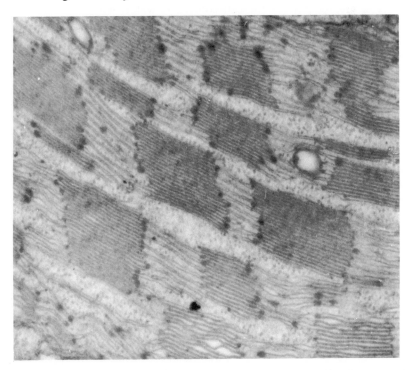

Fig. 3.5. Electron micrograph of a section of maize chloroplast showing the connections between the lamellae of the grana and those in the regions between the grana (×62,000). [Courtesy of Dr. A. E. Vatter.]

be obtained from disrupted bacterial cells by ultracentrifugation. These are known as *ribosomes*, and they seem to be analogous to the small particles found attached to the membranes in the rough-surfaced parts of the micro-somal fraction from larger cells.

Chemical Constitution of Protoplasm

The early analytical studies of protoplasm must have been somewhat disappointing, for they uncovered no clue to its extraordinary properties. The elements which are present are in no sense unusual. The cell is made up largely of carbon, hydrogen, oxygen, and nitrogen, with smaller amounts of the metals potassium, sodium, magnesium, and calcium, and of the nonmetals sulfur, chlorine, and phosphorus. Other elements are present in traces, among them iron, copper, iodine, and manganese.

If protoplasm contains no very exotic or uniquely interesting elements, neither is it built of compounds which are in themselves particularly remark-able. The greater part of the cell content is water, which constitutes over 90 per cent of the total weight in many tissues, and probably accounts for at least 75 per cent of the weight of all living cells. Dissolved or suspended in the water are a number of organic and inorganic compounds. The metallic chlorides, sulfates, and phosphates, present largely in ionic form, make up only a small percentage of the total "dry weight." The greater part of the nonaqueous part of protoplasm consists of organic compounds such as proteins, fatty substances, and carbohydrates, with small amounts of other compounds, many of them containing nitrogen. The simpler carbohydrates, the mono- and disaccharides, are present in solution, but the larger molecules give to the cell contents its colloidal form, on which in turn depend many of its characteristic properties. It is probable that many of the ions and the simpler molecules occur in combination with or adsorbed on the colloidal material of the cytoplasm, and that they are released only during isolation procedures.

Life in a Single Cell

The amoeba, found in quantity in muddy water, is a familiar example of a single-celled animal (Fig. 3.6). Besides the nucleus and granular cytoplasm, there are to be noted inside the cell a vacuole which contains food particles, and a clear contractile vacuole. It is possible by watching the amoeba under the microscope for a time to see food vacuoles form and disappear, and to see the use of the contractile vacuole. If a bit of food is introduced at the edge of the drop of water on the microscope slide, the amoeba advances toward it in a haphazard sort of way by pushing out extensions of its own body in what are called *pseudopodia*, and then flowing along to catch up with the extension. It ultimately flows around the food particle and engulfs it, enclosing a droplet of water at the same time. Food and water are quickly separated from the animal's body by being enclosed in one of the small vacuoles which are visible in the drawing. At first the outlines of the bits of food are perfectly clear, but slowly these become blurred and the particles appear to dissolve. If there is any part of the food which cannot be made soluble, it is ultimately rejected after the amoeba has flowed along and so

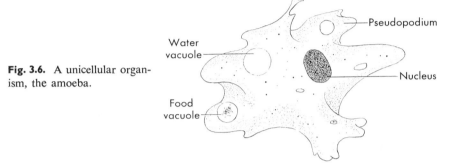

Fig. 3.6. A unicellular organism, the amoeba.

brought the refractory material close to its own outer membrane. At various times the contractile vacuole seems to disappear and then re-form, and it is believed to be acting at such times to excrete from the body of the cell some soluble waste. Thus the amoeba digests its food in an area temporarily set aside for the purpose and the digested fragments dialyze out into the cytoplasm.

If the microscope slide is marked off in squares so that the size of the amoeba can be measured from time to time, it will be seen to grow. Somehow in the subtle chemistry of its tiny laboratory, food is being transformed into a living organism.

In addition to food the amoeba must have oxygen which it obtains from the air dissolved in the water in which it lives. Oxygen is used to oxidize part of its food, as evidenced by the continuous evolution of carbon dioxide. This oxidation provides energy for motion and for the synthetic reactions by which it transforms part of its digested food into cellular fabric. In thus using molecular oxygen in a reaction which makes available to an organism the chemical energy locked up in organic molecules, the amoeba is typical of the vast majority of living cells.

PLANTS AND ANIMALS

Given the basic fact that living cells must be able to obtain energy and to build or maintain their own complex organization, let us next look briefly at the ways in which this is accomplished in plants and in animals.

Habits and Structure

Most higher plants are green; most plants are fixed in position whereas most animals are motile; many plants are heavily branched, with hundreds of identical or similar parts, whereas animals are more compact and less repetitive structurally.

Closer examination reveals other characteristic differences of habit and structure. An animal grows all over its body, so that at one time its internal organs, its limbs, its brain, and its skeleton are all increasing in size. This

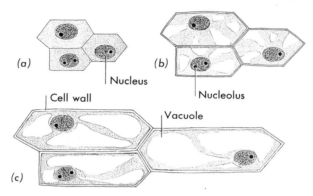

Fig. 3.7. Plant cells at three different ages from the very young cells (*a*), in which the cell walls are filled with protoplasm, to mature cells (*c*) in which the cell contents have become little more than a lining of the cell walls.

continues until it reaches adulthood when growth normally stops. But although the cells cease to grow and multiply, most of them remain actively alive. In contrast to this, plant growth is largely localized, but goes on continuously so long as the plant lives. The tips of the root and the tips of stems grow. The part of the plant behind these growing areas gradually takes on a different structure and becomes a rigid skeleton and a passageway consisting largely of dead cells.

A thin and often invisible surrounding membrane is the only barrier separating one animal cell from another, and normally that membrane is completely filled with protoplasm. Plant cells, on the other hand, have thick and conspicuous cell walls which help to support the plant. Inside this wall is the semipermeable plasma membrane which in young cells is almost filled with cytoplasm and its inclusions. But as plant cells grow older and are left behind the growing tip, they elongate and their protoplasmic contents are transformed into a thin lining within the rigid cell wall (Fig. 3.7). This leaves a large central space or vacuole which holds a watery solution known as cell sap. This is, of course, different from the "cell sap" obtained from disrupted cells.

Use of Solar Energy

Of the differences between plants and animals enumerated above, the first is by all odds the most fundamental. The possession of the pigment chlorophyll makes possible the *autotrophic* or self-nourishing metabolism characteristic of green plants.

Plant cells like those of animals must oxidize organic molecules to obtain energy. But they differ from animal cells in having the ability to build these up by photosynthesis, that is, to synthesize essential foodstuffs from simple inorganic molecules at the expense of energy derived from sunlight. In the presence of chlorophyll and of sunlight, plant cells reduce carbon dioxide to carbohydrates through a complex series of reactions which will be considered later. Meantime the skeleton reaction is now formulated

$$6CO_2 + 12H_2O \rightarrow C_6H_{12}O_6 + 6O_2 + 6H_2O$$
Hexose

in conformity with the experimental evidence that all the oxygen evolved in photosynthesis comes from water molecules. In the simple sugar thus formed, solar energy is stored as chemical energy which may later be released and used by the plant when the compound is oxidized.

But photosynthesis has an importance which far transcends its utility to the plant itself. Animals, lacking chlorophyll, are unable to use radiant energy. They are therefore dependent upon a supply of organic foodstuffs in which the chemical energy lies ready to their use. This supply they obtain either by eating plants or by eating other animals. Thus the organic compounds of the animal body are derived either directly or indirectly from plant products, and in the final analysis it is the green plants which make available to nearly all living organisms on earth the great resources of solar energy.

Alternative Energy Sources

Most organisms follow the pattern which has just been sketched and derive their energy directly or indirectly from solar radiation. But among the microorganisms there is interesting evidence of the great versatility nature has shown in maintaining life on the earth. Most bacteria are *heterotrophs*, that is, they are like the animals in being dependent upon some outside source of organic food. Other microorganisms such as the green algae and a few bacteria contain chlorophyll, and these are autotrophic as are all other organisms which have been provided with this useful catalyst. But there are a few types of bacteria which, although they lack chlorophyll, still are able to live independently of a source of organic foodstuffs provided certain inorganic substances are available. These organisms obtain the energy they need, not from sunlight but from exothermic chemical reactions. The energy thus made available is used as green plants use solar energy to bring about synthesis of foodstuffs from carbon dioxide. Among the reactions which are thus coupled with reduction of carbon dioxide to carbohydrates are the oxidation of ammonia to nitrite and of nitrite to nitrate, as well as oxidation of sulfur, of hydrogen sulfide, and of ferrous compounds.

One imagines that in the course of evolution various possible sources of energy for living organisms have been explored. The widespread development of green plants proves the success of the method in which chlorophyll takes part. The varied forms of animal life indicate that the other really efficient method has been that in which heterotrophic organisms have diverted to their own ends a share of the energy stored up by plants. That oxidation of small inorganic molecules has not been highly esteemed by nature may be deduced from the fact that it is used by only a few unicellular organisms. It is evidently not a plan which can be adapted to the needs of larger and more complex forms. This is easy to understand in the case of a metabolism which requires that an organism live in an atmosphere of hydrogen sulfide and deposit granules of sulfur within its cell walls!

MULTICELLULAR ORGANISMS

As with the amoeba, the metabolism of all unicellular organisms whether plant or animal depends upon direct contact with their aqueous or moist environment. They obtain from this everything that they need either by diffusion or by engulfing small food particles. With equal directness waste materials are expelled or diffuse away. Even some small multicellular

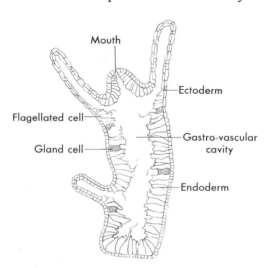

Mouth

Ectoderm

Flagellated cell

Gland cell

Gastro-vascular cavity

Endoderm

Fig. 3.8. A multicellular organism, the hydra, the cells of which are all in contact with its aqueous environment.

organisms such as the hydra have managed to remain in intimate contact with their aqueous medium by developing a crude, infolded digestive tube (Fig. 3.8). Such an organism is not more than two cells thick, every cell is bathed by water, external or internal, and diffusion takes care of all its needs.

As organisms became larger and migrated to dry land they had to develop indirect ways of keeping their cells alive. It was necessary to get water into interior cells, and at the same time to prevent its entering in such volume as to burst the cell walls. Cells far from the surface had to be supplied with food and oxygen, and to be relieved of waste matter. Plants and animals have solved these problems by the development of different organs, but both have had recourse to some sort of division of labor. This has required a complex organization and structure, with each part of the organism carefully integrated with every other part.

Plant Structures

Plants are in general simpler in organization than animals and need only three fundamental structures—the root, the stem, and the leaf—to carry on the life of any individual plant. In the course of that life flowers and fruit may form or other reproductive structures may arise, but these are not essential to the life of the parent plant.

Roots and stems

In such a representative plant as a tree its supply of water and of inorganic compounds is taken in by the microscopic root hairs which are in close contact with the soil. Thence the watery solution moves upward through a series of fine tubelike cells in the centers of roots and stems, which carry it finally along the branches and into the leaves. The tissue concerned with this upward transportation of material is known as *xylem* or wood. It is made up of long slender empty cells with firm supporting walls. These cells connect with each other through thin places in their walls, and are so arranged that there is a continuous conducting system from the roots to every branch and leaf. Part of the water which rises into the leaves is continuously being lost in *transpiration* or evaporation. This loss is minimized by the presence of the impervious waxy cuticle which covers most of the leaf surface, and of the corklike bark, made up of dead cells, which covers the stems.

In addition to the xylem system which carries material up from the soil, there is a second series of tubelike cells involved in the transport of material in the plant. It lies parallel to the xylem and serves to carry to all living parts of the plant the photosynthetic products which constitute the food supply for the whole organism. The tissue involved in this transport is known as *phloem*, the chief cells of which have perforated end walls to facilitate the passage of fluid. Figure 3.9 shows two typical arrangements of phloem and xylem tissues. In (*a*) small bundles made up of both types of vascular tissue form a circle around the periphery of the stem; in (*b*) the xylem forms a cylinder inside the phloem layer.

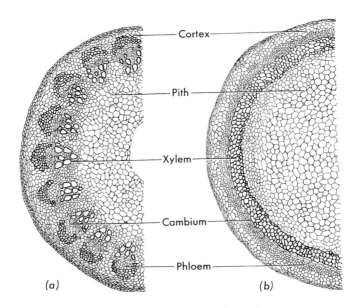

Cortex

Pith

Xylem

Cambium

Phloem

(a)   (b)

Fig. 3.9. Cross sections of two stems to show the disposition of xylem and phloem.

Leaves

The bulk of the living part of a plant consists of leaves, and the structure of these is admirably adapted to giving them access to carbon dioxide and to facilitating the disposal of the oxygen set free in photosynthesis. Leaves are very thin and have the porous structure shown in Fig. 3.10. A waxy cuticle, in conjunction with an upper and a lower epidermis which are usually only one cell in thickness, serves to minimize the loss of water. The inner cells make up the *mesophyll*, and all contain more or less chlorophyll. In the center of the figure are shown the vascular cells of the leaf vein, through which watery solutions are transported to and from the leaf. The small openings in the lower epidermis, the *stomata*, are the paths by which all gas exchange in the leaf takes place. The water which is lost in transpiration passes out through the stomata; carbon dioxide diffuses inward and thus becomes available to the chloroplasts. As photosynthesis proceeds, oxygen is set free and part of this in turn escapes through the stomata during daylight hours. In the dark the plant is entirely dependent upon oxygen of the air which diffuses in to serve its respiratory needs.

To summarize: Even the most complex plants get their raw materials from the soil in the form of an aqueous solution and from the air as carbon dioxide. Because the stomata open into a porous ramifying structure only a few cells in thickness, leaf cells are all in direct contact with the gases which diffuse in. Since plants synthesize their own primary foodstuffs, they have no need of a digestive system, though something resembling digestion must take place whenever a plant begins to use its stored foods. If a plant excretes any waste material except oxygen, the amount is small compared with its total meta-

Fig. 3.10. The essential structures of a leaf, showing how all the cells have free access to air. Note also the vascular bundle of xylem and phloem tissue making up the leaf vein.

bolism. Some crystals occasionally found in plant cells are insoluble calcium salts of acids which are thought to be waste products. Lacking a means of extruding these acids the plant cell simply precipitates them within its own walls.[1]

The essential organs of a higher plant are: (1) widely ramifying roots, from the surfaces of which project fine root hairs, each being a thin-walled projection from a single cell and so very effectively in contact with soil moisture and air; (2) stems with few nutritive needs by way of which solutions pass upward from the roots and downward from the leaves; and (3) an enormous number of flat, thin leaves perfectly adapted to absorbing sunlight and to allowing passage of carbon dioxide and oxygen through the stomata.

Animal Structures

The evolution which has set animals free to wander anywhere on the surface of the earth has also moved them farther than most plants have gone from

---

[1] The animal kingdom uses a similar mechanism with embryos which develop inside an impervious shell. The usual nitrogenous waste of animal cells is the water-soluble amide, urea, which is toxic if present in appreciable concentration. If this were formed by bird and reptile embryos it would soon reach a lethal concentration in the shell. Instead these species excrete waste nitrogen as insoluble uric acid which collects as crystals inside the shell and is thus effectively out of contact with the living tissues.

effective contact with an aqueous environment. The problem thus posed is the more serious in that life is possible only within a rather narrow range of conditions. Salt concentration, osmotic pressure, and acidity can vary only slightly from optimum conditions if cells are to survive. To ensure the required uniformity of what Claude Bernard called the "internal environment" of their cells, animals are equipped with a more complex group of organs than plants have developed. In noting the essential systems in the following paragraphs, the reproductive organs are omitted since they play no large role in the metabolism of the parent organism.

The circulatory system

In most higher animals the transportation of food and oxygen to the cells and the removal of waste from the cells is entrusted chiefly to a system of vessels through which blood of some kind is driven by a heart of greater or less complexity. The effectiveness of such a system depends upon its having places of intimate contact with air and with sources of food as well as with the tissues which must be nourished. This contact between blood and tissues is achieved by a continuous branching of the *arteries* leading from the heart so that they form smaller and smaller vessels which finally become tiny capillaries with walls only a single cell in thickness. These thread their way through a section of tissue and then gradually coalesce again to form the first small *veins* through which the blood begins its journey back to the heart. In the capillary beds, exchange of material between blood stream and tissue cells is a matter of diffusion regulated to some extent by a concentration gradient, but regulated also by active processes in the cell which allow it to accept some molecules and to reject others. This "active transport" is imperfectly understood at present, but is certainly one of the purposes for which the cell must provide energy. Thus things are so arranged that the blood acquires foodstuffs in the digestive tract and oxygen in the lungs and carries these substances to all parts of the organism. It acts also as a scavenger, picking up waste material in the tissues and carrying this to the excretory organs for elimination.

Aside from its function as a common carrier, the chief contribution made by the blood itself to the animal economy is the *respiratory pigment* by virtue of which a given volume of blood carries far more oxygen than it could hold in simple solution. Among vertebrates this pigment is *hemoglobin*. A similar substance, *hemocyanin*, which is found in the blood of molluscs and crustaceans, is blue in oxidized form and colorless when reduced, while certain worms produce a green pigment known as *chlorocruorin*. Whatever the exact nature of the pigment, it acts by virtue of its ability to form a loose compound with oxygen whenever the oxygen pressure is high, and to release the gas when the oxygen tension falls. Thus as blood flows through the capillaries of the lungs or gills, the pigment goes over into the oxygenated form; later when this blood flows through capillaries deep in the tissues, it comes into close contact with the extracellular fluid in which all the body cells are bathed. Here the oxygen pressure is comparatively low and the pressure of carbon dioxide is high. Oxygen dialyzes out into the fluid, and thence across cell membranes into the cells. Meantime carbon dioxide passes into the blood, as do other waste products such as urea and uric acid. The carbon dioxide is carried to the lungs or other respiratory tissue for excretion; the soluble wastes are dealt with by the kidney or some similar organ.

THE LYMPHATIC SYSTEM. In addition to the rapidly circulating blood stream there is another fluid which moves sluggishly through the lymphatic system. The extracellular fluid referred to above is essentially a blood filtrate which is driven through the capillary walls by the blood pressure. In composition it is very like the blood plasma, except that its protein concentration is relatively low. To remove this fluid continually from the tissue spaces into which it is pressing, the mammalian body is provided with a series of drainage channels or lymph vessels. These begin as blind tubes into which the fluid is forced by its own growing pressure in the tissue spaces. These vessels converge upon each other, forming larger vessels which lead ultimately into two main ducts, the *lymphatic* and *thoracic* ducts. These empty their contents into veins near the heart, thus bringing back to the blood the fluid which

Fig. 3.11. Diagram of the relation between tissue cells and blood and lymph capillaries. Note that the blood capillaries form passageways from the artery to the vein, while the lymph vessel begins as blind tubes. [Reprinted with permission from W. C. Curtis and M. J. Guthrie, *General Zoology*, Wiley, New York, 1947.]

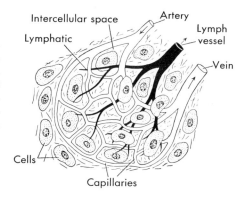

filtered out in the tissues. Here and there the larger lymphatics are interrupted by *lymph nodes* whose chief function seems to be filtration of microorganisms. Since this system has no heart, the fluid moves slowly, driven along, on the one hand, by the pressure of the fluid coming into the tissue spaces and, on the other, by the contraction of muscles along the lymphatic route.

It may at first sight seem strange that any molecules as large as those of proteins are able to migrate from the capillaries into the tissue spaces. It may be that some of them pass through spaces between cells. But it must also be remembered that the membranes which we see under the microscope, and which are drawn as continuous lines, consist of large, unsymmetrical molecules. These are chiefly proteins and fatty substances piled into a sort of dry wall which will inevitably include many open spaces. Through such spaces protein molecules might well find their way.

In Fig. 3.11 is shown the relation between cells, extracellular fluid, lymph vessels, and capillaries. It is clear that the individual cell of a multicellular organism is in the position of a very fortunate amoeba. Its food supply is not a matter of chance encounter, but is delivered in predigested form by capillary. Its waste products are carried away and it is free to get on with whatever work it has to do. Together, the blood and lymph provide it with that stable environment of which Claude Bernard spoke.

Respiratory organs

In the lower reaches of the evolutionary scale, respiratory organs are not needed, even by multicellular forms. In earthworms and amphibia, for example, a large part of the respiratory exchange takes place through the thin, moist skin. But in order that the blood of larger forms may acquire a sufficient supply of oxygen, various more or less effective respiratory organs have been developed. Aquatic forms depend for their oxygen upon the small amount in aqueous solution, and this makes it necessary to bring the blood into contact with large volumes of water. This is achieved by passing it through gills, the thin sheets of which are highly vascular. A continuous stream of water bathes the gill tissue, and the great number of fine capillaries facilitates the passage of oxygen from this water into the blood.

Those animals which have moved into a terrestrial environment have the advantage over aquatic animals that their source of oxygen is the much more concentrated air. On the other hand, in order that diffusion may take place, their lungs have to be kept moist, and the rather heavy fluid layer which coats the lining of the lungs to prevent their drying, also greatly reduces the possible speed of diffusion. To offset this slow passage, the area of the lung epithelium is greatly enlarged by the presence of a vast number of tiny branched sacs, the *alveoli*, which give to that tissue its spongy appearance. It is estimated that the internal respiratory area of adult human lungs is about 100 sq yds. Here as in the gills, the tissue is very vascular, so that all of this large area is in close contact with capillaries.

The type of oxygenation developed among the insects is of interest because it provides another example of a system which has been efficient enough to survive, but has not proved adaptable to the needs of larger forms. The air required by insects is taken directly to all the cells by means of many pairs of fine, branching tubes, or *tracheae* which are open to the air. Some of these end blindly in the deepest tissues while others communicate with the tubes on the opposite side, and thus establish an air passage through the animal. Air is kept moving by contraction and expansion of the body walls; it gives up its oxygen directly to the cells and carries excretory carbon dioxide with it as it moves out to the surface again. With such contact between air and even the deepest tissues, the insect needs only a most rudimentary circulatory system, in spite of the fact that its muscular activity and therefore its energy requirement is relatively large. But although this arrangement is quite satisfactory for organisms the size of a grasshopper, it is not found in larger forms. In the evolutionary struggle the special vascular gill or lung tissue, coupled with a rapid circulation of blood, seems to have proved better adapted to supplying the oxygen needs of organisms of greater size.

The digestive system[2]

In multicellular animals the digestion of food takes place in organs specifically adapted to perform this function. The simplest forms in which this division of labor becomes apparent are those previously mentioned which have formed a short digestive tube by folding one layer of cells within another. Digestive juices are formed by the cells which line this primitive gut and are poured over the food there. As the food is digested, the fragments diffuse directly into all the cells. It is probable that in such forms as these some intracellular digestion goes on as well and that all the cells are able to elaborate digestive catalysts. As forms evolved which were higher in the evolutionary scale, digestion became confined entirely to a digestive tube, and the cells outside the digestive area lost their ability to engulf and digest their own food particles. Finally in the mammals the gut became longer in relation to the length of the animal and was enlarged locally to form one or more stomachs where food could be held to give time for the digestive juices to act. Since herbivorous animals must consume large volumes of food, their intestines have come to be even longer than those of carnivores. In cats, for example, the alimentary canal is three to five times as long as the body, but cows and horses have intestines over twenty times their own length.

With increasing complexity and size came also further subdivision of labor. From certain specialized cells set aside to perform a specific secretory function there developed quite early in evolutionary history such secretory organs or *glands* as the liver and the pancreas. One function of these glands is the elaboration of some of the digestive catalysts. Even among mammals, however, part of the secretory activity is still carried out by cells which make up part of the lining of the digestive tract. The gastric juice and the hydrochloric acid which together initiate digestion in the stomach are each secreted by specialized cells in the gastric mucosa, while secreting cells in the lining of

---

[2] This system is dealt with at greater length in Chapter 10.

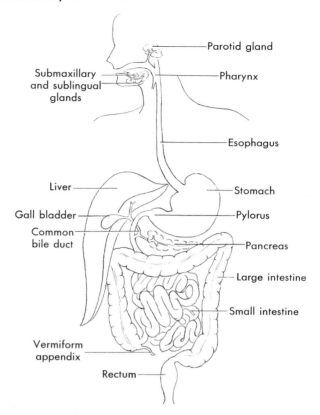

Fig. 3.12. Diagrammatic representation of the digestive tract in man.

the upper intestine provide the intestinal juice. The relation to each other of the various digestive organs in man is shown diagrammatically in Fig. 3.12.

Excretory system

Animals have two kinds of waste material which must be eliminated. There is the solid or semisolid matter which passes to the end of the digestive tract and is there excreted as feces. But in the course of metabolism there are also formed soluble wastes which must be removed. In some of the lower forms this is achieved by means of a system of single tubes or *nephridia* which lead from the tissues directly to the exterior. Cilia located near the internal ends of the tubes set up vibrations which draw fluid in and then propel it to the outside (Fig. 3.13).

Clearly related to these primitive forms are the *uriniferous tubules* which make up the kidney in higher animals. They do not open directly into the body cavity as the nephridia do, but each one begins near the outer surface of the kidney as a knot of arterial blood vessels enclosed in a funnel-like structure known as Bowman's capsule. As the blood flows through this glomerular knot, water and substances in solution are filtered from it and pass into the long convoluted tubule. The circulation of the kidney is so arranged that blood which has passed through Bowman's capsule flows next into vessels which send a network of capillaries around the very tubule through which the blood filtrate is moving. During this passage certain substances including

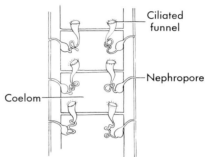

Fig. 3.13. A simple excretory system, the paired nephridia of the segmented worms.

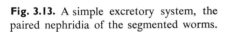

large amounts of water are reabsorbed; at the same time other constituents of the urine are secreted into the tubules along these lower walls. By the process of reabsorption the organism is enabled to recover water and other valuable substances which have passed into the glomerular filtrate. Whatever is not reabsorbed passes into collecting tubes which lead eventually to the bladder in mammals, or into the terminal part of the alimentary canal in lower vertebrates and birds.

Endocrine glands

We have already seen that in higher animals part of the digestive juices are elaborated in two special secreting organs, the liver and the pancreas. These secretions flow into the upper intestine by way of the common bile duct and there act upon the food mass. Such fluids as these, formed in a gland and acting in a specific locality, are known as *external secretions.* In addition to its digestive juice the pancreas also secretes from specialized cells known as "islet cells," a totally different kind of substance which has nothing to do with digestion of food. This is the protein insulin which is absorbed directly from the pancreatic tissue into the blood stream. It is thus carried to all parts of the body and acts upon various tissues far removed from its source. Such a substance is known as an *internal secretion* or *hormone.* Insulin is one of a number of such chemical messengers secreted by different glands. Figure 3.14 shows the location in man of the chief glands of internal secretion, known also as *endocrine* glands. Table 3.2 lists these glands with their

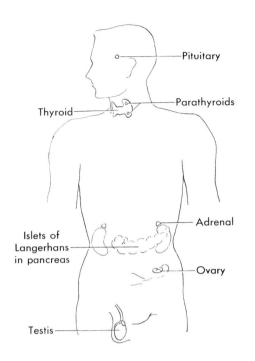

Fig. 3.14. The location of the endocrine glands in man.

TABLE 3.2. The Major Endocrine Glands in Mammals

Gland	Hormone	Principal Known Function
Pituitary		
Anterior lobe	Gonadotropins	Stimulation of gonads
	Lactogenic hormone	Stimulation of milk secretion
	Adrenotropin (ACTH)	Stimulation of adrenal cortex
	Thyrotropin	Stimulation of thyroid
	Growth hormone	Growth of bone and muscle
Posterior lobe	Oxytocin	Contraction of smooth muscle
	Antidiuretic hormone	Control of water metabolism
Ovary	Estradiol ⎫ Progesterone ⎭	Control of the sex cycle, of pregnancy and lactation
Testis	Testosterone	Development of accessory sex organs
Adrenal cortex	Cortical steroids	Metabolism of electrolytes and of carbohydrates
	Epinephrin (adrenaline)	Control of circulation
		Control of deposition of glycogen
Thyroid	Thyroxin	Control of metabolic rate
Pancreas	Insulin ⎫ Glucagon ⎭	Control of several phases of carbohydrate metabolism
Parathyroid	Parathormone	Metabolism of calcium and phosphorus

principal hormones. The commanding position of the pituitary gland is especially noteworthy since it is upon the normal secretory activity of this one small organ that the functioning of most of the other glands depends.

THE AIMS OF BIOCHEMISTRY

The chemical problems set by living tissue are of course greatly simplified by the fundamental resemblances between individual cells, whether plant or animal. In order to elucidate the nature of the chemical transformations by which living cells transmute food and oxygen into energy and use. this energy in synthesis, biochemistry has pursued more or less simultaneously two separate but related aims. In its early years it sought almost exclusively the complete chemical analysis of cellular material. This phase of the investigation is now complete in its major outlines. In the last years of the nineteenth century and the early years of the twentieth, the spectacular progress of organic chemistry, united with the analytical genius of such men as Otto Folin at Harvard and Stanley Benedict at Cornell, provided a knowledge of the chemical and physical properties of the major cell constituents.

The second, more truly biochemical aim of this borderline science was first served by a small group whose primary training was in medicine and physiology. Viewing the cell always as an integrated, living unit they yet believed that its chemical events could be made clear. It is hard to realize now, that no more than twenty-five or thirty years ago some biologists were still insistent that comparison of the living cell with any other physicochemical system was sheer impertinence. They believed that protoplasm had special properties of its own, entirely independent of the actual molecules of which it was constructed, and that even if we knew down to the last atom every single molecule and ion within a cell wall, we could not hope to explain its activity in terms of the ordinary laws of chemistry and physics. One of the earliest champions of the contrary view was F. G. Hopkins of Cambridge University who said of the cell in 1913: "Its life is the expression of a particular dynamic equilibrium which obtains in a polyphasic system." Twenty years later he defined the "essential or ultimate aim" of biochemistry as "an adequate and acceptable description of molecular dynamics in living cells and tissues." Today we accept without question the belief implicit in that statement, that molecular dynamics in the cell follows an orderly pattern, which is the result of the functioning of the same chemical and physical laws which govern matter outside a cell wall. In the following chapters we shall see both how far biochemistry has progressed toward that "adequate description," and also how many problems remain unsolved.

SUGGESTIONS FOR FURTHER READING

Since this chapter gives only a very brief review of biological material which is pertinent to the study of cell metabolism, almost any good modern textbook of botany or zoology would be enlightening. The following references contain interesting material on the subcellular particles.

Gaebler, O. H. (ed.), *Enzymes: Units of Biological Structure and Function*, Academic, New York, 1956.

> One section of this book is concerned with enzymes and cell structure and contains an excellent paper by Dr. G. E. Palade on the properties of the various cellular fractions.

Oncley, J. L. (ed.-in-chief), *Biophysical Science*, Wiley, New York, 1959.

> This carries articles on the fine structure of various cellular particles, illustrated with magnificent electron micrographs and with diagrammatic representations of various lamellar systems.

Roberts, R. B. (ed.), *Microsomal Particles and Protein Synthesis*, Pergamon Press, New York, 1958.

> The Palade article in this book includes a short history of the development of ideas about the subcellular particles.

Part II

THE
ORGANIC
CONSTITUENTS
OF
CELLS

For the study of the chemical processes in animals and plants there is,

except for the proteins, no group of carbon compounds so important

as the carbohydrates. . . .

EMIL FISCHER (1890)

The chemistry of the carbohydrates

4

THE WORD *carbohydrate* reflects the early belief that carbon compounds which contain hydrogen and oxygen in the ratio 2:1 must be hydrates. All the most common and earliest known members of the group, sucrose, $C_{12}H_{22}O_{11}$, starch and cellulose, $(C_6H_{10}O_5)_x$, and glucose, $C_6H_{12}O_6$, can be represented by the general formula $C_x(H_2O)_y$, but it has long been recognized that other substances which clearly belong in the same chemical group are not even formally hydrates. Such, for example, are rhamnose, $C_6H_{12}O_5$, certain acids closely related to the simple sugars, and such nitrogen-containing compounds as glucosamine, $C_6H_{11}O_5(NH_2)$. Nevertheless the name is retained in modern parlance to designate the large group of compounds which either are themselves polyhydroxy aldehydes or ketones or closely related compounds, or yield such compounds on acid hydrolysis.

The carbohydrates are classified in three main groups. Simple sugars like glucose or fructose are known as *monosaccharides* or *monoses*; carbohydrates such as sucrose and raffinose which yield two or more, but fewer than ten, monosaccharide units on acid hydrolysis are called *oligosaccharides*; those which like starch or cellulose set free a large number of simple sugar molecules constitute the group of *polysaccharides*. The number of simple sugars in an oligosaccharide is indicated by such names as *disaccharide* or *tetrasaccharide*. In Table 4.1 is given a classification of the more abundant and better known members of the carbohydrate group.

Individual names were given to many of the sugars long before there was any rational system of scientific nomenclature. Thus glucose gets its name

115

TABLE 4.1. Partial Classification of the Carbohydrates

Monosaccharides
    Trioses $C_3H_6O_3$
        Glyceraldehyde   CHO—CHOH—CH$_2$OH   aldotriose
        Dihydroxyacetone   CH$_2$OH—CO—CH$_2$OH   ketotriose
    Tetroses $C_4H_8O_4$
    Pentoses $C_5H_{10}O_5$
        Ribose, Arabinose, Xylose, and Lyxose   aldopentoses
        Ribulose, Xylulose   ketopentoses
    Hexoses $C_6H_{12}O_6$
        Naturally occurring aldohexoses: Glucose, Galactose, Mannose
        Naturally occurring ketohexoses: Fructose, Sorbose, Tagatose
    Heptoses
        Mannoheptulose, Sedoheptulose   ketoheptoses

Oligosaccharides
    Disaccharides
        Sucrose: yields on hydrolysis glucose and fructose
        Lactose: yields on hydrolysis glucose and galactose
        Maltose: yields on hydrolysis glucose
    Trisaccharides
        Raffinose: yields on hydrolysis galactose, glucose, and fructose

Polysaccharides
    Homopolysaccharides: Compounds which yield on hydrolysis but one type of
        monose
      Dextrans: yield glucose (dextrose) on hydrolysis
        Starch: reserve plant polysaccharide
        Cellulose: structural plant product
        Glycogen: reserve animal polysaccharide
      Levans: yield fructose (levulose) on hydrolysis
        Inulin: found in dahlia tubers
      Polymers of other monoses or monose derivatives
        Xylans: polymers of xylose
        Chitin: polymer of glucosamine
    Heteropolysaccharides: Compounds which yield on hydrolysis more than one
            type of monose or monose derivative. Many of these
            compounds are still imperfectly characterized, and some
            of them yield also some noncarbohydrate units such as
            sulfuric acid or methyl alcohol or acetic acid.
      Hemicelluloses and gums among plant products
      Mucopolysaccharides among animal products: heparin, chondroitin sulfates,
        and hyaluronic acids

from the Greek word for sweet; fructose comes from the Latin *fructus* and indicates that this sugar occurs in many fruits, while the name of arabinose refers to its occurrence in gum arabic. Modern classifications within the monosaccharide group make it possible to indicate in a class name something of the structure of these compounds. Glucose is an *aldohexose*, that is a carbohydrate, indicated by the -ose ending, containing six carbons one of which is present in an aldehyde group. Similarly fructose, which has a carbonyl group at the second carbon is a *ketohexose*, and arabinose with a chain of five carbons is an *aldopentose*.

THE MONOSACCHARIDES

The important monoses are the trioses, the pentoses, and the hexoses. They are colorless crystalline solids having more or less sweet tastes. They are water soluble and form solutions which are optically active and which reduce Fehling's solution and ammoniacal silver nitrate.

Among the simple sugars glucose has a unique importance both in nature and in chemical history. It is the form into which most carbohydrates are converted before being used by living cells, and in the form of various polysaccharides makes up the chief reserve foodstuffs in plants and animals. Historically glucose was the first of the monosaccharides to be characterized and the one on which in 1884 Emil Fischer[1] began his classical study of the carbohydrates and their interrelationships. It is therefore appropriate to center our study of the monosaccharides around the chemistry of glucose.

The Aldehyde Reactions of Glucose

The so-called old structure for glucose $(C_6H_{12}O_6)$ had been formulated between 1868 and 1870, before Fischer's work began. It represents the sugar as a straight chain pentahydroxy aldehyde and rests upon the following reactions:

1. On reduction with sodium amalgam a hexahydroxy alcohol, sorbitol, is formed, which can in turn be further reduced by hydriodic acid to yield 2-iodohexane. This proves that the carbon chain in glucose is not branched.

---

[1] Even in that galaxy of great German scientists whose work made of the nineteenth century a golden age of organic chemistry, Emil Fischer (1852—1919) stands preeminent. His work on the constitution and stereochemistry of the sugars laid the foundation on which modern carbohydrate chemistry is built. But this was only one of his interests and his studies of the amino acids and the proteins opened up that whole fruitful field of research. It is suitable that the second Nobel Prize in Chemistry should have been awarded to him in 1902, the first having gone to van't Hoff in the previous year.

2. On treatment with an acetylating agent such as acetyl chloride or acetic anhydride, a compound is formed which has the formula $C_{16}H_{22}O_{11}$. This represents the introduction of five acetyl groups, and points to the presence of five hydroxyl groups in the sugar molecule.
3. On gentle oxidation with bromine water, an acid, $C_6H_{12}O_7$, is formed. Formation of a carboxyl group by addition of a single oxygen atom indicates that the original molecule must have contained an aldehyde group.

In accordance with these reactions glucose was given the familiar straight chain formula, the carbons of which are now numbered as indicatèd.

$$\underset{1}{\text{CHO}}-\underset{2}{\text{CHOH}}-\underset{3}{\text{CHOH}}-\underset{4}{\text{CHOH}}-\underset{5}{\text{CHOH}}-\underset{6}{\text{CH}_2\text{OH}}$$

This structure not only accounts for the known reactions of the compound, but also for its optical activity, since each of the four central carbon atoms is asymmetric.

Many other reactions of glucose are those which would be expected of a substance having the suggested structure. It reduces Fehling's solution, reacts with hydroxylamine to form an oxime and with hydrogen cyanide to form two isomeric cyanohydrins, since the new compound has an additional asymmetric carbon atom. Strong oxidation converts the sugar to the corresponding dibasic acid, glucaric acid. The class name for these acids is *aldaric acids*, with the individual names showing the hexose from which each is derived. Thus we have glucaric acid from glucose and mannaric acid from mannose.

The addition reaction with hydrogen cyanide, discovered in 1886 by Heinrich Kiliani of Munich, has been of outstanding importance in sugar synthesis. After separation of the two isomeric cyanohydrins they are hydrolyzed separately to the corresponding acids. These compounds readily lose water to give a lactone, and the reduction of the lactone with sodium amalgam yields an aldehyde containing one more carbon than the aldose with which the reaction began. Thus any aldose may be transformed into the next higher aldose, a tetrose yielding two pentoses, these each in turn two hexoses, and so on.

It may be noted here for comparison that the structure assigned to fructose, which also has the empirical formula $C_6H_{12}O_6$, rests upon evidence similar to that outlined for glucose. Fructose can be reduced to a straight chain hexyl iodide and acetylated to a pentaacetate. But in its response to oxidation it differs from glucose. It is not oxidized at all by so gentle an agent as bromine water, and stronger oxidation with nitric acid breaks the carbon chain. Two different two-carbon acids are formed, glycolic acid ($CH_2OH \cdot COOH$) and its oxidation product oxalic acid ($COOH \cdot COOH$), and also the four-carbon *meso*-tartaric acid. Since fructose gives evidence of the presence of a carbonyl group in its reactions with hydrogen cyanide and with other carbonyl reagents,

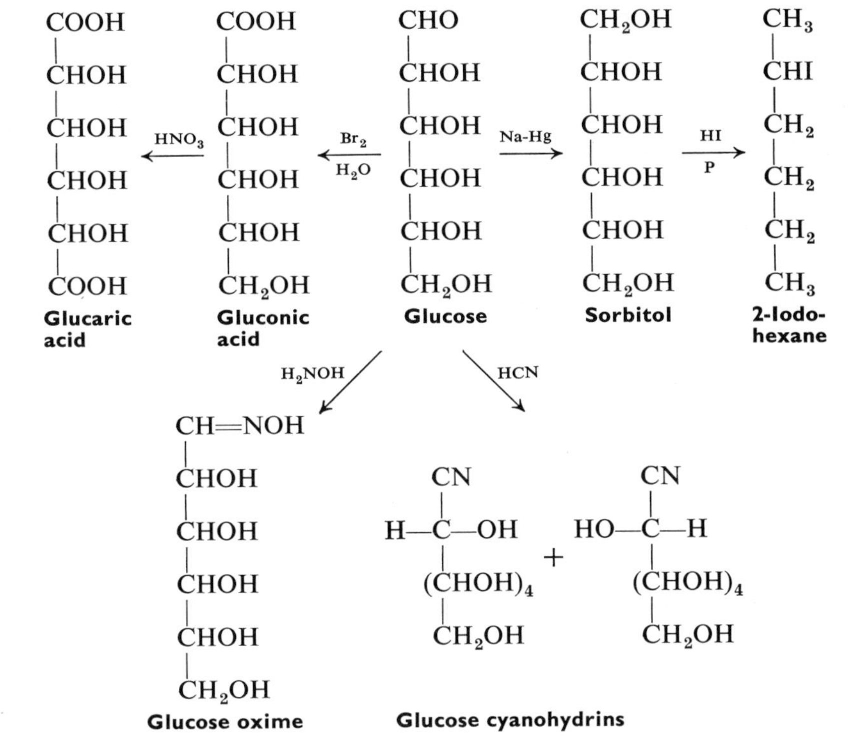

COOH   COOH   CHO   CH₂OH   CH₃

$$
\begin{array}{ccccc}
\text{COOH} & \text{COOH} & \text{CHO} & \text{CH}_2\text{OH} & \text{CH}_3 \\
\text{CHOH} & \text{CHOH} & \text{CHOH} & \text{CHOH} & \text{CHI} \\
\text{CHOH} & \text{CHOH} & \text{CHOH} & \text{CHOH} & \text{CH}_2 \\
\text{CHOH} & \text{CHOH} & \text{CHOH} & \text{CHOH} & \text{CH}_2 \\
\text{CHOH} & \text{CHOH} & \text{CHOH} & \text{CHOH} & \text{CH}_2 \\
\text{COOH} & \text{CH}_2\text{OH} & \text{CH}_2\text{OH} & \text{CH}_2\text{OH} & \text{CH}_3
\end{array}
$$

$\xleftarrow{\text{HNO}_3}$ $\xleftarrow[\text{H}_2\text{O}]{\text{Br}_2}$ $\xrightarrow{\text{Na-Hg}}$ $\xrightarrow[\text{P}]{\text{HI}}$

Glucaric acid   **Gluconic acid**   **Glucose**   **Sorbitol**   **2-Iodo-hexane**

$\xrightarrow{\text{H}_2\text{NOH}}$ $\xrightarrow{\text{HCN}}$

$$
\begin{array}{ccc}
\text{CH=NOH} & & \\
\text{CHOH} & \text{CN} & \text{CN} \\
\text{CHOH} & \text{H—C—OH} & \text{HO—C—H} \\
\text{CHOH} & (\text{CHOH})_4 \;\; + & (\text{CHOH})_4 \\
\text{CHOH} & \text{CH}_2\text{OH} & \text{CH}_2\text{OH} \\
\text{CH}_2\text{OH} & &
\end{array}
$$

Glucose oxime   **Glucose cyanohydrins**

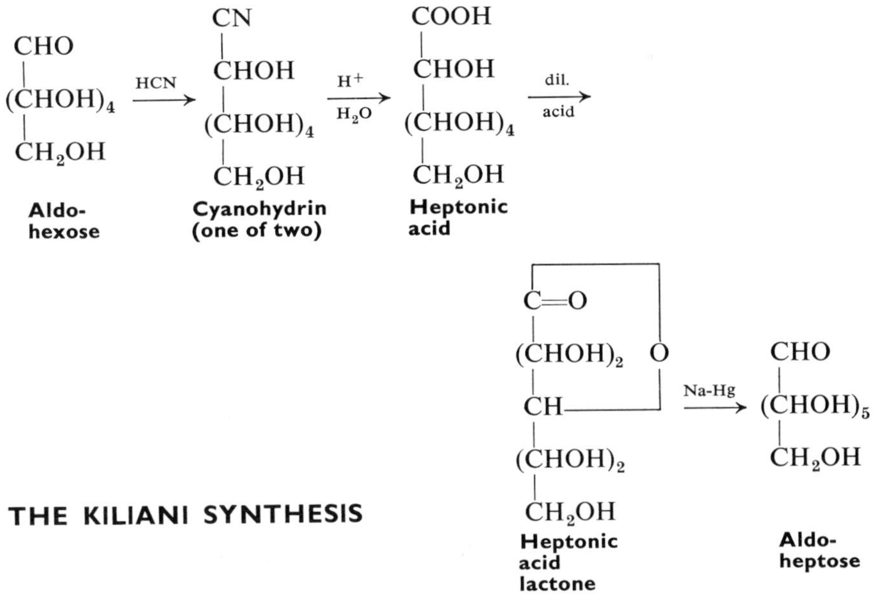

$$
\begin{array}{cccc}
\text{CHO} & \text{CN} & \text{COOH} & \\
 & \text{CHOH} & \text{CHOH} & \\
(\text{CHOH})_4 & (\text{CHOH})_4 & (\text{CHOH})_4 & \\
\text{CH}_2\text{OH} & \text{CH}_2\text{OH} & \text{CH}_2\text{OH} &
\end{array}
$$

$\xrightarrow{\text{HCN}}$ $\xrightarrow[\text{H}_2\text{O}]{\text{H}^+}$ $\xrightarrow[\text{acid}]{\text{dil.}}$

Aldo-hexose   **Cyanohydrin (one of two)**   **Heptonic acid**

$$
\begin{array}{cc}
\text{C=O} & \\
(\text{CHOH})_2 \quad \text{O} & \text{CHO} \\
\text{CH} & (\text{CHOH})_5 \\
(\text{CHOH})_2 & \text{CH}_2\text{OH} \\
\text{CH}_2\text{OH} &
\end{array}
$$

$\xrightarrow{\text{Na-Hg}}$

THE KILIANI SYNTHESIS

Heptonic acid lactone   **Aldo-heptose**

it is formulated as a pentahydroxy ketone with the carbonyl group at position 2.

$$CH_2OH\text{---}CO\text{---}CHOH\text{---}CHOH\text{---}CHOH\text{---}CH_2OH$$
$$1 \qquad 2 \qquad 3 \qquad\quad 4 \qquad\quad 5 \qquad\quad 6$$

Fructose forms an oxime with hydroxylamine and a pair of cyanohydrin addition products with hydrogen cyanide. When it is reduced it yields a

mixture of two hexahydric alcohols, sorbitol and mannitol, since reduction of the carbonyl group introduces a new asymmetric center at carbon 2.

Stereochemistry of the Monosaccharides

Before going on to study further the chemistry of glucose, it will be advisable to consider the general optical properties and relationships within the group of monosaccharides.

Projection formulas

The aldehyde formula for glucose shows it to have four asymmetric carbon atoms, while the corresponding structure for fructose has three. Since the number of possible optical isomers of a compound with n asymmetric carbons is 2^n, there are 16 possible aldohexoses, of which 8 will be mirror images of the other 8. For the ketohexoses there are only 8 possible forms, consisting of 4 isomeric arrangements with their 4 mirror images or *enantiomorphs*. Emil Fischer worked out for the representation of this confusing group of compounds a system of projection formulas derived from the three-dimensional formulas of van't Hoff. Fischer began by actually making tetrahedral models to represent the asymmetric carbon atoms. The simplest optically

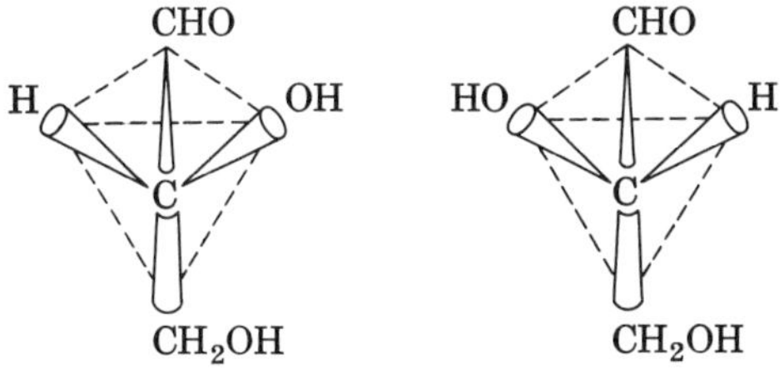

Fig. 4.1. The stereoisomeric forms of glycerose.

active hydroxy aldehyde is the aldotriose, glycerose or glyceraldehyde. The structure of the two forms of this compound, with its single asymmetric carbon, is shown in Fig. 4.1. The —CHO group, the hydroxyl group and the hydrogen are at the points of one face of the tetrahedron, with the CH_2OH— group at the remaining apex. By convention, the functional aldehyde group is written at the top, with the hydrogen and hydroxyl to right and left. Working from similar models, Fischer proposed such formulas as the following as simple projections on a plane of the models pictured above.

$$\begin{array}{cc} \text{CHO} & \text{CHO} \\ | & | \\ \text{HCOH} & \text{HOCH} \\ | & | \\ \text{CH}_2\text{OH} & \text{CH}_2\text{OH} \end{array}$$

Similar formulas may be written for the tetroses.

$$\begin{array}{cccc} \text{CHO} & \text{CHO} & \text{CHO} & \text{CHO} \\ | & | & | & | \\ \text{HCOH} & \text{HOCH} & \text{HOCH} & \text{HCOH} \\ | & | & | & | \\ \text{HCOH} & \text{HOCH} & \text{HCOH} & \text{HOCH} \\ | & | & | & | \\ \text{CH}_2\text{OH} & \text{CH}_2\text{OH} & \text{CH}_2\text{OH} & \text{CH}_2\text{OH} \\ \text{I} & \text{II} & \text{III} & \text{IV} \end{array}$$

Compounds I and II are enantiomorphs, as are III and IV. It should be noted that the conventions governing the use of projection formulas preclude their being removed from the plane of the paper. They may be rotated in that plane by rotating the paper itself, but the paper may not be turned over. If this is done, and a formula is read through the paper, it represents, not the original compound but its mirror image. It should also be pointed out that such projection formulas as these take no account of the fact that the carbon atoms are united at an angle of 109° 28′, and that a "straight chain" of five or six such atoms may in fact be nearly a circle. We shall see later how other types of projection formulas take this into account.

Classification of the monosaccharides

By a combination of brilliant research and masterly reasoning, Emil Fischer had been able by 1891 to establish the fact that the two enantiomorphic forms of glucose must have the configurations represented by formulas V and VI. The numbering of the carbon atoms follows the modern convention. In order to assign one of these to the natural, dextrorotatory form of the sugar, it was necessary to set up some frame of reference. There is no known way in which the configuration of a single form can be determined.

$$
\begin{array}{cc}
\text{CHO} & \text{CHO} \\
| & | \\
\text{HCOH} & \text{HOCH} \\
| & | \\
\text{HOCH} & \text{HCOH} \\
| & | \\
\text{HCOH} & \text{HOCH} \\
| & | \\
\text{HCOH} & \text{HOCH} \\
| & | \\
\text{CH}_2\text{OH} & \text{CH}_2\text{OH} \\
\mathbf{V} & \mathbf{VI}
\end{array}
$$

Some sort of arbitrary decision had to be made, assigning a formula to one of two forms, after which corresponding formulas could be assigned to related substances. Fischer took as his starting point the aldaric acid (then called a saccharic acid) derived from glucose, called it the *dextro*-acid and assigned to it one of the two possible enantiomorphic projection formulas. He then worked out the relationships between this substance and a number of different aldohexoses. As a result he divided all the aldohexoses into two series, the one including all those believed to be structurally related to glucaric acid, the other made up of sugars similarly related to the dibasic acid formed from the enantiomorph of ordinary glucose. On the basis of this classification he assigned to glucose the formula V.

Fischer's idea of dividing all the aldohexoses into two series of mirror images was fundamentally sound, but in choosing the symmetrical dibasic acids as his reference compounds he happened to choose badly. For example, when the two enantiomorphic forms of galactose are oxidized, it is found, because of the symmetry of the galactose molecule, that the same acid arises from both forms. That the two acids are identical may be seen by rotating the formula of one of them through 180°. Clearly if Fischer's classification

$$
\begin{array}{cccc}
\text{CHO} & \text{COOH} & \text{COOH} & \text{CHO} \\
| & | & | & | \\
\text{HCOH} & \text{HCOH} & \text{HOCH} & \text{HOCH} \\
| & | & | & | \\
\text{HOCH} & \text{HOCH} & \text{HCOH} & \text{HCOH} \\
| \quad \xrightarrow{\text{HNO}_3} & | & | & \xleftarrow{\text{HNO}_3} \quad | \\
\text{HOCH} & \text{HOCH} & \text{HCOH} & \text{HCOH} \\
| & | & | & | \\
\text{HCOH} & \text{HCOH} & \text{HOCH} & \text{HOCH} \\
| & | & | & | \\
\text{CH}_2\text{OH} & \text{COOH} & \text{COOH} & \text{CH}_2\text{OH} \\
\textit{dextro-} & \textbf{Identical galactaric} & & \textit{levo-} \\
\textbf{Galactose} & \textbf{acids} & & \textbf{Galactose}
\end{array}
$$

was to have any meaning, enantiomorphic forms of a sugar could not both belong to the same series. Similar difficulties with other sugars have led to the use of a different reference compound by means of which the sixteen aldohexoses are now classified satisfactorily into two groups referred to as the D series and the L series.

The system of classification which is now in use was suggested in 1906 by M. A. Rosanoff who was then at New York University. It is possible to think of all the simple aldoses as derived by repeated Kiliani syntheses from the two glyceraldehydes which are the simplest molecules which can be described as "polyhydroxy aldehydes." Rosanoff arbitrarily assigned to the dextrorotatory form of glyceraldehyde the projection formula with the secondary hydroxyl group written on the right, and classified as members of the D series all sugars which could theoretically have been synthesized from this compound. It should be noted that the letters D and L, which are always to be read "dee" and "ell," are assigned to given sugars regardless of their actual signs of rotation.

$$
\begin{array}{cc}
\text{CHO} & \text{CHO} \\
| & | \\
\text{HCOH} & \text{HOCH} \\
| & | \\
\text{CH}_2\text{OH} & \text{CH}_2\text{OH} \\
\textbf{D(+)-Glyceraldehyde} & \textbf{L(-)-Glyceraldehyde}
\end{array}
$$

The cyanohydrin reaction introduces a new asymmetric carbon atom, hence each step in the progressive building up of the higher sugars gives rise to a pair of stereoisomers. Since, however, the part of the molecule below the new carbon 2 is identical in both isomers they are not enantiomorphs. Compounds of this sort, having several asymmetric centers but differing only in the stereochemical configuration about one of the carbons are known as *epimers*.

The D Series of Aldoses

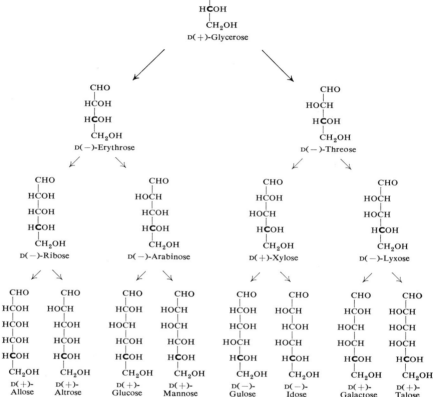

The chart above indicates the relationships which Rosanoff traced between D-glycerose and the tetroses, pentoses, and hexoses which could conceivably have been synthesized from it. As it happens, nearly half of the sugars in this D series rotate plane polarized light to the left, and so it is customary to indicate the direction of rotation by a plus or a minus sign. Thus the levorotatory enantiomorph of glucose is designated L(−)-glucose, while the form of arabinose which is levorotatory belongs to the D series and is therefore D(−)-arabinose. As the sugars of one series are built up from glycerose, the only constant factor is the arrangement of hydrogen and hydroxyl around the original asymmetric carbon atom. Thus all members of the D series have, according to the conventions governing the writing of such projection formulas, the hydroxyl group on the penultimate carbon written to the right. This carbon is the one shown in heavy type in the chart.

Since the Rosanoff classification depends only upon the configuration about this one carbon, it is easily extended to include compounds other than the aldoses. Fructose, for example, in spite of a high levorotation, belongs to the D series, as does the related amino sugar, glucosamine.

$$
\begin{array}{cc}
CH_2OH & CHO \\
| & | \\
C{=}O & CHNH_2 \\
| & | \\
HOCH & HOCH \\
| & | \\
HCOH & HCOH \\
| & | \\
HCOH & HCOH \\
| & | \\
CH_2OH & CH_2OH \\
\text{D(−)-Fructose} & \text{D-Glucosamine}
\end{array}
$$

The keto sugars other than fructose are named from the corresponding aldoses by use of the ending -ulose. Thus ribulose and xylulose are related to ribose and xylose as fructose is related to glucose.

The names of erythrose and threose are now commonly used in prefixes attached to the names of other compounds having two adjacent hydroxyl groups, to differentiate the cis from the trans arrangement. Thus ribulose is an *erythro*-pentulose and xylulose a *threo*-pentulose, as shown in the formulas.

$$
\begin{array}{cc}
CH_2OH & CH_2OH \\
| & | \\
C{=}O & C{=}O \\
| & | \\
HCOH & HCOH \\
| & | \\
HCOH & HOCH \\
| & | \\
CH_2OH & CH_2OH \\
\textbf{\textit{D-erythro}-Pentulose} & \textbf{\textit{L-threo}-Pentulose} \\
\textbf{or \textsc{d}-Ribulose} & \textbf{or \textsc{l}-Xylulose}
\end{array}
$$

Ring Structure of the Monosaccharides

As was briefly indicated above, many of the reactions of the simple sugars can be adequately explained on the assumption that they are straight chain compounds containing a carbonyl group. But from the beginning there were certain facts which could not be reconciled with this formulation. In the first place, the reducing power of glucose solution is far in excess of that to be expected of a compound with but one aldehyde group, and at the same time other properties which such a compound should show are absent. It does not restore the color to Schiff's reagent, and the dry compound is strangely inert to atmospheric oxygen. If the old formula were correct, the pentaacetate should still react as an aldehyde, which it does not do. Finally there was for years the mysterious "mutarotation," first noted in 1846 with glucose solutions. Most optically active substances when put into solution exhibit at once the rotation which is characteristic. This is expressed as a *specific rotation*, defined as the rotation caused by a 1-dm column of a solution containing 1 g of solute per ml.[2] But when the specific rotation of a sugar solution is measured at intervals, it is found to change gradually during the first few hours, finally reaching a constant value. With ordinary glucose the initial specific rotation, $[\alpha]_D$ $+111°$, drops slowly to $+52.5°$ if the solution is allowed to stand. Other sugar solutions undergo similar changes in rotation for which there was no explanation so long as they were formulated as straight chain compounds.

Evolution of the modern formula for glucose

In 1893 Emil Fischer attempted to prepare an acetal by heating glucose with methyl alcohol acidified with hydrochloric acid. This is a typical aldehyde reaction in which one molecule of the aldehyde reacts with two of alcohol. But the reaction between glucose and methyl alcohol proved not to

$$R \cdot CHO + C_2H_5OH \rightarrow R \cdot CH \begin{smallmatrix} OH \\ \\ OC_2H_5 \end{smallmatrix}$$

Hemiacetal

$$R \cdot CH \begin{smallmatrix} OH \\ \\ OC_2H_5 \end{smallmatrix} + C_2H_5OH \rightarrow R \cdot CH \begin{smallmatrix} OC_2H_5 \\ \\ OC_2H_5 \end{smallmatrix} + H_2O$$

Acetal

---

[2] Since in practice it is seldom possible to make a solution as concentrated as the specified one, the actual rotation is measured with a more dilute solution and the specific rotation calculated from the formula

$$[\alpha]_D = \frac{\alpha v}{l w}$$

in which α = observed rotation, v = volume of the solution in milliliters, l = length of the tube in decimeters, and w = weight of the solute in grams. The subscript D indicates that the light used is the yellow sodium light corresponding to the D line in the spectrum. Occasionally the wave length of the light is given in angstrom units.

follow a typical path. Fischer isolated from the reaction mixture a crystalline product which melted at 165°, had a specific rotation of +157°, but did not analyze as an acetal. Its empirical formula was $C_7H_{14}O_6$ which, since it proved to have but one methoxyl group, may be written $C_6H_{11}O_5(OCH_3)$. Fischer called the compound a methyl glucoside since, like the naturally occurring glucosides, it is readily hydrolyzed in acid solution.

$$C_6H_{11}O_5(OCH_3) + H_2O \xrightarrow{\text{acid}} C_6H_{12}O_6 + CH_3OH$$

Fischer suggested that in this reaction the aldehyde group reacted with one hydroxyl group of methyl alcohol and with a second hydroxyl group of its own chain. This can be followed if the reaction is written in two steps, in the first of which the sugar reacts to form a hemiacetal. The second step then gives rise to a ring compound through a splitting out of water between the new hydroxyl group on carbon 1 and an hydroxyl group of the sugar molecule. Fischer wrote the product of this second step, erroneously as it proved, as a five-membered ring.

Glucose hemiacetal

Fischer formula for methyl glucoside

In the paper in which Fischer reported on the methyl glucoside he noted that in this compound carbon 1 had become asymmetric, and that there should therefore be two forms derivable from glucose. In the following year Alberda van Eckenstein at Amsterdam isolated the second methyl glucoside and called it "β-methylglucoside" to distinguish it from Fischer's "α-methylglucoside". The new compound melted at 104° and had a much lower specific rotation ($-33°$) than the α form.

Fischer had been careful to point out that a ring structure for the glucoside did not necessarily indicate a ring structure in the parent sugar. But before the end of 1895 Charles Tanret, a pharmacist in Paris, had shown that glucose itself exists in two modifications. By crystallizing glucose at temperatures above 98° he had obtained an isomeric form, now known as β-glucose, which had an initial specific rotation of $+19°$, contrasted with the initial rotation of $+111°$ given by ordinary or α-glucose. There were thus shown to be one form of glucose with a high initial rotation and a second form with a much lower rotatory power, and these invited comparison with the two methyl glucosides with their very different specific rotations. One of Fischer's students, E. Frankland Armstrong (1878–1945), then at the Central Technical College in London, established the relationship between the sugars and the glucosides when he showed that enzymatic hydrolysis of the α-glucoside resulted in formation of glucose with a high initial specific rotation, while the β-glucoside gave rise to glucose with a low initial specific rotation. Omitting for the moment the question of ring size, the formulas VII to X bring out the relation between the two glucosides and the corresponding sugars. The compounds are named according to modern conventions.

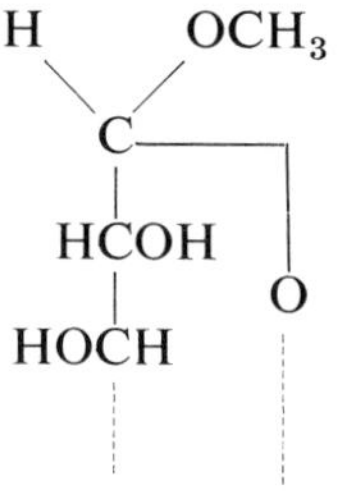

Methyl α-D-glucoside
$[\alpha]_D +157°$
VII

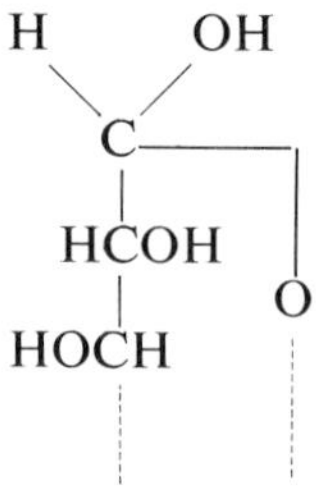

α-D-Glucose
$[\alpha]_D +111°$
VIII

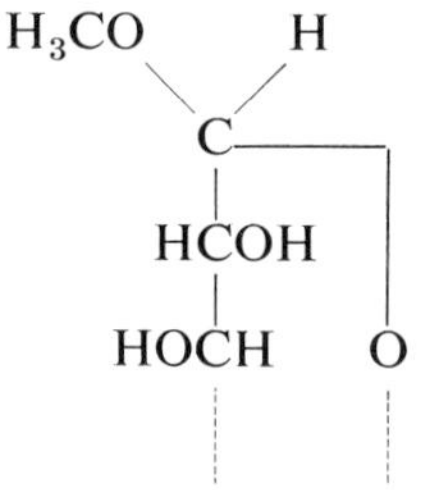

Methyl β-D-glucoside
$[\alpha]_D -33°$
IX

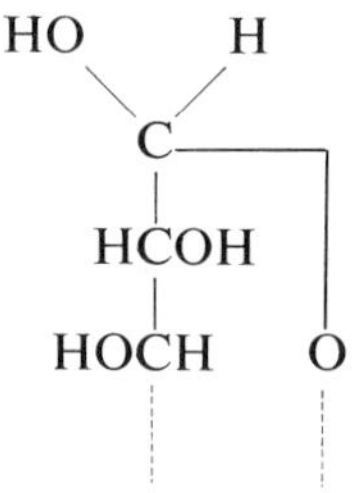

β-D-Glucose
$[\alpha]_D +19°$
X

Such pairs of compounds as α-glucose and β-glucose, in which the asymmetry at carbon 1 depends on ring formation, are known as *anomers*, and in consequence the first carbon of the aldoses is often referred to as the anomeric carbon.

Projection formulas of anomeric forms

The results just outlined established the fact that D(+)-glucose exists in two anomeric forms. It has since been shown that all the aldohexoses and ketohexoses have similar ring structures, and that there are therefore 32 possible aldoses and 16 ketoses. The convention which governs the writing of projection formulas for each pair of compounds was proposed by C. S. Hudson.[3] For pairs of α and β isomers in the D series, the one with the higher rotation is called the α form, and in its projection formula the hydroxyl or methoxyl group is written on the right. In the L series there are of course similar pairs of isomers, the enantiomorph of α-D-glucose, $[\alpha]_D$ +111°, being α-L-glucose, $[\alpha]_D$ −111°. This means that in the L-series the isomer with the lower specific rotation is the α form, and its hydroxyl group is written on the left. Both chemical and physical work has shown that the formulas based on these rules do in fact express correctly the relations in space of the various hydroxyl groups.

Since linkages of the type found in the methyl glucosides are extremely common and very important, it seems appropriate to note here one or two matters of general application. Armstrong found that hydrolysis of an α-glucoside could be catalyzed by the enzyme maltase, present in germinating barley, but that this enzyme does not act upon a β isomer. The latter was, however, readily hydrolyzed under the influence of another enzyme, emulsin, which can be extracted from bitter almonds. Later work showed that maltase acts specifically upon any α-glucosidic link, while emulsin catalyzes hydrolysis of β-glucosides. Another generalization which is sometimes useful in distinguishing between α and β isomers, concerns their relative specific rotations. The differences found in the optical rotations of the α and β isomers of glucose and the methyl glucosides, set the pattern for such differences between other α and β forms. In general, the α configuration leads to higher positive, or lower negative, rotations than result from a β arrangement. While such generalizations may not be pressed too far, they do frequently offer confirmatory evidence for a given structure.

Ring size

For many years the formula of glucose was written as Fischer had formulated the methyl glucoside, with a five-membered ring. As a matter of fact, it was impossible to prove what its size might be until after the discovery of some procedure which would block the hydroxyl groups with some stable linkage. It was of course possible to acetylate them, but the ease with which the acetyl groups were removed by hydrolysis made them unsuitable for structural studies. The method of methylation, yielding not ester but ether

---

[3] During the years in which the structures of the sugars and their derivatives were being worked out, Claude S. Hudson (1881–1952) of the U. S. Public Health Service was the outstanding American in the field.

linkages, opened the way for the work of W. N. Haworth[4] and C. S. Hudson which finally established the structure as that of a six-membered ring, with oxygen linking carbons 1 and 5. This beautiful chapter of structural organic chemistry would take us too far afield, though we shall shortly see how the methylation procedure was used in elucidation of the structures of other sugars. For the moment let us simply revise the Fischer formula to indicate that crystalline glucose exists as a six-membered ring. On pages 143–144 a modern proof of this ring formulation is outlined.

$$
\begin{array}{cc}
\underset{\displaystyle \text{C}}{\overset{\displaystyle \text{H}\quad\text{OH}}{\diagdown\;\diagup}} & \underset{\displaystyle \text{C}}{\overset{\displaystyle \text{HO}\quad\text{H}}{\diagdown\;\diagup}}\\
\text{HCOH} & \text{HCOH}\\
\text{HOCH} \quad \text{O} & \text{HOCH} \quad \text{O}\\
\text{HCOH} & \text{HCOH}\\
\text{HC} & \text{HC}\\
\text{CH}_2\text{OH} & \text{CH}_2\text{OH}\\
\textbf{α-D-Glucose} & \textbf{β-D-Glucose}
\end{array}
$$

Ring projections

Although the stable form of the free hexoses and pentoses contains a six-membered ring, there are compounds in which the oxygen bridge goes to a γ-carbon. For example, Fischer isolated in 1914 a third, very labile methyl glucoside which was truly called a "γ" form, since its oxygen bridge proved to go to the γ-carbon. Likewise the sugar acids such as gluconic acid form stable γ-lactones, and in certain compounds fructose occurs as a five-membered ring. In order to distinguish these various forms names are given which relate a sugar to one or the other of the simple heterocyclic compounds, furan and pyran.

$$
\begin{array}{cc}
\begin{array}{c}
\text{HC}\text{---}\text{CH}\\
\|\qquad\|\\
\text{HC}\qquad\text{CH}\\
\diagdown\;\diagup\\
\text{O}\\
\textbf{Furan}
\end{array}
&
\begin{array}{c}
\text{CH}_2\\
\diagup\quad\diagdown\\
\text{HC}\qquad\text{CH}\\
\|\qquad\|\\
\text{HC}\qquad\text{CH}\\
\diagdown\;\diagup\\
\text{O}\\
\textbf{Pyran}
\end{array}
\end{array}
$$

[4] When Sir Norman Haworth (1883–1950) began his investigations in the field of carbohydrate chemistry about 1912 at St. Andrews University, Thomas Purdie was still active, though retired, and J. C. Irvine was Director of the Chemistry Department. This was a conjunction of stars of the first magnitude, which gives to St. Andrews a very special place in the history of structural sugar chemistry, even though the last twenty-five years of Haworth's professional life were spent at the University of Birmingham. In 1937 Haworth shared with Paul Karrer of Zürich the Nobel Prize in Chemistry.

Sugars with six-membered rings are known as *pyranoses* and the corresponding glucosides as *pyranosides*. Similarly the sugars and glucosides with 1–4 oxygen bridges are named respectively *furanoses* and *furanosides*.

Because the Fischer straight chain projection formulas inevitably distort the bond angles seriously, Haworth suggested drawing the rings in perspective. This gives a much truer picture of the relation between the carbons and the oxygen of the ring. Such formulas are now commonly used with both the carbons and the hydrogens omitted as shown in the formulas on the right, since knowing the disposition of the hydroxyl groups sufficiently defines the entire molecule.

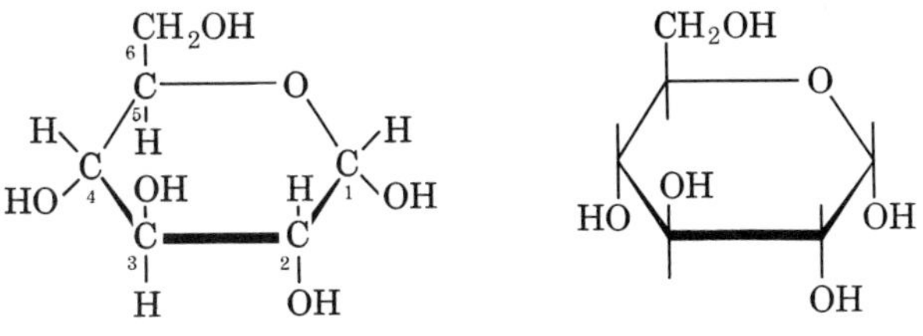

α-D-Glucopyranose

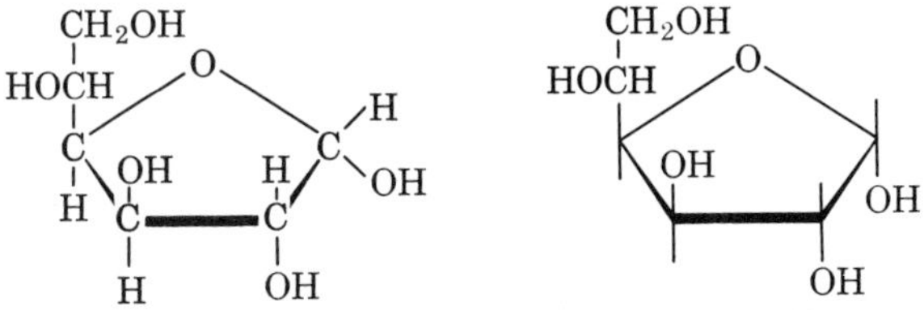

α-D-Glucofuranose

The heavy lines emphasize the fact that we are looking at what is in effect a drawing of a space model in which four or five carbons and an oxygen form a ring in a single plane at right angles to the plane of the paper. The attached groups are disposed above or below this plane. Those groups which were written on the right in the straight chain formula appear below the plane of the ring, while those which were written on the left appear above it. Further illustrations given on page 132 use only the simplified formulations.

The position of the primary alcohol group in the pyranose forms is determined by the position of the hydroxyl on carbon 5. If this hydroxyl group lies to the right in the Fischer formula, the primary alcohol group extends above the plane of the ring, but is below the plane when the adjacent hydroxyl is on the left. This would appear to place the hydrogen attached to carbon 5 on the wrong side of the chain. But with an actual model of the aldehyde form it is found that in order to bring the hydroxyl group on carbon 5 into

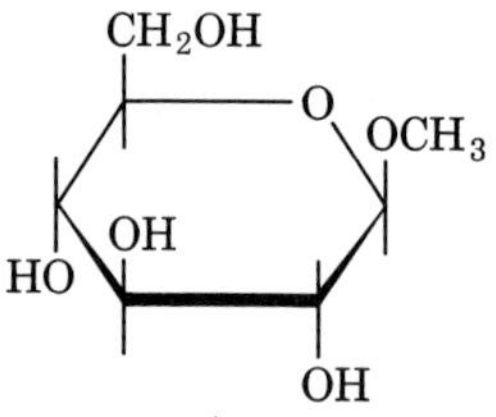

Methyl β-D-glucopyranoside

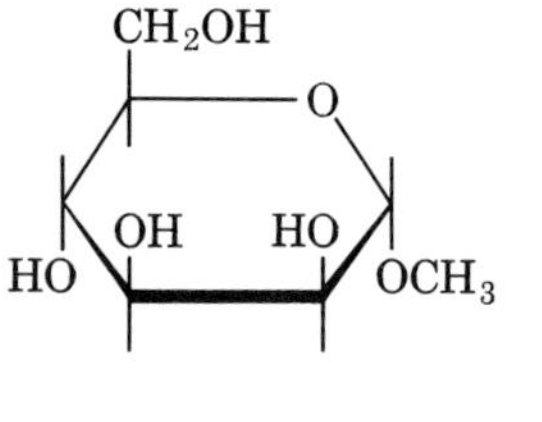

Methyl α-D-mannopyranoside

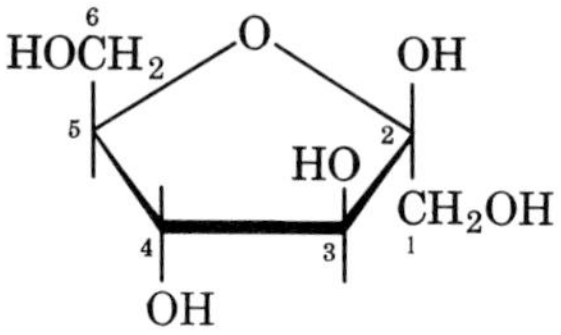

β-D-Fructofuranose

such a position that it can be linked by an oxygen bridge to carbon 1, the chain must be twisted so that the hydrogen crosses to the opposite side of the ring plane.

Value of the ring formula

It was pointed out on page 125 that there were certain objections to the aldehyde formula for glucose. However, this does not change the fact that glucose in solution does react with nearly all aldehyde reagents. Before the ring structure can be accepted it must be reconciled with this fact and be shown to explain also the various anomalous properties referred to above.

There is indirect evidence that when crystalline glucose goes into solution a small amount of the ring compound shifts a proton and takes on the aldehyde structure. The shift is reversible and the proton returning to its position on the anomeric carbon may give either the α or the β configuration. Eventually a mixture results in which the α-glucose in both furanose and pyranose forms is in equilibrium with the two ring forms of β-glucose through intermediate formation of the open chain aldehyde. At equilibrium in neutral solution nearly two-thirds of the glucose is in the β-pyranose form, and just over one-third is present as α-glucopyranose. The other three forms are present in traces only in glucose solutions, but in solutions of ribose over 8 per cent of the sugar is in the aldehyde form.

The fact that there is at any one time so low a concentration of the reducing form accounts for the unexpected slowness of some of the aldehyde reactions of glucose. Thus when an aldehyde reagent is added to the equilibrium mixture, it upsets the equilibrium by reacting with whatever aldehyde is present. In accordance with the law of mass action, more aldehyde then forms and this in turn reacts with the reagent. Eventually all the ring forms

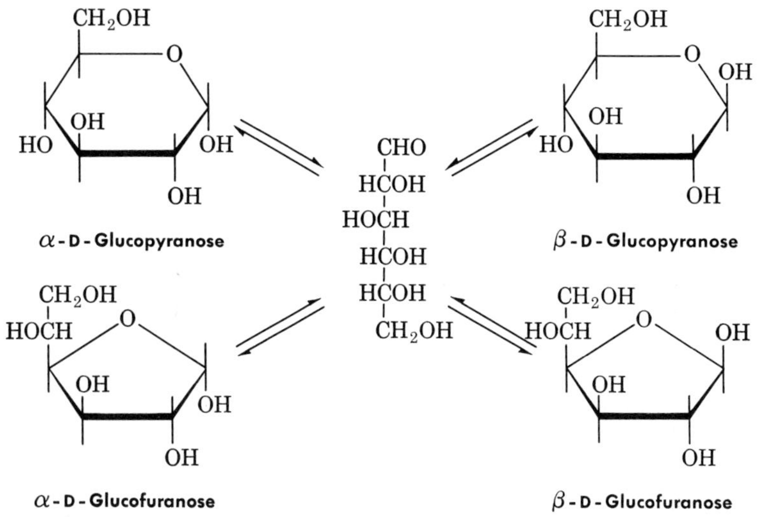

α-D-Glucopyranose

β-D-Glucopyranose

α-D-Glucofuranose

β-D-Glucofuranose

are transformed into the aldehyde form, which is continuously removed. Thus the glucose solution finally reacts as if all the sugar had been present as an aldehyde, giving rise, for example, to such characteristic products as cyanohydrins or oximes. For such reactions the simplest formulation uses the aldehyde formula only, its relation to the ring forms being understood.

Fructose also has the ring structure when in the crystalline form, and gives rise to an equilibrium mixture in solution, which mixture includes both pyranose and furanose forms, though the pyranose ones predominate.

This behavior of the labile sugar molecules in solution explains also why they exhibit mutarotation. Ordinary glucose is the α form, having a specific rotation $+111°$. As it slowly comes to equilibrium with the β form, $[\alpha]_D$ $+19°$, the specific rotation of the mixture falls until equilibrium is established and with it the equilibrium specific rotation of the sugar, $+52.5°$. Similarly the β form of glucose shows an upward mutarotation to the equilibrium value.

Finally, the absence of a reducing group in the glucose pentaacetate is to be expected if almost all the sugar is present in solution in a nonreducing form. The acetylating agent attacks the five hydroxyl groups in the molecule, and once the anomeric hydroxyl has been acetylated the ring form is stabilized. An atom as small as the hydrogen atom can easily slip back and forth between carbon 1 and carbon 5, but this is not true of the large acetyl group. When the α form of crystalline glucose reacts with acetic anhydride in the presence of a catalyst such as zinc chloride, the reaction which takes place yields chiefly a glucose pentaacetate in which one of the five acetyl groups is attached to carbon 1. However, from some such reaction mixtures there has been isolated, in addition to the cyclic, nonreducing pentaacetates, very small amounts of a reducing form. This is a direct demonstration of the presence in the sugar solution of a small amount of the straight chain aldehyde form.

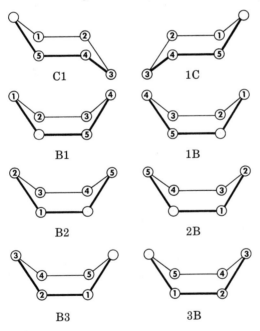

Conformation of pyranose rings

Although the Haworth ring projections were a great improvement on those which had preceded them, they are now in their turn becoming inadequate to represent the pyranose rings. The furanose forms are fairly well represented by the older projections.

In order to take account of the tetrahedral bond angles of 109.3°, a six-membered ring must be buckled in some way. There are for such a ring

Fig. 4.2. A definition of the symbols representing the two chair and six boat conformations for the pyranose ring. The numbering of the atoms is an integral part of the definition and follows the conventions of carbohydrate nomenclature. The heavy lines represent the side of the three-dimensional figure nearest the observer and the open circles, the ring oxygen atoms. [From R. E. Reeves, *Ann. Rev. Biochem.*, **27**, 15 (1958).]

eight theoretically possible arrangements or *conformations*, two of them called "chair" forms and six of them "boat" forms. Figure 4.2 shows these possible forms for a pyranose ring, the open circles representing the oxygen and the numbers being those conventionally given to the carbons of a sugar molecule. The shift from a form in one column to the form beside it results from a reversal of the directions of the "points." To see how such a reversal in C1 for example would give 1C, it is necessary to take account of the conventions used in making these projections. They are drawings of three-dimensional figures, and if two forms are to be compared, the projections must be drawn with the same side of the ring nearest the observer, as is done in the figure. In both C1 and 1C it is the bond between carbons 4 and 5 which is toward the observer. The best way to understand the relation between the various

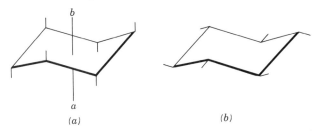

Fig. 4.3. Cyclohexane ring in the two chair conformations showing in (*a*) the axial bonds and in (*b*) the equatorial bonds.

pairs is to make a model and move the points from one position to the other, turning it as necessary to bring the same side toward the observer before making the drawing.

Although there are theoretically eight possible conformations for the pyranose ring, the higher energy of the six boat forms makes them unlikely for the sugars and they may therefore be neglected.

The bonds which hold other atoms or groups to the ring carbons in the chair conformations go out at such angles that one on each carbon is parallel to an axis drawn perpendicular to the plane of the four carbons in the center of the molecule. These are called *axial bonds* and are represented in Fig. 4.3(*a*). It will be noted that they are directed alternately above and below the central plane.

The other bond on each carbon is much more nearly in the plane of the ring and these are therefore called *equatorial bonds*. Actually they form such angles with the other bonds that they jut out alternately slightly above and slightly below the ring plane as shown in Fig. 4.3(*b*), the equatorial bond being above the ring when the corresponding axial bond points downward. Thus these projections preserve, as they must, the proved relations between the groups attached to the various asymmetric carbons. Figure 4.4 shows the C1 and the 1C conformations for methyl β-D-glucopyranoside. The dots stand for the hydrogens, and the double lines indicate the positions of the equatorial bonds. It will be noted that the methoxyl group on carbon 1, for example, is in the equatorial position in the C1 conformation, and in the axial in 1C, but in both its position is above the plane of the ring. This is the pattern followed by all substituents. When the conformation changes, equatorially held substituents become axially bonded, and axial bonds become equatorial, but all groups which were above the ring plane remain so, and those which were below are still below the plane in the new conformation.

The techniques of conformational analysis are in their infancy, but biochemists in the near future are going to have to take account of the new light they are throwing on chemical reactivity. It is found, for example, that

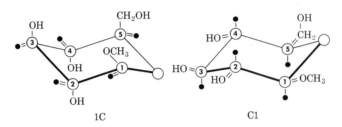

Fig. 4.4. Diagrammatic representation of methyl β-D-glucopyranoside in the 1C and C1 conformations. The single lines are the axial bonds and the double lines the equatorial bonds.

substitution with groups larger than hydrogen in axial positions tends to instability. In the conformations shown for methyl β-D-glucopyranoside, the C1 form has hydrogen in every axial position. The same spatial arrangement would be found in β-glucose, but in α-glucose the hydrogen on carbon 1 would be equatorial, with hydroxyl in the axial position. It is probably because the β forms allow the more favorable conformations that they predominate in the equilibrium mixture which forms in solution.

Chemistry of the Monoses

As indicated above, many of the reactions of the monosaccharides can be satisfactorily explained by the use of simple straight chain formulas, the aldoses reacting by virtue of their aldehyde group and the ketoses reacting as ketones.

Reduction

It has already been noted that treatment of glucose with sodium amalgam yields the expected hexahydric alcohol, sorbitol. Similar reduction of fructose gives rise, as would be expected from its straight chain formula, to two alcohols which differ only in the configuration about the second carbon. The fact that one of the two is the same sorbitol which is formed in the reduction of glucose demonstrates that the configuration about the other asymmetric centers at carbons 3, 4, and 5 are identical in glucose and fructose.

It should be noted that with such symmetrical compounds as the hexahydric alcohols and the dibasic sugar acids, the D and L nomenclature has no meaning. For example, sorbitol is a D compound if written with one primary alcohol group at the top, but is a member of the L series if the formula is inverted.

$$
\begin{array}{cc}
\mathrm{CH_2OH} & \mathrm{CH_2OH} \\
| & | \\
\mathrm{HCOH} & \mathrm{HOCH} \\
| & | \\
\mathrm{HOCH} & \mathrm{HOCH} \\
| & | \\
\mathrm{HCOH} & \mathrm{HCOH} \\
| & | \\
\mathrm{HCOH} & \mathrm{HOCH} \\
| & | \\
\mathrm{CH_2OH} & \mathrm{CH_2OH}
\end{array}
$$

Sorbitol

The hexahydric alcohols, or hexitols, are systematically named by substituting -itol for -ose in the names of the corresponding sugars. For some compounds the older names persist, as with sorbitol which was discovered in the berries of the mountain ash (*Sorbus aucuparia L.*).

Oxidation

When any one of the aldoses is oxidized gently with bromine water, a monobasic acid is formed. All these are named, as is the acid related to glucose, by substituting for -ose in the name of the sugar, the suffix -onic. Thus D-galactose forms D-galactonic acid and L-ribose is oxidized to L-ribonic acid.

This reaction has been adapted to the quantitative estimation of aldoses by oxidation with alkaline hypoiodite. By rigid control of the pH and the temperature, it is possible to estimate the concentration of aldoses in the presence of keto sugars.

$$\mathrm{RCHO + NaIO + NaOH \rightarrow RCOONa + NaI + H_2O}$$

The aldonic acids related to the pentoses and hexoses are α-, β-, γ-, and δ-hydroxy acids, and readily form inner esters or *lactones*. Indeed this elimination of water takes place so readily that the acids scarcely exist as such in solution, but are in equilibrium with their γ- and δ-lactones. Of these the γ forms are the more stable. The lactones are especially important because, while the acids themselves are resistant to reduction, the lactones are readily reduced to the corresponding aldoses.

Another reaction of the aldonic acid lactones which has been valuable in the synthesis of sugars is the change of configuration known as *epimerization*.

```
        O                                              O
        ‖                                              ‖
        C                     COOH                     C
        |                     |                        |
      HCOH                   HCOH                     HCOH
        |                     |                        |
      HOCH     O  ⇌  HOCH                  ⇌  HOCH     O
        |                     |                        |
      HCOH                   HCOH                      HC
        |                     |                        |
      HC                     HCOH                     HCOH
        |                     |                        |
     CH₂OH                  CH₂OH                    CH₂OH
  Gluconic acid                               Gluconic acid
   δ-lactone                                    γ-lactone
```

Gluconic acid
δ-lactone

Gluconic acid
γ-lactone

When such a lactone is heated with aqueous pyridine or quinoline, the arrangement of hydrogen and hydroxyl around carbon 2 is reversed in some of the molecules. This converts part of the lactone to its epimer, which can then be separated and reduced to the corresponding aldose by treatment with sodium amalgam. This reaction was used by Emil Fischer in the synthesis from gulose of the epimeric idose.

```
     CHO                    COOH
      |                      |
    HCOH                   HCOH
      |           Br₂        |          acid
    HCOH        ─────→     HCOH        ─────→
      |           H₂O        |
    HOCH                   HOCH
      |                      |
    HCOH                   HCOH
      |                      |
    CH₂OH                  CH₂OH
  D-Gulose              D-Gulonic acid
```

```
        C=O                      C=O                  CHO
         |                        |                    |
       HCOH                     HOCH                  HOCH
         |                        |                    |
    O  HCOH    quinoline     O  HCOH      Na-Hg      HCOH
         |     ─────────→        |        ───────      |
        CH       140°           CH      dil. acid    HOCH
         |                        |                    |
       HCOH                     HCOH                  HCOH
         |                        |                    |
       CH₂OH                    CH₂OH                 CH₂OH
      Gulonic                   Idonic              D-Idose
     γ-lactone                γ-lactone
```

Although the aldonic acids are the only monobasic acids which can be prepared by direct oxidation of the aldoses, there is a second series of acids which are of great physiological importance and which are clearly related to the sugars. These are the compounds in which the primary alcohol group of the aldose has been oxidized to a carboxyl, though the aldehyde group remains unchanged. The acids of this type are known as *uronic* acids, and the individual members are named by use of the suffix -uronic with the root of the name of the corresponding monose. Glucuronic acid is thus the acid of this structure related to glucose, though it is clearly not possible to prepare it by direct oxidation of the sugar. The entire group of acids is known as the glycuronic acids, the gly- prefix being used here, as elsewhere in sugar chemistry, as a generic term. Thus there are 32 possible *gly*curonic acids, of which 2 are *glu*curonic acids.

α - Glucuronic acid   β - Glucuronic acid   1 - O - Benzoylglucuronic acid

Compounds of this type are very widely distributed in nature, chiefly in the form of heteropolysaccharides. It has been estimated that 10–15 per cent of the organic carbon in the surface soil is in the form of uronic acids, and many plant and bacterial products consist wholly or in part of the uronic acids related to glucose, galactose, and mannose. Glucuronic acid itself serves a special function in animal metabolism because of its ability to form condensation products with various aromatic compounds. Thus administration of various toxic compounds is followed by their excretion in a conjugation product with glucuronic acid. This is true, for example, of benzoic acid and phenol and other aromatic compounds.

Although normally only small amounts of the uronic acids are present in the urine, the body is able to adapt itself to the synthesis of much larger quantities when they are needed for detoxication. In Chapter 13, we shall discover how the body brings about this unusual kind of oxidation.

When an aldose is strongly oxidized, as with nitric acid, both terminal groups react and a dibasic aldaric acid is formed. Most of these acids are named, as noted above, from the corresponding aldose, but the acid related to galactose is called mucic acid. Of all the series of aldaric acids, only mucic acid is insoluble enough to crystallize from a concentrated aqueous solution, and this fact is made the basis of a test to distinguish galactose from other aldohexoses.

Reactions with alkali

All the monoses, ketoses as well as aldoses, react with those oxidizing agents like Fehling's solution and ammoniacal silver nitrate, which are ordinarily used to distinguish between aldehydes and ketones. The reason for this anomalous behavior on the part of the keto sugars is to be found in the great sensitivity of all the simple sugars to alkali. An aqueous solution of glucose, made faintly alkaline with lime water or barium hydroxide, on standing at room temperature will slowly come to an equilibrium in which glucose, fructose, and mannose are all present. It has been shown by the use of molecules labeled with deuterium that the intermediate in this equilibration is fructose, as shown in the formulations below.

Glucose	*Trans* enediol	Fructose	*Cis* enediol	Mannose

It will be noted that all these transformations depend upon migration of a hydrogen from a carbon adjacent to a carbonyl group. This can go on past the point indicated above, to bring about epimerization or ketose formation involving carbon 3. It is of course the lability of this same hydrogen which accounts for the aldol condensation, here shown linking two triose molecules as it does in an important biosynthetic reaction.

Dihydroxy-acetone	D-Glycer-aldehyde	D-Sorbose	D-Fructose

Since two new asymmetric carbons are formed, two other products are, of course, theoretically possible, in which the hydroxyl groups on carbons 3 and 4 are in the cis relationship. Actually these two forms do not appear in detectable amounts.

In the presence of strong alkali such as is present in Fehling's solution, much more deep seated changes take place than those which have just been discussed, and the carbohydrate molecules are broken into fragments. Some of these have been identified, but the whole process is complicated and is still quite obscure. It is therefore impossible to write a chemical equation for the reaction of a reducing sugar with Fehling's solution as there are probably dozens of different reaction products, formed when the various fragments react with the reagent. But the lability which causes the formation of the fragments is due to the presence of the carbonyl group, since no such reduction takes place with polyhydroxy alcohols or acids. In this sense then, the carbonyl groups are the reducing groups, and a positive test indicates the presence of such groups, free or potentially free, in the sugar molecule.

Reactions with carbonyl reagents

Even though the reactions with alkaline oxidizing agents are so complex as to offer little evidence for the aldehyde or ketone structure of the monoses, other carbonyl reagents yield more conventional reaction products. The formation of oximes with hydroxylamine has already been mentioned, and also the formation of an addition product with hydrogen cyanide.

One of the first important contributions to carbohydrate chemistry was the introduction by Emil Fischer of phenylhydrazine as a reagent. The reducing sugars, most of which are very difficult to crystallize, react with phenylhydrazine in the presence of acetate buffers to form yellow, beautifully crystalline phenylosazones. These are compounds in which two phenyl-hydrazine residues are linked to carbons 1 and 2 of either aldoses or 2-ketoses, as shown in the formula for glucosazone. The fact that fructose and

$$
\begin{array}{l}
CH{=}N \cdot NHC_6H_5 \\
| \\
C{=}N \cdot NHC_6H_5 \\
| \\
(CHOH)_3 \\
| \\
CH_2OH
\end{array}
$$

Glucosazone

glucose yield identical osazones furnishes additional proof that the two sugars have identical stereochemical arrangements about carbons 3, 4, and 5.

Although two residues appear in the osazone, three molecules of phenyl-hydrazine are used for every molecule of osazone formed. The third phenyl-hydrazine is reduced in the course of the reaction, and appears as one molecule of NH_3 and one of aniline, $C_6H_5NH_2$. The mechanism of this reaction has been a subject of controversy since Fischer, back in 1887, fitted the facts noted above into a suggested mechanism. It may be doubted whether the last word has yet been said, but work with *p*-nitrophenylhydrazine labeled with N^{15} points to the following reaction sequence for glucose. For simplicity

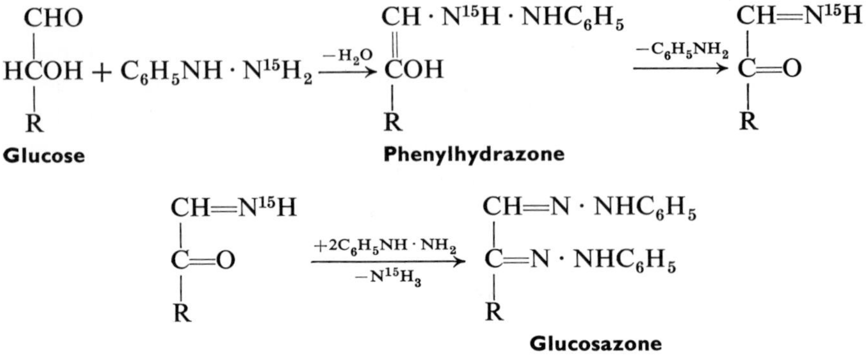

$$
\begin{array}{ccc}
\underset{\text{Glucose}}{\begin{array}{c}\text{CHO}\\ |\\ \text{HCOH} + C_6H_5NH\cdot N^{15}H_2 \\ |\\ R\end{array}} & \xrightarrow{-H_2O} & \underset{\text{Phenylhydrazone}}{\begin{array}{c}\text{CH}\cdot N^{15}H\cdot NHC_6H_5\\ \|\\ \text{COH}\\ |\\ R\end{array}} & \xrightarrow{-C_6H_5NH_2} & \begin{array}{c}\text{CH}=N^{15}H\\ |\\ C=O\\ |\\ R\end{array}
\end{array}
$$

$$
\begin{array}{c}\text{CH}=N^{15}H\\ |\\ C=O\\ |\\ R\end{array} \quad \xrightarrow[-N^{15}H_3]{+2C_6H_5NH\cdot NH_2} \quad \underset{\text{Glucosazone}}{\begin{array}{c}\text{CH}=N\cdot NHC_6H_5\\ |\\ C=N\cdot NHC_6H_5\\ |\\ R\end{array}}
$$

the formulas have been written without the *p*-nitro group. It will be noted that the sequence involves three separate steps, the two-step formation of a labeled derivative, followed by treatment of this compound with unlabeled reagent. This brings about a release of labeled NH_3 and formation of the osazone.

The phenylhydrazine residues can be removed from an osazone by treatment with concentrated HCl, yielding a very reactive compound known as an *osone*. If the osone is then reduced very gently, the aldehyde group reacts preferentially and a ketose results. Thus from the aldose, glucose, by way of its phenylosazone, the ketose, fructose, may be formed.

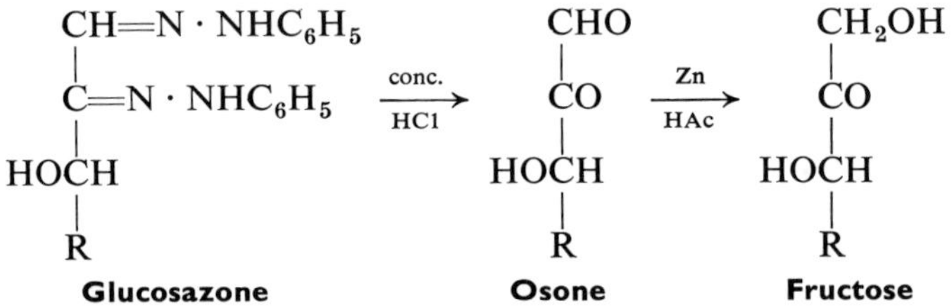

$$
\underset{\text{Glucosazone}}{\begin{array}{c}\text{CH}=N\cdot NHC_6H_5\\ |\\ C=N\cdot NHC_6H_5\\ |\\ \text{HOCH}\\ |\\ R\end{array}} \quad \xrightarrow[\text{HCl}]{\text{conc.}} \quad \underset{\text{Osone}}{\begin{array}{c}\text{CHO}\\ |\\ \text{CO}\\ |\\ \text{HOCH}\\ |\\ R\end{array}} \quad \xrightarrow[\text{HAc}]{\text{Zn}} \quad \underset{\text{Fructose}}{\begin{array}{c}\text{CH}_2\text{OH}\\ |\\ \text{CO}\\ |\\ \text{HOCH}\\ |\\ R\end{array}}
$$

Reactions of the hydroxyl groups

1. OXIDATION WITH PERIODIC ACID. In 1928 Malaprade of the University of Nancy reported that periodic acid (HIO_4) oxidizes α-glycols forming formic acid from a secondary alcohol group and formaldehyde from a primary. One mole of the oxidant is used for each mole of glycolic *pair* oxidized, and the reduction product is iodic acid, HIO_3. When the reaction is applied to a hexahydric alcohol with its five pairs of adjacent hydroxyl groups the following reaction takes place:

$$
\begin{array}{l}
\text{CH}_2\text{OH} \\
| \\
(\text{CHOH})_4 + 5\text{HIO}_4 \rightarrow 2\text{HCHO} + 4\text{HCOOH} + 5\text{HIO}_3 + \text{H}_2\text{O} \\
| \\
\text{CH}_2\text{OH}
\end{array}
$$

With glucose instead of the hexahydric alcohol, reaction is more nearly complete because of the reactivity at the anomeric carbon and the products are 1 mole of formaldehyde and 5 of formic acid.

The course of the reaction may be followed in various ways. The periodate used and iodate formed may be determined by titration as follows. In acid solution the anions of both acids react with iodide ion to set free iodine, but in neutral or faintly alkaline solution only the periodate reacts. Titration of the iodine set free in acid solution measures the total amount of the two acids; a similar determination on another aliquot, carried out in neutral solution measures the amount of periodate which has not reacted. Formaldehyde is estimated gravimetrically as a crystalline condensation product with dimedone (5,5-dimethyl-1,3-cyclohexanedione). If the periodate is used in the form of its potassium salt, and allowance is made for the effect of this cation, the formic acid may be titrated with phenolphthalein as indicator.

When periodic acid is used for the oxidation of such a compound as methyl glucoside, in which the ring is stabilized, the oxidation leaves the oxygen bridge intact and breaks the carbon chain between adjacent hydroxyl-bearing carbons. A primary carbinol of a pair yields formaldehyde; a secondary alcohol group between two other carbinols is oxidized to formic acid, but if it has carbinol on only one side, it remains attached to the chain and becomes an aldehyde group. The general course of such a reaction is as follows:

$$
\begin{array}{l}
\text{H} \quad\;\; \text{OCH}_3 \\
\;\;\backslash \;\; / \\
\;\;\;\text{C} \\
\;\;\;| \\
(\text{HCOH})_n \quad \text{O} + (n-1)\text{HIO}_4 \rightarrow \\
\;\;\;| \\
\;\;\text{HC} \\
\;\;\;| \\
\;\;\text{CH}_2\text{OH}
\end{array}
$$

$$
\begin{array}{l}
\text{H} \quad\;\; \text{OCH}_3 \\
\;\;\backslash \;\; / \\
\;\;\;\text{C} \\
\;\;\;| \\
\text{CHO} \quad \text{O} + (n-2)\text{HCOOH} + (n-1)\text{HIO}_3 \\
\;\;\;| \\
\text{CHO} \\
\;\;\;| \\
\;\text{HC} \\
\;\;\;| \\
\;\text{CH}_2\text{OH}
\end{array}
$$

When this oxidation procedure was applied to methyl glucoside it yielded unequivocal proof of the presence of the pyranose ring.[5] Formulas XI to XV give the ring structures theoretically possible for a methyl glucoside. Under each is indicated (*a*) the moles of periodic acid which 1 mole of a glucoside of the indicated structure would use, (*b*) the moles of formic acid, and (*c*) the moles of formaldehyde which would be formed. All these amounts depend upon the number of *pairs* of adjacent hydroxyl groups, and the pairs are bracketed in the formulas.

Moles oxidant	3	2	2
Moles HCOOH	2	1	0
Moles HCHO	1	1	1
	XI	**XII**	**XIII**

Moles oxidant	2	3
Moles HCOOH	1	2
Moles HCHO	0	0
	XIV	**XV**

When methyl glucoside was oxidized with periodic acid it proved to consume 2 moles of oxidant and to form no formaldehyde, thus establishing the presence of the pyranose ring as shown in structure XIV.

---

[5] The general reaction above as well as the proof of ring structure which follows are quoted with the permission of the publisher from W. W. Pigman and R. M. Goepp, *Chemistry of the Carbohydrates*, Academic, New York, 1948.

2. ESTERS

(*a*) *Acetic Acid Esters.* The acetylation of the sugars has already been referred to. These compounds have been important not only for the light they throw on the structure of the sugar molecule but also because the acetyl group after serving to protect the reactive hydroxyl is easily removed by hydrolysis.

An important use is made of the acetylated sugars in the preparation of the very reactive acetylglucosyl halides which serve as starting material for many syntheses. For example, pentaacetylglucose reacts with concentrated halogen acid in the presence of glacial acetic acid, to replace the acetoxyl

α - D - Glucopyranose pentaacetate

conc. HBr
glacial HAc

Tetra - O - Acetylgluco - pyranosyl bromide

group on the anomeric carbon with halogen. The halogen thus introduced is readily replaceable by various acyl and alkoxyl groups, probably through intermediate formation of an addition product.

(*b*) *Phosphate Esters.* Physiologically the phosphate esters are among the most important carbohydrate derivatives. Orthophosphoric acid with its three hydroxyl groups is ideally formed to link together compounds with which it can be esterified. Thus it occurs in compounds in which it serves to link two sugar residues, or to bind glycerol to one of a number of different compounds. An example of the chemical synthesis of a phosphoric acid ester is the one by which glucose-1-phosphate is prepared. Treatment of the tetra-*O*-acetylglucosyl bromide formulated above, with silver phosphate brings about precipitation of silver bromide and esterification of all three phosphate hydroxyl groups with three separate acetylated glucose residues. Simultaneous deacylation and controlled hydrolysis of this compound removes two of the glucose residues and removes the acetyl groups from the third, leaving the substance known as the Cori ester[6] (glucose-1-phosphate) in honor of its discoverers.

---

[6] Carl Cori and his wife Gerty Cori were born and educated in Czechoslovakia. After coming to the United States in the early 1920's they were associated with the Washington University Medical School in St. Louis. For their joint work in the field of carbohydrate metabolism they were awarded the Nobel Prize in Medicine in 1948, sharing it with Bernardo Houssay of Argentina. Gerty Cori died in 1957.

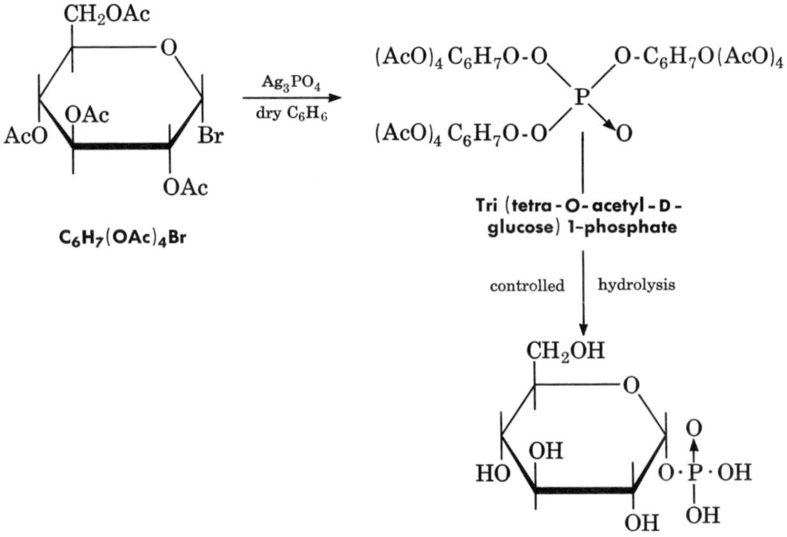

$C_6H_7(OAc)_4Br$

Tri (tetra-O-acetyl-D-
glucose) 1-phosphate

controlled | hydrolysis

Cori ester
α-D-Glucopyranose 1-
phosphate

Synthesis of the phosphate derivative of glucose in which the phosphate group is esterified at carbon 3 makes use of a different protective mechanism. It was Emil Fischer who first noted that glucose would condense with 2 moles of acetone to yield a diacetone derivative now known as di-*O*-isopropylidene-glucose. The reaction is a general one and results from condensation of acetone with a pair of adjacent, cis hydroxyl groups. In glucopyranose only the hydroxyls on carbons 1 and 2 are in this relationship. Since glucose

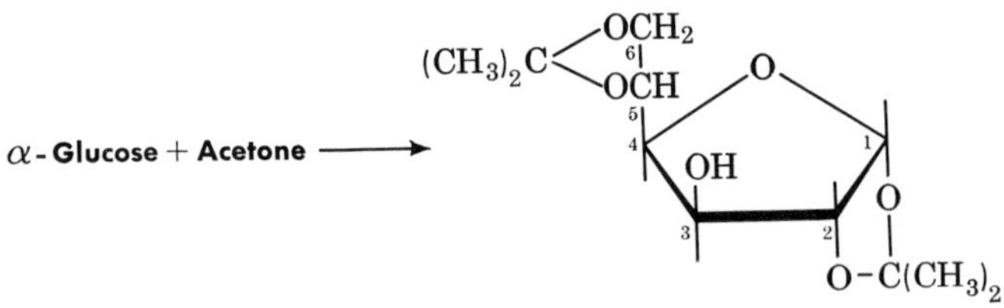

α-Glucose + Acetone ⟶

1,2:5,6-Di-O-isopropylidene-
D-glucofuranose

yields a beautifully crystalline derivative in which it is linked to two acetone residues, there must be in solution at least a small amount of a form with two such pairs. The acetone derivative proves to be 1,2:5,6-di-*O*-isopropylidene-D-glucofuranose in which, with the ring shifted to carbon 4, there are two *cis*-glycol pairs. Experiments such as this justify the formulation on page 133 which indicates that there is always a small amount of the furanose form in a glucose solution. When the acetone reacts preferentially with this form, the equilibrium shifts until all the glucose has been transformed to yield the diacetone derivative.

Other sugars form similar acetone derivatives, sometimes with and sometimes without a preliminary shift in the point of attachment of the oxygen bridge. The importance of the compounds so formed rests largely in the fact that the isopropylidene groups are easily removed by dilute acid hydrolysis after they have served their purpose of protecting some of the hydroxyl groups from reagents. Thus with the glucose derivative above, reaction with phosphorus oxychloride introduces a phosphate group at the only carbon

α - **Glucose - 3 - phosphate**

which has a free hydroxyl group. Subsequent mild hydrolysis removes the blocking groups and allows the 1–5 ring to form again in the glucose-3-phosphate which results.

Similar reactions with other protected molecules have yielded various hexose and pentose phosphate esters. It was in the study of alcoholic fermentation of glucose that the importance of phosphate esters was first recognized. Later work has proved that the same compounds play an essential role in many different metabolic sequences, both in plants and in animals. The first naturally occurring esters to be identified were a hexose diphosphate and two different monophosphates. As often happens in biochemistry, these substances came to be known by the names of their discoverers. The two British pioneers in the field of alcoholic fermentation, A. Harden[7] and W. J. Young, isolated a fructose-1,6-diphosphate which is still known as the Harden-Young ester. The formulas given below indicate the structures of the three most important hexose phosphate esters aside from the Cori ester.

Phosphate groups attached to organic molecules are removed by hydrolysis at different rates, depending upon the point of attachment. Thus the glycosyl phosphates, such as glucose-1-phosphate, hydrolyze readily in acid and the liberation of inorganic phosphate under specific conditions may be taken as a measure of the amount of this type of ester, even in a mixture of phosphate

---

[7] Sir Arthur Harden (1865–1940) was Professor at London University and Head of the Biochemistry Department at the Lister Institute of Preventive Medicine. In addition to the work of research he carried for many years the editorship of the *Biochemical Journal*. In 1929 he shared with the Swedish biochemist, Hans von Euler, the Nobel Prize in Chemistry.

esters. On the other hand, such a true ester as fructose-6-phosphate is much more resistant to acid hydrolysis and requires longer heating to free its phosphate. In $1N$ acid the phosphate group at carbon 1 of fructose-1,6-diphosphate is hydrolyzed approximately twelve times as fast as the phosphate at carbon 6. All such differences are exploited in the standard methods for the estimation of the various types of phosphate compounds.

Harden-Young ester	Robison[9] ester	Neuberg[10] ester
α-D-fructofurano-1,6-diphosphate	α-D-glucose-6-phosphate	α-D-fructofurano-6-phosphate

Not only are the phosphate groups removable by hydrolysis but also under some of the conditions used in studying these compounds they migrate from one carbon to another. This is probably brought about through the formation of a cyclic intermediate. In determinations of the point of attachment of a phosphate group the possibility of such migrations has to be kept in mind.

---

[8] The phosphate group in formulas is abbreviated in many ways. Occasionally, especially if the ionization of the group is important, it is written out as in the formula for the Cori ester on page 146. Sometimes it is given as in the formula for glucose-3-phosphate. But very often the single letter P is used to stand for whatever phosphate residue is present. In $R \cdot O \cdot P$, the P stands for $-PO_3H_2$. In $R \cdot O \cdot P \cdot O \cdot P$ the first P, nearest the R, stands for $-PO_3H$, while the terminal P again stands for $-PO_3H_2$. In this same convention P alone stands for H_3PO_4, sometimes indicated P_i for inorganic phosphate, and PP stands for $H_4P_2O_7$, pyrophosphoric acid.

[9] Professor Robert Robison (1883–1941) was for many years at the Lister Institute in London as Head of its Department of Biochemistry. He was also Professor of Biochemistry at London University.

[10] Carl Neuberg (1877–1956) was for many years an outstanding figure among those concerned with enzyme chemistry in general and with alcoholic fermentation in particular. In 1938 he became Professor Emeritus at the University of Berlin after a long and fruitful career there. Between 1941 and 1948 he was Research Professor at New York University, again becoming Emeritus in 1948. After that he carried on research at the Polytechnic Institute in Brooklyn.

(c) *Tosyl Esters.* The acid chlorides of the aryl sulfonic acids react with glucose as do other acid chlorides to form the corresponding esters. Thus *p*-toluenesulfonyl chloride in pyridine solution reacts with glucose to form a derivative in which four hydroxyl groups have been esterified, while the hydroxyl on carbon 1 has been replaced by chlorine. In the formula, the symbol Ts is used to represent the $CH_3 \cdot C_6H_4 \cdot SO_2$—group.

Tetra - O -tosyl - D - glucopyranosyl chloride

One of the chief uses of the tosyl esters is in testing for the presence of primary alcohol groups. When a polytosyl ester is treated with sodium iodide in acetone solution, the salt reacts preferentially with a tosyloxy group attached to the carbon of a primary alcohol. Iodine replaces the tosyloxy residue and sodium *p*-toluenesulfonate is set free. On treatment of the sugar iodide with silver nitrate, insoluble silver iodide is precipitated and may be determined quantitatively, thus measuring the number of primary alcohol groups in the original compound.

3. ETHERS

(a) *Methyl Ethers.* Brief reference has already been made to the importance of the methylation procedures by which sugar ethers may be prepared. The first successful method was that of the St. Andrews chemists Purdie and Irvine,[11] who made use of a mixture of methyl iodide and silver oxide. The

[11] Thomas Purdie (1843–1916) preceded Irvine (1877–1952) in the Professorship of Chemistry at the University of St. Andrews in Scotland. James Colquhoun Irvine (later Sir James), though burdened with heavy administrative duties after 1921 when he became Principal of the University, yet carried on an active research program until about 1938. His pioneer work on carbohydrate structure was a fundamental contribution to that complex subject.

reaction of alcoholic hydroxyl groups with this reagent was discovered accidentally when Purdie attempted to esterify lactic acid by treating it with methyl iodide in the presence of silver oxide. The properties of the ester which formed proved to differ slightly from those of a supposedly identical ester prepared by Emil Fischer using his methyl alcohol–hydrochloric acid reagent. Search for the cause of the discrepancies led to the isolation of a small amount of a substance which proved to be the dimethyl derivative, $CH_3 \cdot CH(OCH_3) \cdot COOCH_3$. The importance of this formation of an ether linkage led to an elaboration of the method for the preparation of sugar ethers.

The procedure which is now commonly used for methylation was developed by Haworth. The reagent is dimethyl sulfate, used with 30 per cent sodium hydroxide. It is very much cheaper than the Purdie reagent and does not have the disadvantage of including an oxidizing agent (Ag_2O) which attacks the reducing groups if it is used with unsubstituted sugars. Complete methylation with either reagent usually requires several repetitions of the procedure. With methyl iodide and silver oxide the complete methylation of glucose may require six or more treatments with the reagents. The final product is a methyl tetramethylglucoside. It should be noted that while this

Methyl 2, 3, 4, 6-Tetra-O-methyl-
α-D-glucopyranoside

compound contains five methoxyl groups, the group on carbon 1 is not held in a stable ether linkage. If the pentamethyl compound is hydrolyzed, the glucosidic methyl group on carbon 1 is removed and there results a tetramethylglucose.

The partially methylated sugars have been of great importance as reference compounds in determinations of the structure of oligo- and polysaccharides. They are usually prepared by blocking some of the hydroxyl groups before methylating and removing the protecting groups after methylation is complete. By a variety of such procedures all the different partially methylated derivatives of the common hexose and pentose sugars have been prepared. We shall see later how these compounds are used in formulation of the structures of the more complex carbohydrates.

(*b*) *Triphenylmethyl Ethers.* The ethers formed by interaction between triphenylmethyl chloride and alcoholic groups are known as "trityl" ethers.

The reagent attacks any primary hydroxyl group much more readily than a secondary group, and under proper conditions will block only the primary position. For example, methyl glucoside reacts in pyridine solution to form a 6-trityl derivative which can then be methylated or acetylated at the other

Methyl α-D-glucoside

$\xrightarrow[\text{pyridine}]{(C_6H_5)_3CCl}$

Methyl 6-O-trityl-α-D-glucopyranoside

$\xrightarrow[\text{sulphate}]{\text{dimethyl}}$

Methyl (2, 3, 4-O-trimethyl-6 trityl) α-glucopyranoside

$\xrightarrow[\text{HAc}]{\text{HBr}}$

Methyl (2, 3, 4-O-trimethyl) α-glucopyranoside

three hydroxyl groups. Although the trityl group is held in an ether linkage it can be removed by hydrolysis with a mixture of acetic and hydrobromic acids without splitting the glucosidic bond.

4. NATURALLY OCCURRING GLYCOSIDES. There occur naturally in the plant world a large number of compounds which on hydrolysis yield one or more sugar molecules, and one or more molecules of some other type. Many of these were known and had been used in commerce long before Fischer prepared his methyl glucosides. They were originally known as glucosides, but since the sugar moiety is not always glucose, the modern class name is *glycoside*, with glucoside used only for those compounds which yield glucose when hydrolyzed. The nonsugar part of these compounds is known as the *aglycone* or aglucone. It may be a simple compound like methyl alcohol, which is the aglucone of the methyl glucosides, or it may be a much more complex substance. The sugar components are also various, and include besides simple hexose and pentose residues a number of substances closely related to the sugars. Below are given the simple straight chain formulas of several sugar derivatives which have been found in natural products.

CHO	CHO	CHO	CHO
CH_2	HCOH	HCOH	CH_2
HCOH	HOCH	CH_3OCH	$HCOCH_3$
HCOH	HOCH	HOCH	HCOH
HCOH	HCOH	HCOH	HCOH
CH_3	CH_3	CH_3	CH_3
D-Digitoxose	**D-Fucose**	**Digitalose**	**Cymarose**

The aglycone portions of plant glycosides are often toxic substances, and it has been suggested that their condensation with carbohydrates may be a detoxication mechanism of the plant. On the other hand, it may be that they protect the plant in another way. Wherever a glycoside is found in a plant there is also, presumably in neighboring cells, an enzyme or enzymes capable of bringing about its hydrolysis. On this basis it has been suggested that a phenol glycoside, for example, may serve to hold the phenol in a nontoxic form. If a part of the plant is injured, the glycoside and the enzyme come into contact and the antiseptic phenol is set free at the point of injury. This may well be the function also of those glycosides, such as amygdalin, which release hydrogen cyanide on hydrolysis.

Among the phenolic glycosides phlorizin, found in the bark of plum and apple trees, has been widely used in biochemical studies. When injected into an animal it induces an excretion of sugar which simulates diabetes, and this was for many years one of the two standard ways of inducing experimental "diabetes" in animals. On hydrolysis of the glucoside, glucose is

$$OCCH_2CH_2-\langle \ \rangle-OH$$
$$HO-\langle \ \rangle-O \cdot C_6H_{11}O_5$$
$$(\beta\text{-D-glucose})$$
$$OH$$

Phlorizin

set free, leaving the aglucone which is a polyhydroxy aromatic ketone, phloretin [β-(p-hydroxyphenyl)2,4,6-trihydroxypropiophenone].

Many of the plant colors are attributable to the presence of glucosides. One type of aglycone (the hydroxyflavones) introduces yellow and brown tints, while another (the anthocyanins) is associated with reds and blues. The familiar dye, indigo blue, is prepared by oxidation of the hydroxyindole, indoxyl, which is the aglucone of the plant glucoside, indican.

Indican
Indoxyl-β-D-glucoside

Amygdalin is a glucoside of great historical interest, since it was one of the earliest to be formulated, and also because the first recognition of those potent biological catalysts, the enzymes, came about during the study of its properties. It is found in the seeds of the bitter almond, and yields on complete hydrolysis 2 moles of glucose and one each of benzaldehyde and

Amygdalin

hydrogen cyanide. Controlled enzymic hydrolysis as well as synthesis has now established the fact that the sugar occurs as a disaccharide, gentiobiose, while the aglycone is mandelonitrile.

Synthesis and Degradation of the Simple Sugars

Synthesis from noncarbohydrates

The unique example of carbohydrate synthesis from inorganic molecules is photosynthesis by green plants. The chemistry of this process has proved to be so complex that it cannot profitably be considered at this point, but will be taken up in Chapter 15.

Of great historical interest is the fact that in the early years Emil Fischer did succeed in preparing several different hexoses from 1- and 3-carbon precursors. He found that, whether he treated glycerose with bromine and sodium carbonate or allowed mild alkali to act upon acrolein dibromide $(CH_2Br \cdot CHBr \cdot CHO)$ or upon formaldehyde, he obtained optically inactive reducing mixtures which were enough alike to be given the single name "acrose." From several of these reaction mixtures Fischer isolated inactive glucose as the phenylosazone. Using this racemic mixture, he carried out by the usual methods of sugar chemistry an outstanding series

TABLE 4.2. Fischer's Synthesis of Sugars

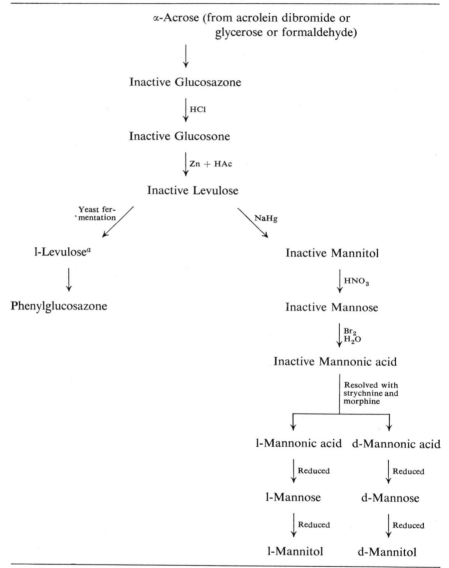

α-Acrose (from acrolein dibromide or
glycerose or formaldehyde)

↓

Inactive Glucosazone

↓ HCl

Inactive Glucosone

↓ Zn + HAc

Inactive Levulose

Yeast fermentation ↙   ↘ NaHg

l-Levulose[a]   Inactive Mannitol

↓   ↓ HNO₃

Phenylglucosazone   Inactive Mannose

                                 ↓ Br₂ H₂O

                            Inactive Mannonic acid

                            Resolved with strychnine and morphine

                    l-Mannonic acid   d-Mannonic acid

                    ↓ Reduced   ↓ Reduced

                    l-Mannose   d-Mannose

                    ↓ Reduced   ↓ Reduced

                    l-Mannitol   d-Mannitol

SOURCE: From E. Fischer, The synthesis of mannose and levulose, *Ber.*, *23*, 370 (1890).
  [a] The d- and l- in this table are used as Fischer used them to indicate the actual rotation of the compounds.

of syntheses of sugars and sugar derivatives which established the relationships between a number of the simple sugars. Some of the transformations
which he effected are shown in Table 4.2, adapted from a similar chart in
Fischer's paper. It would be an excellent exercise in carbohydrate chemistry
to make sure that each step in the procedures is clearly understood!

Lengthening the aldose chain

Reference has already been made to the Kiliani synthesis by which it is
possible to synthesize from one aldose the next higher member of the series
(p. 118). Theoretically it would be possible to prepare all the aldohexoses
by repeated cyanohydrin syntheses from the two glyceroses. Not all these
reactions have actually been carried out but many of them have, and further,
hexose molecules have been lengthened to yield sugars with as many as ten
carbons in a straight chain.

Shortening the aldose chain

One of the best methods for shortening sugar chains depends upon the fact
that a salt of an aldonic acid can be oxidized by hydrogen peroxide in the
presence of ferric ion. Carbon dioxide is liberated yielding the next lower
sugar of the series. Thus D-gluconic acid gives rise to D-arabinose.

$$
\begin{array}{ccc}
\text{COO}^- & & \\
| & & \\
\text{HCOH} & & \text{CHO} \\
| & & | \\
\text{HOCH} & \xrightarrow[\text{Fe}^{+++}]{\text{H}_2\text{O}_2} & \text{HOCH} \quad + \text{CO}_2 \\
| & & | \\
\text{HCOH} & & \text{HCOH} \\
\vdots & & \vdots \\
\textbf{D-Gluconate} & & \textbf{D-Arabinose} \\
\textbf{ion} & &
\end{array}
$$

Bacterial syntheses

Green plants are important because they furnish many carbohydrates of
commercial importance, and certain bacteria are now valuable because carbohydrates and carbohydrate derivatives are by-products of their metabolic
activities. Various strains of *Acetobacter*, for example, ferment sugar
alcohols with formation of ketoses. Thus L-sorbose, an isomer of fructose,
is prepared commercially from D-glucose by first reducing the sugar to the
corresponding alcohol, and then fermenting the alcohol by bacteria. Note
that the sorbitol formula is written with carbon 6 at the top. The ketose
which is formed in this fermentation finds a wide use in the preparation of
vitamin C.

$$
\begin{array}{ccc}
& & \text{CH}_2\text{OH} \\
& & \overset{6}{|} \\
& & \text{HOCH} \\
& & \overset{5}{|} \\
& & \text{HOCH} \\
& \text{reduction} & \overset{4}{|} \\
\text{D-Glucose} \xrightarrow{\hspace{1.5cm}} & & \text{HCOH} \\
& & \overset{3}{|} \\
& & \text{HOCH} \\
& & \overset{2}{|} \\
& & \text{CH}_2\text{OH} \\
& & 1
\end{array}
$$

D-Glucose $\xrightarrow{\text{reduction}}$ **Sorbitol** $\xrightarrow[\textit{suboxydans}]{\textit{Acetobacter}}$ **L-Sorbose**

Sorbitol:
CH$_2$OH
HOCH (6)
HOCH (5)
HCOH (4)
HOCH (3)
CH$_2$OH (2)
1

L-Sorbose:
CH$_2$OH
C=O
HOCH
HCOH
HOCH
CH$_2$OH

A similar pair of reactions serves to transform glycerose to the ketotriose, dihydroxyacetone, thus again achieving the transformation of an aldose to a corresponding ketose.

D-Glycerose:
CHO
HCOH
CH$_2$OH

$\xrightarrow{\text{reduction}}$

Glycerol:
CH$_2$OH
HCOH
CH$_2$OH

$\xrightarrow[\textit{xylinum}]{\textit{Bact.}}$

Dihydroxyacetone:
CH$_2$OH
C=O
CH$_2$OH

D-Glycerose   **Glycerol**   **Dihydroxyacetone**

The field of bacterial synthesis is a wide one and is being exploited in the preparation of other substances than sugars. For a survey of the reactions which can be brought about in this way the student should consult a text devoted to bacterial metabolism.

COMPOUNDS RELATED TO THE MONOSES

Deoxy Sugars

Reference has already been made in connection with the natural glycosides to compounds which differ from the simple sugars only in lacking one or two oxygen atoms. These substances, known as deoxy sugars, occur in several compounds of great physiological importance. One of the nucleic acids which are found in all living cells contains a deoxy derivative of the aldopentose, ribose, while a 6-deoxy hexose, L-rhamnose, is a constituent of many glycosides and polysaccharides. Compounds like rhamnose, having a terminal methyl group, are also named as methyl pentoses, rhamnose itself being methyl-L-lyxose.

The 6-deoxy sugars are readily prepared from the corresponding hexoses through the tosyl derivatives. It will be remembered that a tosyl residue on

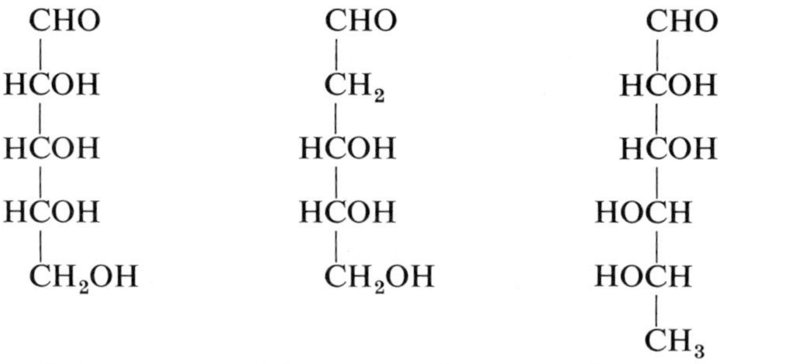

$$
\begin{array}{ccc}
\text{CHO} & \text{CHO} & \text{CHO} \\
| & | & | \\
\text{HCOH} & \text{CH}_2 & \text{HCOH} \\
| & | & | \\
\text{HCOH} & \text{HCOH} & \text{HCOH} \\
| & | & | \\
\text{HCOH} & \text{HCOH} & \text{HOCH} \\
| & | & | \\
\text{CH}_2\text{OH} & \text{CH}_2\text{OH} & \text{HOCH} \\
 & & | \\
 & & \text{CH}_3
\end{array}
$$

| D-Ribose | 2-Deoxy-D-erythro-
pentose | L-Rhamnose or
6-deoxy-L-mannose |

a primary carbon can be replaced by iodine. Reduction of such a compound converts it to the deoxy sugar.

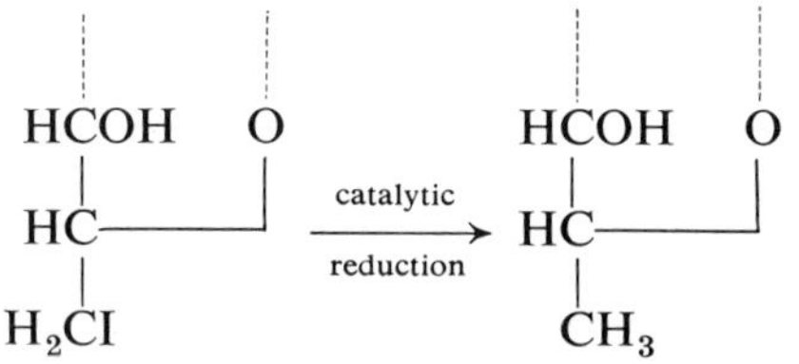

$$
\begin{array}{c}
\text{HCOH} \quad \text{O} \\
| \\
\text{HC}\!-\!\!\!\!\rule{0.6cm}{0.4pt} \\
| \\
\text{H}_2\text{CI}
\end{array}
\quad
\xrightarrow[\text{reduction}]{\text{catalytic}}
\quad
\begin{array}{c}
\text{HCOH} \quad \text{O} \\
| \\
\text{HC}\!-\!\!\!\!\rule{0.6cm}{0.4pt} \\
| \\
\text{CH}_3
\end{array}
$$

6-Deoxy hexose

Amino Sugars

Sugar derivatives in which an amino group replaces an hydroxyl group are known as amino sugars. When the amino group is linked to the anomeric carbon, the compounds are known as glycosylamines, and the amino group is

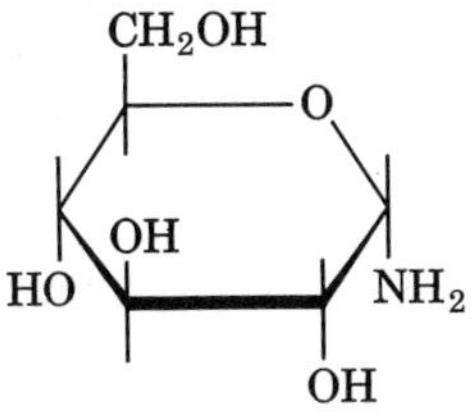

α-D-Glucosylamine

more labile than when it is attached to other carbons. This type of compound forms readily when a sugar is treated with ammonia in alcoholic solution, or with liquid ammonia. Thus D-glucose reacts to form D-glucosylamine. Since similar reactions take place with substituted amines, these compounds may eventually help to elucidate the nature of the linkage between proteins and carbohydrates in the glycoproteins.

The two important natural representatives of the amino sugars have their amino groups on carbon 2 and belong to the group of glycosamines as distinguished from the glycosylamines above. These compounds are *chitosamine*, or D-glucosamine, and *chondrosamine*, or D-galactosamine. The former is obtained by hydrolysis of chitin, the principal polysaccharide of fungi and of the horny parts of crustacea and insects. Chondrosamine is one of the building blocks of another polysaccharide, chondroitin sulfuric acid, which is found in cartilage and tendons. Recent work has shown that these two amino sugars have the configurations indicated:

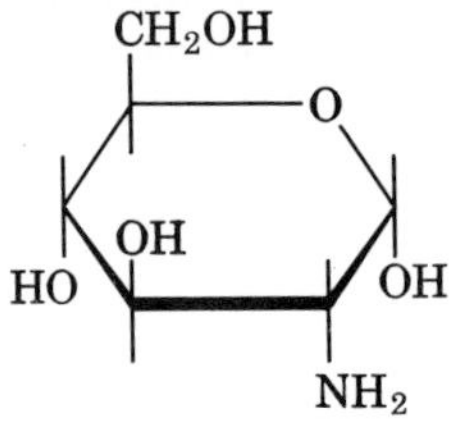

Glucosamine or chitos-
amine
2-Amino-2-deoxyglucose

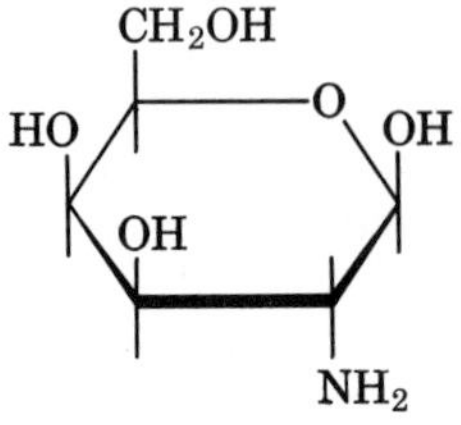

Galactosamine or chon-
drosamine
2-Amino-2-deoxygalactose

With most amino polysaccharides, hydrolysis liberates equimolar amounts of amino sugar and of acetic acid which indicates that in the polymerized form the amino groups are all acetylated.

Special interest attaches to the amino sugars because of their presence both in certain bacterial polysaccharides and in many antibiotics. The significance of the bacterial polysaccharides will be discussed in a later section (p. 181). Streptomycin is also a bacterial product, elaborated by the soil organism, *Streptomyces griseus*. In structure it is a diglycoside in which a methylated

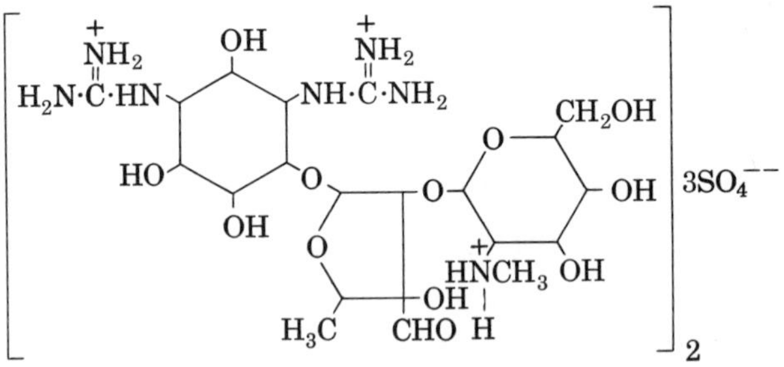

Streptomycin sulfate

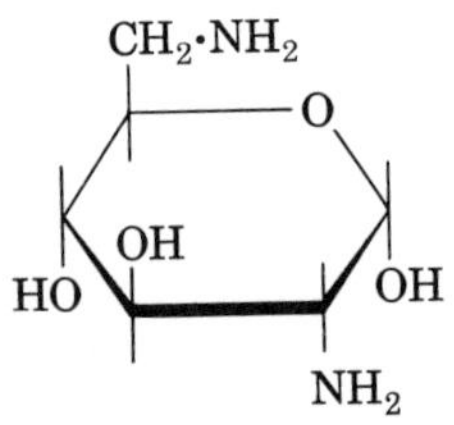

2, 6-Diamino-dideoxy-
D-glucose

L-amino sugar is united through a glycosidic link to a modified, branched chain hexose, which is in turn glycosidically linked to a cyclic alcohol. Other antibiotics have yielded 3-amino-3-deoxy- and 6-amino-6-deoxyglucose, 3-amino-3-deoxy-D-ribose and 2,6-diamino-dideoxy-D-glucose.

An amino sugar derivative which has been found in several different natural products has been variously known as sialic acid, neuraminic acid, gynaminic acid, and lactaminic acid. It is obtained, for example, by hydrolysis of a glycoprotein of the kind known as mucoproteins, in which part at least of the carbohydrate portion is a polysaccharide. It is now suggested that the compound whose formula is given below be called neuraminic acid and that "sialic acids" be the group name for the various derivatives of this compound. The known derivatives include *N*-acetyl neuraminic acid,

$$
\begin{array}{c}
\text{COOH} \\
|\\
\text{C}{=}\text{O} \\
|\\
\text{CH}_2 \\
|\\
\text{CHOH} \\
|\\
\text{H}_2\text{N}{-}\text{CH} \\
|\\
\text{HOCH} \\
|\\
\text{HCOH} \\
|\\
\text{HCOH} \\
|\\
\text{CH}_2\text{OH}
\end{array}
$$

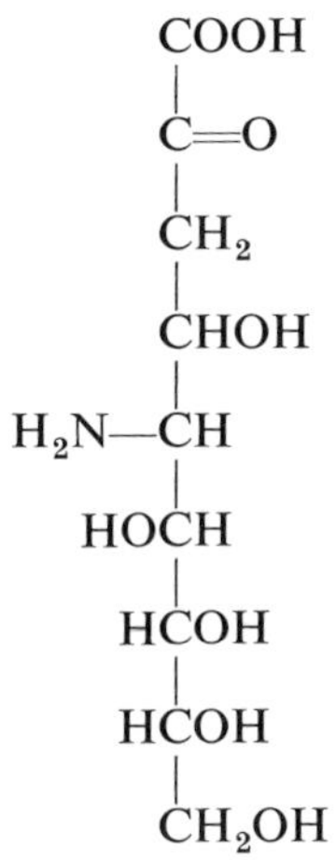

Neuraminic acid

N-glycolyl- and *N,O*-diacetyl neuraminic acids. The structure of the polysaccharides which yield these various compounds is still under investigation.

Ascorbic Acids

Closely related to the sugars are the unsaturated lactones known as ascorbic acids, of which vitamin C is the most important. It is found in many animal tissues and also in plentiful supply in citrus fruits and green vegetables. It was first isolated by Szent-Györgyi[12] in 1928 and because of its acidity and its empirical formula ($C_6H_8O_6$) was named hexuronic acid. It has been shown to have the structure of a lactone of an enediol hexonic acid.

---

[12] One of the most colorful figures in modern biochemistry is that of Albert Szent-Györgyi (1893–). Until 1947 his work was done in Hungary and it was at the University of Szeged that he isolated vitamin C. He is an unconventional thinker whose stimulating ideas are always expressed with wit and charm. In 1937 he was awarded the Nobel Prize in Medicine for his contributions to theories of biological oxidation. He is at present working at the Institute for Muscle Research at Woods Hole, Massachusetts.

Although it behaves like a typical acid, titrating with bases and decomposing carbonates, the acidity of ascorbic acid resides in the hydroxyl groups

$$
\begin{array}{l}
\text{C}=\text{O} \\
|\\
\text{COH} \\
\|\quad\quad \text{O}\\
\text{COH} \\
|\\
\text{HC} \\
|\\
\text{HOCH} \\
|\\
\text{CH}_2\text{OH}
\end{array}
$$

L-Ascorbic acid

attached to the doubly linked carbons. This is shown by the fact that after oxidation, which is readily brought about by iodine, the compound is no longer acidic.

$$
\begin{array}{l}
\text{C}=\text{O} \\
|\\
\text{COH} \\
\|\quad\quad \text{O}\\
\text{COH} \\
|\\
\text{HC} \\
|\\
\text{HOCH} \\
|\\
\text{CH}_2\text{OH}
\end{array}
\xrightarrow{-2\text{H}}
\begin{array}{l}
\text{C}=\text{O} \\
|\\
\text{C}=\text{O} \\
|\quad\quad \text{O}\\
\text{C}=\text{O} \\
|\\
\text{HC} \\
|\\
\text{HOCH} \\
|\\
\text{CH}_2\text{OH}
\end{array}
$$

L-Ascorbic acid   **Dehydroascorbic acid**

Compounds similar in structure to L-ascorbic acid show varying degrees of antiscorbutic activity, but this proves to be true only of those forms in which the lactone ring is on the right. This is one of many examples of the fact that living cells distinguish between stereoisomers and show a specific preference for one of two forms.

Cyclohexanols

Although several straight chain polyhydroxy alcohols occur naturally, none is of biological interest except the one related to ribose. This is the compound ribitol which is part of the molecule of riboflavin or vitamin B_2.

CH₂OH
|
HCOH
|
HCOH
|
HCOH
|
CH₂OH

Ribitol

The cyclic hexahydric alcohols or *inositols*, on the other hand, appear in many compounds of biological importance. In the phytin which is found in many plant seeds and grains, one of the inositols occurs as the calcium magnesium salt of the hexaphosphate ester known as phytic acid. It should be remembered that the P in the formula stands for —PO₃H₂ so that each phosphate group has two ionizable hydrogens. Other phosphoinositol derivatives are found among the phospholipids of many different plant and animal tissues.

O·P

P·O   O·P
     O·P
      P·O

O·P

Phytic acid

If the inositols are represented graphically by planar formulas similar to those which Haworth suggested for the sugars, nine arrangements are possible, as shown in Fig. 4.5. Of these, only the ones designated D and L forms are optically active, any possible activity in the others consisting of rotations which neutralize each other. The commonly occurring inositol is the one numbered V, and called *myo*-inositol because it was originally found in muscle. When "inositol" is used without any identification, it is this form which is intended. *Myo*-inositol is believed to exist largely in the chair form shown below, which gives equatorial attachment to five of the six hydroxyl

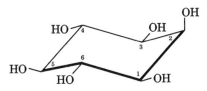

Myo-inositol
cis-1, 2, 3, 5-*trans*-4, 6-Cyclohexanehexol

groups. One of the two yeast growth factors, bios I, is *myo*-inositol; a nitrogenous derivative is one of the components in streptomycin; the alcohol makes up about 7 per cent of a complex phospholipid found in brain tissue and is present in other similar compounds which are widely distributed in cells.

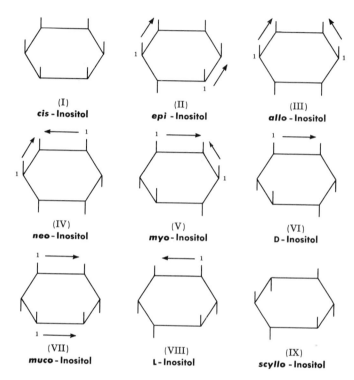

Fig. 4.5. Possible structures for inositol. [From W. W. Pigman (ed.), *The Carbohydrates*, 2nd ed., Academic, New York, 1957.]

THE OLIGOSACCHARIDES

In plant and animal tissues there have been found a number of compounds of lower molecular weights than the polysaccharides, which yield on complete acid hydrolysis either simple sugars or closely related compounds. The empirical formulas of these substances indicate that the monoses are linked by elimination of water between two simple carbohydrate molecules, so that a general formula might be $x(C_nH_{2n}O_n) - (x - 1)H_2O$. These small condensation products are known as oligosaccharides (Gr. *oligos*, a few), though the group is not rigidly defined. At one time it included compounds made up of two to six sugar residues. More recently it has been extended to take in compounds containing as many as nine monose units. Between these and the true polysaccharides there is an enormous gap since the latter are made up of at least several hundred monose residues and may include several thousand.

It is difficult to avoid confusion between the names of the monosaccharides and the oligosaccharides. By convention a diose is a monosaccharide having two carbons, while a disaccharide is an oligosaccharide made up of two monose residues. Yet in naming specific disaccharides the suffix "biose" is used, as for example in the name "melibiose," which is a disaccharide found in plant exudates. Whereas glyceraldehyde is classified as a triose, the same combining form used in the name of a specific sugar indicates that it is a trisaccharide. For example, the melitriose molecule contains a glucose residue linked to one of galactose and one of fructose. The tetroses, such as erythrose, are distinguished from the tetrasaccharides by calling the latter *tetraoses*, and in naming the larger oligosaccharides the "a" is similarly retained. Thus the pentaoses and the hexaoses indicate by their rather awkward names that they are oligosaccharides containing five or six monose residues.

The oligosaccharides include a wide variety of natural products. Some of the compounds are nonreducing, showing that all the potential reducing groups are involved in linkages. Others have one such group free. Some of the compounds yield on hydrolysis only one type of monosaccharide whereas others contain two or more different sugar residues. All are hydrolyzed by one or another of the enzymes which attack glycosidic linkages, and they are therefore essentially glycosides in which the "aglycone" is also a sugar or a sugar derivative.

The chief reactions of the oligosaccharides are those of their constituent monosaccharides. Those compounds which contain a free potential reducing group react as glucose does with carbonyl reagents, forming corresponding oxidation and reduction products, oximes, osazones, etc. The hydroxyl groups react to form similar derivatives, and the glycosidic bonds are broken by the same procedures which bring about cleavage of the simple glycosides. The only matter which need be specially considered in connection with the oligosaccharides is the type of linkage which holds the sugar residues together.

Nonreducing Oligosaccharides

Sucrose ($C_{12}H_{22}O_{11}$) is a disaccharide and the most important non-reducing sugar. Having no free potential reducing group, it neither mutarotates in solution nor reacts with carbonyl reagents. It is hydrolyzed by acids or enzymes to a mixture of equimolecular amounts of glucose and fructose. This transformation is known as *inversion* of sucrose since the optical rotation changes from dextro to levo in the process. The specific rotation of the invert sugar is an average of that of the two components, allowing for the fact that a solution which contained 1 g of sucrose per ml would change to one containing approximately 0.5 g each of the hexoses.

$$C_{12}H_{22}O_{11} + H_2O \rightarrow C_6H_{12}O_6 + C_6H_{12}O_6$$

Sucrose	**Glucose**	**Fructose**
$[\alpha]_D$ +66.5°	$[\alpha]_D$ +52.5°	$[\alpha]_D$ −92.4°

Invert Sugar
$[\alpha]_D$ approx. −20°

Since sucrose is nonreducing, the two monose residues must be linked from carbon 1 of glucose to carbon 2 of fructose. The only question then concerns the positions of the two rings in the disaccharide. The products isolated after inversion are D-glucopyranose and D-fructopyranose, but methylation studies show that this does not necessarily indicate that both rings were six membered in the original sugar.

Purdie and Irvine were the first to methylate sucrose completely. They obtained an octamethyl derivative in which every free hydroxyl was blocked, and the rings therefore prevented from shifting. Hydrolysis of this product yielded the familiar 2,3,4,6-tetra-O-methyl-D-glucose and a tetramethyl derivative of fructose. The first of these indicated that the glucose was present in sucrose in the usual pyranose form. The fructose derivative proved to be 1,3,4,6-tetra-O-methylfructose. This established the fact that in sucrose fructose has a furanose ring. Presumably hydrolysis of sucrose sets free this form of fructose, which immediately rearranges to give the more stable pyranose form.

Before the formula for sucrose can be written, the configurations about the anomeric carbons must be known. When sucrose hydrolyzes under the influence of the enzyme maltase, the glucose which is liberated mutarotates in a downward direction. This indicates that the glucose has the α arrangement at carbon 1. The fact that sucrose is also hydrolyzed by yeast invertase

Sucrose

which is specific for β-fructofuranosides indicates that the fructose moiety has the β configuration. Thus sucrose is (α-D-glucosido)-β-D-fructofuranoside, and the linkage is from carbon 1 of glucose to carbon 2' of fructose. This structure has recently been confirmed by oxidation with periodate. The glucose residue has three adjacent free hydroxyl groups on carbons 2, 3, and 4, and the fructose has one pair on carbons 3' and 4'. Oxidation of this compound should then consume 3 moles of periodate and yield 1 mole of formic acid per mole of disaccharide, and this proved to be true. This kind of method cannot be used with reducing sugars because they tend to be degraded completely by periodate.

Other nonreducing oligosaccharides have been isolated from various plant sources. The trisaccharide melezitose, found in the sweet exudate of some trees, is made up of two glucose residues linked through a fructose as follows:

$$\text{Glucosyl} \xrightarrow{1\rightarrow3} \text{fructosyl} \xrightarrow{2\rightarrow1} \text{glucose}$$

Sugar beets contain a small concentration of another trisaccharide, raffinose. In this compound galactose is condensed with a sucrose residue.

$$\text{Galactosyl} \xrightarrow{1\rightarrow6} \text{glucosyl} \xrightarrow{1\rightarrow2} \text{fructose}$$

Stachyose is a tetrasaccharide which is widely distributed in plants and often occurs associated with raffinose. It appears to be formed by addition of a second galactosyl unit to raffinose.

$$\text{Galactosyl} \xrightarrow{1\rightarrow6} \text{galactosyl} \xrightarrow{1\rightarrow6} \text{glucosyl} \xrightarrow{1\rightarrow2} \text{fructose}$$

Verbascose is a pentasaccharide which occurs in some species of mullein and probably has the structure

$$\text{Galactosyl} \xrightarrow{1\rightarrow6} \text{galactosyl} \xrightarrow{1\rightarrow6} \text{galactosyl} \xrightarrow{1\rightarrow6} \text{glucosyl} \xrightarrow{1\rightarrow2} \text{fructose}$$

Reducing Oligosaccharides

Most of the common oligosaccharides reduce Fehling's solution, show mutarotation in solution, and react with carbonyl reagents to form such derivatives as oximes and osazones. In these compounds the sugar residues are united in such a way that one potential carbonyl group is free.

Lactose ($C_{12}H_{22}O_{11}$)

Lactose or milk sugar is found in mammalian milk in a concentration of approximately 5 per cent. This is one of the few carbohydrates associated entirely with the animal kingdom, most carbohydrates being plant products. The formulation of its structure rests upon the following facts:

1. It is a reducing sugar and after hydrolysis of a given weight of lactose the reducing power of the solution is doubled. This indicates that a second carbonyl group has been set free and that the compound is therefore a glycoside.

2. Acid hydrolysis of lactose sets free equimolecular amounts of glucose and galactose.

3. Oxidation of lactose with bromine water yields lactobionic acid, which can be hydrolyzed to form gluconic acid and galactose. This indicates that in lactose it is the aldehyde group of glucose which is free to be oxidized, and the sugar is therefore a galactoside.

4. Complete methylation yields an octamethyl derivative which on hydrolysis liberates 2,3,6-tri-*O*-methylglucose and 2,3,4,6-tetra-*O*-methylgalactose. The eighth methyl group which was originally introduced into the sugar had been attached at carbon 1 of the glucose, and since it was thus held in a glucosidic link it had been set free when the compound was hydrolyzed. The positions of the methyl groups indicate that the galactose is present in pyranose form, and that lactose must have either one of the two following structures:

(a)   Galactopyranose—$\overset{1\to4}{}$—glucopyranose

(b)   Galactopyranose—$\overset{1\to5}{}$—glucofuranose

5. If lactobionic acid is methylated before it is hydrolyzed, one of the hydrolytic products is the lactone of 2,3,5,6-tetra-*O*-methylgluconic acid. This means that in the lactobionic acid, in which there is no glucose ring, the only hydroxyl which was not free to be methylated was the one at position 4. This must therefore be the point of attachment of galactose to glucose and the disaccharide must have the structure (a) above.

6. The fact that lactose is hydrolyzed by an enzyme which attacks β-galactosidic linkages indicates that the galactose has the β configuration at the anomeric carbon. This is further confirmed by the low specific rotation of the sugar, ($[\alpha]_D +35° \to 55°$). Lactose is then 4-(β-D-galactopyranosyl)-D-glucose.

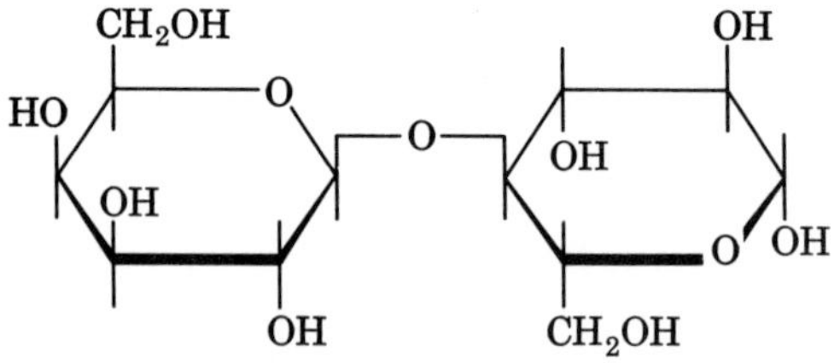

Lactose (β form)

Maltose

The reducing disaccharide which forms in the course of hydrolysis of starch is maltose, which yields on further hydrolysis two molecules of glucose. Proof of its structure parallels that given above for lactose. Its reducing power is doubled on hydrolysis. Methylation studies show that in the two monose units carbon 1 of one glucose is linked to carbon 4 of the other, and that both hexose units have the pyranose ring. Its high specific rotation

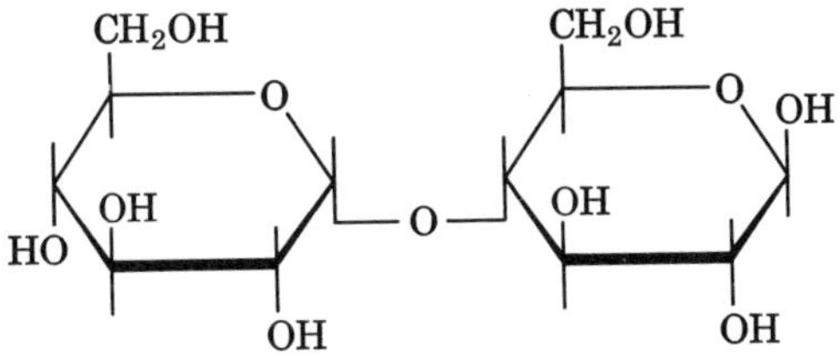

Maltose (β form)

($[\alpha]_D +112° \rightarrow +130°$) and its hydrolysis by maltase indicate the presence of an α-glucosidic link. It is then 4-(α-D-glucopyranosyl)-D-glucose as shown in the formula.

Cellobiose

Of great importance in the elucidation of the structure of cellulose is the disaccharide cellobiose which can be isolated as an octaacetate if cellulose is simultaneously acetylated and hydrolyzed. The disaccharide itself can be obtained by deacetylation of this compound and proves to consist as does maltose of two glucose residues. It has, however, the low specific rotation

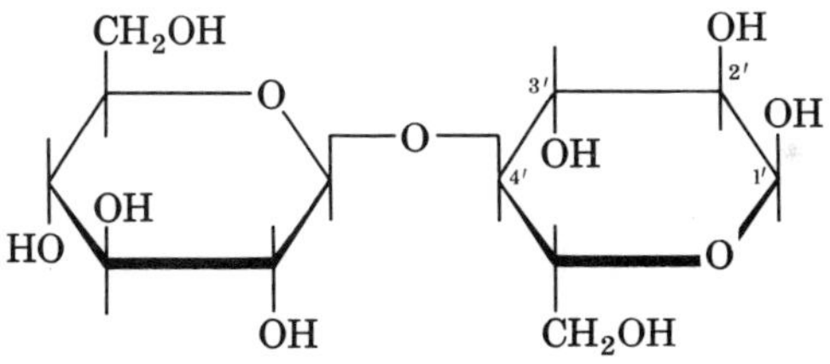

Cellobiose (α-form)

($[\alpha]_D +14° \rightarrow +35°$) characteristic of β-glucosides and is hydrolyzed by emulsin and not by maltase. In other respects it reacts exactly as maltose does, yielding the same products on methylation and hydrolysis. Its formulation as a β-glucoside has been fully confirmed by synthesis.

Although these three important disaccharides are all constituted with a $1 \rightarrow 4$ linkage, it must not be assumed that this is the only type of bond by which monose residues are linked. In various natural glycosides there occurs another disaccharide, gentiobiose, in which carbon 1 of one glucose is linked to carbon 6 of another. Melibiose, which results from partial hydrolysis of the trisaccharide raffinose, is made up of glucose united in a $6 \rightarrow 1$ linkage to galactose. Other oligosaccharides obtained by partial hydrolysis

Gentiobiose (α form)

of more complex substances exhibit $1 \to 2$ and $1 \to 3$ links. In every compound so far studied, the hexose rings are pyranose except in fructose residues. This sugar assumes the furanose form not only in sucrose but also in several trisaccharides.

THE POLYSACCHARIDES

The polysaccharides serve both as reserve food substances and as structural material. They are defined as polymerized products of high molecular weights in which monoses or their derivatives are united, usually through glycosidic bonds. The most important polysaccharides are cellulose and starch among plant products, and glycogen which is the reserve carbohydrate of animals.

Complete hydrolysis of the polysaccharides yields either monoses or closely related compounds. The most common constituent is D-glucose, but several different pentoses and uronic acids as well as amino sugars and other hexoses occur in polysaccharide molecules. Some of these compounds yield on hydrolysis only one type of monosaccharide. They may then be classified by replacing the terminal -ose by -an. Thus starch, cellulose, and glycogen, all of which are made up of glucose residues, are glucans or dextrans; polysaccharides which yield mannose on hydrolysis are mannans, while those made up of fructose residues are levans (from levulose).

More complex than these compounds, and not as yet completely formulated, are a number of polysaccharides made up of more than one type of monose or monose derivative. Such, for example, are the gums and mucilages, certain polysaccharides of bacterial origin, and the polymers known as mucopolysaccharides. All of these contain uronic acids in addition to one or more simple monoses.

Procedures for the Determination of Polysaccharide Structure

A number of monosaccharide units may be linked together to form a long chain, no single residue being attached to more than two others, or the large molecule may be branched, some of the inner residues being attached to three others at what is known as a branching point. In the first type of polysaccharide the two terminal residues differ from all the central ones in having at one end of the chain an extra free hydroxyl group and at the other a free reducing group. But if a polysaccharide has a branched structure, the number of end residues is correspondingly increased and the number of free hydroxyl groups on internal residues reduced.

Because of their commercial importance starch and cellulose have been exhaustively investigated and their structures established. This has been achieved partly by the use of procedures which are applicable to smaller molecules, and partly by the use of special techniques. The presence or absence of free reducing groups is determined by familiar procedures such as titration with iodine in sodium hydroxide or preparation of phenylhydrazine derivatives or estimation of free carboxyl groups following gentle oxidation. Methylation establishes the number of unsubstituted hydroxyl groups while periodic acid oxidation will show whether or not these groups are adjacent to each other. For example, in a glucose polymer $1 \rightarrow 6$ links can be differentiated from $1 \rightarrow 4$ links since in compounds of the first type there are three adjacent unsubstituted hydroxyl groups on each inner residue, whereas in the other type of polymer there are only two. In Fig. 4.6(*a*) a hypothetical chain molecule of glucose residues in $1 \rightarrow 6$ linkages is shown, while the compound represented in (*b*) is a $1 \rightarrow 4$ glucan. The oxidation of the compound in (*a*) would use 2 moles of periodate and yield 1 mole of formic acid for each internal residue, and for molecules the size of the natural polysaccharides these make up the bulk of the molecule. In computing the results the terminal residues must of course be allowed for. Fig. 4.6(*b*) shows how the oxidation of a straight chain $1 \rightarrow 4$ glucan would lead to a complex aldehyde and 3 moles of formic acid and 1 of formaldehyde per *chain*. If a molecule were branched, with $1 \rightarrow 4$ chains attached through their terminal reducing groups to various branching points on carbon 6, the molecule would still contain only one reducing group, but the number of nonreducing end groups would be correspondingly increased. This would be indicated by an increased amount of formic acid after the oxidation. These results can be checked by independent determination of the number of free primary alcohol groups in a polymer, using either the tosyl derivative or the trityl derivative.

Complete acid hydrolysis of a polysaccharide determines the type or types of monoses of which it is built. Further light on the structure is often obtained by partial hydrolysis, usually catalyzed by enzymes. Isolation of a disaccharide from such a reaction mixture makes it possible to determine the nature of some of the glycosidic links on these smaller units. For example, maltose is formed when starch hydrolyzes in the presence of malt diastase. The presence of the α-$1 \rightarrow 4$ link in this sugar points to the presence of such links in starch. Furthermore, in certain compounds some of the linkages

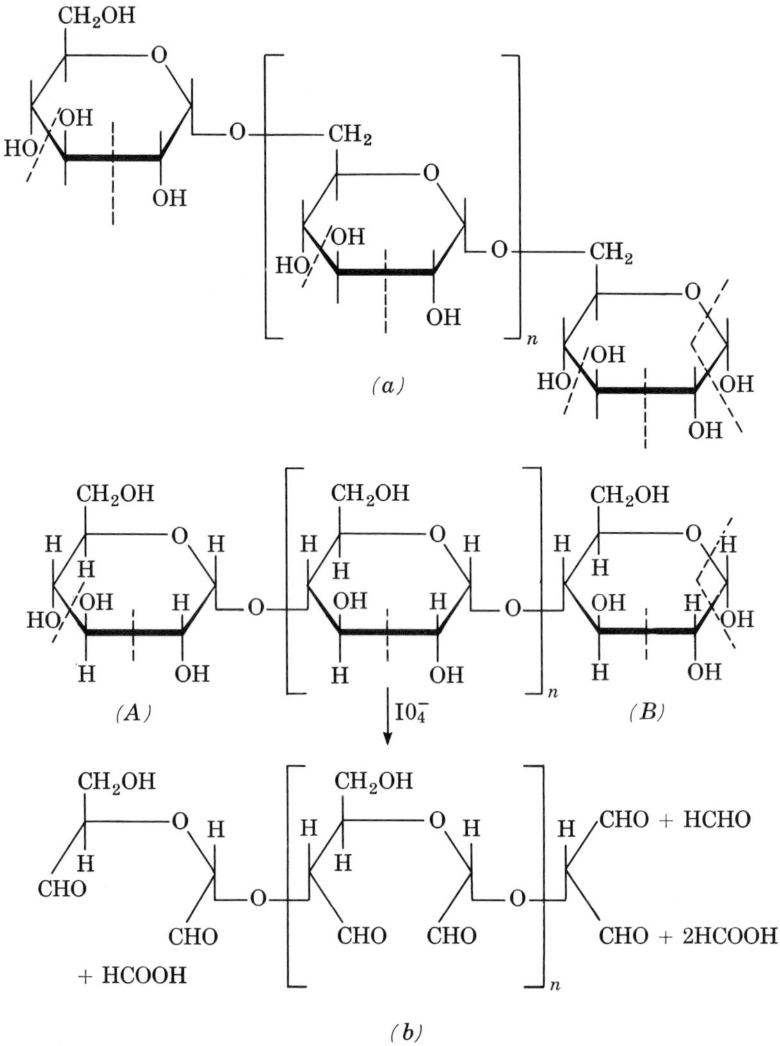

Fig. 4.6. Indication of the points of attack of periodic acid on a $1 \rightarrow 6$ and a $1 \rightarrow 4$ polysaccharide. [Diagram (b) from W. W. Pigman (ed.), *The Carbohydrates*, Academic, New York, 1957.]

prove more resistant than others to hydrolysis. In such cases determination of the type of sugar freed in the early stages of hydrolysis may indicate which are in terminal positions and therefore exposed to early attack by enzymes.

The method of "end group" analysis is a chemical procedure which has contributed greatly to the elucidation of polysaccharide structure. When a polysaccharide is first methylated and then hydrolyzed, it yields trimethyl derivatives from those internal residues which are linked to only two others. Any internal residue which contains a branching point and hence is linked to three others will form a dimethyl substitution product, while terminal non-reducing units will give rise to tetramethyl derivatives. The reducing terminal residues cannot be differentiated from internal ones with two links, since their fourth methyl group is held in glycosidic linkage and is lost during hydrolysis of the polysaccharide. Determination of the percentage of tetramethyl compound in the hydrolytic mixture indicates the number of non-reducing terminal units, while the amount of dimethyl derivative is a measure of the number of branching points. By comparison with known methylated derivatives of the monose, the positions of the methyl groups can be determined, and these serve to define the positions at which there were linkages in the original polysaccharide.

X-ray analysis is a physical method which has been widely used in structural studies, especially with cellulose. A fine beam of x-rays emerging from a slit in a lead screen passes through the material under examination. In the course of that passage it is scattered by the electrons which it encounters, and the rays which emerge are then allowed to fall upon a sensitive plate. If the particles within the molecule are arranged regularly enough for one diffracted beam to reinforce another, the plate will show a diagram made up either of concentric circles or of symmetrical arcs or dots. Even though the polysaccharides do not have the regularity of crystals, they do yield x-ray diffraction diagrams from which it has been possible to calculate certain intramolecular distances, and also the dimensions of any units which are repeated regularly within the molecule. For example, from x-ray evidence it appears that the "unit cell" or repeating unit in the cellulose molecule contains four glucose residues and has the dimensions indicated in Fig. 4.7 on page 173.

Molecular Weight Determinations

Determination of the molecular weights of the polysaccharides has proved to be extremely difficult, and there are still many unanswered questions. These substances as obtained from natural sources are far from homogeneous and the preliminary purification has undoubtedly been inadequate in many experiments. There is no clear criterion of purity such as the melting point of a crystalline compound, and it has been necessary to decide on some indirect basis whether or not a given sample is homogeneous. In one study, for example, when it was found that corresponding molecular weights were given by purified cellulose, by several of its acetylated derivatives and by the polysaccharides regenerated from these derivatives, it was felt that the original sample had been uniform in composition.

The ultracentrifuge (see p. 82) is used both to estimate the purity of a sample and to determine its molecular weight. If only a single boundary forms, this indicates that the material is probably homogeneous, and from the rate at which the boundary moves the weight of the particles may be calculated.

In spite of the fact that classical osmotic pressure determinations are difficult to apply to substances of high molecular weight, many polysaccharide molecular weights are being determined in this way.

The estimation of molecular weights by viscosity measurement depends upon the fact that the viscosity of substances of colloidal dimensions increases with the molecular weight. As originally elaborated this method depended upon empirical equations to calculate the molecular weight from an observed viscosity, but the method has since been put upon a firmer theoretical basis.

The actual molecular weights of the polysaccharides are still being actively investigated. It is probable that most polysaccharide samples include a range of particle sizes. It is furthermore being found that some of the early extraction methods caused more degradation of the polymers than had been supposed. For example, glycogen was for many years extracted from tissue with hot 30 per cent KOH. Samples obtained in this way gave molecular weights of 2 to 6×10^6, but extraction with cold water or with trichloroacetic acid has yielded samples with molecular weights as high as 200×10^6. Cellulose molecules seem to be smaller than this, but molecular weights have been reported which vary between 150,000 and 1,000,000. To what extent the higher figure represents association of smaller "molecules" is not known. Indeed one definition of the polysaccharides describes them as "collections of polymeric homologues, each based on the same chemical ground plan, but displaying a range of molecular weights."

Phytopolysaccharides

Cellulose

The heavy cell walls of plants are composed largely of cellulose which constitutes more than 50 per cent of woody tissue and more than 90 per cent of cotton. It is extracted by cuprammonium solution [$Cu(OH)_2$ in NH_4OH] or by very strong acids, but is otherwise insoluble. It is a glucose polymer for which the vertebrates have no digestive enzymes, though some invertebrates are able to digest it. It is however a valuable foodstuff for herbivorous animals, thanks to the cellulose-splitting enzymes elaborated by the microorganisms of their digestive tracts.

Most of the structural studies of cellulose have been made on material derived from cotton, since it occurs there in a relatively pure form, and the further purification requires only gentle manipulation. The evidence points to a structure in which more than 2000 β-glucose residues are linked to form a long chain molecule. This formulation is based upon the following evidence.

1. The empirical formula is $(C_6H_{10}O_5)_x$.
2. Complete hydrolysis yields only D-glucose.

3. Formation of triacetates and trimethyl ethers indicates that each glucose residue has three unsubstituted hydroxyl groups. The fact that the yield of these compounds is practically quantitative means that the molecule has almost no end groups and is therefore a long straight chain of glucose residues.
4. Formation of a monotosyl derivative, which reacts with sodium iodide to replace the tosyloxy group with iodine, shows that each residue has one unsubstituted primary alcohol group.
5. When cellulose is acetylated and hydrolyzed, the only product other than acetylated glucose is the octaacetate of the disaccharide cellobiose. This compound has been shown to be a β-1 → 4-glucoside, hence it is concluded that the cellulose chain is linked in this same way.
6. As previously noted, the molecular weights obtained with cellulose vary widely, but it is clear that the chain must consist of 1000 to 3000 glucose units.

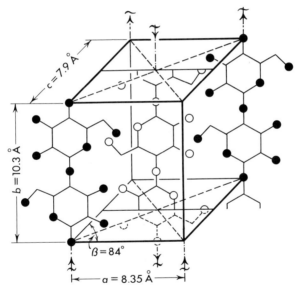

Fig. 4.7. Diagrammatic representation of the unit cell of cellulose. Note that each unit cell contains four glucose residues. These include the two in the center of the figure and one-fourth of each of the eight which are placed at the corners of the cell. The corner residues are shared by each of the four unit cells which meet at these corners. Of the eight residues which make up the corners of the cell in the diagram only four are represented. Similar pairs at the other two corners complete the cell. [From K. H. Meyer and L. Misch, *Helv. Chim. Acta*, **20**, 232 (1937).]

Figure 4.7 gives a spatial diagram of the repeating unit in cellulose. This is believed to represent part of a crystalline area in a cellulose fiber, such areas being intermingled with amorphous regions in which the chains are less symmetrically disposed. The exact orientation was determined by comparing actual x-ray diagrams formed by purified cellulose with those to be expected from various spatial models. It should be noted that adjacent chains extend in opposite directions in this formulation, with the oxygen of the ring at the "upper" part of the hexagon in one chain and at the "lower" end in the neighboring chain. With chains thus disposed in close proximity it is assumed that cross linkages occur in the form of hydrogen bridges, thus giving to cellulose its great stability.

Starch

A more complex polysaccharide than cellulose is another dextran, starch, which occurs in the form of characteristic granules in seeds, roots, and fruits. It serves as a reserve food either for the plant itself, which stores in this form any excess carbohydrate formed in photosynthesis, or for the new plants which will form when the starch-packed seeds germinate. Indirectly of course it also constitutes a generally useful food supply for animals, since it differs from cellulose in being easily split by digestive enzymes.

Starch as extracted from different plants is not a single individual, but differs slightly from plant to plant, being in all cases a complex mixture of related substances. On the basis of end group assay and of methylation studies it was originally formulated by Haworth as a short chain molecule containing 25 glucose residues held in 1 → 4-glucosidic bonds. This structure was based on the formation from starch of methylated glucose derivatives of which approximately 90 per cent were 2,3,6-tri-*O*-methylglucose and 4.5 per cent were 2,3,4,6-tetra-*O*-methylglucose. Since partial enzymic hydrolysis of starch yields largely maltose, the glucose residues are believed to be linked as in maltose by α-glucosidic bonds. This view is supported by the high optical rotation of starch derivatives.

From the first there were objections to this simple formulation. In the first place, the molecular weight of starch was known to be far larger than the 4000 which would represent about 25 glucose residues. Moreover, in hydrolysis of the polysaccharide by the starch splitting enzyme, β-amylase, only about 70–80 per cent of the starch was transformed to maltose. The unexplained residue, known as "limit dextrins," was of much lower molecular weight than the original starch.

Meantime it began to appear that "starch" is in fact a mixture of two components now known as amylose and amylopectin. Many methods of separating these substances have been devised, but one of the simplest depends upon precipitation of the amylose fraction. The starch is first dispersed in water by autoclaving or by other less drastic methods such as refluxing in strong lithium bromide solution. Saturation of the resulting solution with butanol or amyl alcohol causes a very nearly quantitative separation of the amylose as a precipitate. In Table 4.3 are brought together the properties of the two substances, on which depends their identification as separate entities.

For amylose, which in most starches makes up about 20 per cent of the total, end group assay indicates that only one glucose unit in every 300 is capable of forming tetramethylglucose. Since molecular weight estimations

Table 4.3. Properties of the Two Main Constituents of Starch

Property	Amylose	Amylopectin
Color with iodine	Deep blue	Red to purple
Stability of solutions	Yields gels which "retrograde"	Solutions stable
Molecular weights	Usually not greater than 50,000	As high as 500,000
Approximate number of glucose units per molecule	300	1300–3000
Proportion of end groups	1 : 300	1 : 27
Effect of β-amylase	Complete hydrolysis to maltose	Hydrolysis to extent of about 50 per cent, leaving a nonreducing limit dextrin of mol. wt. about 80,000

show that approximately 300 glucose units make up the amylose molecule, it is evident that it must consist of a single straight chain of glucose units. The hydrolysis of amylose by β-amylase, which acts on α-1 $\rightarrow$ 4 linkages, results in its complete transformation to maltose, hence the linkages are believed to be α-glucosidic. This picture of amylose as a long slender chain explains many known properties of the substance. On cooling a hot solution of amylose it sets to a gel very rapidly. This may well result from formation of a network of interlacing, randomly distributed linear molecules. But when such a solution is allowed to stand, the solute slowly deposits as a fine crystalline mass. This process is known as *retrogradation* of the starch and might be expected if similar slender molecules gradually line up in such a way that they can form loose aggregations which are too large to remain in solution.

It has been suggested that the glucose chains in amylose differ from those in cellulose in having the ability to coil in the form of a helix (Fig. 4.8) in which there are six glucopyranose units in each turn. X-ray studies support this structure, and it is of interest to note that while the α-glucosidic form of amylose lends itself to such a coiling, a straight chain of glucose units is enforced upon cellulose by the β configuration at the anomeric carbons in that compound.

The helical formulation of amylose has been especially useful in explaining the intense blue color given by amylose with iodine. The inner dimensions

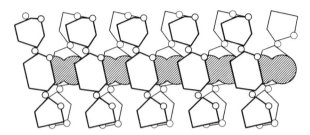

Fig. 4.8. Diagram of a helical starch chain with iodine molecules in the center of the helix. [From R. E. Rundle and R. R. Baldwin, *J. Am. Chem. Soc.*, **65**, 555 (1943).]

of the spiral which has been postulated are such that an iodine molecule can just be fitted inside. It is therefore suggested that the starch-iodine complex may consist of iodine molecules lining the center of the helix, with one iodine molecule associated with each turn.

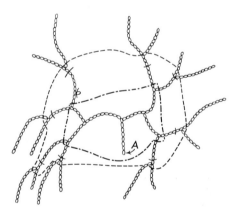

Fig. 4.9. Diagrammatic representation of amylopectin. Each small circle stands for a glucose residue. The outermost dotted line represents the point to which β-amylase degrades such a molecule. The short lines mark the extent of the hydrolysis by α-glucosidase which has split the 1-6′ bonds. A second treatment with β-amylase degrades the chains until new branching points are reached as indicated by the inner dotted line. *A* is the reducing end of the molecule. [From K. H. Meyer and P. Bernfeld, *Helv. Chim. Acta*, **23**, 880 (1940).]

Molecular weight estimations and end group assay of amylopectin point to a molecule made up of over 1000 glucose units, so arranged that there is a nonreducing end group for every twenty to twenty-six residues. Various types of branched or laminated molecules have been postulated, but a multiply branched form suggested by the late Kurt Meyer of the University of Geneva is now widely accepted (Fig. 4.9). Support for this structure is found in the behavior of amylopectin with β-amylase, which hydrolyzes only about half of the molecule to maltose. The residue consists of limit dextrins, polysaccharides having molecular weights of approximately 80,000 and very highly branched chains, i.e., one end group for every eleven or twelve glucose residues. It is believed that β-amylase attacks the free ends of the glucose chains, splitting off maltose units until it meets a variation in the pattern such as would be offered by a 1 → 6 link at a branching point of the chain. The dextrins would then consist of the truncated, highly ramified molecules left when the enzyme has come as close as it can to each branching point. As indicated in the figure, Meyer suggests that a second enzyme, α-glucosidase, is able to act upon the dextrin because it is able to break the link at the branching point, thus freeing the chains of the remaining dextrin so that they can be attacked again by β-amylase. If this branched structure for amylopectin is assumed, its stability in solution depends on such molecules offering no opportunity for close aggregations. In solutions of whole starch the amylopectin probably acts as a protective colloid for the less stable amylose.

Although amylose and amylopectin constitute probably 99 per cent of the starch complex, the remaining 1 per cent varies from starch to starch and may be important in determining the structure of the starch grains. For example, the water which is present in the granules seems to play a part in their crystalline structure, for when it is removed the crystalline pattern disappears. Most starches are also associated with small amounts of fatty acid, but whether they are really combined chemically or merely adsorbed is not clear. The same question arises in relation to the phosphate which occurs in native starch grains. From some starches it can be washed away in the form of soluble phosphate compounds by repeated extraction with warm water. In others, of which potato starch is an example, the phosphate seems actually to be combined with the starch itself. In general, the root starches include phosphate esterified with the starch itself, while the phosphate of cereal or seed starches is in combination with smaller, soluble molecules. The function of these traces of noncarbohydrate substances in starch grains is unknown.

Hemicelluloses

Polysaccharides which are extractable with 17.5 per cent NaOH are called hemicelluloses. They vary in amount and kind from plant to plant and from tissue to tissue. The most abundant members of the group are xylans, sometimes occurring as homopolysaccharides and sometimes as copolymers of xylose with arabinose or D-glucuronic acid. Mannans and galactans and the so-called pectic substances also belong in the group of hemicelluloses.

The pectic substances consist of a mixture of three polysaccharides: a galactan, a polymerized methyl ester of galacturonic acid and an araban. This latter has an unusual type of branched chain. It consists of α-L-arabofuranose in a 1 → 5 chain, with a single arabinose attached to every other member of the chain as a one-residue side chain held in a 3 → 1 linkage.

To what extent the three types of polysaccharide are bound to each other is not known.

Gums

Plant gums are exudates which appear as a covering material on wounds or abrasions. They have highly branched structures and include several different monose units. Uronic acids are nearly always present and may form copolymers with one or several different pentoses or hexoses.

Animal Polysaccharides

Glycogen

Animal carbohydrate reserves are stored largely in the liver and muscles in the form of the polysaccharide glycogen. Although hydrolysis and end group assay indicate a molecule containing twelve to eighteen glucopyranose units in a chain, the molecular weight of glycogen is certainly more than 10^6. As with amylopectin, this discrepancy is explained if glycogen is formulated

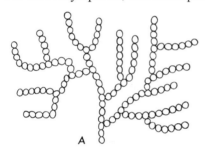

Fig. 4.10. Diagram of the structure of glycogen. The one reducing group represented is at *A*. Each circle indicates a glucose residue. [From K. H. Meyer and M. Fuld, *Helv. Chim. Acta*, **24**, 376 (1941).]

A

as a multiply branched molecule in which about 9 per cent of the residues branch by means of $1 \rightarrow 6$ links (Fig. 4.10). Hydrolysis with β-amylase transforms about 50 per cent of the polysaccharide to maltose, leaving a product of high molecular weight in which the average chain length has dropped to 5.5 glucose units. Meyer and Fuld interpret this to mean that each branch in glycogen consists of six to seven glucose units joined by $1 \rightarrow 4$ glucosidic links, and that β-amylase shortens each such chain to one or two units by removing successive maltose molecules from the free ends. At this point the enzyme is halted by the new configuration at the branching point, and there is left a truncated polysaccharide residue. Thus the glycogen macromolecule is like that of amylopectin except that it is somewhat more highly branched.

Chitin

Reference has already been made (page 158) to chitin, the polysaccharide which is the organic skeletal substance of insects, crustacea, and fungi.

Chemically and structurally chitin resembles cellulose. It is a polymer of *N*-acetylglucosamine linked in $1 \rightarrow 4$-β-glycosidic linkages. It therefore differs from cellulose only in having on carbon 2 an acetylated amino group instead of an hydroxyl group.

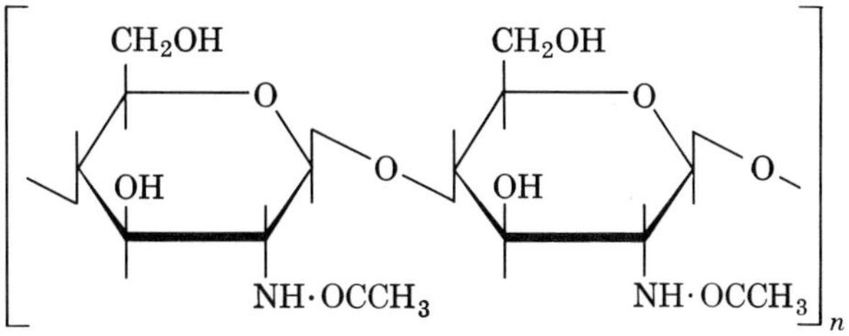

CH₂OH ... O ... CH₂OH ... O
OH ... O ... OH ... O
NH·OCCH₃ ... NH·OCCH₃

Portion of a chitin chain

The mucopolysaccharides

The polysaccharides so far considered have been made up of uncharged units. In the group of polysaccharides which are known as "mucopolysaccharides" are three important types of compounds in which the units are sugar derivatives which carry charges. These are hyaluronic acid, heparin, and the chondroitin sulfates. These are reactive substances, more difficult to work with than the uncharged compounds and consequently less completely characterized.

Hyaluronic acid makes up part of the gel-like ground substance of connective tissue and of the material which acts as a lubricant in the joints. It is usually prepared from umbilical cords, though it is found also in synovial fluid, vitreous humour, and skin and has been obtained from bacteria. It is a copolymer of glucuronic acid and *N*-acetylglucosamine, the probable structure of which is:

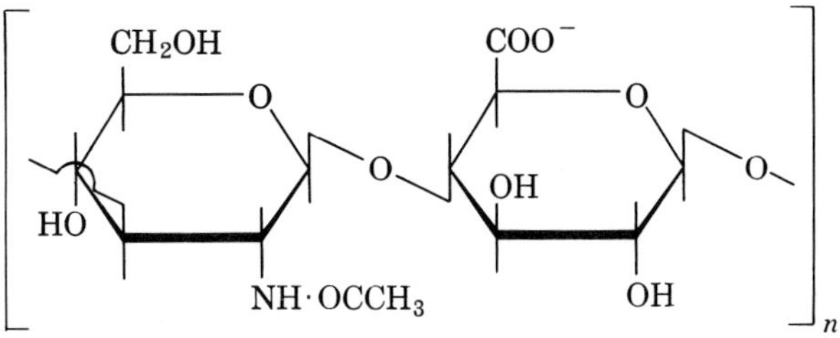

CH₂OH ... O ... COO⁻ ... O
HO ... O ... OH ... O
NH·OCCH₃ ... OH

Repeating unit of hyaluronic acid

Quite recently a special function has been suggested for hyaluronic acid. It forms experimentally a complex with water and the fibrous protein, collagen, which complex shows a definite resistance to compression. Since hyaluronic acid occurs in several regions which are exposed to local compression, it may well be that it forms such a complex or meshwork *in situ* where its own stiffly coiled particle can effectively protect against compression.

Part of the ground substance in tissue and cartilage consists of substances known as the chondroitin sulfates. Three of these compounds have been isolated and distinguished as chondroitin sulfates A, B, and C. These compounds are *β*-glycosides and are copolymers of a uronic acid and an amino

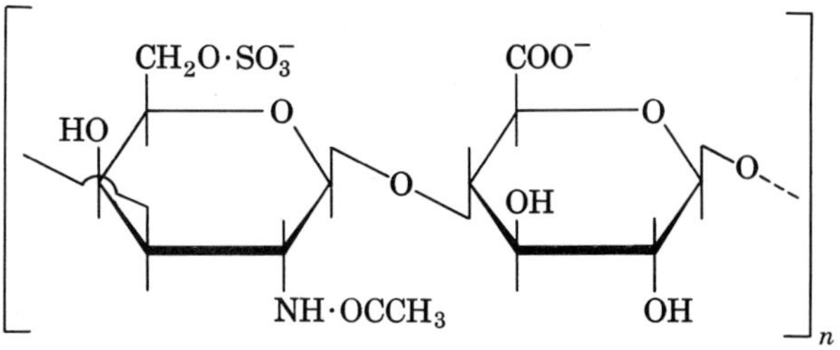

Repeating unit for chondroitin sulfate

sugar which also carries a sulfate group. Chondroitin sulfates A and C are alike in being copolymers of *N*-acetylgalactosamine and D-glucuronic acid. They differ in the position of the sulfate group. The B polymer contains iduronic acid instead of glucuronic. The repeating unit for the A and C forms is indicated above.

Heparin, an anticoagulant, is found in several mammalian tissues and in blood where it is associated with protein, which can be removed by tryptic

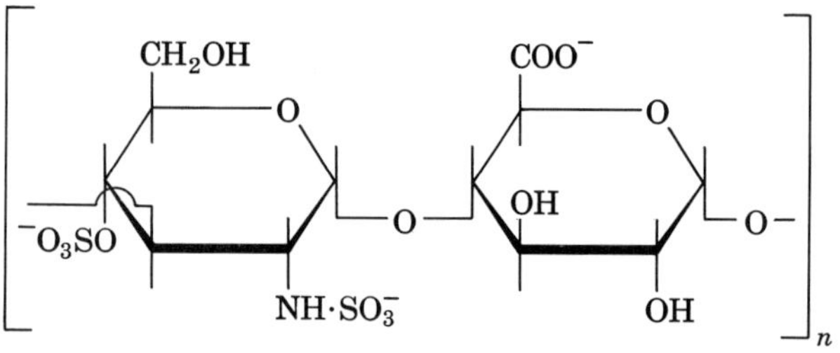

Repeating unit for heparin

digestion. Heparin is also a copolymer of a uronic acid and glucosamine, but in heparin the amino group, as well as one of the free hydroxyl groups, has been esterified with sulfate. The structure which at present seems the most probable one is shown above. Note that all these compounds are mixed $1 \rightarrow 4$, $1 \rightarrow 3$ polymers.

In addition to these fairly well-characterized substances there are several similar compounds found associated with proteins and known as *mucoproteins* or *glycoproteins*. Some of the carbohydrate residues are charged and others are not. One such compound, known as α_1-acid glycoprotein, yields on hydrolysis *N*-acetyl-D-glucosamine, *N*-acetylneuraminic acid, D-galactose, D-mannose, and L-fucose (6-deoxygalactose). At the present time nothing can be said about the structures of these substances.

Bacterial Polysaccharides

Perhaps the most interesting of the heteropolysaccharides are those which are produced by microorganisms and which have immunological properties. The immunity which is conferred upon a person who has recovered from such a disease as smallpox resides in the presence in his blood stream of protective substances called *antibodies*. These form in response to the presence in the patient of a foreign substance elaborated by the infective agent and known as an *antigen*. The relation between antibody and antigen can be demonstrated experimentally. If to one sample of serum from the immune person there is added an extract of the infective agent, a precipitate will form. But if the immune serum is tested with another type of microorganism, there will be no flocculation. This indicates that an antibody is specifically fashioned to fit in some way the particular invader with which the patient is having to cope, and that its own shape does not allow it to react in the same way even with molecules which closely resemble its antigen in structure.

It has been found that the polysaccharides elaborated by pneumococci and present in the blood and urine of pneumonia patients are responsible for the immunological specificity of the bacteria. Since this discovery was made, other bacteria including *B. dysenteriae* and tubercle bacilli have been shown to produce immunologically specific polysaccharides. Some of these are themselves antigenic and stimulate formation of antibodies if injected into animals. Others show that they contain the specific groups involved in the precipitation, for they do cause flocculation of the corresponding antisera, but they are unable to stimulate antibody formation. They become true antigens only in combination with protein.

Many of these immune polysaccharides contain uronic acids and amino sugars, but their constituents vary widely, some containing no nitrogen while others contain bound phosphorus. The only one of the pneumococcal polysaccharides for which structural information is available is the one from Type III. This is a linear molecule composed of equal numbers of D-glucose and D-glucuronic acid residues, linked alternately so that the molecule is a chain of aldobionic acids in $1 \rightarrow 4$ linkages.

SUGGESTIONS FOR FURTHER READING

General

Advances in Carbohydrate Chemistry, Academic, New York.
> This series began in 1945. The yearly volume carries authoritative articles on various phases of carbohydrate chemistry. The most recent volumes are very specialized, but the earlier ones have many articles of general interest.

Annual Review of Biochemistry, Annual Reviews, Inc., Palo Alto, Calif.

> Each volume carries an article on "Carbohydrate Chemistry" which summarizes recent developments in this field.

Haworth, W. N., *The Constitution of the Sugars*, Arnold, London, 1929.

> In this delightful small book is summarized, by one who took a major part in the work, those experiments which established the structure of the simple sugars.

Hudson, C. S., *Collected Papers*, R. M. Hann and N. K. Richtmeyer (eds.), Academic, New York, 1946.

McIlroy, R. J., *The Plant Glycosides*, Arnold, London, 1951.

Percival, E. G. V., *Structural Carbohydrate Chemistry*, Muller, London, 1950.

> This book does for 1950 what Haworth's book did 20 years earlier. It is called a textbook, but the author's style and his interest in the history of the subject give the book a charm which is rarely found in texts.

Pigman, W. W. (ed.), *The Carbohydrates*, Academic, New York, 1957.

> This book is a completely revised form of a book published by Pigman and Goepp in 1948. The sections have been written by experts in the individual fields and the book is a mine of information both chemical and biochemical.

Papers of Historical Interest

Armstrong, E. F., The correlation of the stereoisomeric α- and β-glucosides with the corresponding glucoses, *J. Chem. Soc.*, *83*, 1305 (1903).

Fischer, E., Compounds of phenylhydrazine with the sugars, *Ber.*, *17*, 579 (1884). Syntheses of the sugars, *Ber.*, *23*, 370, 2114 (1890). Concerning the glucosides of alcohols, *Ber.*, *26*, 2400 (1893).

Hudson, C. S., The significance of certain numerical relations in the sugar group, *J. Am. Chem. Soc.*, *31*, 66 (1909).

Purdie, T., and J. C. Irvine, The alkylation of sugars, *J. Chem. Soc.*, *83*, 1021 (1903).

Tanret, C. J., Concerning the molecular modifications of glucose, *Compt. rend.*, *120*, 1060 (1895).

Classification of the Sugars

Fischer, E., Concerning the configuration of glucose and its isomers, *Ber.*, *24*, 1836, 2683, (1891).

Hudson, C. S., Historical aspects of Emil Fischer's fundamental conventions for writing stereo-formulas in a plane, *Advances in Carbohydrate Chem.*, *3*, 1 (1948).

Rosanoff, M. A., On Fischer's classification of stereo-isomers, *J. Am. Chem. Soc.*, *28*, 114 (1906).

Polysaccharides

Abdel-Akher, M., and F. Smith, The repeating unit of glycogen, *J. Am. Chem. Soc.*, *73*, 994 (1951).

Abdel-Akher, M., *et al.*, A new procedure for determination of the fine structure of polysaccharides, *J. Am. Chem. Soc.*, *74*, 4970 (1952).

Bell, D. J., and D. J. Manners, The action of crystalline β-amylase on some glycogens, *J. Chem. Soc.*, 3641 (1952).

Cori, G. T., and J. Larner, Action of amylo-1,6-glucosidase and phosphorylase on glycogen and amylopectin, *J. Biol. Chem.*, *188*, 17 (1951).

Myrbäck, K., Products of enzymic degradation of starch and glycogen, *Advances in Carbohydrate Chem.*, *3*, 251 (1948).

Schlamowitz, M., On the nature of rabbit liver glycogen, *J. Biol. Chem.*, *188*, 145 (1951).

Schoch, T. J., Fractionation of starch, *Advances in Carbohydrate Chem.*, *1*, 247 (1945).

Structural Studies

Barker, S. A., *et al.*, Infra-red spectra of carbohydrates. I. Some derivatives of D-glucopyranose, *J. Chem. Soc.*, 171 (1954).

Gould, E. S., *Mechanism and Structure in Organic Chemistry*, Henry Holt, New York, 1959.
    This carries a good introductory discussion of the conformation of organic molecules.

Hough, L., and D. B. Powell, Methylation and periodate oxidation studies of the alkali-stable polysaccharide of sugar beet, *J. Chem. Soc.*, 16 (1960).

Jackson, E. L., and C. S. Hudson, Studies on the cleavage of the carbon chain by oxidation, *J. Am. Chem. Soc.*, *59*, 994 (1937).
    This gives a clear discussion of the use of periodate.

Malaprade, L., Action of polyalcohols on periodic acid, *Bull. soc. chim.*, *43*, 683 (1928).

Morrison, M., *et al.*, Periodate oxidation of hexose phosphates, *J. Am. Chem. Soc.*, *77*, 5156 (1955).

Since, in one way or another, the proteins are involved in all the chemical processes in living organisms, one may expect discoveries of fundamental importance to biological chemistry to result from the elucidation of their structure and reactions.

EMIL FISCHER (1906)

The compounds of nitrogen 5

·THE AMINO ACIDS AND THE PROTEINS

The most abundant nonaqueous constituents of protoplasm are the nitrogenous compounds of high molecular weight known as proteins. The name originated with the Dutch chemist Mulder who first recognized the similarities between the various compounds then being isolated from plant and animal tissues. Believing that these substances must play a fundamental role in the cell economy, he gave to them a name which comes from the Greek and means "of first importance." All subsequent work has confirmed Mulder's judgment, so that in a recent discussion of the origin of life our present terrestrial biology is spoken of as "protein-centered."

Protein Characteristics

The protein group includes a wide variety of substances which appear superficially to have few properties in common. Horn and hair consist largely of protein, and so do egg white and milk curd. In spite of the obvious differences between such representative substances as these, they do have certain properties which justify their inclusion in a single chemical classification.

In the first place they have, as Mulder suspected, a unique place in the living economy. They form the structural basis of every living cell, and no organism from the smallest bacterium to the largest mammal can continue to live unless it is furnished material from which it can build cell proteins. All the enzymes elaborated by living cells are protein in whole or in part. The proteins differ from the lipids and the carbohydrates in that they are not stored to any appreciable extent, except in eggs or seeds where they are used in the formation of new tissue. Nor are they used primarily as sources of energy as are both fats and carbohydrates. Ingested protein is digested, part of it is built into the proteins of the organism and each day's excess of nitrogen is excreted. It is true, as we shall see, that the non-nitrogenous parts of the

TABLE 5.1. Average Elementary Composition of Some Representative Proteins

Constituent	Percentage
Carbon	50–55
Hydrogen	6.8–7.3
Nitrogen	15.5–18.7
Oxygen	20–23
Sulfur	0.3–1.7
Phosphorus	About 0.8

protein of the diet are ultimately used as sources of energy. But it is only on a high protein diet that these fragments contribute significantly to the energy requirements of the organism, and if they are stored for future use they are stored, not as protein, but as fat or carbohydrate.

Even more striking is the specificity of the body proteins. Glucose is glucose whether it comes from a plant or an animal. The general structure of the simple fats is the same whatever their source, all being glyceryl esters of fatty acids. But each species of animal builds its own specific proteins, very like—but clearly distinguishable from—the proteins of every other species. No variations of diet influence in the slightest the structure of this specific pattern. The protein of duck egg is "foreign protein" to an animal of another species, even though it is so similar chemically to the egg protein of the other species that ordinary chemical tests reveal no differences.

Not only do the proteins have these unique characteristics which set them in a class apart, but among themselves they exhibit certain rather striking similarities. As indicated in Table 5.1, their average elementary compositions are very similar. They are all substances of high molecular weights which, if they dissolve at all, form colloidal suspensions. While many proteins do not dissolve in pure water, most can be dispersed in dilute salts or in dilute acids or alkalies. The solutions so formed all react similarly with a varied group of so-called protein precipitants. For example, they flocculate in the

TABLE 5.2. The Natural Amino Acids

Name[a]	Formula[b]	Residue Symbol	pK_a^c at 25°C pK_1	pK_2
	The Neutral Amino Acids			
Glycine	$H_2N \cdot CH_2 \cdot COOH$	-gly-	2.35	9.78
Alanine	$H_2N \cdot CH \cdot COOH$ $\quad\ \ |$ $\quad\ \ CH_3$	-ala-	2.35	9.87
Valine	$H_2N \cdot CH \cdot COOH$ $\quad\ \ |$ $\quad\ \ CH(CH_3)_2$	-val-	2.29	9.72
Leucine	$H_2N \cdot CH \cdot COOH$ $\quad\ \ |$ $\quad\ \ CH_2 \cdot CH(CH_3)_2$	-leu-		
Isoleucine	$H_2N \cdot CH \cdot COOH$ $\quad\ \ |$ $CH_3 \cdot CH \cdot C_2H_5$	-ileu-		
Phenylalanine	$H_2N \cdot CH \cdot COOH$ $\quad\ \ |$ $\quad\ \ CH_2$⬡	-phe-		
Proline[d]	H_2C———CH_2 $\ |\qquad\quad |$ $H_2C\qquad CH \cdot COOH$ $\quad \diagdown N \diagup$ $\qquad\ \ |$ $\qquad\ H$	-pro-	1.95	10.64
Tryptophan	⬡$—C \cdot CH_2 \cdot CH \cdot COOH$ $\quad \| \qquad\qquad\ |$ $\diagdown N \diagup CH \qquad\quad NH_2$ $\quad |$ $\ H$	-try-		
Serine	$H_2N \cdot CH \cdot COOH$ $\quad\ \ |$ $\quad\ \ CH_2OH$	-ser-	2.19	9.21
Threonine	$H_2N \cdot CH \cdot COOH$ $\quad\ \ |$ $\quad\ \ CHOH \cdot CH_3$	-thr-	2.09	9.10
Methionine	$H_2N \cdot CH \cdot COOH$ $\quad\ \ |$ $\quad\ \ (CH_2)_2 \cdot SCH_3$	-met-		
Cystine	$\quad\ COOH \qquad COOH$ $\qquad\ |\qquad\qquad\ \ |$ $H_2N \cdot CH \qquad CH \cdot NH_2$ $\qquad\ |\qquad\qquad\ \ |$ $\quad CH_2 \cdot S \cdot S \cdot CH_2$	-cyS -cyS		
Asparagine	$H_2N \cdot CH \cdot COOH$ $\quad\ \ |$ $\quad\ \ CH_2 \cdot CONH_2$	NH_2 $|$ -asp-		

Name[a]	Formula[b]	Residue Symbol	$pK_a{}^c$ at 25°C	
			pK_1	pK_2
Glutamine	$H_2N \cdot CH \cdot COOH$ | $CH_2 \cdot CH_2 \cdot CONH_2$	NH_2 | -glu-		

The Acidic[e] Amino Acids

			$pK_a{}^f$
Aspartic acid	$H_2N \cdot CH \cdot COOH$ | CH_2COO^-	-asp-	3.9–4.7
Glutamic acid	$H_2N \cdot CH \cdot COOH$ | $CH_2 \cdot CH_2 \cdot COO^-$	-glu-	3.9–4.7
Tyrosine	$H_2N \cdot CH \cdot COOH$ | CH_2—⬡—O^-	-tyr-	8.5–10.9
Cysteine	$H_2N \cdot CH \cdot COOH$ | $CH_2 \cdot S^-$	-cySH-	About 10

The Basic Amino Acids

Histidine	$H_2N \cdot CH \cdot COOH$ | CH_2—C$=$CH | | HN NH \ /+ C H	-his-	6.4–7.0
Lysine[d]	$H_2N \cdot CH \cdot COOH$ | $(CH_2)_4 \cdot NH_3^+$	-lys-	8.5–10.9
Arginine	$H_2N \cdot CH \cdot COOH$ | $(CH_2)_3 \cdot NH \cdot C{=}NH_2^+$ | NH_2	-arg-	11.9–13.3

[a] The systematic names, which are almost never used, are omitted.

[b] For simplicity the formulas are written with free amino and carboxyl groups, and charges are omitted on the two groups attached to the α-carbon.

[c] Most of these values were obtained using concentrations rather than activities.

[d] Hydroxyproline, $HOCH$—CH_2
$$H_2C \quad CH \cdot COOH$$
$$\diagdown N H \diagup$$
and hydroxylysine, $^+H_3N \cdot CH_2 \cdot CHOH(CH_2)_2 \cdot CH \cdot COOH$ are found only in collagen.
$$\underset{NH_2}{|}$$

[e] The acidic and basic amino acids are written in ionized form to show the net charge resulting from the third functional group.

[f] The constants given are those referable to the third ionizable group.

presence of strong acids or of many heavy metal salts or of organic solvents such as acetone or ethyl alcohol. They are precipitated also by the group of substances known as alkaloidal reagents, which includes trichloroacetic acid, picric acid, and various complex phosphotungstic or phosphomolybdic acids. Many proteins can also be "salted out" of solution by high concentrations of such salts as sodium or ammonium sulfate. Finally, the proteins are alike in yielding, on complete hydrolysis, mixtures of α-amino acids. Furthermore in view of the differences between the proteins themselves, the amino acid compositions of the various mixtures obtained by hydrolysis of different proteins are remarkably alike. The 21 amino acids listed in Table 5.2 make up the currently accepted list of natural amino acids, that is, of acids which are found in a wide variety of common proteins. From these relatively few building blocks living cells synthesize all their diverse proteins by varying the acids used, their ratios to each other, and their positions within the molecule. Before attempting to unravel the complexity of such molecules, it will be necessary to gain an understanding of the properties of these funda-mental simple molecules, the α-amino acids.

The α-Amino Acids

Excepting only proline and hydroxyproline, which are α-imino acids, all the acids which are known to be constituents of the common proteins are α-amino acids. Except for glycine (α-aminoacetic acid) all have centers of asymmetry at the α carbon and occur in an optically active form. The actual sign of rotation varies from acid to acid, and indeed the rotation of a single acid changes with changes in pH. But it has been shown that, with rare exceptions, all have the same stereochemical configuration. That is to say, the spatial relation to each other of the amino group, the carboxyl group, the hydrogen, and the fourth or "R" group is identical in all the acids. Since, as indicated in the formulas, this configuration is similar to that of L(+)-lactic acid, the natural amino acids are said to belong to the L series.[1] In the formula shown for lactic acid, the hydroxyl group, the carboxyl group,

L(+)-Lactic acid   Alanine   General formula   Residue formula

---

[1] The presence of D-amino acids is reported from time to time especially in bacterial proteins and polypeptides. *Streptococcus faecalis* requires D-alanine for growth, and

and the hydrogen are at the points of one face of the tetrahedron, with the methyl group at the remaining apex. When this type of formula is written for an amino acid, the amino group takes the place of the hydroxyl group and amino, carboxyl, and hydrogen in that order occupy the points of one tetrahedral face. The general formula represents any α-amino acid, the various acids with the exception of the prolines, differing only in the nature of the R group.

It will be found (see page 203) that the linking of many amino acids in a protein molecule takes place through the formation of "peptide bonds," that is, formation of an amide linkage between the carboxyl group of one acid and the amino group of another. Since each acid contains both an amino and a carboxyl group, one amino acid can form such bonds with two others, as in the compound, known as a tetrapeptide, for which the formula is:

$$\underset{\textbf{Glycyl}}{H_2N \cdot CH_2 \cdot CO} \cdot \underset{\textbf{alanyl}}{NH \cdot \underset{\underset{CH_3}{|}}{CH} \cdot CO} \cdot \underset{\textbf{valyl}}{NH \cdot \underset{\underset{\underset{H_3C \diagdown \diagup CH_3}{CH}}{|}}{CH} \cdot CO} \cdot \underset{\textbf{tyrosine}}{NH \cdot \underset{\underset{\underset{C_6H_4OH}{CH_2}}{|}}{CH} \cdot COOH}$$

By convention the free amino group in such a compound is written to the left, and the parts of each amino acid which appear in the peptide chain between broken lines are called the "residues." Just as acetic acid becomes "acetyl" chloride when its carboxyl —OH group is replaced by chlorine, so each residue in a peptide except the one with a complete carboxyl group is named from the acid, using the -yl ending. For the acid at the carboxyl end the unchanged name is used, thus making the compound a substitution product of that acid. To indicate briefly the composition of such a peptide, the name of each residue is abbreviated, with the exceptions noted in Table 5.2, to the first three letters of the commonly used name of the acid. Thus the structure of the tetrapeptide would be given as gly-ala-val-tyr. The order makes it clear that the free amino group is in the glycine and the free carboxyl in the tyrosine. In Table 5.2 are given the commonly used or trivial names of the natural acids and the residue abbreviations. Up to the present there is no indication that the trivial names are to be superseded by systematic ones. The acids are grouped as neutral, acidic, or basic, depending on whether they are monoamino and monocarboxylic, or monoamino and dicarboxylic, or diamino and monocarboxylic. At the end of the list of neutral acids, appear two acid amides of the two dibasic acids, aspartic and glutamic acids. These

---

several of the antibiotics contain, among other amino acids, significant amounts of D forms. It still is true however that nearly all known plant and animal proteins and many proteins from bacteria are made up entirely of L-amino acids.

are listed separately from the acids themselves because the amides appear as such in various proteins and are therefore true protein constituents.

For all the natural amino acids except the prolines the general formula given on page 188 may be used. In glycine the R stands for hydrogen, and in six other neutral acids it stands for a simple alkyl or aryl group. The reactions of these seven acids will depend almost entirely upon the two functional groups, the amino and the carboxyl group. The remaining members of this class possess other functional groups such as the aliphatic hydroxyl group in serine and the indole group in tryptophan. Proline and hydroxyproline are exceptional both in structure and solubility. The α-imino group in these acids is part of a ring, and the acids therefore have anomalous properties and their presence in a protein confers special properties on the molecule.

The acidic amino acids have two carboxyl groups and but one amino group. This gives these compounds an acid reaction in water solution. The basic amino acids are those which contain more than one basic nitrogen grouping. In lysine this consists of a second free amino group; in arginine it is a guanido group. Since the substance guanidine $NH_2 \cdot C(\!=\!NH) \cdot NH_2$ is as strong a base as sodium hydroxide, the basicity of this group is marked. The imidazole group in histidine is, on the other hand, only very slightly basic, so that histidine resembles the neutral acids in solubility. Note that there is a fourth acid which contains more than one nitrogen. This is tryptophan which contains an indole group but is listed with the neutral acids. This is in accord with the fact that indole itself is not basic, but very slightly acidic in reaction.

Indole

Physical properties of amino acids

The amino acids have physical properties which are very different from those of unsubstituted fatty acids. Saturated fatty acids above butyric are either only slightly soluble in water or are indeed quite insoluble. They are, on the other hand, very soluble in such an organic solvent as ether. They are either liquids at room temperature, or low-melting solids. Stearic acid, with eighteen carbons, melts at 69°C. In sharp contrast to these, the corresponding α-amino acids are extremely soluble in water and quite insoluble in ether. They are nonvolatile, and they melt only with decomposition at temperatures above 200°C. These properties are reminiscent of those we associate with the crystal lattices of inorganic salts, held together by electrostatic attraction. It is now believed that the neutral amino acids exist largely in the form of molecules which may be thought of as salts. Neutralization has taken place within the molecule, yielding an "inner salt," $^+NH_3 \cdot CH(R) \cdot COO^-$. Such a self-neutralized molecule is known as a dipolar ion or a *zwitterion* from the German word meaning hybrid. The molecule is believed to exist in this form in water solution also, thus explaining the fact that in an electric field the neutral amino acids in essentially neutral solutions (near pH 6) do not move toward either electrode.

Chemical properties of the amino acids

Since all amino acids except the prolines share the properties of the two functional groups, the amino and the carboxyl groups, those reactions will be considered first. Later the special reactions characteristic of individual amino acids will be reviewed. Although the α-amino acids undergo the reactions of the amino group and of the carboxyl group, those of the carboxyl group in particular are somewhat modified by the proximity of the basic amino group.

1. Reactions with Acids and Bases. When a mineral acid is added to the solution of an amino acid, the dipolar ion functions as a conjugate base. It acquires a proton which neutralizes the charge on the carboxyl group, thus making the molecule into a cation. Similarly, on addition of alkali the dipolar

$$^+H_3N \cdot CH(R) \cdot COO^- + H^+ \rightarrow {}^+H_3N \cdot CH(R) \cdot COOH$$

  Conjugate base   **Cationic acid**

ion furnishes a proton to the added hydroxyl ion, thus itself acting as an acid. The base which remains carries a single negative charge and is therefore an

$$^+H_3N \cdot CH(R) \cdot COO^- + OH^- \rightarrow H_2N \cdot CH(R) \cdot COO^- + H_2O$$

         Acid   **Conjugate base**

anion. Thus the three forms, anion, cation, and dipolar ion are freely interconvertible.

$$
\begin{array}{ccccc}
NH_2 & & NH_3^+ & & NH_3^+ \\
| & & | & & | \\
CHR & \underset{OH^-}{\overset{H^+}{\rightleftharpoons}} & CHR & \underset{OH^-}{\overset{H^+}{\rightleftharpoons}} & CHR \\
| & & | & & | \\
COO^- & & COO^- & & COOH
\end{array}
$$

2. Behavior in an Electric Field. It has been noted that if a nearly neutral aqueous solution of a monoamino, monocarboxylic acid is subjected to an electric field, the dipolar ion does not move toward either electrode. Its net charge is zero. The basic acids on the other hand, carrying a net positive charge, migrate toward the cathode, while the dicarboxylic acids are attracted to the anode because of their net negative charge.

$$H_2N(CH_2)_4CH \cdot COO^- + H_2O \rightarrow {}^+H_3N(CH_2)_4CH \cdot COO^- + OH^-$$

| |
| NH$_3^+$ |

Lysine, a basic   **Cationic form**
amino acid

$$HOOC \cdot CH_2 \cdot CH \cdot COO^- + H_2O \rightarrow {}^-OOC \cdot CH_2 \cdot CH \cdot COO^- + H_3O^+$$

| |
| NH$_3^+$ |

Aspartic acid,   **Anionic form**
a dibasic acid

These facts have made it possible to separate an amino acid mixture by electrophoresis (see page 214), at least into three major groups.

Although the neutral amino acids are the only ones whose net charge is close to zero when they are dissolved in water, it is possible to find for every amino acid a *p*H at which it will fail to migrate toward either electrode. If hydroxyl ions are added to a solution of a cationic or basic amino acid, these ions compete with the acid for protons, and at some definite *p*H, characteristic for each acid, a simple dipolar ion results.

$${}^+H_3N(CH_2)_4CHCOO^- + OH^- \rightarrow H_2N(CH_2)_4CHCOO^- + H_2O$$

| |
| NH$_3^+$ |

Similarly, hydrogen ion added in just the right amount to an acidic or anionic acid suppresses the ionization of one of the carboxyl groups and brings about formation of a dipolar ion with a net charge of zero.

$${}^-OOC \cdot CH_2 \cdot CH \cdot COO^- + H^+ \rightarrow HOOC \cdot CH_2 \cdot CH \cdot COO^-$$

| |
| NH$_3^+$ |

Thus, for each amino acid there is a definite *p*H at which it fails to migrate toward either electrode. This *p*H is called the *isoelectric point* of the acid. For the neutral acids this *p*H is in the vicinity of *p*H 6; for the acidic ones it is well on the acid side of neutrality while the basic acids carry a net charge of zero when their solutions have some definite *p*H above 7.

3. IONIZATION CONSTANTS.   A solution of glycine in water has, as noted above, a *p*H of about 6. When it is titrated with hydrochloric acid the *p*H gradually falls and becomes about 1.5 when an equimolar amount of acid has been added. Similarly, addition of sodium hydroxide brings about first a rapid, then a slow rise in *p*H until, when an equivalent amount of base has been added, the *p*H is about 11.5. A compound which thus acts as glycine does, both as an acid and a base is known as an *ampholyte*, or amphoteric electrolyte. Such behavior is, of course, characteristic of all the amino acids.

The titration curves for glycine with acid and base are shown in Fig. 5.1 on which the added equivalents of acid and alkali run in opposite directions from the zero point in the center of the ordinate. The curve shows two points of inflection, one at pH 2.4 and the other at pH 9.6. These, as with other titration curves, come at the points at which half the molar equivalent of acid or base has been added. It will be remembered (see page 53) that at

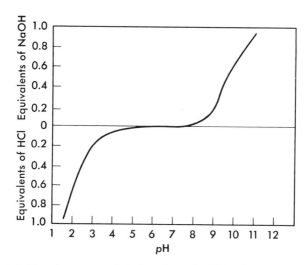

Fig. 5.1. Titration curves of glycine, titrated with NaOH and with HCl.

this point in a titration, when the concentration of base equals the concentration of acid, $pK_a = pH$. The curve thus shows that glycine has two pK values, or two ionization constants. It has been established that the lower pK_a corresponds to the neutralization of the carboxyl group, while the higher is referable to the reaction of the $—NH_3^+$ group with base.

To relate this curve for glycine to more familiar titration curves for a dibasic acid, consider that the titration begins with a solution containing equimolar amounts of glycine and hydrochloric acid. Such a solution will have a pH of 1.5 and will contain glycine in the cationic form, $HOOC \cdot CH_2 \cdot NH_3^+$. Added base will compete with the carboxyl group for its proton, and pH measurements will give the lower half of the curve in Fig. 5.1, to the point at which the pH of the solution has reached 6.

$$HOOC \cdot CH_2 \cdot NH_3^+ + OH^- \rightarrow {}^-OOC \cdot CH_2 \cdot NH_3^+ + H_2O$$

As the equation shows, titration to this point has brought the glycine back to the form of a dipolar ion, one equivalent of sodium hydroxide having been used. As the second equivalent of sodium hydroxide is added, the base competes now with the positively charged —NH_3^+ group for its proton in the reaction:

$$^-OOC \cdot CH_2 \cdot NH_3^+ + OH^- \rightarrow {}^-OOC \cdot CH_2 \cdot NH_2 + H_2O$$

At the equivalence point the amino acid has become an anion, that is to say the solution contains the sodium salt of glycine, and of course the ions of sodium chloride because of the acid used to prepare the original solution.

Table 5.2 lists the two *pK* values for several of the neutral acids, and gives a single *pK* value for the acidic and basic acids. Amino acids with other functional groups than the α-amino and the adjacent carboxyl yield titration curves with a third point of inflection. Two of these points correspond to similar points in the glycine curve. The third arises from the presence of such other groups as a second amino or carboxyl group or the guanido group of arginine, the phenolic hydroxyl of tyrosine or the imidazole ring of histidine. Each of these is capable of furnishing or accepting a proton, thus making the amino acid essentially tribasic. The pK_a values given in the table for the acidic and basic amino acids are the ones which are referable to the third functional groups, it being understood that the groups which form the dipole have pK_a values which correspond roughly to those indicated for the neutral acids. The constants for glutamic acid, for example are: $pK_1 = 2.2$, pK_2, which is referable to the second or γ-carboxyl group, is about 4.3 and pK_3, for the —NH_3^+ group is about 9.7. When an acid has more than one pK_a, they are listed in the order of ascending *pK*, with subscripts numbered in the same order.

4. REACTIONS OF THE CARBOXYL GROUP

(*a*) *Salt Formation.* As indicated above, the amino acids react with strong bases to form salts.

$$CH_3 \cdot CH \cdot COO^- + Na^+ + OH^- \rightarrow CH_3 \cdot CH \cdot COO^- + Na^+ + H_2O$$

| NH_3^+ | NH_2 |
| **Alanine** | **Alanate ion** |

The amino acids also form a more complex type of salt. If a suspension of cupric hydroxide is added to a solution of a monobasic α- or β-amino acid, it dissolves with formation of a complex copper salt in which two amino acid residues are united through copper. These compounds are of the *ammine* type in which both the primary and the secondary valences of copper are involved, yielding a coordination compound. For such a glycine salt the following structure has been suggested:

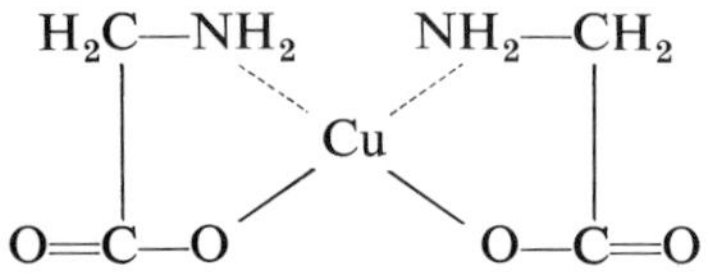

$$
\begin{array}{ccc}
H_2C-NH_2 & & NH_2-CH_2 \\
| & Cu & | \\
O{=}C-O & & O-C{=}O
\end{array}
$$

If cupric hydroxide is added to a solution containing a mixture of amino acids, the complex may hold together two different amino acids. Pope and Stevens made use of this type of salt formation in their titrimetric method for the estimation of free amino acids. Insoluble cupric phosphate is added to the solution of amino acids and reacts with them to form soluble complex cupric salts. This solution is filtered from excess of the insoluble cupric phosphate reagent, and the amount of cupric ion in solution is determined by iodometric titration. When a large excess of iodide ion is added to cupric ion, the cupric ion is reduced:

$$2Cu^{++} + 4I^- \rightarrow 2Cu^+ + 2I^- + I_2$$

Titration with sodium thiosulfate measures the amount of iodine set free, which is in turn a measure of the amount of cupric ion which formed a salt with the amino acids. This method has two advantages over the earlier Van Slyke nitrous acid method (see p. 196) for total free amino acids. It estimates proline and oxyproline, and it is not sensitive to the presence of free ammonia.

(*b*) *Esterification.* Esterification of amino acids was first carried out by Emil Fischer as a step toward the separation of individual acids from a protein hydrolyzate. This separation is rendered very difficult by the great similarity of the amino acids and by the fact that they are not volatile and cannot, therefore, be separated by distillation. Fischer was able to esterify the mixture by heating it with alcohol saturated with hydrogen chloride, and he found that the resulting esters were low-boiling liquids. By fractional distillation at diminished pressure he isolated some of the previously known amino acids and discovered hydroxyproline.

$$R \cdot CH(NH_3^+)COO^- + CH_3OH \xrightarrow{HCl} R \cdot CH(NH_2)COOCH_3 + H_2O$$

(*c*) *Acid Chloride Formation.* Because of the adjacent amino group, it is difficult to form the acid chloride directly from an amino acid. These compounds may be prepared, however, if the amino group is first protected by acetylation. Thus addition of acetyl chloride and phosphorus pentachloride to an amino acid brings about simultaneous acetylation of the amino group and formation of the acid chloride.

$$R \cdot CH(NH_3^+)COO^- + CH_3COCl \rightarrow R \cdot \underset{\underset{NH \cdot COCH_3}{|}}{CH} \cdot COOH + HCl$$

$$R \cdot \underset{\underset{NH \cdot COCH_3}{|}}{CH} \cdot COOH + PCl_5 \rightarrow R \cdot \underset{\underset{NH \cdot COCH_3}{|}}{CH} \cdot COCl + POCl_3 + HCl$$

The protected molecule which is formed at this stage is often used in synthesis, especially in condensation with another amino acid.

(*d*) *Decarboxylation.* When amino acids are heated, especially in the presence of a weak base like barium hydroxide, many of them decompose with evolution of carbon dioxide.

$$R \cdot \underset{\underset{NH_2}{|}}{CH} \cdot COOH \xrightarrow{Ba(OH)_2} R \cdot CH_2 \cdot NH_2 + CO_2$$

Similar reactions are catalyzed by enzymes which are widespread in living organisms. The products, the amines, often possess potent physiological activities. Histamine, resulting from the decarboxylation of histidine, is thought to play an important role in the allergic conditions, perhaps by affecting cell permeability. Certain bacteria are particularly active in the decarboxylation of amino acids. The amines formed, especially those from the basic amino acids, are responsible for the odors of putrefying tissues.

5. REACTIONS OF THE AMINO GROUP. With the exception of the prolines, the amino acids undergo all the reactions characteristic of the primary amino group.

(*a*) *Reaction with Nitrous Acid.* This reaction, in which nitrogen is set free, is the basis of the Van Slyke[2] method for estimation of free primary amino groups. The nitrogen gas is collected and the equivalents of free amino

$$R \cdot \underset{\underset{NH_2}{|}}{CH} \cdot COOH + HONO \rightarrow R \cdot CHOH \cdot COOH + N_2 + H_2O$$

nitrogen are calculated from the volume of nitrogen evolved. It should be noted that only half of the nitrogen actually collected comes from the amino acid.

(*b*) *Reaction with Formaldehyde.* Formaldehyde reacts with the primary amino group in such a way as to eliminate that center of positive charge. There is some question about the actual structure of the derivative which forms, but with some acids at least the reaction seems to take place in two steps as follows:

$$R \cdot \underset{\underset{COO^-}{|}}{CH} \cdot NH_3^+ \xrightarrow{HCHO} R \cdot \underset{\underset{COOH}{|}}{CH} \cdot N\overset{H}{\underset{CH_2OH}{\diagdown}} \xrightarrow{HCHO} R \cdot \underset{\underset{COOH}{|}}{CH} \cdot N\overset{CH_2OH}{\underset{CH_2OH}{\diagdown}}$$

When the basic quality of the amino group has been suppressed in this way

---

[2] Dr. Donald D. Van Slyke (1883–   ) was for many years a member of the Rockefeller Institute for Medical Research in New York. He is now Member Emeritus of the Institute and Research Chemist at the Brookhaven National Laboratory. He is known especially for his work on the acid-base balance in blood and for a number of excellent microanalytical methods.

it is possible to titrate the carboxyl group as in any acid-base titration. This is the basis for Sørensen's "formol" titration method for estimation of free carboxyl groups.

(c) *Acetylation.* As suggested above, the amino group reacts characteristically with acetylating agents such as acetyl chloride or acetic anhydride, forming an *N*-acetyl amino acid.

$$\text{R} \cdot \underset{\underset{\text{COOH}}{|}}{\text{CH}} \cdot \text{NH}_2 + \begin{array}{c} \text{CH}_3\text{CO} \\ \diagdown \\ \text{CH}_3\text{CO} \end{array}\hspace{-0.5em}\text{O} \rightarrow \text{R} \cdot \underset{\underset{\text{COOH}}{|}}{\text{CH}} \cdot \text{NH} \cdot \text{COCH}_3 + \text{CH}_3\text{COOH}$$

A similar reaction takes place in the body when glycine is conjugated with the toxic benzoic acid to yield the nontoxic product, hippuric acid, or *N*-benzoylglycine. The benzoyl compound $(C_6H_5CO \cdot X)$ is a complex activated derivative of benzoic acid.

$$C_6H_5CO \cdot X + H_2N \cdot CH_2COOH \rightarrow C_6H_5CO \cdot HN \cdot CH_2COOH + HX$$

(d) *Reaction with 1-Fluoro-2,4-dinitrobenzene (FDNB).* A reaction which is widely used in studies of protein structure is the one in which a free amino group reacts with fluoro-2,4-dinitrobenzene. The substituted amino acid which forms is colored yellow and is stable enough to withstand mild hydrolysis.

2,4-Dinitrophenyl amino acid
DNP Amino acid

It should be noted here that the reagent also reacts to replace other hydrogens than those of the α-amino group. Tyrosine, for example, reacts to form a di-DNP derivative, the phenolic as well as the amino hydrogen having reacted with the reagent. Serine, on the other hand, forms a mono-DNP substitution product, indicating that FDNB does not react with an aliphatic hydroxyl. Histidine reacts with two moles of the reagent, the second nitrophenyl group attaching itself to the charged nitrogen of the imidazole ring. The sulfhydryl group of cysteine is also attacked so that cysteine yields an *S:N*-di-DNP derivative. And of course lysine, with its two free amino groups reacts to form an *N*-di-DNP compound. When fluorodinitrobenzene is used with large peptides which may contain many different amino acids all these possibilities have to be kept in mind.

(*e*) *Reaction with Phenylisothiocyanate.*   Another valuable reaction even though its use is somewhat limited is the one with phenylisothiocyanate, C_6H_5NCS. Amino groups react with this substance to form phenylthiohydantoic acids which can be converted to phenylthiohydantoins.

$$R \cdot CH \cdot NH_2 + S{=}C{=}N \cdot C_6H_5 \rightarrow$$
$$\underset{\displaystyle COOH}{\mid} \qquad \text{\textbf{Phenylisothiocyanate}}$$

$$R \cdot CH \cdot \overset{\displaystyle S}{\overset{\displaystyle \|}{NH \cdot C}} \cdot NH \cdot C_6H_5 \xrightarrow[\text{pyridine}]{\text{dry}} R \cdot CH \cdot NH \cdot C{=}S$$
$$\underset{\displaystyle COOH}{\mid} \qquad\qquad\qquad\qquad \underset{\displaystyle CO\text{------}N \cdot C_6H_5}{\mid}$$
$$\text{\textbf{Phenylthiohydantoic acid}} \qquad\qquad \text{\textbf{Phenylthiohydantoin}}$$

6. Reactions of Individual Amino Acids.   Each amino acid has, in addition to the reactions common to all, certain reactions which are characteristic of its own particular R group. A few of these, which are important for later discussions of protein structure and metabolism are considered in this section.

Those acids, listed at the beginning of Table 5.2 in which the R groups are simple alkyl radicals, have no reactions of importance other than those of their amino acid groups. *Phenylalanine* and *tyrosine* both have the reactions characteristic of the phenyl ring and tyrosine has, in addition, the reactions of a phenolic hydroxyl. It is this group, of course, which makes tyrosine an acidic amino acid.

Proline and *hydroxyproline* do not react typically with nitrous acid to liberate nitrogen, since they are not primary amines. They do, however, react with acylating agents to form *N*-acyl derivatives. Proline is the only one of the amino acids which is soluble in alcohol. Isolation of proline makes use of the fact that it is precipitated from acid solution by ammonium rhodanilate, the salt of a complex acid in which the coordination positions of chromium are filled by the six groups within the square brackets.

$$NH_4[Cr(CNS)_4(C_6H_5NH_2)_2] \cdot 1\tfrac{1}{2}H_2O$$
Ammonium rhodanilate

A similar salt known as Reinecke salt or ammonium Reineckate precipitates not only proline but also hydroxyproline and various other amino acids.

$$NH_4[Cr(NH_3)_2(SCN)_4] \cdot H_2O$$
Ammonium Reineckate

Tryptophan was first identified by the color reaction known as the Adamkiewicz, or later, as the Hopkins-Cole or Acree-Rosenheim reaction. A protein treated with either glyoxylic acid (CHO · COOH) or formaldehyde in the presence of concentrated sulfuric acid developed a violet color which proved to be due to the presence of tryptophan. The color results from a reaction between the indole nucleus of the amino acid and an aldehyde, to form a condensation product having the structure shown in the formula.

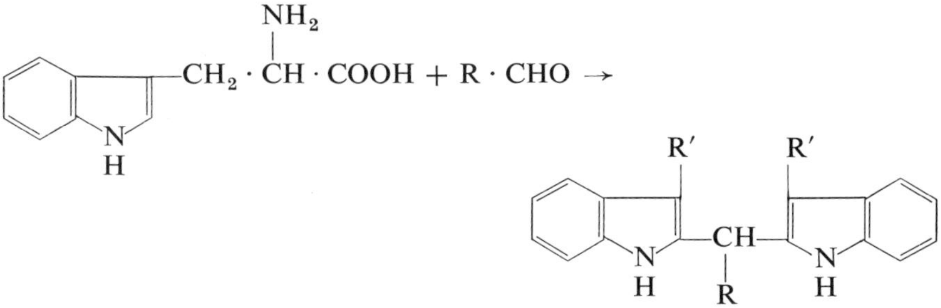

R′ stands for —CH₂CH(NH₂)COOH.
R is hydrogen when the reagent is formaldehyde, or —COOH
if glyoxylic acid is used.

Serine and *threonine* are oxidized by periodic acid as shown in the equations, the amino group on a carbon adjacent to one which carries an hydroxyl making the molecule reactive just as two adjacent hydroxyls do.

$$CH_3 \cdot CHOH \cdot CH(NH_2) \cdot COOH + HIO_4 \rightarrow$$
Threonine
$$CH_3CHO + CHO \cdot COOH + NH_3 + HIO_3$$

$$CH_2OH \cdot CH(NH_2) \cdot COOH + HIO_4 \rightarrow$$
Serine
$$HCHO + CHO \cdot COOH + NH_3 + HIO_3$$

In addition, these two amino acids have of course the typical reactions of aliphatic secondary or primary alcohols and can form esters with carboxylic acids or with such an inorganic acid as phosphoric acid. The phosphate which is attached to certain proteins by covalent bonds is believed to be held there in the form of a phosphate ester of serine.

$$NH_2 \cdot CH \cdot COOH$$
$$CH_2O \cdot PO_3H^-$$
Phosphoserine

Cysteine contains the very reactive sulfhydryl group which accounts for the following reactions:

1. The amino acid is unstable in alkaline solution and releases its sulfur as sulfide ion. This can be identified in the usual way as lead sulfide.

2. Cysteine gives a purple red color with sodium nitroprusside in the presence of sodium hydroxide.

$$Na_2[Fe(CN)_5NO] + 2NaSH \rightarrow Na_4[Fe(CN)_5NOS] + H_2S$$
Sodium nitroprusside   **Colored derivative**

3. Cysteine is reversibly oxidized to the disulfide, cystine, by oxygen of the air or other oxidizing agents.

$$2HS \cdot CH_2 \cdot CH(NH_2)COOH \underset{2H}{\overset{\frac{1}{2}O_2}{\rightleftarrows}} \begin{array}{l} S \cdot CH_2 \cdot CH(NH_2)COOH \\ | \\ S \cdot CH_2 \cdot CH(NH_2)COOH \end{array} + H_2O$$

     Cysteine   **Cystine**

4. Strong oxidation of cysteine yields cysteic acid, $HO_3S \cdot CH_2 \cdot CH(NH_2) \cdot COOH$.
5. Any free sulfhydryl group reacts with maleic acid, or with *N*-ethyl-maleimide to form addition products. This type of reaction can be used in enzyme experiments, for example, to mask a free sulfhydryl group, and

$$RSH + \begin{array}{l} CH \cdot COOH \\ \| \\ CH \cdot COOH \end{array} \rightarrow \begin{array}{l} HCH \cdot COOH \\ | \\ RS \cdot CH \cdot COOH \end{array}$$

$$RSH + \begin{array}{l} CH \cdot CO \\ \| \\ CH \cdot CO \end{array}\!\!\!\!\Big\rangle NC_2H_5 \rightarrow \begin{array}{l} HCH \cdot CO \\ | \\ RS \cdot CH \cdot CO \end{array}\!\!\!\!\Big\rangle NC_2H_5$$

so to determine whether or not the presence of such a group is essential to the biological activity of the enzyme.
6. Cysteine reduces the complex phospho-18-tungstic acid to yield the deep blue lower oxide of tungsten. The reaction may be indicated as follows, allowing $(WO_3)_{18}$ to stand for the tungsten-containing part of the complex acid:

$$- - -(WO_3)_{18} + 2H \rightarrow - - -(WO_3)_{17}WO_2 + H_2O$$

This reaction is the basis for the Kassell and Brand colorimetric procedure for estimation of cysteine or cystine, the latter having first to be reduced with sulfite to free the sulfhydryl group.

Methionine differs from the other two sulfur-containing acids in not releasing its sulfur in alkaline solution. Biologically its ability to form a sulfonium derivative is of great importance. The formula indicates the structure of a compound of this type formed by reaction of a simple alkyl halide with methionine.

$$CH_3S \cdot CH_2 \cdot CH_2 \cdot CH(NH_2) \cdot COOH + RI \rightarrow$$

$$CH_3 \cdot \overset{+}{\underset{R}{S}} \cdot CH_2 \cdot CH_2 \cdot CH(NH_2) \cdot COOH + I^-$$

Sulfonium derivative

When methionine is oxidized it forms first a sulfoxide and then a sulfone.

$$\underset{R}{\overset{CH_3}{\mid}} \; S{=}O \qquad\qquad \underset{R}{\overset{CH_3}{\mid}} \; O{=}S{=}O$$

Sulfoxide   **Sulfone**

Tyrosine has the reactions of an aromatic phenol. The Folin and Looney test for this acid makes use of one of the numerous solutions of complex phospho acids. This particular reagent consists of a mixture of phosphotungstic and phosphomolybdic acids. These acids, singly or together, are reduced by a number of different substances to give a clear blue color of unknown composition. In the "phenol reagent" used for detection of tyrosine, the solution is adjusted as to acidity and reagent concentration so that the appearance of the familiar blue color indicates the presence of a phenolic hydroxyl group. Like all benzene rings, that of tyrosine is easily nitrated, and it is the nitration product of such rings in skin proteins which causes the yellow stain when skin comes in contact with concentrated nitric acid. Treatment of tyrosine with iodine in alkaline solution results in substitution in the

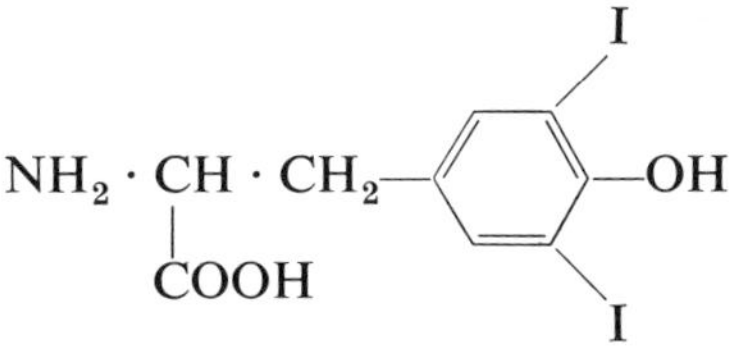

$$NH_2 \cdot CH \cdot CH_2 - \underset{\overset{\mid}{COOH}}{} \; \begin{array}{c} I \\ \diagdown \\ \end{array} - OH$$

Diiodotyrosine

ring. The 3,5-diiodotyrosyl residue occurs in thyroglobulin and in the proteins of some marine organisms.

Histidine contains the imidazole ring which occurs in many other compounds of biological importance. It is responsible for the color which develops in reaction with diazobenzenesulfonic acid and which is used for colorimetric estimation of histidine. The reaction, known as the Pauly reaction, begins with diazotization of benzenesulfonic acid. The diazo compound then reacts with the imidazole ring to form a red substitution product.

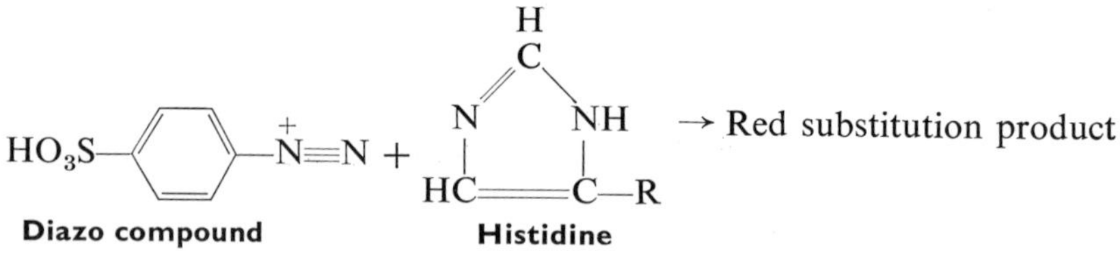

Diazo compound   Histidine   → Red substitution product

When histidine is in water solution the doubly linked nitrogen acquires a proton and becomes a center of positive charge. It is the removal of this proton by a base which gives rise to the *pK* of 6.4–7, noted in Table 5.2.

Arginine contains the strongly basic guanido group:

$$-HN \cdot C \cdot NH_2$$
$$\|$$
$$NH$$

This group is responsible for the bright red color which arginine develops in the Sakaguchi test. When the amino acid is treated with α-naphthol and sodium hypobromite, a red color appears which is used for quantitative estimation of arginine. The formula given below for the product is one of several which have been suggested and may be taken to indicate that the guanido group condenses with two molecules of the naphthol.

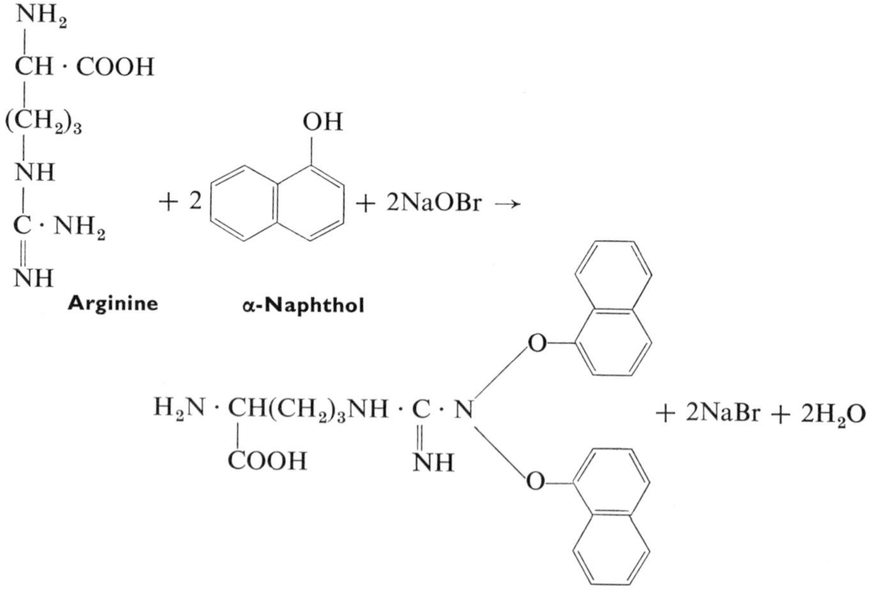

Arginine decomposes on treatment with alkali. In boiling barium hydroxide urea is split out, leaving ornithine, while less drastic treatment releases ammonia and leaves a third amino acid, citrulline.

$$
\begin{array}{cc}
 & \text{NH}_2 \\
 & | \\
 & \text{CO} \\
\text{NH}_2 & | \\
| & \text{NH} \\
(\text{CH}_2)_3 & | \\
| & (\text{CH}_2)_3 \\
\text{H}_2\text{N} \cdot \text{CH} \cdot \text{COOH} & | \\
 & \text{H}_2\text{N} \cdot \text{CH} \cdot \text{COOH} \\
\textbf{Ornithine} & \textbf{Citrulline}
\end{array}
$$

These amino acids do not commonly occur in proteins, but are of considerable importance in nitrogen metabolism.

7. THE LINKING OF AMINO ACIDS: POLYPEPTIDES. The fundamental problem in amino acid chemistry, at least for the biochemist, is the manner of their combination in the complex protein molecule. From the beginning of his interest in proteins, Emil Fischer addressed himself to this problem. Side by side with his work on protein analysis, he carried out experiments designed to link several amino acids into a single molecule. His methods are now of historical interest only, but modern techniques must still find ways to block or protect the amino group. Only after this has been achieved can an acid halide be prepared. This then is used to form a peptide bond ($-\text{CO} \cdot \text{NH}-$) by a reaction resembling that by which a simple acid amide is prepared.

$$
\underset{\textbf{Acid chloride}}{\text{RCOCl}} + \text{HNH}_2 \rightarrow \underset{\textbf{Acid amide}}{\text{RCONH}_2} + \text{HCl}
$$

For some amino acids special methods have had to be developed for peptide formation, and always the possibility of racemization has to be guarded against. The two methods described below have been used successfully with several amino acids.

(a) *Through the Carbobenzoxy Derivative.* About 1932 Bergmann[3] introduced a method of protecting the amino group which revolutionized the preparation of peptides. We have already seen that an acid chloride may be prepared if the amino group is protected by acetylation. But this is of no use in the synthesis of peptides, because the acid hydrolysis which must later be used to remove the protecting group also splits the peptide bond. Bergmann

---

[3] Dr. Max Bergmann (1886–1944) became interested in amino acid chemistry while he was a student in Emil Fischer's laboratory. His research in the field of protein chemistry and structure was carried on first in Dresden, and after 1933 at the Rockefeller Institute in New York.

introduced the use of a protecting group which can be removed by reduction instead of hydrolysis. The reagent is prepared by interaction of phosgene with benzyl alcohol:

$$COCl_2 + C_6H_5CH_2OH \rightarrow C_6H_5 \cdot CH_2 \cdot O \cdot COCl$$
Phosgene   **Benzyl alcohol**   **Benzoxycarbonyl chloride**

This reagent reacts with amino acids to block the primary amino group as follows:

$$CH_3CH \cdot COOH + C_6H_5 \cdot CH_2 \cdot O \cdot COCl \rightarrow$$
$$\qquad\quad |$$
$$\qquad NH_2$$

$$CH_3CH \cdot COOH \qquad\qquad + HCl$$
$$\qquad\quad |$$
$$\qquad NH \cdot CO \cdot O \cdot CH_2 \cdot C_6H_5$$
Carbobenzoxy derivative

The protected derivative may now be treated as an acid. It forms an acid chloride or bromide which will condense with an amino acid to give a substituted dipeptide.

$$CH_3CH \cdot COBr \qquad\qquad + H_2N \cdot CH \cdot COOH \rightarrow$$
$$\qquad\quad | \qquad\qquad\qquad\qquad\qquad |$$
$$\qquad NH \cdot CO \cdot O \cdot CH_2 \cdot C_6H_5 \qquad\quad R$$
        Acid bromide   **Amino acid**

$$\qquad\qquad\qquad\qquad\qquad\qquad R$$
$$\qquad\qquad\qquad\qquad\qquad\qquad |$$
$$CH_3CH \cdot CO \cdot NH \cdot CH \cdot COOH + HBr$$
$$\qquad\quad |$$
$$\qquad NH \cdot CO \cdot O \cdot CH_2 \cdot C_6H_5$$
              Substituted dipeptide

To free the dipeptide it is only necessary to reduce with hydrogen in the presence of colloidal platinum. The protecting group is split out with formation of toluene and carbon dioxide, and the dipeptide is set free.

$$C_6H_5 \cdot CH_2 \mid \cdot O \cdot CO \mid \cdot NH \cdot CH \cdot CO \cdot NH \cdot CH \cdot COOH \rightarrow$$
$$\qquad\qquad\qquad\qquad\qquad\quad | \qquad\qquad\qquad |$$
$$\qquad\qquad\qquad\qquad\qquad CH_3 \qquad\qquad\quad R$$

$$\quad H \mid \qquad\quad \mid H$$

$$C_6H_5CH_3 + CO_2 + H_2N \cdot CH \cdot CO \cdot NH \cdot CH \cdot COOH$$
$$\qquad\qquad\qquad\qquad\qquad\qquad | \qquad\qquad\qquad |$$
$$\qquad\qquad\qquad\qquad\qquad CH_3 \qquad\qquad\quad R$$
        Toluene   **Dipeptide**

Alternatively, the substituted dipeptide may be transformed into an acid halide and linked to other amino acids before removal of the protecting group.

(b) *Through the Phthalyl Derivative.* Although the Bergmann method made it possible to prepare a wide variety of peptides, it proved to have some disadvantages, particularly when the sulfur-containing amino acids were to be used. These disadvantages have been circumvented in a method which makes use of the phthalyl group to mask the amino group during the actual coupling. Removal of the protecting group from the phthalyl dipeptide is brought about by reaction with hydrazine (N_2H_4), a reagent to which the peptide bond is insensitive under the specified experimental conditions. The preparation of the hydrochloride of glycylglycine by this method is illustrated by the following equations adapted from Sheehan and Frank's paper:

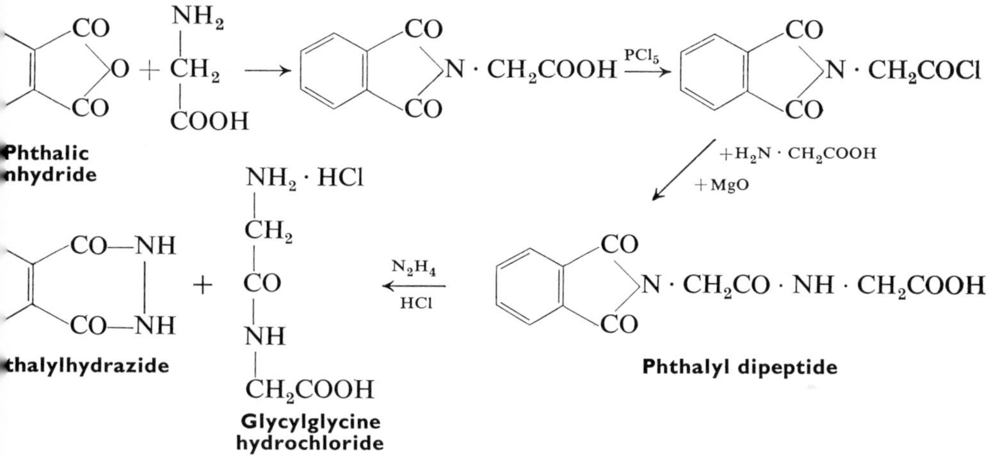

The advantage of this method over that of protection by the carbobenzoxy group lies chiefly in the fact that the various phthalyl compounds are obtained as readily crystallizable substances. This is not always true of the carbobenzoxy derivatives. At the same time, the phthalyl method gives at least as high yields as the older method at its best.

8. SIGNIFICANCE OF THE SYNTHETIC POLYPEPTIDES. Working long before either of the modern methods had been developed, Emil Fischer succeeded in building a polypeptide containing eighteen amino acid residues linked by a series of peptide bonds and having a molecular weight of 1213. Later the Swiss biochemist Emil Abderhalden prepared a slightly heavier polypeptide containing a wider variety of acids. A section of such a compound might be represented very approximately as shown in the formula, with a "backbone" made up of the α-carbons plus the carbons and nitrogens of the amide groupings. The zigzag chain is to be thought of as lying in the plane of the

paper, with R groups jutting out at an angle, alternately above and below this plane. (See page 225 for further discussion of this.)

$$\begin{array}{ccccccc}
\text{R} & & & & \text{R} & & \\
| & & & & | & & \\
\text{CH} & \text{NH} & \text{CO} & & \text{CH} & \text{NH} & \text{CO} \\
& & & & & & \\
\text{H}_2\text{N} & \text{CO} & \text{CH} & \text{NH} & \text{CO} & \text{CH} & \\
& & | & & & | & \\
& & \text{R} & & & \text{R} &
\end{array}$$

The name "polypeptide" is given not only to synthetic substances of known structure, such as those just referred to. If a protein is hydrolyzed, it goes through a number of stages before it is entirely broken down to amino acids. With care the process may be interrupted at the stage at which the molecules are about the size of those formed when eighteen to twenty amino acids have been linked together to form a synthetic polypeptide. Such a solution contains what may be called "natural polypeptides."

The justification for the name is found in a comparison of the properties of the natural and the synthetic substances. They are alike in solubility, and both respond positively to the general protein color reaction known as the biuret test (see page 207). This is dependent upon the presence in a molecule of at least two peptide bonds, separated by no more than a single carbon or nitrogen atom. The test is positive, for example, with biuret itself, $NH_2 \cdot CO \cdot NH \cdot CO \cdot NH_2$.

Both the natural and the synthetic polypeptides can be hydrolyzed by heating with acids, or by the use of digestive enzymes. As the hydrolysis progresses, the number of free carboxyl and amino groups in each digest increases, and at approximately the same rate. This is, of course, to be expected of the synthetic substance since hydrolysis of such a compound must rupture peptide bonds and set free carboxyl and amino groups in equal numbers.

$$-CH_2 \cdot CO \cdot NH \cdot CH_2- + H_2O \rightarrow -CH_2 \cdot COOH + H_2NCH_2-$$

But the fact that the hydrolysis evidently progresses in much the same way with the natural products points to the existence of similar linkages in the two compounds.

Far more striking than this, however, is the fact that both compounds are attacked by the same digestive enzymes. One of the most characteristic properties of those natural catalysts is their extreme specificity. An enzyme designed to bring about the hydrolysis of sucrose will not attack lactose. Even a change in optical rotation about a single carbon may render a molecule inert toward a particular enzyme. It is therefore extremely significant that enzymes which digest natural proteins also hydrolyze the synthetic polypeptides.

From these facts it was concluded long ago that the amino acids in proteins are probably linked, at least in part, through peptide bonds. Later work has confirmed and extended this conclusion so that it is now recognized that these bonds constitute the chief linkages in the protein molecule. This conclusion has been confirmed again and again as new techniques have made it possible to test it in different ways.

The Proteins

Having now learned something of the chemical properties of the individual amino acids we are ready to consider their condensation products, the proteins.

Color tests for proteins

There are a few classical color tests which were long used to test for the presence of protein although most of them actually indicate only the presence of certain specific amino acids which are commonly found in proteins.

1. THE BIURET TEST. This is the most general of the color tests and is given not only by proteins but by many of their hydrolytic products and indeed by many quite simple molecules. When a drop of very dilute cupric sulfate solution is added to a protein solution containing excess of potassium hydroxide a characteristic violet or rose-violet color develops. The simplest molecule which gives a positive test is one containing two peptide linkages, either directly attached to each other, as in oxamide, or separated by a single carbon or nitrogen atom as in malonamide or in biuret itself. This last is formed by loss of ammonia when urea is heated to a high temperature.

$$\begin{array}{ccc} CONH_2 & CONH_2 & CONH_2 \\ | & | & | \\ CONH_2 & CH_2 & NH \\ & | & | \\ & CONH_2 & CONH_2 \\ \textbf{Oxamide} & \textbf{Malonamide} & \textbf{Biuret} \end{array}$$

The colored substance which forms is a complex, reminiscent of those formed by cupric ion and free amino acids. In it the cupric ion is believed to be coordinated with at least four nitrogens of peptide groups. One suggested structure is the following:

$$\begin{array}{ccc} & H_2O & \\ R \cdot OC \cdot HN\text{:} & | & \text{:}NH \cdot CO \cdot R \\ & Cu^{++} & \\ R \cdot OC \cdot HN\text{:} & | & \text{:}NH \cdot CO \cdot R \\ & H_2O & \end{array}$$

2. MILLON'S TEST. Millon's reagent consists of a mixture of mercuric nitrate and mercuric nitrite in excess of the two acids. It cannot be used with alkaline solutions nor in the presence of a high concentration of inorganic salts.

Most proteins when warmed with Millon's reagent develop a brick-red color. A similar though deeper color appears when any compound containing a phenolic hydroxyl group is tested with the reagent. Since the only naturally occurring amino acid which contains this group is tyrosine, the development of the typical color establishes the presence of tyrosine in a protein.

3. HOPKINS-COLE TEST. As noted on page 198 this test, known also as the Adamkiewicz and the Acree-Rosenheim test, depends upon the presence of tryptophan in a protein. The reagent is either glyoxylic acid or formaldehyde, either of which is used with concentrated sulfuric acid to form the violet condensation product whose formula was given in the earlier discussion.

4. XANTHOPROTEIC ACID TEST. The intense yellow color which develops when concentrated nitric acid comes in contact with skin is the result of nitration of aromatic rings in the protein, specifically those of tyrosine and of tryptophan. This color is intensified to a deep orange by treatment with a base.

5. NINHYDRIN REACTION. Although ninhydrin is used for quantitative determination of free amino acids if the acidity is kept below pH 4 (see page 216), it also yields a blue color with proteins under other conditions of acidity. The positive test indicates the presence in the protein of a certain number of free amino and carboxyl groups.

Isolation of proteins from tissues

Many proteins occur in solution in natural fluids such as blood serum or digestive juices. Others may be extracted from tissues by the use of such solvents as dilute acid or base or sodium chloride solution. Either solution will contain many different proteins with nearly identical properties as well as a number of small organic and inorganic molecules. The isolation of a single protein from such a mixture is a difficult matter, and all that can be done here is to indicate some of the methods by which it may be attempted.

It has already been indicated that certain protein precipitants can be counted upon to throw out of solution almost all proteins. Alcohol in sufficient concentration is such a general precipitant, and the alkaloidal reagents also remove protein from solution, presumably by forming such salts as protein picrate or phosphotungstate. Such a procedure serves to separate the extracted protein from soluble nonprotein material. Sometimes it is possible even at this stage to make a partial separation of the proteins themselves. Some proteins precipitate if their solution is partially saturated with such a neutral salt as ammonium or magnesium sulfate. Others separate only from the completely saturated solutions. The "globulin" extracted from fat-free peanut meal is divided into two fractions if its solution is first made 0.2 saturated with respect to ammonium sulfate. This throws down part of the dissolved protein, which may be separated from the solution by filtration, or better by use of a centrifuge. Complete saturation of the filtrate "salts out" a second protein fraction.

Some proteins precipitate when their solutions are brought to a definite acidity. Like the amino acids, the proteins have isoelectric points which depend upon the nature of the constituent amino acids and upon the number and nature of the links between them. At some definite pH the net charge on the molecule is zero, and at this pH certain physical properties of protein solutions have a maximum or minimum value. Viscosity, osmotic pressure, and solubility in water, for example, are at minimum values at the isoelectric point. Some proteins precipitate directly if the pH of the solution is brought to this critical value. Casein, the chief protein of milk, is thus separated from other proteins when milk is brought to pH 4.6.

Dialysis is frequently employed in the process of isolating proteins. Sometimes a crude extract is dialyzed against running water to separate it from small molecules which have been extracted with the protein and which pass through the membrane and are carried away. In other procedures a protein precipitate, obtained by salting out, may be suspended in water and the suspension dialyzed against water. As the small salt molecules which brought about the precipitation pass into the water, the protein goes back into solution. With proteins which cannot be crystallized this process of alternate precipitation and dissolution may be repeated again and again to effect a partial purification.

The ultracentrifuge has proved to be an instrument of great value both in purification of proteins and in assessing the purity of a supposedly homogeneous sample. As previously noted, these instruments are capable of speeds of more than 100,000 revolutions per minute and develop a centrifugal force equivalent to 1,000,000 times gravity. When a protein mixture is subjected to such a force as this, any molecules which are conspicuously heavier than others go quickly to the bottom, leaving the lighter molecules suspended in the liquid. When skimmed milk is spun in the ultracentrifuge, its casein separates readily, leaving behind in the "milk serum" a number of protein constituents of lower molecular weights.

Criteria of purity of proteins

Some proteins remain amorphous through repeated precipitations and dissolutions but are by such procedures separated into fractions which become progressively more homogeneous. Others separate as crystals quite readily. But not even with the crystalline proteins is it a simple matter to determine when a sample is pure. None of the usual criteria for the purity of organic compounds can be applied. The proteins do not melt but decompose at elevated temperatures. No distinction between fractions can be made on the basis of elementary analyses since the elementary analysis of one protein is very like that of another. Fortunately, however, there are now available physical methods which not only facilitate the isolation of proteins but help to assess the purity of the final sample.

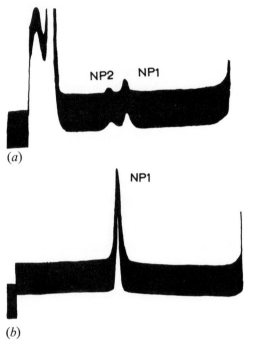

(a)

(b)

Fig. 5.2. Ultracentrifuge diagrams. (*a*) Clover leaf extract, diluted with an equal volume of water. (*b*) Purified nucleoprotein fraction obtained from clover leaf extract. [From J.W. Lyttleton, *Biochem. J.*, **74**, 84 (1960).]

Many supposedly pure proteins have proved in the ultracentrifuge to be mixtures. Figure 5.2 shows in (*a*) the ultracentrifuge pattern obtained with a crude aqueous clover leaf extract. The peaks labeled NP_1 and NP_2 are due to heavy nucleoprotein particles with sedimentation coefficients of approximately 55 and 65 S, while the peaks to the left (nearer the meniscus) represent two lower molecular weight components. In (*b*) the single peak indicates that the purification procedure used has successfully isolated the NP_1 component and freed the solution of contaminants. In this particular experiment the ultracentrifuge was also used in the purification, the particles differing enough in their sedimentation coefficients to be separated by differential centrifugation.

The electrophoresis technique offers another method both for fractionation of protein mixtures and for examining the purity of a supposedly homogeneous sample. Just as simple amino acids in solution carry a net charge which is negative or positive depending on their isoelectric points and on the *p*H of the solution, so do the proteins. The isoelectric point of a protein depends upon its amino acid composition. A high percentage of dicarboxylic acids will cause a protein to carry a negative charge, while a high percentage of the basic acids will make the protein a cation.

Apparatus designed for the separation of protein mixtures uses a large cell, of which Fig. 5.3 is an example. The divisions between compartments are made of sintered glass. The solution of protein is put in the center compartment and buffer solutions in the others. After the current has run for a suitable length of time, the contents of the various compartments are examined

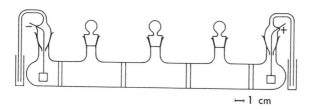

⊢1 cm

Fig. 5.3. An electrophoresis cell in which the compartments are separated by sintered glass disks. Capacity of cells I and V, 40 ml; cells II, III, and IV, 80 ml; platinum electrodes. [From G. W. Irving, H. M. Dyer, and V. duVigneaud, *J. Am. Chem. Soc.*, **63**, 505 (1941).]

separately and subjected when necessary to further purification. In one such experiment with a relatively pure protein it was found that about 70 per cent of the total solute had concentrated in the cathode compartment. The use of simple electrophoresis for preparative work is now less important than its use for assessing the purity of a sample, but as a preliminary step the method is frequently of value.

When electrophoresis is carried out, not for the purpose of fractionation, but to determine the purity of a sample, a very small aliquot will serve the purpose and the cell shown in Fig. 2.30 on page 85 is used. If but one boundary appears, moving smoothly toward one electrode even when the solvent and the *p*H of the solution are varied, the solute is said to be electrophoretically homogeneous. If the same substance appears also to be homogeneous in the ultracentrifuge, again when dispersed in various buffers at different *p*H values, its purity is as nearly proved as is possible at present.

How complex such an entity is and how inadequate are our chemical and physical tests of purity become clear when the immunological reactions of proteins are considered. A protein of moderate molecular weight contains about three hundred amino acid residues, representing about twenty different amino acids. One needs only an elementary understanding of permutations and combinations to realize that the number which represents all possible arrangements of these residues is so large as to be quite inconceivable. It should therefore be clear that proteins might be elaborated in living tissues, identical in all the physical and chemical properties which can be measured without disruption of the molecule and yet not identical in their ultimate molecular architecture. They might differ, for example, in the actual number of different acids present, or in their ratio to each other, or in the order of their arrangement in the polypeptide chain. This type of difference between proteins can best be detected serologically.

When a protein from one species of animal is injected into another species, it acts as a foreign substance or antigen and gives rise in the blood of the host to antibodies which are themselves protein in nature. The flocculation which results when serum of the host is mixed with a solution of the antigen is believed to depend upon a specific structural relationship between the two proteins. It is therefore of great interest that antibodies formed in response to serum albumin of one species do not precipitate in the presence of serum albumin of another species. This must indicate fine structural differences between proteins which respond identically to the ordinary chemical tests. Apparently under the mediation of cell catalysts, each species uses the twenty-one or twenty-two fundamental amino acids to build highly individual and specific protein molecules, each generation reproducing faithfully its own ancestral pattern.

In spite of the difficulties which have just been indicated, a few proteins have been prepared in apparently pure form. Even when absolute purity has not been achieved it has been possible to carry out many satisfactory studies of protein chemistry with samples which approach homogeneity. Indeed much of our present information about proteins has been obtained by the use of partially purified substances.

Classification of proteins

The proteins were classified near the turn of the century on a purely empirical basis, which depended chiefly on differences in solubility. No fundamental revision of this classification has been made in the intervening years. It was never very satisfactory but does separate a large number of very similar compounds into classes which are useful in separation of mixtures. A real classification must await a much more detailed knowledge of the chemistry of the proteins.

All proteins may be roughly divided into three main groups as follows:

1. Simple proteins are compounds which occur in nature and yield on hydrolysis only α-amino acids or their derivatives.
2. Conjugated proteins also occur naturally but when they are hydrolyzed they set free in addition to α-amino acids various nonprotein molecules, such as carbohydrate or hemin. The nonprotein part of such a molecule is known as a "prosthetic group."

3. Derived proteins, as the name implies, are substances formed from native proteins. The molecules are still of colloidal size but may be formed by partial hydrolysis or by other slight modification of the natural protein.

These main classes are further subdivided as follows:

1. SIMPLE PROTEINS

Albumins. Soluble in water and in neutral salt solutions; coagulable by heat. Examples are serum albumin from blood and ovalbumin from white of egg.

Globulins. Insoluble in water but soluble in dilute solutions of neutral salts; coagulable by heat; insoluble in saturated solutions of neutral salts or in half-saturated ammonium sulfate. Examples are serum globulin and edestin from hemp seed. The antibodies are among the serum globulins.

Glutelins. Insoluble in water or neutral salt solutions but soluble in dilute acid or alkali. An example is glutenin from wheat. This type of protein has been found only in plants.

Prolamines. These are also plant proteins. Their solubility is like that of the glutelins but they differ in being soluble in 75 per cent alcohol. Contain a high percentage of proline. An example is gliadin from wheat.

Albuminoids (*Scleroproteins*). Extremely insoluble except in reagents which bring about decomposition. Examples are keratin from wool and fibroin from silk.

Histones. Soluble in water and in dilute acids or strong bases; weakly basic in character due to a high percentage of diamino acids. An example is globin from hemoglobin.

Protamines. Soluble in water and in dilute acids; not coagulable by heat; composed largely of diamino acids so that their aqueous solution is basic to litmus; occur chiefly in combination with nucleic acid; the molecules are smaller than most proteins, and so diffuse through collodion. An example is salmin from salmon sperm.

2. COMPOUND OR CONJUGATED PROTEINS

Nucleoproteins. The prosthetic group is nucleic acid, a complex substance of high molecular weight containing both nitrogen and phosphorus.

Chromoproteins. Compounds of protein with some colored molecule which contains a metal. An example is hemoglobin from which may be set free the iron-containing substance, heme, and the protein, globin.

Phosphoproteins. According to British classification these are simple proteins, though hydrolysis frees phosphoric acid which is neither combined in a phospholipid nor in nucleic acid in the original molecule. An example is casein from milk.

Glycoproteins. The prosthetic group is carbohydrate in nature. Mucin from saliva is an example.

Several of the enzymes are conjugated proteins and will be considered later.

3. DERIVED PROTEINS

Primary Protein Derivatives. These are substances derived from proteins by changes less drastic than hydrolysis. *Denatured proteins*, representing the least possible change in the protein molecule, belong in this group. Non-hydrolytic changes brought about by brief exposure to acids or alkalis result in *metaproteins*. *Coagulated proteins* are also considered primary derivatives.

Secondary Protein Derivatives. While still having molecules large enough to exhibit many of the properties of proteins, these are early products of protein hydrolysis. Hydrolysis of proteins does not, as might have been expected, proceed by a splitting of amino acids one by one from the ends of the molecule. Rather, it begins with a splitting of the huge molecule into two or three roughly similar fragments. As this process is repeated the molecules finally become too small to be considered proteins any longer. The gradual change in molecular size is reflected in changes in coagulability, in solubility, in sedimentation constants and in rates of diffusion. On this basis the hydrolysis of proteins is believed to go through the following stages:

Proteoses. Soluble in water and not coagulated by heat. Precipitate from saturated ammonium sulfate solution.

Peptones. Water-soluble and not coagulable by heat. Not precipitated by saturated ammonium sulfate but are precipitated by some alkaloidal reagents.

Peptides. This group includes all the smaller fragments which are not precipitated by any of the protein reagents. The largest of these are called *polypeptides*, and they are degraded to tri- and dipeptides and finally to free acids.

Quantitative analysis of proteins

To obtain information about the amino acids present in a protein it must be hydrolyzed completely, and its constituent amino acids must be determined quantitatively. Emil Fischer devised the first satisfactory separation when he transformed into esters the mixture of acids obtained by hydrolysis of protein and separated these esters by fractional distillation under diminished pressure. This procedure, however, is more satisfactory for isolation from a hydrolyzed protein of those amino acids which are present in high proportion than for identifying all the amino acids present. The method requires at least 100 g of protein and never yields even approximately complete analytical figures.

Modern methods have improved upon Fischer's separation in various ways. After hydrolysis of the protein is complete, the mixture of amino acids may be subjected to a preliminary fractionation. For example, a separation into three fractions may be achieved by use of one of the large electrophoresis cells. The basic amino acids concentrate near the cathode, the dicarboxylic acids move toward the anode compartment, while the large group of neutral acids remains in the central part of the cell. For such a separation a cell of the type shown in Fig. 5.3 may be used.

After such a preliminary separation, the concentration of the individual acids may be determined in different ways. Some are precipitated by specific reagents. Histidine, for example, may be separated from the other basic acids by precipitation as the insoluble silver salt. Other acids lend themselves to quantitative colorimetric estimation without preliminary separation from a mixture. For example, the characteristic color of arginine with the Sakaguchi reagent (see page 202) may be used to determine its concentration. Several other acids with functional groups other than the amino and carboxyl groups may be estimated colorimetrically, but for a complete analysis it is necessary to turn to other methods.

1. MICROBIOLOGICAL ASSAY. A method which was very useful before chromatography became so common was the procedure known as *bioassay*. It depends upon the fact that microorganisms can be bred so that a certain strain requires in its nutrient medium a specific amino acid. Over a certain concentration range of this acid, the growth rate of the organism is then proportional to the amount of acid present in the nutrient medium, as shown in Fig. 5.4. If a protein hydrolyzate is used as the source of the amino acid,

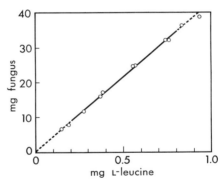

Fig. 5.4. The relation between the weight of leucine added to the medium and the weight of fungus which has formed at the end of 8½ days of incubation. [From F. J. Ryan and E. Brand, *J. Biol. Chem.*, **154**, 167 (1944).]

the growth rate measures the amount of that particular acid present in the mixture. Even though such experiments involve incubation periods of eight to ten days, they are simple compared with the elaborate and often frustrating chemical manipulations involved in the quantitative separation of the kind of mixture provided by a protein hydrolyzate. Bioassay requires comparatively small amounts of protein, and can be used to detect the presence of amino acids which make up only a small proportion of the total mixture. Bacterial strains have now been developed which can be used in the bioassay of all the known natural amino acids.

2. CHROMATOGRAPHIC ANALYSIS.   The method of separation of amino acids which now seems to take precedence over all others is the chromatographic.   As a matter of fact the present modern use of this method began when Martin and his colleagues first worked out procedures for separating amino acids on gelatine.   Now, with a suitably chosen method, whether on paper or on a column, an extraordinarily small amount of protein hydrolyzate can be separated into its constituent amino acids.

The identification of the positions of the various acids usually depends upon the fact that most amino acids yield a blue condensation product with ninhydrin.   In the formulation, the triple arrows indicate that several steps have been omitted.

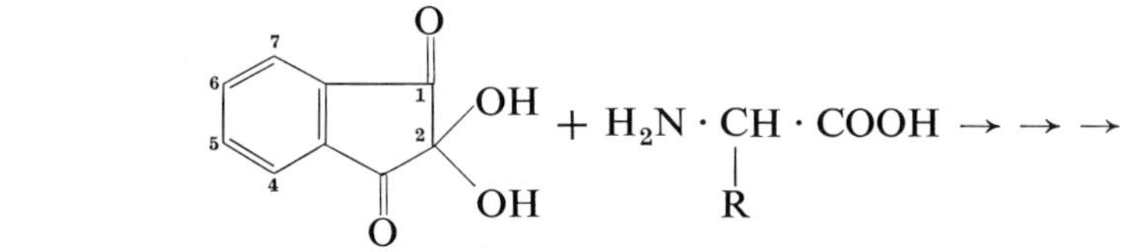

Ninhydrin
Triketohydrindene
hydrate

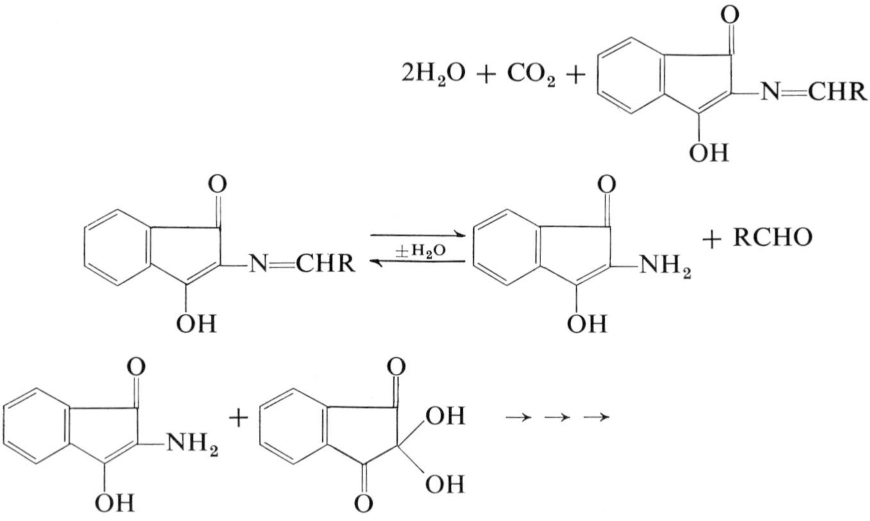

Ninhydrin

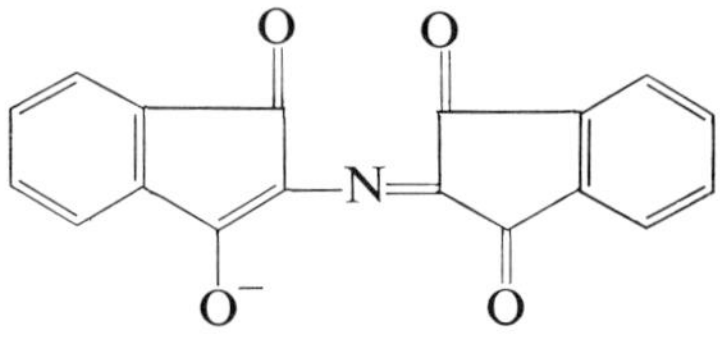

Ruhemann's purple

The only ones of the natural amino acids which do not normally give a clear blue are the prolines which first form a yellow product. This on heating goes over to a purple by condensation with a third molecule of ninhydrin, but often the prolines are simply identified by the yellow spots.

Yellow product   **Purple from the prolines**

Amino acids separated by two-dimensional chromatography are identified as shown in Fig. 2.7 on page 30. The paper is sprayed with ninhydrin and warmed to bring out blue or purple spots wherever an amino acid has accumulated. Identification of the spots of course depends upon knowing the R_f values of the different acids in the solvents used and having as a standard a "map" on which the positions of all the acids with those solvents have been determined.

Since two-dimensional chromatography is rather time-consuming, a recent technique which avoids the necessity for a second development is of interest. This depends upon the fact that the different amino acids give rise to different colors when sprayed with a modified ninhydrin reagent. The reagent consists of two solutions which are mixed just before using. One is a solution of ninhydrin in a mixture of ethyl alcohol, glacial acetic acid and 2,4,6-collidine (2,4,6-trimethylpyridine). The other is a solution of cupric nitrate trihydrate in absolute alcohol. The mixture of the two is a ninhydrin-copper complex which reacts when warmed with amino acids to yield a characteristic color with each of the naturally occurring L-amino acids. There is some duplication of colors, but this occurs with acids which have such different R_f values that they can easily be differentiated by their positions on the paper. It is claimed that with the ninhydrin-copper reagent the chromatogram need be developed in only one direction for a clear identification even of those acids with very similar migration rates.

Probably the most elegant and generally satisfactory chromatographic method is the one developed by Moore and Stein. This uses column chromatography and catches the effluent solution in small equal volumes, collected automatically. The original packing material was starch, but later experiments have used various synthetic sulfonated polystyrene resins such as Dowex 50 or Amberlite IR-120. The concentration of amino acid in each 2-ml fraction of effluent was originally determined by separate colorimetric estimation of the ninhydrin color, but apparatus is now available for automatic recording of this color. The stream of effluent meets a capillary stream of ninhydrin solution and the mixture then passes through tubing immersed in boiling water, to bring out the color. As the colored stream emerges from the bath its light absorption at 570 and at 440 mμ is recorded automatically.

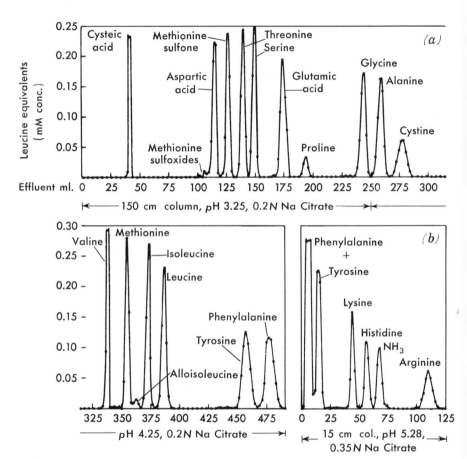

Fig. 5.5. Chromatographic fractionation of synthetic mixture of amino acids on columns of Amberlite IR-120. Load on 0.9 × 150 cm column was 1 μmole of each amino acid (0.5 μmole of cystine). (*a*) Obtained by elution of neutral and acidic amino acids at 50° from column at flow rate of 12 ml per hour. (*b*) Elution of the basic amino acids (at half the above load) from a 0.9 × 15 cm column of the resin at 50° and at a flow rate of 25 ml per hour. Effluent collected in 2-ml fractions. [From S. Moore and W. H. Stein, *Anal. Chem.*, **30**, 1185 (1958).]

The absorbance at 440 mμ is for identification of proline; that at 570 mμ records the amount of blue color given by other amino acids.

Before such an analysis can be carried out with unknown mixtures, the order of emergence of the individual acids from a particular adsorbent column, with specific buffers as eluants must be mapped. Figure 5.5 shows in (a) how a synthetic mixture of neutral and acidic amino acids emerges from a polystyrene column if eluted with citrate buffers, first at pH 3.25 and then at pH 4.25. In (b) the separation of the basic amino acids is shown, using a much shorter column and buffer at pH 5.28. Since the areas under the peaks are proportional to the amounts of amino acid present, such curves yield a quantitative analysis of a protein hydrolyzate. With the automatic recording of concentrations, such an analysis can be carried out in 22 hours and requires only 1–2 mg of hydrolyzed protein. This is to be contrasted with Fischer's separations which began with at least 100 g of protein, and even then could identify only those acids which were present in fairly high concentration.

The number of proteins whose amino acid content is known accurately is increasing rapidly. It is in the indication of the composition of such a large and complicated molecule as a protein that the use of residue abbreviations is particularly convenient. In the early stages of the study of a pure protein its amino acid composition is indicated as shown for pepsin. The subscripts of course indicate the number of residues of each acid per molecule of protein.

Pepsin, MW 34,400, Total N 14.60%

$Gly_{29}Ala \ldots Val_{21}Leu_{27}Ileu_{28}Pro_{15}Phe_9(CySH)_2(CyS-)_4Met_4Try_4Arg_2His_2$

$Lys_2Asp_9Glu_{28}(Asp-NH_2)_{32}Ser_{40}Thr_{28}Tyr_{16}(H_2O)_2(H_2PO_3)$

In later stages when the actual order of the amino acids is known, the residue abbreviations show this clearly and as briefly as possible. Such a formulation for beef insulin is shown in Fig. 5.6 on page 221.

Structure of proteins

As soon as it became possible to obtain data on the amino acid composition of pure proteins, two problems arose: (1) in what order are the many acids attached to each other in a molecule with a molecular weight of, for example, 34,000, and (2) how are the resulting polypeptides disposed in space to yield molecules of such different sizes and shapes as those represented in Fig. 2.24 on page 72.

1. THE AMINO ACID SEQUENCE. The pioneer attack on the first problem was made by Frederick Sanger at Cambridge University. Very sensibly, he chose for examination the low molecular weight protein insulin, which could be obtained in pure form. His plan was first to determine the number of free amino groups in the molecule by treating the protein with 1-fluoro-2,4-dinitrobenzene (FDNB) which reacts with any free amino group to form a yellow dinitrophenyl (DNP) derivative. Thinking of the protein as a long

polypeptide chain and indicating only its N-terminal end, the reaction may be represented:

$$\text{NO}_2\text{—}\underset{\text{NO}_2}{\bigcirc}\text{—F } + \text{ H}_2\text{N} \cdot \underset{\text{R}}{\text{CH}} \cdot \text{CO—protein } \rightarrow$$

$$\text{NO}_2\text{—}\underset{\text{NO}_2}{\bigcirc}\text{—NH} \cdot \underset{\text{R}}{\text{CH}} \cdot \text{CO—protein } + \text{ HF}$$

Subsequent hydrolysis sets free a mixture of amino acids of which only those which were N-terminal are marked with the color-producing dinitrophenyl group. From the mixture the yellow ones are separated and identified by paper chromatography. Of course the ε-amino group of any lysine would also react with the reagent. The first report indicated that for each molecule, which was then believed to have a molecular weight of 12,000, there were two free amino groups in glycine, two in phenylalanine and two in lysine. Since insulin was known to contain cystine, but no DNP derivative of cysteine appeared, these results were interpreted to mean that the molecule of insulin consisted of four polypeptide chains held together by disulfide links between the chains. Two of the chains (A chains) have glycine at the N-terminal end, and the other two (B chains) have phenylalanine. The molecular weight has now been found to be only 6000 and so each molecule consists of one A and one B chain.

The chains can be separated by oxidation at room temperature with performic acid (formic acid in hydrogen peroxide) which ruptures the disulfide bonds, forming cysteic acid residues in the chains but otherwise leaving the chains intact. The separated chains can then be isolated and purified by fractional precipitation.

Further work with the isolated single chains has been described as being rather like dropping a pile of plates on the floor and then trying to reconstruct the design from a study of the pieces. Partial hydrolysis yielded complex mixtures of small polypeptides for the separation of which into manageable groups most of the available methods had to be called upon. These included adsorption on charcoal and on resins and separation of basic and acidic fractions by electrophoresis in three- and four-compartment cells. The partially separated peptides were then subjected to paper chromatography and the individual peptides eluted from the cut-out spots on the filter paper. Each peptide was then analyzed, both for its N-terminal acid and for its complete amino acid content. For the elucidation of the B chain about 65 peptides had to be completely characterized. Then, knowing the molecular weight of the chain and the ratio in which the various acids occurred, Sanger found that only one sequence of acids would fit all the pieces into a single chain, using the 30 acids known to be present. Figure 5.6 shows the structure of beef insulin which could be assigned when the positions of the crosslinkages and of the one intrachain disulfide link had been determined by methods, applied to insulin itself, which follow the pattern just outlined for elucida-

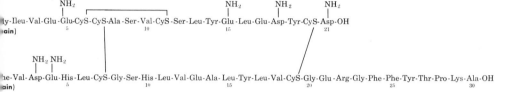

Fig. 5.6. Amino acid sequences in the A and the B chains of beef insulin.

tion of the single chains. Insulins from other sources prove to differ in the three residues at positions 8, 9, and 10 in the A chain but to be otherwise identical.

One of the most recent and spectacular applications of the methods which Sanger initiated has given the complete structure of the enzyme ribonuclease which contains 124 amino acid residues in a single chain of molecular weight 13,700. Partial hydrolysis of a protein is usually achieved by use of enzymes, and the study of ribonuclease made use of several digestive enzymes in order to split the chain in different places. (See chapter on Digestion for a discussion of the specificity of digestive enzymes.) In addition to determination of the amino acid at the N-terminal ends of the fragments, analyses were also carried out to discover which acids were at the carboxyl end of the various polypeptides.

For identification of the amino-terminal residues both the DNP method and the one using phenylisothiocyanate (see page 198) were used. The latter method is particularly useful for stepwise degradation of a peptide from the amino end. This process is known as the Edman degradation. After reaction with phenylisothiocyanate, the peptide is heated under a stream of dry hydrogen chloride, with the result that the phenylthiohydantoin of the N-terminal amino acid is set free and can be extracted with ether and identified by paper chromatography. Repetition of the procedure on the residual peptide will reveal the new N-terminal acid. This type of degradation can be repeated for identification of a few more residues. But after four to six residues have been removed, it ceases to perform reliably. However, the authors state that without the Edman procedure the work with ribonuclease would have been impossible.

Estimation of the acid at the carboxyl end of a chain is in general less satisfactory than that of the acid at the amino end. An enzyme known as a *carboxypeptidase* removes most acids from the free carboxyl end and in spite of various disadvantages its use often yields valuable data. Since it removes the new terminal carboxyl residue as soon as the first residue has been set free, and repeats this until blocked by a prolyl residue, use of this method involves time studies to determine the order in which residues must have been set free. However, a very recent modification circumvents this necessity by carrying out the hydrolysis in water labeled with O^{18}. Under these conditions only the terminal carboxyl will be free of O^{18} when hydrolysis is complete, since all the other carboxyl groups are formed by interaction of the peptide group with water. Identification of the acid which contains only the normal concentration of the oxygen isotope will therefore identify the acid which was at the C-terminal end of the polypeptide.

$$-NH-CH-CO-NH-CH-CO-NH-CH-COOH$$
$$\qquad \quad R_3 \qquad\qquad\quad R_2 \qquad\qquad\quad R_1$$

$$\quad HO^{18}H \qquad\qquad HO^{18}H$$

$$H_2N \cdot CH \cdot COO^{18}H + H_2N \cdot CH \cdot COO^{18}H + H_2N \cdot CH \cdot COOH$$
$$\qquad R_3 \qquad\qquad\qquad R_2 \qquad\qquad\qquad R_1$$

Ribonuclease proved to contain four disulfide bonds, the positions of which were determined in a five-step procedure which was first used with insulin.

1. Partial hydrolysis of the protein in such a way that the disulfide bonds are not broken.
2. Isolation of the cystine-containing peptides.
3. Oxidation of each peptide to two cysteic acid derivatives.
4. Isolation of the two cysteic acid peptides from each oxidation.
5. Determination of the amino acid composition of each cysteic acid peptide.

A part of the results obtained with ribonuclease are shown in Fig. 5.7. The enzyme protein has been subjected to digestion by trypsin and chymotrypsin in sequence. These enzymes split various peptide bonds but do not attack disulfide bonds. In the upper curve the distribution of the resulting peptides in the effluent from a column is recorded. The peptide concentrations in the various fractions were obtained by subjecting a small aliquot portion to alkaline hydrolysis and measuring the resultant amino acid concentration with ninhydrin. Since each fraction would yield an unknown mixture of acids, the concentration of peptide in each fraction is reported in "leucine equivalents," that is, as the amount of leucine which would be indicated by the color obtained. Simultaneously the concentration of cystine-containing peptides in each fraction was determined in another aliquot, using the Kassell and Brand color reaction (see page 200). The data from this second type of analysis are plotted in terms of the phosphotungstate color in the lower part of the upper graph. This curve shows that only in those parts of the effluent represented by the peaks labeled A, B, C, and D were there peptides containing cystine. The remainder of the fractions corresponding to each of the lettered areas A, B, C, and D were then pooled to give four solutions. These were oxidized

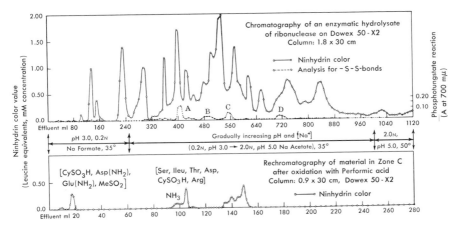

Fig. 5.7. (*Upper curve*) Separation of cystine-containing peptides formed from ribonuclease by the action of trypsin and chymotrypsin in 2 M guanidinium chloride. (*Lower curve*) Separation of cysteic acid peptides present after performic acid oxidation of the peptides present in Zone C of the upper curve. [From D. H. Spackman *et al.*, *J. Biol. Chem.*, **235**, 651 (1960).]

with performic acid to form cysteic acid-containing peptides, which were then subjected to chromatography. The lower curve in the figure shows the results of chromatography of one of the original four fractions. Because of the acidity of the cysteic acid-containing peptides, they move on the Dowex 50 column more rapidly than other peptides, and so are found within the first 120 ml of effluent, and emerge well before any other peptides in the mixture.

The experiments outlined above represent a tiny fraction of the information which had to be gathered before the amino acid sequence in ribonuclease could be established. References are given at the end of the chapter to the most recent papers which finally reported the complete primary structure of bovine pancreatic ribonuclease. Figure 5.8 shows this structure and the folds which must be made in the long polypeptide chain in order that the intrachain disulfide links may form.

2. THREE-DIMENSIONAL STRUCTURE OF PROTEINS. Long before any attempt had been made to determine the order of amino acids in a protein, chemists

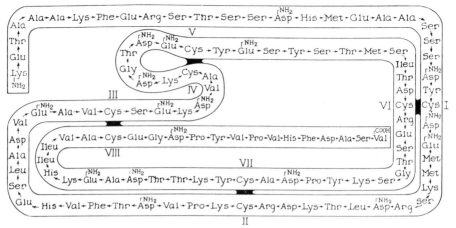

Fig. 5.8. A two-dimensional schematic diagram of the structure of bovine ribonuclease showing the arrangement of the disulfide bonds and the sequence of the amino acid residues. The arrows indicate the direction of the peptide chain starting from the amino end. [From D. H. Spackman *et al.*, *J. Biol. Chem.*, **235**, 656 (1960).]

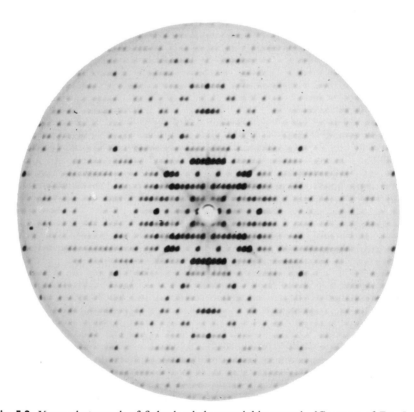

Fig. 5.9. X-ray photograph of finback whale myoglobin crystal. [Courtesy of Dr. J. C. Kendrew.]

and biochemists and especially the x-ray crystallographers had begun to speculate upon the disposition in space of the polypeptide chain or chains in various proteins. Although most proteins do not crystallize readily, many of them proved to have a regular repeating pattern which gave rise to usable x-ray diffraction diagrams. Much of our present knowledge of protein structure is based upon the analysis of such diagrams, one of which is shown in Fig. 5.9. Although such a diagram conveys nothing to the uninitiated, it is from such patterns that much of our present knowledge of interatomic distances and bond angles has been derived.

(*a*) *The Fibrous Proteins.* The first molecules to yield useful x-ray data were the long slender molecules of *fibroin* from silk and of the *keratins* which come from wool and hair. Fibroin is especially suited to structural studies. It is secreted in relatively pure form as a double filament, enveloped in a sticky coating which dissolves in hot detergent and leaves pure fibers of fibroin. Its composition is relatively simple, 45 per cent of its amino acid residues coming from glycine, 26 per cent from alanine, and 12 per cent from serine, with only very small amounts of other amino acids. As early as 1920 silk fibroin yielded an x-ray diffraction pattern which proved to be characteristic for silks from various sources. The spacing of the spots indicated that the identity period along the fiber axis, i.e., the distance from one group to an exactly similar one on the same side of the chain, was 7.00 A. A diagram of the simplest possible configuration of a polypeptide chain is shown in Fig. 5.10 with all the peptide units lying in a single plane, and the R groups jutting out alternately above and below this plane. This means that the identity period would be for example the distance between the R″ and the next but one in the chain, R⁗. The length of a single residue in the chain would be half of this.

In such a fully extended chain the identity period, or *fiber-axis repeat distance*, proves to be 7.2 A. The fact that this distance in fibroin is somewhat less than 7.2 A means that the chain is slightly rotated between residues so that the backbone itself has a zigzag form though each individual peptide group is planar. Such a chain is shown in Fig. 5.11(*a*). In Fig. 5.11(*b*) several such chains are shown, adjacent ones running in opposite directions. This brings into juxtaposition carbonyl groups of one chain and amino groups of its neighbor, and allows formation of hydrogen bonds between the two. The structure here shown, known as the antiparallel chain pleated sheet, is now believed to be a reasonable representation of a silk fiber. The involvement of all the carbonyl and amino groups in hydrogen bonding gives stability to the arrangement. The actual identity period for silk has recently been measured as 6.97 A and in the antiparallel pleated sheet this distance is 7.00 A. Other measurements also show a good correspondence and indicate that the distance between adjoining chains in the sheet is 4.75 A and the distance between sheets or molecular layers is 9.20 A.

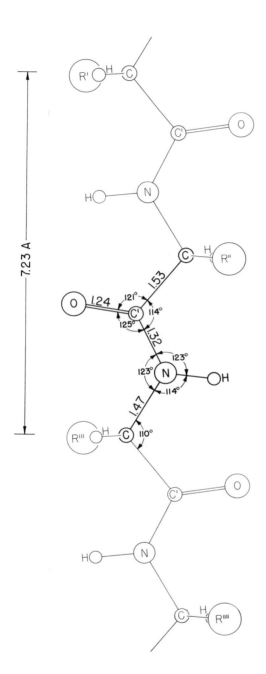

Fig. 5.10. Diagram of a fully extended polypeptide chain. [From R. B. Corey and L. Pauling, *Proc. Roy. Soc.* (London), **B141,** 10 (1953).]

The protein from wool, known as keratin, is one of a group of substances sometimes referred to as the keratin-myosin-epidermin-fibrinogen (k-m-e-f) group, all of which give similar x-ray patterns of the two types discussed below. Chemically these proteins are far more complex than fibroin, containing appreciable amounts of fifteen or more different amino acids, and so

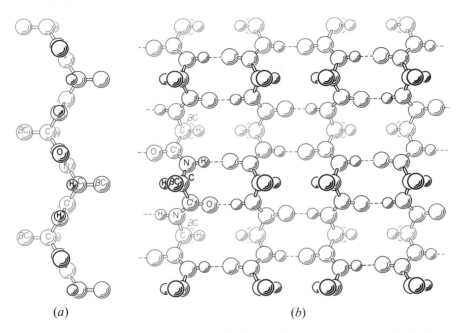

(a)   (b)

Fig. 5.11. A diagram of the antiparallel chain pleated sheet structure, with a single chain represented at the left. [From L. Pauling and R. B. Corey, *Proc. Natl. Acad. Sci. U.S.*, **37**, 729 (1951).]

including many more large R groups. In native keratin a conspicuous feature is the large number of cystine residues.

Like the wool from which it is derived, keratin immersed in steam can be stretched to twice its original length, and when the tension is removed, it springs back to its original length. But if it is dried under tension it maintains its stretched length until it is again moistened. The two forms of keratin, the natural unstretched one and the extended form, are known as α-keratin and β-keratin. That they show quite different x-ray reflections was first shown by W. T. Astbury[4] and his colleagues in England. Their pictures indicated that in β-keratin each residue in the polypeptide was of about the

---

[4] William Thomas Astbury (1898—) began his professional career at University College, London, but has been at Leeds University since 1928. He has been chiefly interested in the structure of fibers and crystals particularly as they can be studied in x-ray diffraction pictures.

same length as those in fibroin, namely 3.33 A. This means that the chain is almost completely extended. The best interpretation of the data now available leads to a structure for the extended keratin fiber very like that suggested for fibroin, and shown in Fig. 5.12. In this arrangement, known as the parallel chain pleated sheet, all the polypeptide chains run in the same direction, but hydrogen bridges are still formed as shown by the dotted lines. As in the

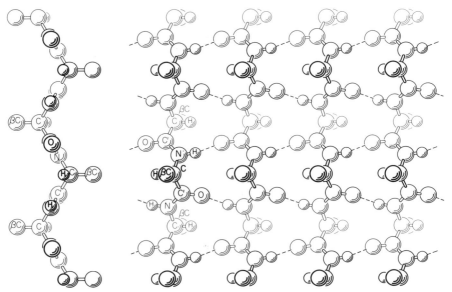

Fig. 5.12. Diagram of the parallel chain pleated sheet structure, with a diagram of a single chain at the left. [From L. Pauling and R. B. Corey, *Proc. Natl. Acad. Sci. U.S.*, **37**, 729 (1951).]

fibroin structure, the distance between one chain and the next in the sheet (backbone spacing) is approximately 4.7 A, and the sheets themselves lie 9.7 A apart. This distance is determined by the size of the R groups which both serve to hold the sheets apart sterically, and to hold them together by forming bonds through ester formation or formation of disulfide or amide links. The importance of the disulfide bonds becomes apparent if wool is treated with a reducing agent. This ruptures the disulfide links, and it is found that at the same time the mechanical strength of the fiber has been greatly lessened.

X-ray data for α-keratin indicate an identity period which is only about half that for the β form. This must mean that the polypeptide backbone is folded or pleated in some way. Evaluation of the x-ray patterns for both types of keratin is complicated by the fact that only part of the protein has a well ordered, crystalline form which yields a clear x-ray pattern. The amorphous parts give diffuse x-ray scattering which lessens the sharpness of the whole pattern. It is therefore not strange that many different proposals have been made for the structure of α-keratin, and that Kendrew could write as late as 1954 that "the dust of battle is still rather thick and in some directions quite impenetrable."

In the early days, Astbury and his school evolved a shortened structure in which a single polypeptide chain formed a series of planar loops held in place by hydrogen bonds between amide and carbonyl groups of a single chain. The geometry of the arrangement was such that only about one-third of the peptide groups could form such bonds.

The shortened form which is now given widest acceptance is the α helix proposed by Pauling[5] and Corey in 1951. Other helical structures had been suggested earlier, but this was the first one to take meticulous account of bond angles, interatomic distances, the space requirements of the larger R groups, coplanarity of the peptide grouping, and the necessity for providing for the largest possible number of hydrogen bonds. Previously suggested helical forms had assumed that each turn of the helix must involve an even number of amino acid residues. The Pauling model succeeded in meeting all the requirements listed above by so adjusting the size and pitch of the helix that there were 3.6 residues per turn. Such a structure allows each carbonyl group to be bonded to an amide group three residues along the chain and this network of hydrogen bonds down the center of the helix is believed to be the predominant stabilizing factor. The spatial relations of such a helix are indicated diagrammatically in Fig. 5.13, in which the heavy lines indicate the side of the helix nearest the observer. Although other helices have been proposed which are almost as satisfactory as the α helix, this latter is at present the preferred structure. Not only does it interpret the x-ray data for α-keratin, but it gives a good picture of the structure of all the proteins of the k-e-m-f group. Furthermore, it is probable that this same kind of coiling exists in parts at least of the more compact globular proteins.

(*b*) *Globular Proteins.* All the fibrous proteins described above are extremely inert chemically. All the physiologically active proteins, such as the serum proteins, hemoglobin and the enzymes, have physical properties which indicate that they are quite differently shaped from those proteins just discussed. The proteins in this second group are known as globular or corpuscular proteins, though many of them are far from being truly spherical. For example, x-ray studies show that hemoglobin is cylindrical in shape, having a radius of 27.5 A and a height of 65 A. Table 5.3 gives approximate dimensions of four serum globulins. Three of the four are clearly

---

[5] Linus Pauling (1901–) is Professor of Chemistry and Director of the Gates and Crellin Chemistry Laboratories at the California Institute of Technology. He has been interested chiefly in crystal structure and the sizes of ions, in the nature of the chemical bond, and in the structure of proteins.

unsymmetrical but all are far more compact than the molecules of fibrous proteins. This makes it much more difficult to picture them as long polypeptide chains, yet all the evidence indicates that the acids in the corpuscular proteins are linked exactly as they are in fibroin, through a succession of peptide

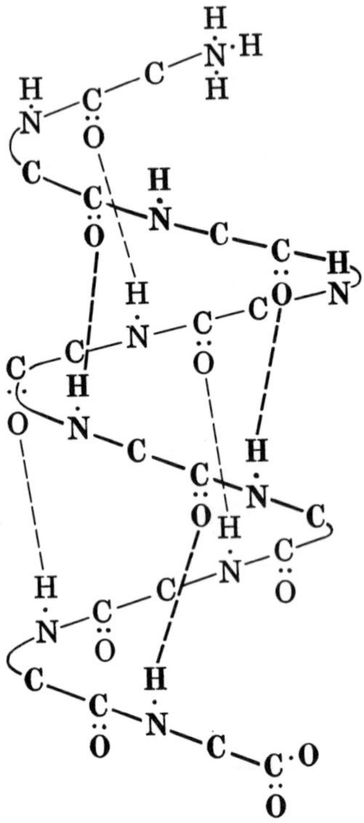

Fig. 5.13. Hydrogen bonding in an α helix. [From L. E. Orgel, "The Hydrogen Bond," in J. L. Oncley (ed.-in-chief), *Biophysical Science*, Wiley, New York, 1959.]

TABLE 5.3. **Dimensions of Globulins**

Length, A	Diameter, A
150	38
300	50
185	185
235	44

bonds. The corpuscular shape must arise therefore from some kinking or folding of the chain. There is at present no agreement on the type of folding involved, though it begins to seem that this may often be a very irregular arrangement.

Assume for the moment that a globular protein consists, as it is known to do for several relatively simple ones, of a single polypeptide chain.

Myoglobin, for example, with a molecular weight of 18,000, consists of 153 amino acid residues arranged in a single chain. X-ray studies indicate a long, irregularly folded rod which gives a molecule 45 A by 35 A by 25 A. Kendrew and his colleagues at Cambridge University picture this molecule as shown in

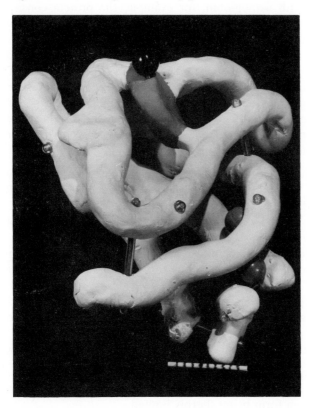

Fig. 5.14. Model of the myoglobin molecule. The gray disk seen nearly edge on is the heme group; the small spheres are heavy atoms that were attached to the myoglobin to facilitate the x-ray analysis. The marks on the scale are 1 A apart. [From J. C. Kendrew, "Three-Dimensional Structure of Globular Proteins," in J. L. Oncley (ed.-in-chief), *Biophysical Science*, Wiley, New York, 1959.]

Fig. 5.14, which is a photograph of a model made after an extensive x-ray analysis of the protein. Certain segments of the rod give an x-ray pattern which fits the α helix and it seems likely that this or some very similar coiling does in fact exist in these regions. In other places, where the rod bends sharply, the coiling must be less tight in order to allow for the total measured length of 300 A for the polypeptide. Comparison of this measurement with the 230 A which would be the length of the chain if it consisted entirely of an α helix, indicates that approximately 70 per cent of the chain is in the helical form. In this molecule then the primary structure is that represented by the formation of the long polypeptide chain. The secondary structure is given by the coiling of this chain, chiefly as an α helix, and the tertiary structure is determined by the highly irregular folding of this long rod upon itself. When, as happens with hemoglobin, for example, the protein consists of several distinct layers, it is said to show a quaternary structure in the relation of these coiled and folded layers to each other.

The great importance of the hydrogen bonds in maintaining the structure of the coiled protein has been stressed, but other links are also of importance in maintaining secondary and tertiary and possibly quaternary structure. Disulfide links play a role in many other proteins than the keratins. For example, Fig. 5.8 showed how the positions of the disulfide links determine the way the ribonuclease chain must fold. Other forces which come into play in protein molecules are:

1. Electrostatic forces of attraction or repulsion between areas carrying charges.
2. Van der Waals forces of attraction between hydrocarbon R groups at suitable distances from each other.
3. Bonds formed by phosphate residues linking, for example, seryl or threonyl residues by formation of a diester.
4. Phosphate bonds of an amide character, linking an hydroxyl group of one residue to a free amino group of another. This yields a crosslink: $-CH_2 \cdot O \cdot PO_2H \cdot NH-$.
5. Something which has been called a "hydrophobic bond," resulting from the strong hydrogen bonding of water molecules, which tend to exclude any groups such as the hydrocarbon side chains, and to push them together in what are effectively oil drops in the aqueous phase.

How many of these various crosslinkages will appear in any one protein will depend, of course, upon its composition and shape, the distances over which such bonds can form being sharply limited.

How general a pattern is represented by the two folded molecules, ribonuclease and myoglobin, no one can say. As noted above, there is evidence that some globular proteins consist of thin layers piled up "like a stack of pancakes." It may well be that each layer consists of a single coiled chain, folded to give a thin, roughly circular particle. Hemoglobin, for example, has such a layered structure and has been shown to consist of four polypeptide chains made up of two identical pairs.

Denatured proteins

Whatever its structure may ultimately prove to be, any native protein depends for its unique properties upon that arrangement. Any treatment, chemical or physical, which alters that structure but does not split the molecule is said to have *denatured* the protein. In the early days of protein chemistry, many of the procedures for extraction and isolation undoubtedly caused denaturation.

Many proteins are denatured by heat, and heat coagulation is believed to consist of denaturation followed by aggregation of the denatured molecules. Subtler changes are brought about by treating a protein with a concentrated solution of urea or of guanidine or by sharply increasing or decreasing the *p*H of the solution. These treatments all lower the solubility of the protein and change various other physical properties. If the original protein was biologically active as an antigen or infective agent or enzyme, it becomes inactive.

Frequently chemical changes accompany the changes in biological activity. For example, most native proteins give no test for free sulfhydryl or phenolic groups. When proteins are denatured, the presence of such groups is readily detectable by color tests. On the basis of these facts, denaturation has been defined as "any nonproteolytic modification of the unique structure of a native protein giving rise to definite changes in chemical, physical or biological properties."

In the light of what has been said about the structure of native proteins, it is possible to draw a reasonable picture of what may happen when a protein is denatured. In the native protein there is a long polypeptide chain, coiled or folded upon itself in a very definite pattern. Some of the side chains or R groups will be folded in, forming crosslinks with other interior side chains. These will build up inside the molecule a kind of lattice work in which the gratings consist of such linkages as result from formation of esters, of disulfide bonds, and of supplementary peptide linkages as well as the many hydrogen bonds. It is not hard to see why any tampering with the elaborate pattern so set up would change the properties of the molecules. Urea, for example, is believed to denature proteins by rupturing the hydrogen bonds which are essential to maintaining its secondary structure.

According to present theories, denaturation consists of a destruction or modification of the unique protein pattern. This may range from the breaking of a few minor crosslinks to such disorganization that the polypeptide chain becomes completely extended, or at any rate, folded in only a haphazard fashion. In the process certain groups may actually be freed. Sulfhydryl groups would appear if disulfide bonds were opened. Free carboxyl, amino, and hydroxyl groups would appear wherever amide and ester crosslinks were hydrolyzed. But not all groups which become manifest as a result of denaturation need actually have been "formed" by ruptured linkages. A free sulfhydryl group, for example, might be so buried within a molecule, or so hemmed in by large adjacent groups, that no nitroprusside (see page 200) could reach it. After denaturation the molecule is disoriented and its chains at least partially extended. In this condition the sulfhydryl groups might be readily available for reaction with nitroprusside and so would seem to have been newly freed.

NONPROTEIN COMPOUNDS OF NITROGEN

In addition to the proteins, there are in living tissue other nitrogenous compounds which are of biological importance. The place of some of these substances in the chemistry of cell metabolism is known; the importance of others is inferred from their wide distribution in living material though their exact function remains to be discovered.

Glutathione

Although isolated native proteins give no test for free sulfhydryl groups, living tissues quite uniformly respond to the nitroprusside test. Search for the cause of the positive test revealed the presence in nearly all living cells of a tripeptide named "glutathione" by Hopkins[6] who first isolated it. Glutathione consists of residues of glutamic acid, cysteine, and glycine condensed to form a tripeptide.

$$\text{HOOC} \cdot \underset{\underset{\text{NH}_2}{|}}{\text{CH}} \cdot \text{CH}_2 \cdot \text{CH}_2 \cdot \text{CO} \cdot \text{NH} \cdot \underset{\underset{\text{CH}_2\text{SH}}{|}}{\text{CH}} \cdot \text{CO} \cdot \text{NH} \cdot \text{CH}_2\text{COOH}$$

  γ-Glutamyl   **cysteinyl**   **glycine**

Since the important reactions of the molecule center about the sulfhydryl group, the abbreviation GSH is frequently used, and its ready reversible oxidation is then indicated:

$$2\text{GSH} + \tfrac{1}{2}\text{O}_2 \rightleftharpoons \text{GSSG} + \text{H}_2\text{O}$$

Since its discovery in 1921 many attempts have been made to assign a significant biological function to this compound. It has proved to be an essential participant in several enzymic reactions, but so far it has not been shown to be an obligatory component of any of the major metabolic systems. On the other hand, there are many enzymes which depend for their activity on the presence of free sulfhydryl groups in the enzyme molecule. Since such groups are readily oxidized and the resulting enzyme is entirely inactive, it may well be that one function of glutathione is to keep these enzymes in reduced form.

---

[6] Sir Frederick Gowland Hopkins (1861–1947) was an outstanding member of the small group of scientists who at about the turn of the century gave biochemistry the standing of an independent discipline. His own brilliant contributions to the science were a result of a rare combination of meticulous chemical technique and insight with a biologist's feeling for the cell as a complex living organism. As Head for many years of the Sir William Dunn Institute of Biochemistry at Cambridge he attracted students from all over the world and fostered research on a wide variety of biochemical problems. He was awarded every scientific honor which England has in her gift, and was a corecipient of the Nobel Prize in Medicine in 1929.

Glutathione has also a theoretical importance from the circumstance that it was through a consideration of its reversible oxidation-reduction that Hopkins in 1926 was led to postulate what he described as a "ferrying" action. Suppose that TH_2 represents some metabolite in the cell which is to react with oxygen and form water. For this substance oxidized glutathione could act as a ferry by accepting two hydrogen atoms to form GSH and then passing them on to molecular oxygen. This would reconstitute the oxidized glutathione molecule which could then pick up another pair of hydrogens from another molecule of the metabolite. The net result would be oxidation of the metabolite and the formation of water. It is probable that glutathione actually does take part in such a sequence in some plant oxidations, but this is not a major metabolic expedient. More important is the fact that this

$$TH_2 + GSSG \rightarrow T + 2GSH$$
**Oxidized
metabolite**

$$2GSH + \tfrac{1}{2}O_2 \rightarrow GSSG + H_2O$$

suggested mechanism for the course of oxidative reactions proved enormously fruitful in work with cell oxidizing systems. Cyclic changes of just the type suggested have proved to be very common in the chemistry of living tissues.

Urea and Guanidine

In man and in some other species, the end product of nitrogen metabolism is urea, the diamide of carbonic acid. Another important nitrogen compound is the much more strongly basic substance guanidine. The relation between the two compounds is evident from their formulas. It is the δ-guanido group in arginine which makes it a basic amino acid.

$$
\begin{array}{cc}
\begin{array}{c} \diagup NH_2 \\ C{=}O \\ \diagdown NH_2 \end{array} &
\begin{array}{c} \diagup NH_2 \\ C{=}NH \\ \diagdown NH_2 \end{array} \\
\textbf{Urea} & \textbf{Guanidine}
\end{array}
$$

Urea forms molecular compounds with acids in the cold. The characteristic forms of the saltlike crystals of these compounds are sometimes used to identify urea in biological fluids.

$$CO(NH_2)_2 \cdot HNO_3 \qquad CO(NH_2)_2 \cdot C_2H_2O_4$$
Urea nitrate **Urea oxalate**

If, however, urea is treated with an acid chloride instead of a free acid, a condensation takes place, yielding a compound known as a *ureid*. The product of the reaction with acetyl chloride is a straight chain compound, but with the dibasic acids the important cyclic ureids are formed. For example, diethyl malonate condenses with urea in the presence of sodium

$$H_2N \cdot CO \cdot NH_2 + 2CH_3COCl \rightarrow CH_3CO \cdot NH \cdot CO \cdot NH \cdot COCH_3$$

Diacetylurea

$$
\begin{array}{c}
NH_2 \\
| \\
CO \\
| \\
NH_2
\end{array}
+
\begin{array}{c}
C_2H_5O\text{—}OC \\
| \\
CH_2 \\
| \\
C_2H_5O\text{—}OC
\end{array}
\xrightarrow{\text{NaOC}_2\text{H}_5}
2C_2H_5OH +
\begin{array}{c}
\overset{1}{NH}\text{—}\overset{6}{CO} \\
| \qquad | \\
\overset{2}{CO} \quad \overset{5}{CH_2} \\
| \qquad | \\
\underset{3}{NH}\text{—}\underset{4}{CO}
\end{array}
$$

Barbituric acid

ethoxide to form the six-membered ring compound, malonyl urea or barbituric acid. Derivatives of barbituric acid in which one or both hydrogens on carbon 5 are substituted are important soporifics. Veronal, for example, is diethyl barbituric acid. This particular arrangement of carbons and nitrogens in a 6-membered ring is found in a number of compounds of great biological importance. Two compounds of the vitamin B complex, B_1 and B_2, each contain this ring as do the bases which make up part of the nucleic acid molecule.

Creatine and Creatinine

Related to guanidine is the basic substance, creatine, and its anhydride, creatinine.

$$
\begin{array}{c}
CH_3 \\
| \\
HN\text{=}C\text{—}N\text{—}CH_2COOH \\
| \\
NH_2
\end{array}
\rightarrow H_2O +
\begin{array}{c}
CH_3 \\
| \\
N \\
\diagup \quad \diagdown \\
HN\text{=}C \qquad CH_2 \\
| \qquad\qquad | \\
HN\text{———}CO
\end{array}
$$

**Creatine or N-methyl-
guanidoacetic acid**   **Creatinine**

The phosphoric acid derivative of creatine, sometimes called phosphagen, plays an important part in muscle metabolism.

$$
\begin{array}{c}
CH_3 \\
| \\
HN\text{=}C \cdot N \cdot CH_2COOH \\
| \\
NH \cdot PO_3H_2
\end{array}
$$

Phosphocreatine

The linkage between phosphorus and nitrogen in phosphocreatine is an example of the type of bond which is often referred to as an "energy rich" bond. This concept arose because when this bond is broken by hydrolysis of the compound, there is a large drop in free energy. Actually of course there is no way of knowing how the energy of the molecule is distributed or what changes in distribution result from the hydrolysis. Nevertheless, it is customary to differentiate, by using a wavy line, the bond whose rupture results in a freeing of a large amount of energy.

$$\underset{\overset{|}{NH{\sim}PO_3H_2}}{HN{=}C \cdot \overset{\overset{\displaystyle CH_3}{|}}{N} \cdot CH_2COOH}$$

We shall find that one of the prime functions of oxidation in the muscles is provision of the energy necessary for formation of such energy-rich compounds as phosphocreatine.

Nucleic Acids

The nonprotein nitrogen compounds so far considered are all simple substances, the formulas of which are known. The nucleic acids on the other hand are giant or macromolecules whose structures have been as difficult to unravel as those of proteins, and for many of the same reasons.

The nucleic acids were first discovered toward the end of the last century, after the isolation from salmon sperm of an unusual phosphorus compound which is now known as a nucleoprotein. This substance was shown to consist of an acidic constituent which was named nucleic acid, and a protein, known as protamine, which is basic because most of the amino acid residues are those of diamino acids. For many years the parent compound has been classified as a conjugated protein, nucleic acid being considered the prosthetic group. Since it is now known that most nucleoproteins consist of a nucleic acid unit with a molecular weight of 2 to 10×10^6, to which are attached hundreds of identical protein molecules, these aggregates are perhaps better referred to as nucleoprotein particles, rather than molecules. They are certainly not typical conjugated proteins in which the prosthetic group is a relatively small molecule. The relationship of these fundamental particles to protein synthesis and to the beginnings of life itself will be considered in Chapter 13.

Isolation of nucleic acids

As the name indicates, nucleoprotein was originally believed to be the characteristic protein of the cell nucleus. It is now known that nucleoproteins occur in both the nucleus and the cytoplasm of all living cells. Extraction of these compounds is nearly always accompanied by more or less degradation, so that it is not easy to determine the actual weight of the original aggregates. The nucleic acid, bound to the proteins by hydrogen bonds and by salt bridges, may be freed in a number of ways most of which involve denaturation of the protein. These include treatment with alcohol or other organic solvents, or with a detergent such as sodium dodecylsulfate or even simply with heat. The nucleic acid may be separated from the precipitated protein as its soluble sodium salt which yields the insoluble acid on acidification. There are now available methods for obtaining nucleic acids from animal tissues, from various viruses which are pure nucleoprotein, from plant material, and from microbial cells.

Hydrolysis of nucleic acids

Two types of nucleic acid have been distinguished, but it must not be assumed that this means that there are only two nucleic acids. Indeed it is likely that any one sample as now prepared is more or less heterogeneous and includes some products of partial degradation. When any nucleic acid is hydrolyzed completely whether by acids or by enzymes, the products are phosphoric acid, a sugar, and a mixture of basic substances. From some acids the sugar obtained is ribose; from others deoxyribose is isolated. Both sugars occur in the furanose form.

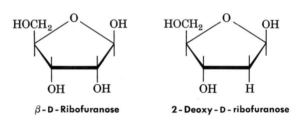

β-D-Ribofuranose   2-Deoxy-D-ribofuranose

The two general types of acid are symbolized by RNA for ribose nucleic acid and DNA for the one which contains the deoxy sugar. Both of these abbreviations stand for generic names, so that a substance called DNA, isolated from one organ or organism, is not identical with DNA from another source. Of the ribose-containing nucleic acids, that from yeast has been most thoroughly studied. Thymus nucleic acid is the best known of the deoxyribose compounds. The lists below give the products obtained by complete hydrolysis of the two types of nucleic acids.

RNA		DNA	
Phosphoric acid		Phosphoric acid	
D-Ribose		D-2-Deoxyribose	
Adenine	Purine bases	Adenine	
Guanine		Guanine	
Cytosine	Pyrimidine bases	Cytosine	
Uracil		Thymine (5-methyluracil)	

It will be noted that the mixture of bases obtained by hydrolysis of a nucleic acid usually consists of two purine bases and two pyrimidine bases.

1. PYRIMIDINE BASES. It is customary to say that the parent heterocyclic compound of this group of bases is pyrimidine, which it will be noted has the same ring form that is found in barbituric acid. In actual fact several of the "derivatives" were synthesized or discovered before it was suggested that they might all be considered to be substitution products of the simple ring compound to which the name pyrimidine had been given.

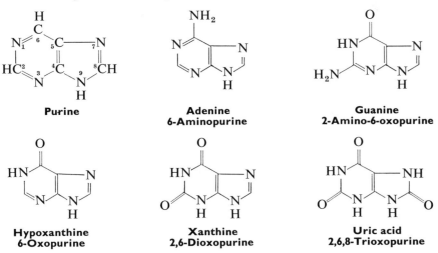

The relation of those pyrimidine bases which occur commonly in nucleic acids to each other and to pyrimidine itself is indicated in the formulas. It should be noted that when the ring includes a carbonyl carbon the neighboring nitrogen holds a hydrogen, and a double bond is replaced by a single one.

2. PURINE BASES. The first of this group to be isolated was uric acid, separated from urinary calculi and from mammalian urine by Scheele in 1776. When it had become clear, toward the end of the nineteenth century, that the same fundamental ring structure was common to uric acid, caffeine, and several other basic substances extracted from living tissue, Emil Fischer suggested that they all be named as derivatives of a hypothetical substance to which he gave the name "purine."

The purine bases consist of two condensed heterocyclic rings. The six-membered ring is identical with the pyrimidine ring, and the five-membered ring may be thought of as resulting from condensation of a reduced urea at

TABLE 5.4. Purine and Pyrimidine Bases

Base	Chemical Name[a]	Occurrence
Purines		
Adenine	6-Aminopurine	In all cells in nucleic acids, and in nucleotides; free in plants; in ATP and in oxidative coenzymes
Guanine	2-Aminohypoxanthine 2-Amino-6-oxypurine	In nucleic acids and nucleotides; free in plants
Xanthine	2,6(1,3)-Purinedione[b] 2,6-Dioxypurine	Free in small amounts in plants and animals
Hypoxanthine	6(1)-Purinone 6-Oxypurine	In inosinic acid in muscle; free in small amounts
Uric acid	2,6,8(1,3,7)-Purinetrione 2,6,8-Trioxypurine	In animal excreta and in plants
Heteroxanthine	7-Methylxanthine 2,6-Dioxy-7-methylpurine	In sugar beet
Theophylline	1,3-Dimethylxanthine 1,3-Dimethyl-2,6-dioxypurine	In tea leaves
Theobromine	3,7-Dimethylxanthine 3,7-Dimethyl-2,6-dioxypurine	In cocoa, cola, and tea leaves, and cocoa berries
Caffeine	1,3,7-Trimethylxanthine 1,3,7-Trimethyl-2,6-dioxypurine	In cocoa, cola, and tea leaves, and in maté
Pyrimidines		
Uracil	2,4(1,3)-Pyrimidinedione 2,4-Dioxypyrimidine	In plant and animal ribose nucleic acids (RNA)
Cytosine	4-Amino-2(1)-pyrimidone	In plant and animal RNA
5-Methylcytosine		In plant and animal deoxyribose nucleic acid (DNA)
Thymine	5-Methyluracil	In deoxyribose nucleic acid (DNA)

[a] The first name in the list for each compound is the modern one, the ones which follow are in accordance with the earlier system of nomenclature.

[b] The number in parentheses indicates the nitrogen of the ring to which the added hydrogen is attached when a neighboring carbon becomes part of a keto group.

carbons 4 and 5. Thus the purines are reduced cyclic diureids. The five-membered ring is the same imidazole ring which appears in histidine. The formulas given indicate the structural relationships among the various purine bases which occur commonly in living tissue. Table 5.4 lists the chief natur-ally occurring purine and pyrimidine bases with their names and sources.

Both the purines and pyrimidines have high absorbances for ultraviolet light of about 2600 A. This fact can be used to show the localization of nucleoprotein in a cell. When ultraviolet light of the proper wavelength is used in a quartz microscope to illuminate a thin slice of tissue, regions of high nucleoprotein concentration appear dark in the photomicrograph, whereas other cell proteins transmit most of this light and appear bright.

3. NUCLEOTIDES. When a nucleic acid is subjected to less drastic con-ditions than those which lead to complete hydrolysis, various fragments may be identified which throw light on the structure of the acid. RNA for example is split by prolonged, mild alkaline hydrolysis at room temperature to a mixture of four different pairs of compounds known as *mononucleotides*. These are compounds of phosphoric acid, ribose, and one of the four bases, and the pairs consist of compounds having the same base but differing in the point of attachment of the phosphoric acid. Since the mononucleotides are acids because of the ionizable hydrogens on the phosphate group, they are so named. The acids containing guanine, adenine, cytosine, and uracil are therefore called guanylic acid, adenylic acid, cytidylic acid, and uridylic acid.

The nature of the products formed on further hydrolysis of the mono-nucleotides depends upon whether the reaction is carried out in acid or alkaline solution. Alkaline hydrolysis sets free phosphoric acid leaving a sugar-base compound which is known as a *nucleoside*. The nucleosides formed by removal of phosphate from the four mononucleotides above are named guanosine, adenosine, cytidine, and uridine. In contrast, very mild acid hydrolysis of the original mononucleotides sets free, not phosphoric acid, but the bases, leaving the sugar-phosphate links intact. These results indicate that the sugar lies between the other two constituents and that the structure of a mononucleotide may be indicated:

Acid hydrolysis

Base——sugar——phosphate

Basic hydrolysis

The bases prove to be attached to carbon 1 of the sugar through a nitrogen, the pyrimidine bases being linked through N 1[7] and the purines through N 9. For some time the position of the phosphate link was in doubt. The pairs of

---

[7] The atoms in the pyrimidine ring are numbered in accordance with the modern American usage, but many people still number those atoms as they are numbered in the six-membered ring of the purine, and as they were numbered for many years in the pyrimidine ring. If the older convention is followed, the point of attachment of the pyrimidines to the sugar is N 3.

isomeric mononucleotides referred to above consisted of one in which the phosphate group was linked to carbon 3 of the ribose and another in which the phosphate was esterified with carbon 2. It was eventually shown that this mixture was obtained because of the intermediate formation of a cyclic 2′,3′-phosphate. The structure of the cyclic ester is:

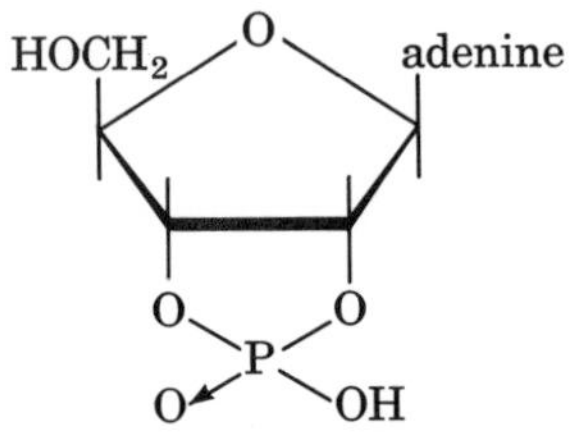

Adenosine - 2′, 3′- phosphate

It has now been shown that in an alkaline solution of nucleic acid a phosphate attached to carbon 3 of ribose forms a cyclic ester with the adjacent hydroxyl on carbon 2 before any hydrolysis takes place. The cyclic mononucleotides which are freed by the subsequent hydrolysis of the nucleic acid themselves undergo further hydrolysis which breaks the link between the phosphate and one or the other of the carbons of ribose. This gives rise to a mixture of 2′- and 3′-mononucleotides. In the next paragraph the experimental evidence will be given for the present belief that it is the 2′ ester which is the artifact, and that phosphate was originally attached to carbon 3′ of the ribose.

When RNA is hydrolyzed by enzymes the products which form show that different enzymes bring about cleavage of different links. Hydrolysis of RNA by the pancreatic enzyme, ribonuclease, yields chiefly 3′-nucleotides containing pyrimidine bases. On the other hand, a nuclease from snake venom frees nucleotides in which phosphoric acid is esterified at carbon 5 of the sugar. The structures of compounds of the two types are:

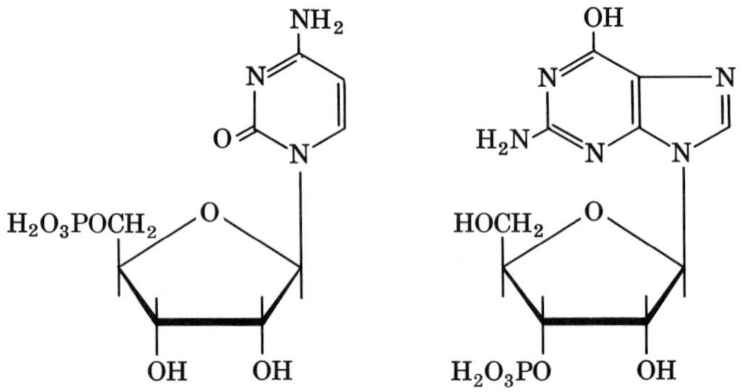

Cytidine - 5′- phosphate   **Guanosine - 3′ - phosphate**

Note that oxygen attached to the ring is sometimes written as an —OH group, and that in this case the double bond remains.

The formation of two different phosphate esters when nucleic acid is hydrolyzed by different enzymes indicates that in the original molecule phosphoric acid forms a bridge from one nucleoside to its neighbor, linking carbon 5 of the ribose of one nucleoside to carbon 3 of the ribose of another. This results in a molecule which may be roughly represented as follows:

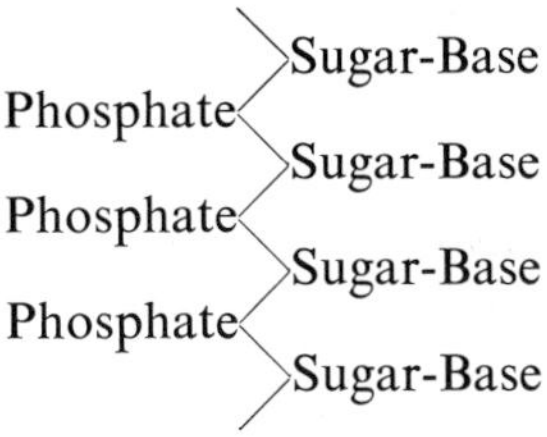

Nucleic acid pattern

Several mono- and dinucleotides occur free in living tissue and play essential roles in tissue metabolism. The first of these to be isolated was inosinic acid which Liebig prepared from beef extract. The base in this

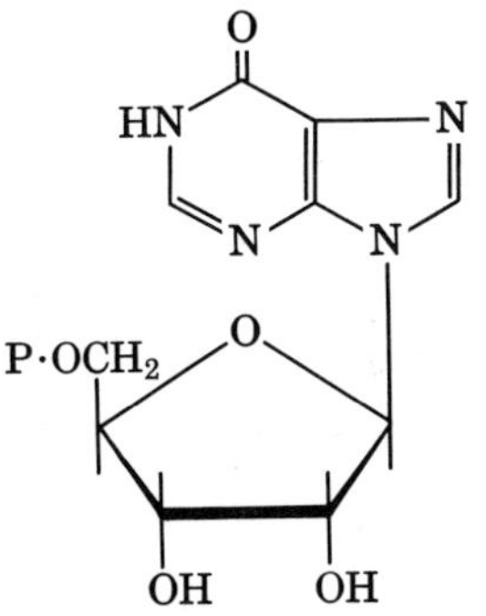

Inosinic acid (IMP)
9-Hypoxanthine-5′-phosphoribofuranoside

compound is hypoxanthine, and phosphoric acid is linked to carbon 5 of ribose.

Adenylic acid is another mononucleotide which occurs free. It is found in muscle and two of its derivatives play an important part in muscular contraction. The pyrophosphate derivative of adenylic acid, known as adenosine triphosphate (ATP), is a key compound in the metabolic chemistry of the cell, having, as shown by the wavy lines in the formula, two bonds whose hydrolysis results in a large drop in free energy.

	Adenylic acid (AMP)	A5′-P
	Adenosine diphosphate (ADP)	A5′-PP
	Adenosine triphosphate (ATP)	A5′-PPP

Localization of the nucleic acids

In recent years it has been found that the two types of nucleic acid differ in their localization in the cell, in their size and shape, and in their functions. DNA is found characteristically in the nucleus where it appears in the jacket surrounding the nucleolar material, and most specifically in the chromosomes. The DNA content per nucleus in the different tissues of a given species remains fixed in spite of changes in nutritional conditions. It has been said, in fact, that "DNA appears to be the least variable of all cell constituents."

TABLE 5.5. Distribution of Nucleic Acids and of Nitrogen in Liver Tissue

(All figures are percentages of the total in the cell)

	Nitrogen	RNA	DNA
Nuclei	15	12	100
Mitochondria	17	4	0
Microsomes	26	50	0
Cell sap	42	34	0

SOURCE: From J. N. Davidson, *The Biochemistry of the Nucleic Acids*, 3rd ed., Methuen, London, 1957.

RNA on the other hand, though it is found in small amounts in the central portions of the nucleoli, is chiefly localized in the cytoplasm. Table 5.5 indicates the distribution of the two nucleic acid types among the various particles in the cell and the fluid which makes up the cell sap. (For definition of the particles, see page 91.)

Structure of DNA

In the early years "nucleic acid" was formulated as a tetranucleotide in which were united four mononucleotides, each containing a different base. This idea arose because the bases seemed to be present in equimolar amounts, and because of mistaken estimations of the molecular weight. Recent work has shown in the first place that the bases are not always present in a 1:1:1:1 ratio, and may depart from these figures appreciably. Table 5.6 gives the molar proportions found in the two types of nucleic acid obtained from various sources. As for molecular weights, viscosity and light scattering experiments have shown that typical DNA samples have average molecular weights of 5 to 10×10^6. The molecule is very long compared with its diameter and has indeed been described as the "most extended ever examined." As indicated on page 243, the primary structure of both nucleic acids consists of a phosphoester polymer, a section of which is represented in the following formula:

There is, of course, no assurance that the four different bases would be found in sequence in any given segment of a chain, and in some parts the same one might fill all four positions.

One of the most valuable structural suggestions made in recent years was that proposed by Watson and Crick in 1953 for the structure of DNA. This envisaged the acid as a pair of polynucleotide chains running in opposite

TABLE 5.6. Molar Proportions of Nucleotides (as moles per 100 moles nucleotide) in RNAs and DNAs from Different Sources

Source	Adenine	Guanine	Cytosine	Uracil	Thymine	5-Methyl-cytosine
In RNA from:						
Ox liver	17.1	27.3	33.9	21.7		
Rat kidney	19.4	29.5	30.7	20.4		
Sea urchin embryos	22.6	29.4	27.2	20.8		
Yeast	25.4	24.6	22.6	27.4		
E. coli	25.3	28.8	24.7	21.2		
In DNA from:						
Bovine thymus	28.2	21.5	21.2	—	27.8	1.3
Bovine sperm	28.7	22.2	20.7	—	27.2	1.3
Rat bone marrow	28.6	21.4	20.4	—	28.4	1.1
Yeast	31.3	18.7	17.1	—	32.9	—
E. coli	26.0	24.9	25.2	—	23.9	—

SOURCE: Parts of two tables from J. N. Davidson, *The Biochemistry of the Nucleic Acids*, 4th ed., Methuen, London, 1960.

directions, wrapped around each other to form a double helix. It has long been known that the plane of the bases is perpendicular to that of the chain axis. In the Watson and Crick formulation, the bases fill the center of the helix, with the two phosphoester chains making up the outside. As with the proteins, this helix is stabilized by hydrogen bond formation between bases in the two chains. When Pauling investigated the actual spatial relations between the chains, he found that if the backbones of the two chains were to be kept equidistant throughout, adenine must always be bonded to thymine and guanine to cytosine, thus putting a purine always opposite a pyrimidine base. Figure 5.15 shows how the base pairing takes place and gives the dimensions on which this structure depends. It allows formation of two hydrogen bonds between adenine and thymine and three between cytosine and guanine. It will be noted that the resulting distance between backbones is approximately 11 A with both pairs. Figure 5.16 reproduces a photograph of a model of a DNA helix with the bases filling the center and two helical grooves of unequal depth on the outside. It has been computed that the smaller of these grooves will just accommodate such a basic polypeptide chain as is found in nucleoproteins, the positively charged residues of the basic amino acids interacting

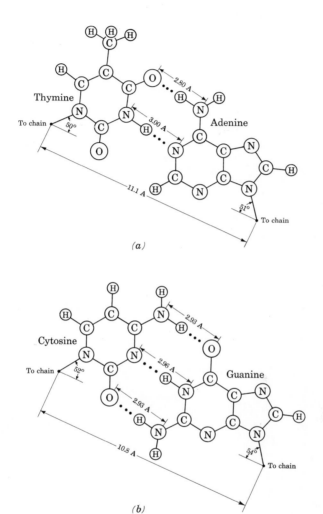

Fig. 5.15. Drawings showing in (a) how molecules of adenine and thymine may form a complementary pair held together by two hydrogen bonds and in (b) the same sort of relationship for cytosine and guanine held by three hydrogen bonds. The distances in (b) were kindly corrected by Dr. Corey. [From L. Pauling and R. B. Corey, *Arch. Biochem. Biophys.*, **65**, 164 (1956).]

Fig. 5.16. Photograph of a recent model of DNA. (Courtesy of Dr. M. F. H. Wilkins.)

with the negatively charged phosphate groups on the outside of the helix. The total nucleoprotein would then consist of a three-stranded helix.

Structure of RNA

The molecular weight of RNA is still an uncertain quantity. Estimates usually vary between 10,000 and 250,000, though RNA has been extracted from tomato mosaic virus with a molecular weight many times this. Since any cell contains a mixture of different RNAs, and extraction may involve varying degrees of degradation, this uncertainty is not to be wondered at, and it is probable that the higher figures are the better. Although the primary structure of RNA is, like that of DNA, a long unbranched polynucleotide chain, it is beginning to appear that their configurations differ. The viscosity of solutions of RNA is surprisingly low, and this and other evidence suggests that the molecules are tightly coiled, and that these coils are more contracted than is usual in polymer chains. This structure can be maintained only by some sort of intramolecular attractions, and one suggestion is that these may result from base pairing and hydrogen bond formation between bases *in the same chain*. The RNA molecule might then be considered to be folded in the same sense as are the globular proteins.

It should be noted here that a form of RNA has been isolated from cell saps which has rather special properties and which performs a unique function in the cell which will be considered in Chapter 13. This substance is known as soluble RNA or SRNA. As at present isolated, it is undoubtedly a heterogeneous mixture, but it contains a high proportion of atypical bases, including methylated purines and 5-methylcytosine, and it yields a pseudouridylic acid in which the base is attached through carbon 5 to ribose instead of through nitrogen 1. Compared with SRNA, the other nucleic acids contain only traces of bases other than the typical ones. The average molecular weight of SRNA has been recently estimated at 30,000–35,000. As nucleic acids go, this is a small molecule.

Importance of the nucleotide structure

It has been known for many years that mono- and dinucleotides perform unique functions in various metabolic cycles. Reference has already been made to adenylic acid and its pyrophosphate derivative, ATP. There are also found in living tissue a number of compounds having the structure of two nucleotides, united to each other through their phosphate groups. These substances, in which are found other bases than those which occur in nucleic acids, have proved essential to the activity of various oxidizing enzymes. They will be considered in connection with cell oxidations. Meantime let us glance briefly at two nucleoproteins which exemplify the special importance of these substances.

Chromosomes and genes

Within the nuclei of cells are the tiny, threadlike chromosomes which go through a characteristic series of changes leading up to cell division. In the course of these changes each chromosome splits lengthwise and one half goes to each of the two daughter cells. Figure 5.17 shows a chromosome as

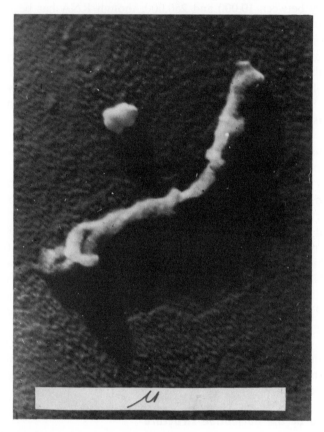

Fig. 5.17. An electron micrograph of a chicken chromosome after five extractions with *M* NaCl, showing intertwining and crossbanding. [From A. R. T. Denues, *Science*, **113**, 203 (1951). Reprinted from *Science* by permission.]

revealed by the electron microscope. The twisted structure is especially interesting. Since nearly all the DNA of the cell is concentrated in the chromosomes, this appearance may well reflect the fundamental helical nucleoprotein structure postulated by Watson and Crick.

The orderly development of an organism and its final form and properties all depend upon the small structures within the chromosomes known as genes. In higher plants and animals thousands of them lie along the main axis of the chromosome, each one concerned with passing on to daughter cells some one specific characteristic. What this means at the molecular level is that each gene controls the synthesis of some one enzyme, and the enzyme in turn supervises its own part of some metabolic or synthetic sequence. It has now been clearly shown that genetic information can be transferred from one cell to another by transfer of purified DNA. For example, if pure DNA from one bacterial suspension is added to bacteria having different genetic properties, the recipient cells develop the characteristics of the donor bacteria. This indicates that DNA must be a kind of coding device, roughly like a punched tape in a computer. Instead of holes, it carries base pairs. Since the rest of the molecule is identical in all chains, it must be the order in which the bases occur in certain portions of the helix which determines the nature of the enzyme protein which will be synthesized. This coded information is believed to be transferred to RNA which is synthesized in the nucleus according to the DNA code. This RNA with its specific pattern is then extruded into the cytoplasm, perhaps as a microsomal particle, which in its turn will supervise the assembling of amino acids to form a protein. This process will be considered in more detail in Chapter 13.

Viruses

The larger infectious agents such as bacteria and amoebae readily reveal themselves under the microscope, and are held back if a liquid in which they are suspended is passed through an unglazed porcelain filter. But a number of plant and animal diseases are caused by submicroscopic particles which are not retained by a filter and which are therefore known as filterable viruses. In the presence of the living cells of a suitable host, the viruses multiply and spread and cause characteristic manifestations of disease.

From tobacco plants affected with a mosaic disease Stanley[8] isolated and ultimately crystallized the first example of a pure chemical compound having the properties of a virus. This substance proved to be a nucleoprotein of the ribose type. Even after repeated chemical manipulations it was still an infective agent, capable of multiplication. Thus was obtained for the first time an *infective molecule*, the comparative chemical simplicity of which must be contrasted with the complexity of a bacterial cell.

In recent years the infective agents of many virus diseases both of plants and of animals have been isolated. All have proved to be nucleoproteins of very high molecular weight and rather low nucleic acid content, in spite of the fact that the infectivity resides in the nucleic acid portion. In most of the compounds the sugar has been found to be ribose, though quite recently

---

[8] Dr. Wendell M. Stanley worked for many years at the Rockefeller Institute in New York and is now in charge of Virus Research at the University of California in Berkeley. He is known best for his isolation of virus proteins. In 1946 he shared the Nobel Prize in Chemistry with J. B. Sumner and J. H. Northrop.

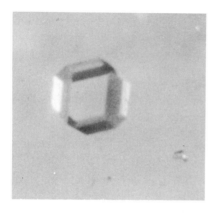

Fig. 5.18. A single large crystal of type 1 poliomyelitis virus (×80). [From R. L. Steere and F. L. Schaffer, *Biochim. et Biophys. Acta*, **28**, 241 (1958).]

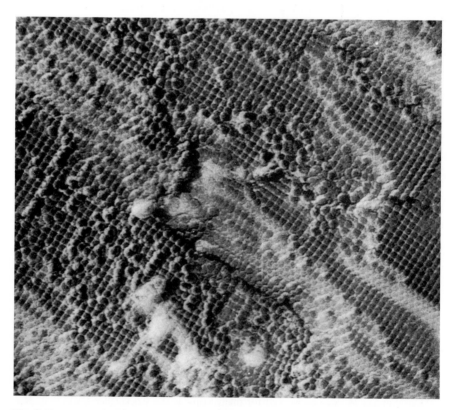

Fig. 5.19. Electron micrograph of a fractured, frozen crystal of poliovirus (×65,000). [From R. L. Steere and F. L. Schaffer, *Biochim. et Biophys. Acta*, **28**, 241 (1958).]

deoxyribonucleic acids have been extracted from some tumor-inducing viruses. Tobacco mosaic virus is estimated to have a molecular weight of 25 to 60 × 10⁶, and other viruses have molecular weights of roughly this order of magnitude.

Figure 5.18 shows a single large crystal of type 1 poliomyelitis virus, one of the first such crystals ever prepared with an animal virus. When the nucleic acid was separated from the protein it proved to be of the ribose type, to have a molecular weight of about 2 million and to account for about 30 per cent of the crystal. The remaining 70 per cent is protein with a molecular weight of a few hundred thousand. This means that each nucleic acid molecule must have associated with it a large number of these relatively small protein molecules.

Figure 5.19 shows the crystalline virus as revealed by the electron microscope. It is seen to consist of billions of tiny identical spheres or particles, each about 27 mμ in diameter. It is estimated that as few as 30 of these particles would induce severe paralysis in man. Since the nucleic acid alone is infective and can bring about self-duplication, it must carry in the form of base pairs what are essentially genes, or the coded information needed to bring about replication of itself. It is thus clear why one of the great workers in the field of nucleic acid chemistry, J. M. Gulland, said the nucleoproteins "stand on the threshold between the living and the never-having-lived."

SUGGESTIONS FOR FURTHER READING

General

Advances in Protein Chemistry, Academic, New York.

This series began in 1944; each volume carries articles written by specialists in the various fields.

Annual Review of Biochemistry, Annual Reviews, Inc., Palo Alto, Calif.

Recent numbers carry articles on amino acid chemistry and on protein structure which bring together the information on these subjects published in the previous year.

Neurath, H., and K. Bailey (eds.), *The Proteins*, 4 vols., Academic, New York, 1953–1954.

These volumes bring together papers by a large group of people who represent all sorts of approaches to the problems of protein chemistry and structure.

Stereochemistry of Amino Acids

The configuration of the natural amino acids has been studied both by direct conversion of one acid to another, and by various ingenious indirect methods. Both methods are illustrated in the references given.

Fischer, E., and K. Raske, Conversion of *levo*-serine to *dextro*-alanine, *Ber.*, *40*, 3717 (1907).

Karrer, P., *et al.*, On the configuration of *d*-glutamic acid, *d*-ornithine and *d*-lysine, *Helv. Chim. Acta, 9*, 301 (1926).

Freudenberg, K., and F. Rhino, The configuration of alanine, *Ber., 57*, 1547 (1924).

Peptide Bond Formation

Bergmann, M., and L. Zervas, A general method of peptide synthesis, *Ber., 65*, 1192 (1932).

Fischer, E., Synthesis of polypeptides, *Ber., 40*, 1754 (1907).

    It is in this paper that Fischer reported the successful preparation of his octadecapeptide.

Sheehan, J. C., and V. S. Frank, A new synthetic route to peptides, *J. Am. Chem. Soc., 71*, 1856 (1949).

Chromatography of Amino Acids and Peptides

Consden, R., *et al.*, Qualitative analysis of proteins: A partition chromatographic method using paper, *Biochem. J., 38*, 224 (1944).

Dent, C. E., Study of the behaviour of some sixty amino acids and other ninhydrin-reacting substances on phenol-"collidine" filter paper chromatograms, *Biochem. J., 43*, 169 (1948).

Hirs, C. H. W., Studies on the structure of ribonuclease.

    This is one of three papers which report work done by Drs. Hirs, S. Moore, W. H. Stein, and D. H. Spackman which unraveled the structure of ribonuclease. The references are, *J. Biol. Chem., 235*, 625, 633, 648 (1960). The material is presented clearly and interestingly and makes clear the monumental labor that lies behind formulation of a protein structure.

Moffat, E. D., and R. I. Lytle, Polychromatic technique for identification of amino acids on paper chromatograms, *Anal. Chem., 31*, 927 (1959).

Moore, S., and W. H. Stein, Chromatography of amino acids on sulfonated polystyrene resins, *J. Biol. Chem., 192*, 663 (1951).

Moore, S., *et al.*, Chromatography of amino acids on sulfonated polystyrene resins, *Anal. Chem., 30*, 1185 (1958).

Protein Structure

Fraenkel-Conrat, H., N-Terminal amino acids by the phenylisothiocyanate procedure, *J. Am. Chem. Soc., 76*, 3606 (1954).

Astbury, W. T., X-Rays and the stoichiometry of the proteins, *Advances in Enzymol., 3*, 63 (1943).

Edsall, J. T., and J. Wyman, *Biophysical Chemistry*, Academic, New York, 1958. Chapter III.

Kowalsky, A., and P. D. Boyer, A carboxypeptidase-H_2O^{18} procedure for determination of COOH-terminal residues . . . , *J. Biol. Chem., 235*, 604 (1960).

Oncley, J. L. (ed.-in-chief), *Biophysical Science*, Wiley, New York, 1959.

    Papers by J. C. Kendrew, A. Rich, and by Oncley himself are especially recommended.

Neurath, H., and K. Bailey, *The Proteins, loc. cit.*

    Papers in these volumes by J. C. Kendrew and by K. Bailey are concerned with the structural proteins.

Pauling, L., *et al.*, Structure of proteins: Two hydrogen bonded helical configurations, *Proc. Natl. Acad. Sci. U.S.*, *37*, 205 (1951).

Pauling, L., and R. B. Corey, Stable configurations of polypeptide chains, *Proc. Roy. Soc. (London)*, *B141*, 21 (1953).

Corey, R. B., and L. Pauling, Fundamental dimensions of polypeptide chains, *Proc. Roy. Soc. (London)*, *B141*, 10 (1953).

Perlmann, G. E., and R. Diringer, Structure of proteins, *Ann. Rev. Biochem.*, *29*, 151 (1960).

Ryle, A. P., *et al.*, The disulfide bonds of insulin, *Biochem. J.*, *60*, 541 (1955).

Sanger, F., and H. Tuppy, The amino acid sequence in the phenylalanine chain of insulin, *Biochem. J.*, *49*, 463 (1951).

Sanger, F., and E. O. P. Thompson, The amino-acid sequence in the glycyl chain of insulin, *Biochem. J.*, *53*, 353, 366 (1953).

Scheraga, H. A., Structural studies of ribonuclease. III. A model for the secondary and tertiary structures, *J. Am. Chem. Soc.*, *82*, 3847 (1960).

Nucleic Acids

Davidson, J. N., *The Biochemistry of the Nucleic Acids*, 4th ed., Methuen, London, 1960.

Feughelman, M., *et al.*, Molecular structure of DNA and nucleoprotein, *Nature*, *175*, 834 (1955).

Franklin, R. E., and R. G. Gosling, Molecular configuration in sodium thymonucleate, *Nature*, *171*, 740 (1953).

Pauling, L., and R. B. Corey, Specific hydrogen-bond formation between pyrimidines and purines in deoxyribonucleic acids, *Arch. Biochem. Biophys.*, *65*, 164 (1956).

Rich, A., and D. R. Davies, A new two stranded helical structure, *J. Am. Chem. Soc.*, *78*, 3548 (1956).

Davies, D. R., and A. Rich, Formation of a helical complex between polyinosinic acid and polycytidylic acid, *J. Am. Chem. Soc.*, *80*, 1003 (1958).

Watson, J. D., and F. H. C. Crick, A structure for DNA, *Nature*, *171*, 737 (1953).

Wilkins, M. H. F., *et al.*, Molecular structure of deoxypentose nucleic acids, *Nature*, *171*, 738 (1953).

The true Experimenting *has this one thing inseparable from it,*
never to be a fixed *and* settled Art,
and never to be limited by constant Rules.

THOMAS SPRAT: *History of the Royal Society* (1665)

The lipids 6

THE LIPIDS CONSIST OF a large and varied group of compounds which are
now sometimes defined as "actual or potential derivatives of fatty acids,"
but which were actually first classified together because of their solubilities.
These are the compounds which are almost insoluble in water but are quite
soluble, though to differing degrees, in the so-called fat solvents. The chief
of these solvents are acetone, alcohol, ether, petroleum ether or ligroin,
chloroform, and carbon tetrachloride. The separation of lipids from tissues
rich in fat, such as adipose tissue or fatty seeds, is readily achieved by some
sort of continuous extraction such as the Soxhlet extraction, in which a hot
solvent is allowed to drip repeatedly through the dried and minced tissue.
The material which dissolves under these circumstances contains several
different kinds of compounds which may be roughly classified into *simple
lipids*, which are fatty acid[1] esters of various alcohols of which glycerol is by
far the most abundant, *compound lipids* which yield on hydrolysis three or
more different compounds in addition to fatty acids, and the *steroids* which
make up the major part of the nonsaponifiable material left as an insoluble
residue after the total lipids have been subjected to alkaline hydrolysis. The
steroids are polycyclic compounds related to cyclopentanoperhydrophenan-
threne, and so chemically quite distinct from the compounds in the other two

---

[1] In organic chemistry the fatty acids are the homologues of acetic acid, but the word
as used by biochemists is hard to define. In order to avoid a wordy discussion let us
consider that the term refers to all the acids obtained from lipids by hydrolysis. This means
that it will include some which are unsaturated, a few with branched chains and, as indicated
in Table 6.2, some which are partly cyclic.

groups. The first two main classes have each been separated into several subgroups depending chiefly upon differences in solubility in the various fat solvents. Table 6.1 gives one classification, though it will be found that it is not entirely free of overlapping.

TABLE 6.I. Classification of the Lipids

Simple Lipids
 Fats and oils: Fatty acid triglycerides
 Waxes: Esters of long chain fatty acids with higher aliphatic alcohols or with sterols
 Glyceryl ethers
Compound Lipids
 Phosphatidyl compounds or glycerophosphatides
  Phosphatidic acids
  Phosphatidyl esters
  Phosphatidyl inositides
  Lysophosphatides
  Plasmalogens
 Sphingolipids
  Sphingomyelins
  Cerebrosides
  Gangliosides
Steroids

STRUCTURE OF THE SIMPLE LIPIDS

In the chapters dealing with carbohydrates and proteins, the chemistry of the simplest units was first discussed in order to clarify the structures and reactions of the more complex compounds. In the course of these discussions the reactions of the aliphatic hydroxyl group, the amino group, and the carboxyl group have been reviewed. These same groups are major functional groups through which the various small molecules are linked together in the lipids, hence it is possible to go in this chapter directly to a consideration of the structures of the various types of compounds which make up this heterogeneous group.

The Triglycerides

The most abundant of the simple lipids are the triglycerides which are fatty acid esters of glycerol. They are called fats if they are solid or semisolid at room temperature, and oils if they are liquids. These differences in melting point reflect differences in the degree of saturation of the constituent fatty acids. Since the saturated acids are themselves solid at room temperature, fats containing a high percentage of saturated acids are also solids. The presence in a triglyceride of appreciable amounts of the lower melting unsaturated acids lowers the melting point of the compound and makes it an oil. Structurally the fats and oils are identical, and both are represented by the formulation below and by the drawing in Fig. 6.1. The latter gives an

$$CH_2O \cdot OCR_1$$
$$R_2CO \cdot OCH$$
$$CH_2O \cdot OCR_3$$

Mixed triglyceride

idea of the spatial relations in this large uncharged molecule. In the formula R_1CO—, R_2CO—, and R_3CO— stand for residues of fatty acids which are usually long straight chain compounds containing an even number of carbon atoms. One or more of these acid residues may be unsaturated, and recent

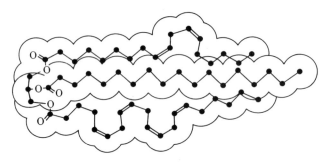

Fig. 6.1. A triglyceride molecule containing two unsaturated acid residues. [Reproduced by permission from J. L. Oncley, in *Biophysical Science*, p. 47, J. L. Oncley (ed.-in-chief), Wiley, New York, 1959.]

evidence indicates that when there is only one such residue in a triglyceride it is attached preferentially to the center or β-carbon of glycerol. Although it had long been known that isovaleric acid occurs in the fat of dolphins and porpoises, it is only in the last decade that higher branched chain acids have been identified in animal fats. These prove to be saturated acids, some with odd numbers of carbons, ranging from C_{13} to C_{18} or even C_{20}. Thus it seems that as much as 1 per cent of the total acid may be exceptional either in having a branched chain or an odd number of carbons or both.

When the three acids in a triglyceride molecule are identical, the compound is said to be a *simple triglyceride* as opposed to a *mixed triglyceride* which contains residues of two or three different acids. Actually mixed triglycerides are far more abundant in nature than the simple molecules. Table 6.2 lists some of the important acids which have been obtained by hydrolysis of fats and oils.

TABLE 6.2. Some Representative Acids Which Occur in Natural Fats and Oils

Acid	Formula	Sources
Saturated Acids		
Butyric	$CH_3(CH_2)_2COOH$	Butter fat
Isovaleric	$(CH_3)_2CH \cdot CH_2COOH$	Porpoise fat
Caproic	$CH_3(CH_2)_4COOH$	Butter fat and coconut oil
Caprylic	$CH_3(CH_2)_6COOH$	Butter fat and coconut oil
Capric	$CH_3(CH_2)_8COOH$	Coconut oil
Lauric	$CH_3(CH_2)_{10}COOH$	Coconut oil
Myristic	$CH_3(CH_2)_{12}COOH$	Coconut oil
Palmitic	$CH_3(CH_2)_{14}COOH$	Animal and vegetable fats
Stearic	$CH_3(CH_2)_{16}COOH$	Animal and vegetable fats
Arachidic	$CH_3(CH_2)_{18}COOH$	Peanut oil
Cerotic	$CH_3(CH_2)_{24}COOH$	Wool fat
Unsaturated Acids		
Palmitoleic	$CH_3(CH_2)_5CH{=}CH(CH_2)_7COOH$	Butter fat
Oleic	$CH_3(CH_2)_7CH{=}CH(CH_2)_7COOH$	All fats
Linoleic	$CH_3(CH_2)_4(CH{=}CH \cdot CH_2)_2(CH_2)_6COOH$	Linseed oil
Linolenic	$CH_3CH_2(CH{=}CH \cdot CH_2)_3(CH_2)_6COOH$	Linseed oil
Arachidonic	$CH_3(CH_2)_4(CH{=}CH \cdot CH_2)_4(CH_2)_2COOH$	Compound lipids
Erucic	$CH_3(CH_2)_7CH{=}CH(CH_2)_{11}COOH$	Rapeseed oil
Ricinoleic	$CH_3(CH_2)_5CHOH \cdot CH_2CH{=}CH(CH_2)_7COOH$	Castor oil
Chaulmoogric	$\begin{array}{l} CH{=}CH \\ \quad\diagdown \\ \quad\quad CH(CH_2)_{12}COOH \\ \quad\diagup \\ CH_2{-}CH_2 \end{array}$	Chaulmoogra oil
Hydnocarpic	$\begin{array}{l} CH{=}CH \\ \quad\diagdown \\ \quad\quad CH(CH_2)_{10}COOH \\ \quad\diagup \\ CH_2{-}CH_2 \end{array}$	Chaulmoogra oil
Tariric	$CH_3(CH_2)_{10}C{\equiv}C(CH_2)_4COOH$	Seed fat of a Central American shrub
Eleostearic	$CH_3(CH_2)_3(CH{=}CH)_3(CH_2)_7COOH$	Tung oil
Clupanodonic	$C_{22}H_{34}O_2$ with 5 double bonds	Fish oils

As indicated in the table, most of the common acids have been given trivial names which are simple and will surely continue to be used. But newly discovered acids, such as some of the intermediates in fatty acid metabolism, are named according to the scientific system. This system shows the chain length by a numerical prefix from the Greek, numbers the carbons from the carboxyl end, indicates unsaturation by changing -an in the name to -en, and the position of a double bond by giving the position in the chain of the lower-numbered carbon involved. Originally a double bond was indicated also by use of a Δ with the number used as a superscript, and this is still used by some writers, though the present trend is toward a dropping of this symbol. In the examples given below both systems are illustrated.

$$CH_3 \cdot (CH_2)_{16} \cdot COOH$$
Octadecanoic acid

$$CH_3 \cdot (CH_2)_7 \cdot CH{=}CH \cdot (CH_2)_7 \cdot COOH$$
9-Octadecenoic acid or
Δ^9-Octadecenoic acid

$$CH_3(CH_2)_7CH{=}CH \cdot CH_2 \cdot CH{=}CH \cdot CH_2 \cdot CH{=}CH \cdot (CH_2)_3 \cdot COOH$$
5,8,11-Eicosatrienoic acid or
$\Delta^{5,8,11}$-Eicosatrienoic acid

$$CH_3 \cdot CH_2 \cdot CH \cdot (CH_2)_5 \cdot CH{=}CH \cdot CH_2 \cdot CH{=}CH \cdot (CH_2)_7 \cdot COOH$$
$$\overset{|}{CH_3}$$
19-Methyl-9,12-heneicosadienoic acid

Any given sample of fat, even after extensive purification yields at least five and may yield as many as twelve or more different acids. This means that a fat sample is always a mixture of triglycerides, and often a very complex mixture.

The Waxes

A second group of compounds which consists largely of esters is the waxes. Although some of the waxes are of commercial importance, they usually do not play an active role biologically. They occur as a coating on the cuticle of leaves and the surfaces of seeds and fruit. However, waxes do sometimes replace triglycerides as in the "fat" of the castor oil fish, *Ruvettus pretiosus*, and of the sperm and the bottlenose whales. These compounds make up as much as 70 per cent of the "oil" from the two last named, and approximately 100 per cent of the "oil" from the castor oil fish. In at least one plant (*Simmondsia californica*) waxes constitute the entire seed lipid.

In general the waxes consist of esters of even-numbered fatty acids either with sterols or with monohydric aliphatic alcohols. The sterols are solid alcohols of the steroid group; the aliphatic alcohols found in waxes usually contain 16 to 18 carbons and the acids are of greater chain length than those found in other lipids, containing as they do from 26 to 36 carbon atoms. The acids are saturated in those waxes which serve only as protective coatings, but when the waxes replace triglycerides and are to be used metabolically the chains are shorter and the constituents show some degree of unsaturation. Among bacterial waxes occasional branched chain acids are found, also hydroxy acids and those with odd numbers of carbon atoms. For example, the wax of certain tubercle bacilli yields a 10-methylstearic acid known as tuberculostearic acid, and "mycolic acid" which is a mixture of branched chain hydroxy acids containing 87 or 88 carbons. The compounds in the mixture have similar structures which is indicated in the formula

$$CH_3 \cdot (CH_2)_{23} \cdot \underset{\underset{CHOH \cdot R}{|}}{CH} \cdot COOH$$

Mycolic acid

in which R may stand for $C_{60}H_{121}$— or $C_{60}H_{120}(OH)$— or $C_{60}H_{120}(OCH_3)$—.

The wax esters are usually found mixed with varying amounts of paraffin hydrocarbons and with free alcohols and acids. The alcohols and acids correspond to those found in the wax esters both in chain length and in having even numbers of carbons; the hydrocarbons are odd-numbered compounds with 25 to 37 carbons.

Glyceryl Ethers

Long chain aliphatic alcohols are also found in some marine animal oils attached to glycerol by an ether linkage. In these compounds which are known as alkoxydiglycerides, the other two hydroxyl groups of the glycerol are esterified in the usual way with fatty acids. Hydrolysis removes the two fatty acid residues but leaves the ether link intact. The resulting ether-alcohols are insoluble in water and therefore form part of the unsaponifiable fraction of these particular oils. In the formulas R stands for one of three aliphatic

$$\begin{array}{cc} CH_2 \cdot O \cdot R & CH_2 \cdot O \cdot R \\ | & | \\ HOCH & R_1CO \cdot O \cdot CH \\ | & | \\ CH_2OH & CH_2 \cdot O \cdot OCR_2 \\ \textbf{Glyceryl ether} & \textbf{Alkoxydiglyceride} \end{array}$$

alcohols. Because of the two free hydroxyl groups on the glycerol in the ethers, these compounds are named as alcohols. Table 6.3 lists these trivial names which reflect the sources from which the compounds were originally isolated.

TABLE 6.3.   The Glyceryl Ethers

Name	Structure
Chimyl alcohol	$CH_2 \cdot O \cdot (CH_2)_{15}CH_3$ $\mid$ $HOCH$ $\mid$ CH_2OH
Batyl alcohol	$CH_2 \cdot O \cdot (CH_2)_{17}CH_3$ $\mid$ $HOCH$ $\mid$ CH_2OH
Selachyl alcohol	$CH_2 \cdot O \cdot (CH_2)_8 \cdot CH{=}CH \cdot (CH_2)_7 \cdot CH_3$ $\mid$ $HOCH$ $\mid$ CH_2OH

STRUCTURE OF THE COMPOUND LIPIDS

In living cells there are a number of compounds which are soluble in some fat solvents but which contain in addition to carbon, hydrogen, and oxygen either nitrogen or phosphorus or both. These are the compound lipids. The pioneer work on these substances was done by Thudicum[2] who named them phosphatides in the mistaken belief that they all contained phosphorus. Recent additions to the group have made necessary some type of classification. None so far proposed is entirely satisfactory, but the one shown in Table 6.1 has a minimum of overlapping.

Glycerophosphatides

A large group of compounds which seem to be as universally present in living organisms as the fats are the compound lipids which are derivatives of α-glycerophosphoric acid. It was believed for many years that some of these compounds were derived from β-glycerophosphoric acid, in which the phosphoric acid residue is attached to the central carbon of glycerol. But it has now been shown that the procedures by which the β compounds were

---

[2] Johann L. W. Thudicum (1829–1921) was born in Germany and took his medical degree there, but spent most of his professional life in London, first at St. George's School of Medicine, and later as Pathologist at St. Thomas' Hospital. He is chiefly remembered for his pioneer work on the chemical composition of the brain.

isolated lead to phosphate migration, and that all the natural glycerophosphatides are derivatives of α-glycerophosphoric acid. Furthermore, all have

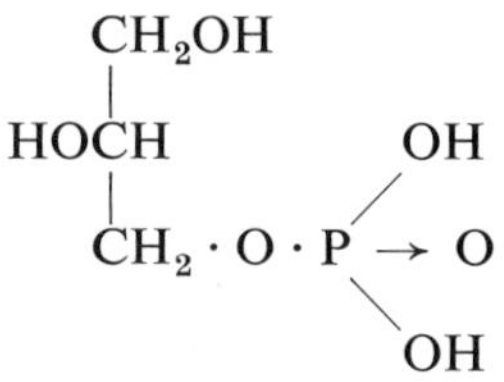

$$CH_2OH$$
$$|$$
$$HOCH \qquad OH$$
$$| \qquad \diagup$$
$$CH_2 \cdot O \cdot P \rightarrow O$$
$$\diagdown$$
$$OH$$

α-Glycerophosphoric acid

the L configuration, that is, they are structurally related to L-glyceraldehyde, indicated by writing the hydroxyl on the asymmetric carbon on the left.

Phosphatidic acids

When the two free hydroxyl groups of α-glycerophosphoric acid are esterified with fatty acids the resulting compound is known as a phosphatidic acid. There is some question as to whether or not this type of compound actually occurs free in living tissues, but it does certainly form part of several

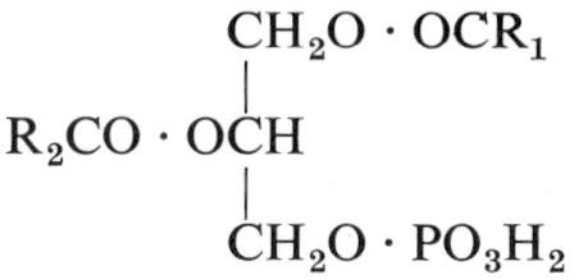

$$CH_2O \cdot OCR_1$$
$$|$$
$$R_2CO \cdot OCH$$
$$|$$
$$CH_2O \cdot PO_3H_2$$

Phosphatidic acid

more complex molecules, many of which contain nitrogen in addition to phosphorus. An interesting derivative found in heart muscle and known as *cardiolipin* has had several different structures suggested for it. According to the most recent formulation, the compound consists of two molecules of phosphatidic acid linked through glycerol as shown.

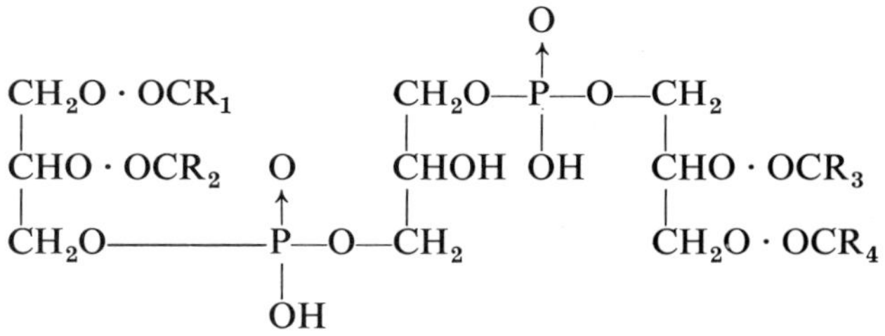

Cardiolipin

Phosphatidyl esters

Three different nitrogen-containing alcohols form esters with one of the hydroxyl groups of the phosphoric acid residue in phosphatidic acid. Two of the resulting compounds have long been known. The third was discovered more recently as a contaminant in preparations of one of the older compounds. The two original compounds were called lecithin and cephalin and are now known respectively as phosphatidyl choline and phosphatidyl ethanolamine. The newer compound separated from cephalin proved to be phosphatidyl serine.

The compound which is still frequently referred to by the old name of lecithin has the structure of an ester of phosphatidic acid and choline. In lecithin as in the triglycerides, a single unsaturated acid is esterified preferentially on the β-carbon. As the formula indicates, lecithin is believed

$$\begin{array}{l} CH_2O \cdot OCR_1 \\ | \\ R_2CO \cdot OCH \qquad O \\ | \qquad\qquad \uparrow \\ CH_2O \cdot P \cdot O \cdot CH_2 \cdot CH_2 \cdot \overset{+}{N}(CH_3)_3 \\ \qquad\quad | \\ \qquad\quad O^- \end{array}$$

Lecithin or phosphatidyl choline

to have the structure of a dipolar ion, the phosphoric acid having a pK_a of approximately 1, while the pK_a which is due to the nitrogen is higher than 14. Since at least five different fatty acids are obtained on hydrolysis of highly purified lecithin, samples of this substance must be mixtures of several different glycerides. Strictly speaking then one should not refer to lecithin but to the lecithins or the phosphatidyl cholines, but actually the simpler and older of the two names continues to be used in the singular since it involves no real uncertainty.

The substance once called cephalin has proved to include more than one contaminant and so it seems best to drop that older name entirely and to call the major component of the mixture phosphatidyl ethanolamine.

$$\begin{array}{l} CH_2O \cdot OCR_1 \\ | \\ R_2CO \cdot OCH \qquad O \\ | \qquad\qquad \uparrow \\ CH_2O \cdot P \cdot O \cdot CH_2CH_2\overset{+}{N}H_3 \\ \qquad\quad | \\ \qquad\quad O^- \end{array}$$

Phosphatidyl ethanolamine

As the formula indicates, this compound is also a dipolar ion in which the phosphoric acid has a pK_a of about 1 and the amino group a pK_a of approximately 10.

Phosphatidyl serine differs from the ethanolamine compound only in having a serine residue in place of that of ethanolamine. Since phosphatidyl serine has two acid groups and one basic group it reacts as an acid, the two functional groups attached to the α-carbon of the serine forming the usual dipolar ion. The drawing in Fig. 6.2 again indicates the shape of the molecule and gives the pK_a values of two of the ionizable groups. Lecithin and phosphatidyl

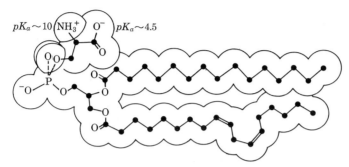

Fig. 6.2. Phosphatidyl serine. [Reproduced by permission from J. L. Oncley, in *Biophysical Science*, p. 47, J. L. Oncley (ed.-in-chief), Wiley, New York, 1959.]

ethanolamine have essentially the same structures but lack the carboxyl group which accounts for the pK_a near 4.5. The close relationship of the three

$$CH_2O \cdot OCR_1$$
$$R_2CO \cdot OCH \qquad O$$
$$CH_2O \cdot P \cdot O \cdot CH_2 \cdot CHNH_3^+$$
$$O^- \qquad\qquad COO^-$$

Phosphatidyl serine

nitrogenous residues in these compounds is obvious from the formulas, and indeed these compounds are mutually interconvertible in the cell.

Phosphoinositides

   Comparatively recently a new group of compound lipids has been discovered in which *myo*-inositol is a constituent. The group as a whole is incompletely

$$CH_2O \cdot OCR_1$$
$$R_2CO \cdot OCH \qquad O$$
$$CH_2O \cdot P \cdot O$$
$$O^-$$

Monophosphoinositide or
phosphatidyl inositol

characterized, but one or two structures seem to be fairly well documented. One of these is assigned to a compound which has been isolated from wheat germ, and from heart and liver and which is known as a monophosphoinositide. On hydrolysis this compound frees fatty acid, glycerol, phosphoric acid, and inositol in the molar ratios 2:1:1:1, and on this basis it has been assigned the structure of a phosphatidyl inositol.

In 1949 Folch announced the isolation from brain of an inositol compound which yielded on hydrolysis equimolar amounts of *meta*-diphosphoinositol, fatty acid, and glycerol. This compound has recently been re-examined by Grado and Ballou, who find that the main constituent set free by hydrolysis is inositol 1,4,5-triphosphate. A second triphosphate, with phosphate

Myo-inositol 1,4,5-triphosphate

Tentative formula for
beef brain phosphoinositide

groups at positions 2, 4 and 5, is obtained in smaller yield, as well as two different diphosphates. These products could all arise from an inositide like the one shown on page 265, if the phosphatidyl group were attached at position 1 and the inositol carried two other phosphate groups at positions 4 and 5. It would then have to be assumed that during the hydrolysis the phosphate at position 1 formed a bridge to position 2 (see p. 148), and that the reopening of the bridge left the phosphate attached, sometimes to position 1 and sometimes to position 2. Elimination of the diglyceride would then yield the two triphosphates mentioned above.

In plant seeds a number of more complex compounds have been found which are related to the phosphoinositides. One such compound yields on hydrolysis inositol, glycerol, phosphoric acid, fatty acids, nitrogenous bases, and sugars. A partial, tentative structure has been advanced for this phytoglycolipid and is reproduced below, as an indication of the complexity which is encountered among these compounds.

$$CH_3 \cdot (CH_2)_{13} \cdot CH \cdot CH \cdot CH \cdot CH_2O \cdot P \overset{\nearrow O}{\underset{\searrow O^-}{\longrightarrow}} \text{inositol-mannose}$$

with the branches:

$$
\begin{array}{l}
\underset{OH}{|} \quad \underset{OH}{|} \quad \underset{NH}{|} \\
\qquad\qquad CO \\
\qquad\qquad CHOH \\
\qquad\qquad (CH_2)_{21} \cdot CH_3
\end{array}
$$

inositol-mannose
glucuronic acid
glucosamine
galactose
arabinose

Partial structural representation of a phytoglycolipid

Lysophosphatides

An enzyme known as lecithinase A or phospholipase A was originally found in snake venom but has since been isolated from mammalian and other sources. It acts upon the phosphatidyl esters of choline, ethanolamine, and serine to free the fatty acid residue attached to the β-carbon of glycerol. The resulting compounds are known as lysophosphatides and have recently been shown to have the structure indicated. Since the phosphatidyl com-

$$
\begin{array}{l}
CH_2O \cdot OCR \\
|\\
HOCH \qquad\qquad O \\
|\qquad\qquad\quad \nearrow \\
CH_2O \cdot P \cdot O - \left\{ \begin{array}{l} \text{ethanolamine or} \\ \text{choline or} \\ \text{serine} \end{array} \right. \\
\qquad\qquad \searrow \\
\qquad\qquad O^-
\end{array}
$$

Lysophosphatide

pounds tend to include at least one unsaturated acid residue, and this is preferentially esterified on the β-carbon, the action of phospholipase A releases chiefly unsaturated acids. It should perhaps be noted that proof of this structure has come during 1960 and reverses the positions of the saturated and unsaturated acids in those glycerides which include only one unsaturated residue. The same results also indicate that phospholipase A attacks the β-ester and not the α-linkage as had previously been reported.

Lysophosphatides in any appreciable quantity are strongly hemolytic, hence it was assumed that such compounds would not be found in animals. It now appears that they do occur naturally in small amounts in egg yolk and among the plasma phospholipids.

Plasmalogens

Preparations of lecithin and of phosphatidyl ethanolamine from many different sources contain varying and sometimes quite large amounts of related compounds known as plasmalogens. These are compounds which on hydrolysis set free higher fatty aldehydes as well as fatty acids. It was originally believed that in these compounds there was an acetal linkage involving the α- and the β-carbons of glycerol, while the structure about the third carbon was identical with that of the classical phosphatidyl compounds. For example, the compound related to phosphatidyl ethanolamine was believed to have the formula:

$$
\begin{array}{l}
CH_2O \\
\quad\diagdown \\
\quad\quad CHR \\
\quad\diagup \\
CHO \\
\qquad\qquad\quad O \\
\qquad\qquad\nearrow \\
CH_2O \cdot P \cdot O \cdot CH_2 \cdot CH_2 \cdot \overset{+}{N}H_3 \\
\qquad\quad\diagdown \\
\qquad\qquad O^-
\end{array}
$$

Old plasmalogen formula

It has now been shown that compounds of this type are artifacts arising in the course of the separation of the plasmalogens from the related phosphatidyl compounds. In the compound as it actually occurs the α- and β-carbons are involved in linkages with separate long chain compounds. One of these is an unsaturated acid which is esterified as usual on the β-carbon. The other is a long chain aldehyde which has reacted with the α-hydroxyl group to form a vinyl ether derivative as indicated in the formulations below. The structure of the plasmalogen is based on a report made in the summer of 1960 by

$$R \cdot CH_2OH + OHC \cdot CH_2R' \rightarrow R \cdot CH_2O \cdot CH{=}CH \cdot R' + H_2O$$

$$
\begin{array}{l}
CH_2O \cdot CH{=}CH \cdot R' \\
\quad| \\
RCO \cdot OCH \qquad\qquad O \\
\quad| \qquad\qquad\quad \nearrow \\
CH_2O \cdot P{-}O{-}\left\{ \begin{array}{l} \text{choline} \\ \text{or} \\ \text{ethanolamine} \end{array} \right. \\
\qquad\quad\diagdown \\
\qquad\qquad O^-
\end{array}
$$

Plasmalogen

Hanahan and his group at the University of Washington in Seattle. In placing the vinyl grouping on the α- instead of the β-carbon he has reversed the arrangement which he had previously suggested and which had been accepted by many other workers. The reason for the discrepancies is not clear, but the latest results appear to offer conclusive proof of the structure given.

It has been suggested that the plasmalogens be called phosphatid*al* choline or ethanolamine to distinguish them from the phosphatid*yl* compounds, but the difference of a single letter seems more likely to be confusing than helpful, especially when the two pronunciations are so similar. It is to be hoped that some more distinctive nomenclature will be provided if the old "plasmalogen" is to be discarded.

The Sphingolipids

The compounds which contain the hydroxy base sphingosine or its saturated analogue, dihydrosphingosine, are for the most part incompletely characterized. They consist of complex mixtures in which both bases are likely to be present as well as a mixture of fatty acids.

Sphingomyelins

The best known of the sphingolipids is sphingomyelin, which yields on hydrolysis phosphoric acid, choline, fatty acids, and the aliphatic hydroxy base, sphingosine. The structure of this base should be compared with the

$$CH_3 \cdot (CH_2)_{12} \cdot CH{=}CH \cdot CHOH \cdot CHNH_2 \cdot CH_2OH$$
Sphingosine

one shown on page 267 as part of the complex plant, or phyto-, glycolipid. In that compound hydrolysis of the amide link and the phosphoester link would free the base which is known as phytosphingosine to emphasize its similarity to the base found in analogous compounds in animal tissues.

Sphingomyelin has been known in a relatively pure form for many years, and has been shown to have the structure below. Hydrolysis of sphingo-

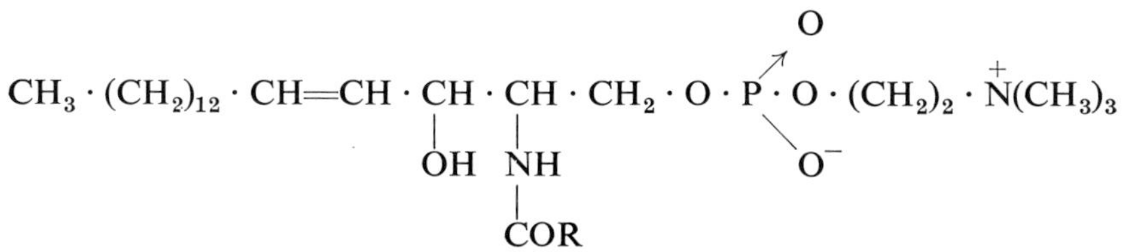

$$CH_3 \cdot (CH_2)_{12} \cdot CH{=}CH \cdot \underset{\underset{\displaystyle \underset{\displaystyle COR}{NH}}{|}}{CH} \cdot \underset{\underset{\displaystyle OH}{|}}{CH} \cdot CH_2 \cdot O \cdot \underset{\underset{\displaystyle O^-}{\diagdown}}{\overset{\overset{\displaystyle O}{\nearrow}}{P}} \cdot O \cdot (CH_2)_2 \cdot \overset{+}{N}(CH_3)_3$$

Sphingomyelin

myelin always yields a mixture of fatty acids, but each molecule holds only one, bound in an amide linkage. In general, the acids in the sphingomyelins are more saturated than those found in lecithin, lignoceric acid, $C_{24}H_{48}O_2$, being the chief acidic constituent.

Cerebrosides

Although they occur in many cells of the animal body and have been found in some plant tissues, the group of compounds known as the cerebrosides are particularly abundant in nervous tissue. They differ from most lipids in being insoluble in ether and petroleum ether, but they are extracted by warm alcohol. The cerebrosides were discovered and named about 1874 by Thudicum, but our information about their structure is still very incomplete. On complete hydrolysis they yield 1 mole each of fatty acid, sphingosine or dihydrosphingosine, and hexose. It was believed at one time that the sugar was always D-galactose, but it has now been found that it is sometimes D-glucose. The fatty acids are like those of sphingomyelin in being predominantly saturated, but some contain an hydroxyl group in the α position and some are unsaturated. Four acids which occur commonly in cerebrosides are listed below, though it should be noted that the so-called lignoceric acid from a brain cerebroside has been shown to be a mixture of the C_{22}, the C_{24}, and the C_{26} saturated acids.

$CH_3 \cdot (CH_2)_{22} \cdot COOH$ Lignoceric acid

$CH_3 \cdot (CH_2)_{21} \cdot CHOH \cdot COOH$ Cerebronic acid

$CH_3 \cdot (CH_2)_7 \cdot CH{=}CH \cdot (CH_2)_{13} \cdot COOH$ Nervonic acid

$CH_3 \cdot (CH_2)_7 \cdot CH{=}CH \cdot (CH_2)_{12} \cdot CHOH \cdot COOH$ Oxynervonic acid

From the formula below it will be seen that the cerebrosides show a general similarity to sphingomyelin not only in using acids of the same average

$$CH_3 \cdot (CH_2)_{12} \cdot CH{=}CH \cdot CH \cdot CH \cdot CH_2 \cdot O \cdot CH \cdot CHOH \cdot CHOH \cdot CHOH \cdot CH \cdot CH_2OH$$

with OH, NH (COR) substituents and O linkage

Cerebroside

molecular weights, but in binding them to sphingosine in a peptide linkage.

Gangliosides

Compounds resembling the cerebrosides have been found in tissues of the nervous system, in red blood cells, and in spleen. Klenk, who was the original discoverer of these compounds, called them gangliosides since he had found them in ganglion cells. The name is now given to a growing group of related compounds. They differ from the cerebrosides in yielding on hydrolysis either the compound which is called neuraminic acid (page 159) or its N-acetyl derivative, one of the compounds to which the name *sialic acid* has been given. The other hydrolytic products are fatty acids, sphingosine and a hexose. The last named is usually D-galactose but occasionally either D-glucose or galactosamine is obtained. The structure of these compounds is not known.

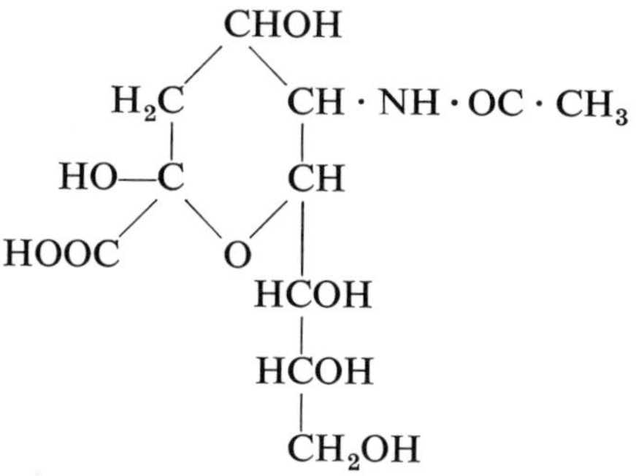

CHOH
/ \
H₂C   CH · NH · OC · CH₃
|
HO—C   CH
/ \ / |
HOOC   O   HCOH
|
HCOH
|
CH₂OH

N-acetylneuraminic acid
(O-sialic acid)[3]

THE STEROIDS

In addition to such readily hydrolyzable compounds as have just been considered, the fat solvents extract from plant and animal tissues a certain amount of material which does not become soluble during hydrolysis. This nonsaponifiable matter includes any long chain aliphatic alcohols, the glyceryl ethers and representatives of the group of substances which were originally known as sterols, or solid alcohols, since nearly all of them carry at least one hydroxyl group. In order to include all the compounds which are now known to be structurally related to the sterols, the group name *steroid* has been coined. The steroids are all derivatives of the aromatic hydrocarbon, phenanthrene, or more exactly of its cyclopentano derivative.

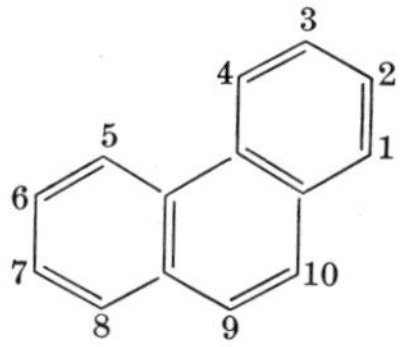

Phenanthrene

The first of this group of compounds to be recognized was the major animal sterol, cholesterol, first isolated from gallstones in 1775. It occurs both free and esterified with long chain fatty acids, in the blood and in all animal cells. The structure of cholesterol is indicated by the conventional formula and by the drawing in Fig. 6.3. The somewhat irrational numbering system shown on the structural formula has grown up over the years and is in part the

---

[3] O-sialic acid is ovine sialic acid. B-sialic acid (bovine) contains an additional, labile *O*-acetyl group. Note that this is an acetyl derivative of the compound shown on page 159 in straight chain form.

result of false starts made during the early investigations. The rings indicated are not aromatic rings but are fully saturated except where the double bond is shown. The compound is therefore an hydroxyl derivative of a substituted perhydro-1,2-cyclopentanophenanthrene. The presence of the methyl groups

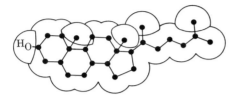

Fig. 6.3. The cholesterol molecule. [Reproduced by permission from J. L. Oncley, in *Biophysical Science*, p. 47, J. L. Oncley (ed.-in-chief), Wiley, New York, 1959.]

at positions 10 and 13 is characteristic of most of the natural compounds in the steroid group, as is some sort of substituent at position 17. As indicated, the rings are often identified by letter. Note that the numbering of the

Cholesterol

steroids does not follow that of phenanthrene, and so the 1,2 positions in phenanthrene become 14,13 in cholesterol.

Systematic nomenclature of the steroids has to take account not only of the positions of substituents on the ring but of various stereochemical possibilities. These last include the relationship between pairs of condensed rings, which may be cis or trans, as well as the arrangement about the various asymmetric carbons.

In order to explain the meaning of cis and trans as applied to fused ring systems, it is necessary to recall that cyclohexane rings are not planar but may be buckled into boat or chair conformations. Of these two the chair conformation is the more stable. Assuming then that the rings have this form, the diagrams in Fig. 6.4 indicate the two conformational relationships which are designated cis and trans. The ring pair at the left illustrates the cis relationship; that on the right the trans arrangement.

Substituents on an asymmetric carbon may project above or below the plane of the ring system, and by convention those which project above are connected in the formulas by solid lines and are said to have the β orientation. Those which project behind or below the plane of the rings have the α orientation and are shown with dotted bonds.

Fig. 6.4. Perspective formulas of a pair of fused cyclohexane rings in the cis and in the trans relationship to each other.

Cis relationship   Trans relationship

The saturated hydrocarbon related to cholesterol is named cholestane. Saying that it is related means that the relationships of the various pairs of rings to each other are those found in cholesterol. These are all trans relationships. As shown in the formula, the hydroxyl group in cholesterol has the β orientation. Thus cholesterol, with its one double bond at carbon 5, is Δ^5-cholesten-3β-ol. One more example given below will perhaps serve to clarify this complex subject enough to make the nomenclature in the literature intelligible without giving so much detail as to confound the reader. Fortunately whole groups of steroids prove to have so-called parent hydrocarbons to which they are all related as cholesterol is related to cholestane. All in such a group will be named as derivatives of their particular hydrocarbon, thus obviating the necessity for specifying an entire structure in the name. Some of the parent hydrocarbons of the physiologically active steroids are referred to in Chapter 14.

A compound which is believed to be an intermediate in the biosynthesis of cholesterol is a methylated compound with the trivial name methostenol. Its systematic name is 4α-methyl-Δ^7-cholesten-3β-ol. This tells us that it is like cholesterol except for the position of the double bond and the presence of an extra methyl group at carbon 4. These differences are illustrated in the formula below.

Methostenol

Many biologically active compounds have proved to be closely related in structure to cholesterol. The sex hormones both male and female, the major moiety of the bile acids, and the steroid hormones of the adrenal cortex are among the animal products having structures very like that of cholesterol. The sterols of plant origin are known as phytosterols and include sitosterol and ergosterol, the latter yielding the closely related vitamin D on irradiation with ultraviolet light. The formulas for some of these compounds are given in Chapter 14.

Another group of plant products which are partly steroid in structure are the cardiac glycosides, so-called because of the stimulating effect which they exert on the heart. These substances are found in the seeds and leaves of the purple foxglove from which they are extracted to yield the medicinal "digitalis." This is a mixture of glycosides in which various simple sugars are condensed with ring compounds closely related to cholesterol.

The chemistry and stereochemistry of all this group of compounds is complex in the extreme, and cannot be considered in detail here. For a discussion of the isolation, purification, and properties of the steroids the reader is referred to the book by the Fiesers, *Steroids*.

ANALYSIS AND CHARACTERIZATION OF THE LIPIDS

It will be obvious that such mixtures as occur in cells, of compounds as much alike as the various lipids, will present many technical problems. In the following paragraphs some of these will be considered in general terms, in order to show the methods of lipid chemistry and to give some experimental basis for the statements already made about lipid structure.

Isolation and Purification of Lipids

Although triglycerides are relatively easy to extract from tissues such as adipose tissue in which they are the major lipid constituents, the other types of lipids and some of the triglycerides usually occur in combination with protein or with carbohydrate in *lipoprotein* or sometimes in *glycolipid* macromolecules. These complexes tend to be water soluble rather than soluble in fat solvents, and must therefore be disintegrated if their lipid portions are to be extracted. Detergents will often release the lipids from such complexes. Acetone and alcohol will accomplish the same thing and use of one or the other, usually followed by some other solvent or solvent mixture will ensure a relatively complete lipid extraction.

Unfortunately these extracts will contain some nonlipid material either because the compounds are themselves soluble in the solvents used or because they become soluble in the presence of compound lipids, which are good emulsifying agents. Sometimes extraction of the solution with a different organic solvent, or even with water, will remove the nonlipid material. Recently chromatographic methods and adsorption on ion exchange resins have both been used to free the lipids of contaminating material.

Given then a mixture of lipids free of other types of compounds, there arises the problem of separating one class of lipid from the others. This originally depended entirely upon solubility differences. For example, the phosphatidyl compounds and the sphingolipids are insoluble in cold acetone, while triglycerides and sterols dissolve. Selective extraction or crystallization from different solvents is still used to take advantage of such differences. But as might be expected, chromatographic procedures have now been developed for dealing with lipid mixtures. Another very useful technique is known as countercurrent distribution. In this process the mixture is distributed between two solvents in an operation which allows as many as 1000 or more separate extractions in a single operation. In the end, the various components of the mixture will have been distributed between the various solvent fractions in accordance with their differing solubilities and their gradually changing ratios in the material being extracted.

Frequently no attempt is made to achieve a complete analysis of a lipid mixture. Instead methods are used which will ensure separation from the original extract of one or two lipid types in which the experimenter is interested, no account being taken of the loss of other components.

Preliminary Approximations

Because it has been almost impossible to isolate a truly homogeneous lipid sample, characterization of individual samples has had of necessity to be approximate. For example, it is often of interest to have some idea of the chain lengths of the acids in a given fat or of their degree of unsaturation.

The figure which represents the degree of unsaturation of a fat is known as its *iodine number*. It is defined as the number of grams of iodine which react with 100 g of fat. Since free iodine does not react readily, the more active iodine bromide (Hanus' solution) or iodine chloride (Wijs' solution) is used for the addition reaction, and the iodine equivalent calculated. Pure oleic acid with one double bond has an iodine number of 90, while for clupanodonic acid with five such bonds the number is 384. Therefore when a sample of butter gives an iodine number of about 25, while that for linseed oil is nearer 200, it is clear that the latter mixture includes far more unsaturated acids than the former. In Table 6.4 are given figures for several common fats and oils.

Another indication of the nature of the major fatty acids in a lipid is given by its *saponification number*. This is defined as the number of milligrams of potassium hydroxide required to saponify 1 g of fat. Obviously, since 1 g will

TABLE 6.4. Degree of Unsaturation of Fats and Oils[a]

Fat or Oil	Iodine Number	Saturated Acids, %	Unsaturated Acids		
			One Double Bond, %	Two Double Bonds, %	Three Double Bonds, %
Butter	26–38	61.3	32		
Lard	46–66	49	41	6	
Beef tallow	32–47	49	48	3	
Olive oil	80–85	10	83	7	
Cottonseed oil	108	28	19	53	
Tung oil	163–171	3.4	8	10	78
Linseed oil	175–202	10.3	21	15	53
Perilla oil	185–206	6.7	23	—	70

[a] Percentages are given as mole per cent, not weight per cent.

contain more molecules if the average molecular weight is low, a high saponification number indicates a relatively large number of short chain acids in the molecule. As shown in Table 6.5, the number is higher for butter than for most fats and this is in agreement with the fact that milk fats contain unusually high percentages of acids with fewer than 14 carbon atoms.

TABLE 6.5. Average Molecular Weights of Fats and Oils

Fat or Oil	Saponification Number	Reichert-Meissl Number
Butter	210–230	17–34.5
Lard	195–203	0.5–0.8
Beef tallow	193–199	0.3
Cottonseed oil	194–196	0.95
Olive oil	185–196	0.6–1.5
Linseed oil	188–195	0.95
Tung oil	190–191	0.35

The *Reichert-Meissl number* is the number of milliliters of $0.1N$ alkali required to neutralize the soluble, volatile acids from 5 g of fat. Of the acids set free by hydrolysis of a fat, only those of short chain length are volatile with steam. A high Reichert-Meissl number is therefore also indicative of a relatively high proportion of acids having fewer than 12 carbons. The high butter value differentiates this mixture from most other fats and has made it simple to detect its adulteration.

Analysis of Triglycerides

Such information as is obtained by the two determinations just described is of course very vague. Though often commercially useful, it is not satisfying to a chemist. Ideally the objective is the isolation and characterization of pure samples. Practically this is almost impossible with the lipids, but given a sample that is "pure" in the sense of being entirely triglyceride or entirely phosphatidyl choline, it has proved possible to obtain a good deal of very useful information about such mixtures. In the following paragraphs some of the methods used to characterize the triglycerides will be outlined. It will be seen that while it is relatively easy to determine the proportions in which the different fatty acids occur in a given sample, it is far more difficult to determine the actual structure of any individual triglyceride.

Identification of the fatty acids

The analysis of a fat begins with its hydrolysis. This is usually brought about by heating the lipid with an alcoholic solution of KOH in which both fat and reagent are soluble. After distillation of part of the alcohol the unsaponifiable matter is separated from the water-soluble potassium salts and from glycerol by extraction with ether. This removes sterols and long chain aliphatic alcohols. The acids are then precipitated by addition of mineral acid and removed by ether extraction, leaving the glycerol in the water layer. Steam distillation separates the group of lower fatty acids, up to and including lauric with 12 carbons. The higher acids are then transformed into their lead salts and crystallized from alcohol or ether. This effects the separation of the saturated and the unsaturated acids, the lead salts of the latter being much the more soluble in organic solvents. After this preliminary separation into three groups the acids were originally esterified, and the esters were separated by fractional distillation under diminished pressure. Of recent years other methods of separation have come into use. Among these are crystallization of the acids from organic solvents at very low temperatures, countercurrent distribution, various chromatographic procedures and separation of fatty acid esters by gas chromatography. Quantitative analysis of the various fractions then gives the acid composition of the original fat sample.

In general, the acids found to occur naturally in fats and oils comprise a list of about 50 saturated and unsaturated acids, among which those with 14 or more carbons make up by far the largest proportion. With the exception of isovaleric acid $[(CH_3)_2 \cdot CH \cdot CH_2 \cdot COOH]$, which occurs in the fat of the dolphin and the porpoise, and occasional trace amounts of a few other odd-numbered acids, they all contain an even number of carbons and are nearly all of the straight chain type.

Of all the acids, oleic acid with its single, central double linkage is by far the most widespread, making up in some fats 50 per cent of the total acids, and appearing in significant amounts in every fat and oil so far examined. Nearly as abundant are two other unsaturated acids, linoleic acid (9,12-octa-decadienoic acid) and palmitoleic acid (9-hexadecenoic acid). The saturated acid which occurs most frequently is palmitic acid, $C_{16}H_{32}O_2$, which is almost as ubiquitous as oleic. Myristic ($C_{14}H_{28}O_2$) and stearic ($C_{18}H_{36}O_2$) acids are also widely distributed.

As noted above, fat from a single source contains at least five different acids and may contain many more. Of these there are usually only 2 or 3 which are present to the extent of 10 per cent or more. Hilditch[4] refers to these as "major constituents" as opposed to the "minor" acids which occur in smaller percentages. On this basis there may be two or three major constituents.

Since it has become possible to survey broadly the composition of many plant and animal fats, a pattern begins to be evident. Except for a very few plant oils in which there may occur an acid peculiar to a given plant or to its species, all the acids which make up the fats come from a relatively short list. The same acids occur again and again in animal, fish, and plant fats, the different properties of which depend quite as much on differences in relative proportions as on actual differences in component acids. In general, the fats of the simplest and most primitive organisms are the most complex in composition, while those of the higher forms contain fewer different acids. Furthermore, the fats from organisms which have been grouped together by the biologists or the botanists are often found to share the same acids as major constituents. Thus in aquatic forms the unsaturated acids predominate, with those containing 16, 18, 20, and 22 carbons making up the major part. Among these aquatic fats, there is a distinction to be drawn between those of marine organisms and those of fresh water forms, the latter showing a tendency to utilize C_{16} and C_{18} unsaturated acids, while the marine fats include higher proportions of the C_{20} and especially the C_{22} unsaturated acids. The body fat of the salmon alters progressively in conformity with this generalization as the fish go from their breeding grounds in fresh water, out to the open sea.

The depot fats of land animals are on the whole simpler than those of aquatic origin, and include higher proportions of saturated acids and much smaller amounts of the very long chain unsaturated ones. Some of these differences are illustrated in Table 6.6, the data for which come from Hilditch's book.

Among the plants the same progression is apparent, with the more primitive

---

[4] Thomas P. Hilditch (1886–) was for many years Professor of Industrial Chemistry at the University of Liverpool. He became Professor Emeritus in 1951. A third edition of his encyclopedic volume, *The Chemical Constitution of the Natural Fats*, came out in 1956.

plants elaborating the more complex fats. Here the same acids appear as in animal fats, their distribution often seeming to follow family lines. The pattern is, however, varied to this extent, that in certain species the seed fats contain a high percentage of an acid which is not otherwise known as a fat constituent of that plant. Outstanding examples are the cyclic acids

TABLE 6.6.   Component Acids in Depot Fats of Animals on Natural Diets[a]

Animal	Saturated, %	Unsaturated, %			
	Palmitic Acid	C_{16}	C_{18}	C_{20}	C_{22}
Fish, fresh-water	13–15	ca. 20	40–45	ca. 12	0–5
Fish, marine	12–15	15–18	27–30	20–25	8–12
Frog	11	15	52	15	
Lizard	18	10	56	5	
Rat	24–28	7–8	ca. 60	0.3–0.5	
Cat	29	4	43	Trace	
Ox	27–30	2–3	40–50	0.2–0.5	
Lion	29	2	40	3	
Man	24–25	5–7	53–57	2–2.5	

SOURCE: Data from T. P. Hilditch, *Chemical Constitution of Natural Fats*, 2nd ed., Chapman & Hall, London, 1947.
[a] Percentages are weight percentages.

chaulmoogric and hydnocarpic acids, found in chaulmoogra oil. This oil is the product of a thorny shrub which grows in tropical Asia and Africa and belongs to the *Flacourtiaceae*. In the East the oil was used medicinally for leprosy for generations before modern medicine discovered its efficacy. Other acids which are narrowly distributed are the acetylenic tariric acid which is found in one Central American genus, *Picramnia*, of the family Simarubaceae; eleostearic acid with its three double bonds which is confined to only a few species of three different families, and ricinoleic acid which constitutes about 85 per cent of the acid in castor oil.

Component triglycerides of fats

Our knowledge of the actual composition of natural triglycerides depends largely upon the monumental labors of Hilditch and his group. One of his procedures will be roughly outlined. It begins with the separation of fully saturated triglycerides from those which contain one or more unsaturated acids. This is achieved by subjecting the fat to oxidation with potassium permanganate. This splits any unsaturated acid at the double linkage forming a pair of carboxyl groups and gives rise as chief product to acidic compounds known as "azelao-glycerides," since one or more of the acid residues still attached to glycerol is that of the dibasic acid azelaic acid, $HOOC(CH_2)_7$-COOH. This results from the fact that many natural unsaturated acids have seven CH_2— groups between the double link and the carboxyl group. Thus a triglyceride in which two saturated (S) acids plus oleic acid made up the triglyceride would on oxidation give the monoazelao-glyceride below:

$$CH_2O \cdot OC \cdot S$$
$$S \cdot CO \cdot OCH$$
$$CH_2O \cdot OC(CH_2)_7COOH$$

Having now a free carboxyl group, this compound is soluble in KOH. By extracting with alkali, potassium salts of all the azelao-glycerides may be separated from those which were fully saturated and were therefore not attacked by permanganate at all. The potassium salts are then fractionated, making use of the lower solubility in ether of those having only one carboxyl group. Given such quantitative data as may be obtained in this sort of

TABLE 6.7. Triglyceride Composition of Fats and Oils

Triglyceride	Cocoa Butter, mol. %	Shea Butter, mol. %	Butter, mol. %	Ox Depot Fat, mol. %
Trisaturated glycerides	2.5	2.3	34	17
Disaturated-monounsaturated glycerides	77	30–65	37–51	49
Monosaturated-diunsaturated glycerides	16	70–0	30–0	34
Triunsaturated glycerides	4	0–35	0–15	Trace

SOURCE: The data in this table have been adapted from figures obtained by Hilditch and his associates and quoted by H. E. Longenecker, *Chem. Revs.*, *29*, 201 (1941).

estimation, plus a knowledge of the actual component acids of a fat, it is possible to calculate the distribution of saturated and unsaturated acids in the mixed triglycerides. Table 6.7 gives the triglyceride distribution in four representative fats as revealed by the type of experiment just described.

It was found rather surprisingly that even when saturated acids make up 25 per cent or more of the total, the percentage of fully saturated *triglycerides* is small. This can only mean that the saturated acids are distributed among many triglyceride molecules, and that most triglycerides contain at least one unsaturated acid residue. In the early days of fat chemistry the simple triglycerides were named from the acids involved, as tristearin, triolein, etc. Recent work makes it clear that such molecules, if present at all, make up only a very small fraction of the total mixture. It is also generally accepted that the arrangement of acids in triglycerides is not a result of random distribution. There is still some argument about the actual pattern followed in the assembling of triglyceride molecules, but the theory which seems at present to be supported by the most convincing experimental evidence is that of Hilditch. According to his "principle of even distribution," each fatty acid is as widely distributed as possible among the different triglycerides so that it will occur once in nearly every molecule if it makes up about one-third of the total acids and will occur in simple triglycerides only if it makes up 60 per cent or more of the total. As noted above, in both triglycerides and lecithins a single unsaturated acid is attached preferentially to the β-carbon of glycerol.

There are exceptions to this rule of even distribution. There is a high concentration of trilaurin in laurel seeds, and in some other seeds and an occasional animal fat a high percentage of fully saturated triglycerides has been found. Whether these were originally assembled in this form, or result from changes in the molecules after assembly, is not known. In this connection it should be noted that one of the pitfalls of structural studies of the lipids is the ready migration of acyl radicals not only from one position in a molecule to another but also from one molecule to another. Such migrations, either *in vivo* or in the course of analytical manipulations could change the character of the individual molecules even if they had originally been assembled to give an even distribution of the acids. This problem still awaits solution.

SUGGESTIONS FOR FURTHER READING

General

Deuel, H. J., Jr., *The Lipids*, 3 vols. Interscience, New York, 1951–1957.
   The first volume is concerned with the chemistry of the lipids.
Fieser, L. F., and M. Fieser, *Steroids*, Reinhold, New York, 1959.
Hilditch, T. P., *Chemical Constitution of the Natural Fats*, 3rd ed., Chapman and Hall, London, 1956.
Hanahan, D. J., *Lipide Chemistry*, Wiley, New York, 1960.
Lovern, J. A., *Chemistry of Lipids of Biochemical Significance*, 2nd ed., Methuen, London, 1957.
   This is an excellent brief summary of structural information and of laboratory techniques and the pitfalls they entail.
Mattson, F. H., and R. A. Volpenhein, Specific distribution of fatty acids in the glycerides of vegetable fats, *J. Biol. Chem.*, 236, 1891 (1961).

Lipid Structure

Obviously the information about structure that was available when the books listed above were published will be found there. The following references are included because they have been referred to in the text or because they represent later information.

Brockerhoff, H., and C. E. Ballou, Structure of the phosphoinositide complex of beef brain, *J. Biol. Chem.*, *236*, 1907 (1961).

Carter, H. E., *et al.*, Structure of the cerebrosides from wheat flour, *J. Biol. Chem.*, *236*, 1912 (1961).

Grado, C., and C. E. Ballou, *Myo*-inositol phosphates obtained by alkaline hydrolysis of beef brain phosphoinositide, *J. Biol. Chem.*, *236*, 54 (1961).

Hanahan, D. J., *et al.*, . . . Position of fatty acids on lecithins and triglycerides, *J. Biol. Chem.*, *235*, 1917 (1960).

Klenk, E., and H. Debuch, The lipides, *Ann. Rev. Biochem.*, *28*, 39 (1959).

   This article is more concerned with questions of structure than many in the *Annual Review*. It indicates the questions which have been recently studied, and gives a full bibliography.

Marinetti, G. V., *et al.*, Structure of beef heart plasmalogens, *J. Am. Chem. Soc.*, *81*, 861 (1959).

It is ... sure that the inter-related activity of highly specific catalysts represents a notable device of Nature which has supported during the course of evolution those dynamic manifestations which characterize living things.

F. G. HOPKINS

The enzymes 7

IT IS A FAMILIAR FACT that if bacteria and molds are excluded, solutions of sucrose or glucose are perfectly stable and can be kept unchanged for months. Yet both, if introduced into living organisms, undergo rapid chemical transformation. Polar explorers report that within twenty minutes the heating effect of an ingested chocolate bar can be noted with a thermometer. This means that within so short a time sucrose has been hydrolyzed, the split products have been absorbed, and at least some of them have been oxidized. Outside the body these reactions could have been brought about only under conditions of temperature or acidity which would be lethal to living tissue. The agents which give to living organisms the ability to digest, to oxidize and to carry out a host of synthetic reactions are the catalysts or enzymes which every living cell elaborates. Those enzymes which are secreted into the digestive tract act outside the cells, but a far greater number carry out their functions intracellularly.

EARLY WORK ON ENZYMES

Although fermentation of grape juice and the making of cheese and souring of milk had been known from very early times, the study of the agents concerned in such catalytic processes goes back only to the early years of the nineteenth century. In 1830 Robiquet and Boutron-Charlard obtained by distillation of bitter almonds the fragrant "volatile oil" which we call benzaldehyde. In a study of the properties of this substance and of its relationship to the inert, odorless "fixed oil" which they obtained if they simply expressed the juice from the kernels by pressure in the cold, they were puzzled by the apparently unpredictable appearance of the fragrant substance. They decided that "quelques corps occulte" must be involved but made no attempt to identify it.

A few years later Wöhler and Liebig[1] solved the mystery by showing that the liquid obtained from bitter almonds by pressure contains a glucoside, amygdalin. At an elevated temperature this substance hydrolyzes readily to yield glucose, benzaldehyde, and hydrogen cyanide. They proved that the "vegetable proteins" of the almond itself, left as a residue after extraction of amygdalin by pressure, contained some substance which greatly hastened hydrolysis of the glucoside at room temperature. They named the active agent emulsin because it was found in the emulsion formed when the protein residue was extracted with water. In the light of his results with the extract Liebig wrote: "The small amount of emulsin which is necessary . . . to bring about the breakdown of amygdalin . . . shows that we are dealing here with no ordinary chemical reaction; there is a definite resemblance to the action of yeast on sugar, which Berzelius describes as catalytic." Even in these early papers Liebig foresaw the possibility that there were in organic nature other agents of a similar nature, "each concerned with the preparation of a special substance." Later chapters will show how good a prophet he was, for the economy of living cells, whether plant or animal, is mediated and controlled by a whole battery of such catalytic agents, each of which fulfills a unique function.

For many years there was no uniformity in the nomenclature of these new organic catalysts. Malt diastase, found in sprouting barley, was one of the first of these agents to be precipitated from solution, and as a result many writers, especially in France, refer to all such active agents as *diastases*. Pasteur (1822–1895) who did much of the pioneer work on alcoholic fermentation, used the word *ferment* to designate the entire group of catalysts, and in Germany the use of that name has persisted. But in English-speaking countries the name which has come into general use is "enzyme," first proposed by Willy Kühne in 1878. The substance on which an enzyme exerts its catalytic effect is known as a *substrate*, and many individual enzymes are now named by adding *-ase* to the name, or part of the name, of the substrate. *Urease* is thus the enzyme which brings about hydrolysis of

---

[1] Justus von Liebig (1803–1873) and Friedrich Wöhler (1800–1882) were friends and research associates for many years, Wöhler often attempting though with scant success to stem the tide of his colleague's scientific polemics. It would be hard to overestimate the debt which organic chemistry owes them for the long series of brilliant researches which they carried out, sometimes in collaboration and sometimes working separately. Wöhler was Professor at Göttingen and Liebig first at Giessen and later at Munich.

urea, and *sucrase* catalyzes the inversion of sucrose. Class names often indicate the type of reaction catalyzed. Thus hydrolytic enzymes are known as *hydrolases*, and enzymes concerned with formation of new bonds are *synthetases*.

Although the next few years following the publication of Wöhler's and Liebig's papers on emulsin saw the identification of many enzymes of plant and animal origin, the chief interest of scientists centered in the studies of the nature of alcoholic fermentation. As early as 1837 Berzelius had recognized the catalytic nature of the reaction, but the names chiefly associated with the early studies are those of Liebig and Pasteur. For many years these two eminent scientists engaged in a running battle over the nature of enzyme action. Pasteur's views were colored by his own microscopic study of yeasts, while Liebig was thinking in terms of the enzyme he knew best, emulsin.

Pasteur had proved that such processes as alcoholic fermentation and the souring of milk and wine took place only in the presence of certain definite microorganisms. He knew that the organisms were alive, for he found that they multiplied rapidly while exerting their catalytic activity. He deduced from this that the chemical changes taking place were inseparable from the simultaneous vital activities of the organisms involved. Liebig, on the other hand, had seen and indeed taken a leading part in the triumphant advances in organic chemistry which followed the overthrow of the old "vital force" theory. He was therefore understandably averse to allowing a similar theory to come to the fore in the field of enzyme chemistry. His emulsin was certainly not a product of a reproducing microorganism, and he therefore argued for a purely chemical explanation of all enzyme activity. He pictured a stable molecule as one in which the "amplitude of vibration" of its atoms does not exceed a certain amount. He argued that if a substance, itself unstable and therefore decomposing, were brought into contact with a more stable one, it would so upset the vibration equilibrium of the stable molecule as to cause it to begin to decompose also. He thought emulsin acted upon amygdalin because the vegetable proteins were decomposing, and he insisted that yeast acted upon sugar because the yeast, or some part of it, was also undergoing putrefaction. In just these terms, Liebig's theory is of course untenable. But it will be found that modern ideas of enzyme action are not so very far from Liebig's, though couched now in more precise terms.

Liebig had been dead for twenty-four years and Pasteur for two when, in 1897, Eduard Buchner[2] settled the dispute in Liebig's favor. He showed that yeast cells, ruptured by grinding with sand, yield under high pressure a juice which, though entirely cell-free, yet brings about the fermentation of sugar. This

---

[2] Eduard Buchner (1860–1917) was Professor of Chemistry at Tübingen when he separated the yeast enzymes from the cells. He was awarded the Nobel Prize in Chemistry in 1907. In 1911 he went to Würzburg as Director of the Chemical Institute of the University, but was on war duty at the time of his death.

experiment opened a whole new field in enzyme chemistry. Once it had been shown that one catalyst could be separated in solution from the cells which elaborated it, it was inevitable that other microorganisms as well as plant and animal tissues should in turn be subjected to the action of solvents. Certain enzymes, of course, such as the digestive ones are found already in solution in the various digestive secretions. Many others, however, are formed and act within the cells. Most of these are readily separated from the cells by suitable solvents. A few proved refractory to extraction, and these were for long believed to be inseparable from the cell structure. More recent methods have overcome the technical difficulties until now most of the known enzymes have been removed from the cells in which they occur. Indeed our present knowledge of enzyme properties and activities results largely from studies of cell-free preparations. Waldschmidt-Leitz,[3] who did much of the early work on protein-splitting enzymes, defined enzymes as "material catalyzers of an organic nature, elaborated by living cells, but independent of their presence in operation." A more recent definition describes an enzyme as "a protein with catalytic properties due to its power of specific activation."

ISOLATION OF ENZYMES

Liebig commented on the small amount of emulsin needed to bring about hydrolysis of amygdalin. We know now that his emulsin, as well as Buchner's press juice from yeast cells, contained a high proportion of inert substances extracted or pressed out with the active catalytic agents. One of the most important accomplishments in the field of enzyme chemistry has been the separation of minute amounts of catalyst from contaminating material in the crude extracts. This has led with some enzymes to isolation of pure substances, many of which have been crystalline, and in all cases to a great reduction in the actual weight of material associated with a given degree of enzyme activity.

Extraction from Cells

Except for a few which are secreted in the digestive juices, enzymes must be extracted from the interior of cells. This requires a destruction of cell walls. Buchner achieved this by grinding the yeast cells with sand. A similar mechanical destruction of cell structure is now achieved by grinding

---

[3] Ernst Waldschmidt-Leitz (1894–) was Professor of Biochemistry at the German University of Prague and later published from the Bayer Institute in Munich. He has held a Professorship at the University of Erlangen and is now Professor of Biochemistry at the Munich Technische Hochschule.

tissue between metal plates in a mincer, or between ground glass surfaces rotated against each other. Alternatively the cells may be exposed to sonic or ultrasonic vibrations, or to alternate freezing and thawing. A different and in some ways less satisfactory method is to rupture the cells by *autolysis*, or self-digestion of its membranes. This is brought about by protein-splitting enzymes found in all cells and known as *cathepsins*. In living cells these enzymes are segregated with other hydrolytic enzymes in tiny cytoplasmic granules known as lysosomes. These particles are impermeable to the substrates present in the cytoplasm, and so during normal cell life the enzymes appear to be inactive. When normal metabolic processes stop, there ensues a disruption or weakening of the lipoprotein envelope around the granules, and enzymes and substrates then come into contact. As a result the various cell membranes in turn are hydrolyzed, and the cytoplasmic contents are thus made available to solvents. This method has the disadvantage that the enzyme which is to be extracted, being itself a protein, may be digested, but in practice autolysis has proved a useful tool in many enzyme extractions. Yeast for example contains the enzyme sucrase or invertase which catalyzes the hydrolysis of sucrose. The first step in the extraction of this enzyme is autolysis of the cells for several days at room temperature in the presence of toluene to maintain aseptic conditions. There results a complete liquefaction of the cell mass. Spinning in a centrifuge then throws down some insoluble matter and leaves a cloudy supernatant solution containing the enzyme. A third common preliminary treatment is *dehydration* with acetone or other dehydrating solvent. The finely minced tissue is stirred or allowed to stand with several times its own volume of acetone, and finally filtered. If necessary, this process may be repeated several times. After the final filtration, the tissue is dried in air and can then be finely powdered in a mortar. Such acetone-dried preparations often retain their activity for months. Extraction of the powder with a suitable solvent yields a cloudy, crude solution containing the enzyme contaminated with varying amounts of inert soluble material.

Purification of Enzymes

With such a crude extract, the next step is separation of the enzyme from as much as possible of the inert material which has dissolved with the catalyst. This requires a method of testing for the presence or absence of the enzyme and usually involves setting up some sort of arbitrary unit in which to express its concentration.

Enzyme tests

The test for the enzyme will depend upon the type of reaction which it catalyzes. One or two examples should make clear the general principles on which such testing is based. When an ester is hydrolyzed the products are an alcohol and an acid. Of the four substances involved, one, the acid, can be easily identified with a suitable titration indicator. To find out whether or not a given extract contains an enzyme capable of catalyzing the hydrolysis of an ester it is necessary only to add some of the extract to a mixture of the ester and water and to test from time to time to see whether acid is being formed. Another type of testing is used if the enzyme reaction being studied is one which involves the use or evolution of a gas. Delicate and ingenious apparatus is available for the measurement of small changes in the volume of gas enclosed within the apparatus. Many enzymes catalyze reactions in which molecular oxygen is used. Others either promote the direct evolution of carbon dioxide, or the formation of an acid which, in the presence of bicarbonate, will set free an equivalent amount of carbon dioxide. The presence of the fermentation enzyme can be proved by showing that the solution being examined does, under certain definite conditions, bring about the evolution of carbon dioxide from a sugar solution. With other enzymes a decrease in the volume of gas within the apparatus indicates that oxygen is being used under the catalytic influence of an oxidizing enzyme.

A different sort of test which is simple, elegant, and rapid can be applied to reactions in which the light absorption of the substrate differs from that of its transformation product or when the absorption spectrum of an enzyme itself changes in the course of its catalytic action. There is, for example, an enzyme which catalyzes the dehydration of 2-phosphoglyceric acid to phosphoenolpyruvic acid.

$$\begin{array}{ll} \text{CH}_2\text{OH} & \text{CH}_2 \\ | & \| \\ \text{CHO} \cdot \text{PO}_3\text{H}_2 & \text{CO} \cdot \text{PO}_3\text{H}_2 \\ | & | \\ \text{COOH} & \text{COOH} \end{array}$$

2-Phosphoglyceric acid   **Phosphoenolpyruvic acid**

The phosphoenolpyruvic acid absorbs ultraviolet light of 240 mμ wavelength; the substrate transmits this wavelength. When a tissue extract is added to the substrate, the appearance of the absorption band at 240 mμ indicates that the product has formed, and therefore that the enzyme is present. Furthermore, the rate at which the band appears is a measure of the concentration of the enzyme solution. Figure 2.13, on page 39, illustrates how a change in light absorption while an enzyme is acting catalytically could be used to determine whether or not the enzyme was present in a solution or extract.

The purification of a crude enzyme extract involves the removal of much inert material. In one preparation, for example, 16.5 g of material were extracted, but of this only 1.14 g remained after purification. To express the ratio of active to inert substances in a solution, it is customary to refer to the number of arbitrary activity units per milligram of dry weight. A unit consists of the amount of enzyme which will change a specified weight of substrate under well-defined conditions. Such an arbitrary unit for sucrase was defined in one study of the enzyme as that amount of enzyme which would reduce the rotation of 4.0 g of cane sugar in 25 ml of a carefully defined solution, to zero degrees in one minute. As an enzyme preparation is progressively freed of inert matter, the actual weight of substance required to change a given weight of substrate becomes quite fantastically small. The enzyme peroxidase, which catalyzes a reaction between hydrogen peroxide and various oxidizable substrates, has now been prepared in so pure a form that 0.001 mg of the enzyme in a liter of water gives a solution which has catalytic activity.

Separation from inert matter

The methods in use for the purification of enzymes are essentially those developed for the purification of proteins. A very general method makes use of protein precipitants to separate active and inactive material. Repeated precipitations and dissolutions yield at each step two fractions, each of which must be tested for the presence of enzyme. With many extracts so high a proportion of the activity will be found in one fraction that the other can be discarded. Electrophoresis has proved a valuable tool in enzyme purification, as has the method of repeated adsorption on, and elution from, various finely divided adsorbents. The latter process has been useful not only in separation of an enzyme from inactive material but also in concentration of enzyme solutions, since the volume of liquid used for elution may be only a fraction of that from which the enzyme was originally adsorbed.

Some of the procedures which have led to enzyme preparations of high potency are long and complicated and arduous. One method began with 18 months' autolysis! On the other hand, it may happen that the process is very simple. The enzyme urease may be extracted at room temperature from finely ground jack bean meal with dilute acetone. During overnight filtration in a refrigerator the enzyme crystallizes. Urease was, in fact, the first enzyme to be obtained in pure crystalline form. This was announced by Sumner[4] in 1926. He substantiated his claim that the crystals *are* the enzyme, and not simply a carrier of minute amounts of a much more active substance, by comparing activity before and after repeated recrystallizations. His crystals hydrolyze urea 700 to 1400 times as fast as equal weights of the bean meal from which the enzyme was extracted, and for a given sample this activity is neither increased nor decreased by repeated recrystallizations. Since this first crystallization of urea many other enzymes have been obtained

---

[4] James B. Sumner (1885–1955) was Professor of Biochemistry at Cornell University and after 1947, Director of the Laboratory of Enzyme Chemistry. He prepared the first crystalline enzyme in 1926 and shared the Nobel Prize in Chemistry with Stanley and Northrop in 1946.

in crystalline form. It should be noted that this does not mean that these enzymes are "pure." A protein often forms crystals which enclose impurities, but such preparations have certainly been freed of the major part of the contaminating material. Every day the number of highly purified enzymes, crystalline or not, is increasing, so that there are probably now more than 200 which have been freed of most inert material.

With some extracts the problem of purification is of the type outlined above, that is it requires only the removal from the enzyme solution of a certain amount of inert material. With other enzyme extracts the reaction catalyzed proved to require a whole group of enzymes which had been extracted together. With such extracts it was necessary to identify and separate one enzyme after another. An early example of this type of purification was afforded by Buchner's press juice which was originally supposed to contain a single enzyme, called "zymase," which caused fermentation of sugar. Soon it was discovered that in the cell extract there was more than one catalytic agent and that there were also other, nonprotein factors which were essential to the catalysis. It was found that when the enzyme solution was dialyzed it lost its activity, but addition of the dialyzate reactivated it. The nonprotein material which passed through the dialyzing membrane was called a *coenzyme*, since it included small molecules essential to the catalytic activity of an enzyme. The process of separation so begun went on until we now know that "zymase" contains at least 14 enzymes and 5 coenzymes all essential to the catalysis by which glucose is fermented to alcohol and carbon dioxide.

Potency of enzymes

The specific activity of an enzyme is defined as the activity per unit weight, but there is at present no generally accepted way of expressing this. Results are often reported in terms of the so-called turnover number, defined originally as the number of moles of substrate transformed per mole of enzyme per minute at some fixed temperature. This gives a useful figure for comparative purposes if the molecular weight of the enzyme is known, and if each enzyme molecule acts catalytically upon a single substrate molecule at a time. As we shall see later in the chapter, an enzyme in exerting its catalytic function must form a compound with its substrate, and the place on the enzyme surface at which this takes place is known as the *active site* or center. It has been found that enzymes differ in the number of active sites per molecule, and when the true number of such sites is known, it would be more informative to report the activity of an enzyme in terms of moles of substrate transformed per active enzyme center. It has been suggested[5] that the figure

---

[5] This suggestion, like much else in this chapter, is taken from *Enzymes*, by Dixon and Webb (see bibliography). This book, published in 1958 and already in process of revision, has brought together an enormous amount of information about all those enzymes which have been obtained in a pure enough form so that they clearly have an individual existence.

which expresses the turnover per mole of enzyme be called the *catalytic constant*, and that the term *turnover number* be reserved to indicate the turnover per active center. With these definitions, the catalytic constant for catalase, which catalyzes the breakdown of hydrogen peroxide to water and oxygen, would be 5×10^6, but since each catalase molecule has four active centers, its turnover number would be one-quarter of this. For many enzymes neither the molecular weight nor the number of active sites is known, yet the activity of such enzymes is often reported as a turnover number which may be given an arbitrary definition, or may represent moles of substrate acted upon per milligram of enzyme or per 100,000 g of enzyme. Comparison of turnover numbers of enzymes should therefore be undertaken with caution. The figure given above for the catalytic constant for catalase is said to be the highest so far determined; similar figures for other enzymes may be as low as 10,000, but they cover a wide range, some of the higher figures approaching that for catalase.

Nomenclature

In the early years, names were given to individual enzymes at the pleasure of the discoverer. Emulsin was so named, because it was found in an emulsion. Trypsin comes from the Greek word meaning "a rubbing," and was chosen because the enzyme was first obtained by grinding pancreas with glycerol. Pepsin means "to cook" or "digest." With the introduction of a rational system of nomenclature in other chemical fields, a system of naming enzymes has come into use in which the ending *-ase* indicates an enzyme. Originally the ending was used with the substrate name, as in urease or sucrase. More recently it has been used more flexibly, especially with words which indicate the type of reaction involved. This is the case with the names given to groups of enzymes which bring about similar reactions. Those which catalyze the hydrolysis of their substrates are called *hydrolases*. Such are all the digestive enzymes. A similar reaction is the splitting of polysaccharides in which phosphoric acid is involved instead of water.

$$(C_6H_{10}O_5)_n + nH_3PO_4 \rightleftharpoons nC_6H_{11}O_6{-}PO_3H_2$$

Starch or glycogen   **Glucose-1-phosphate**

This reaction is spoken of as phosphorolysis, and the active agents are grouped together as *phosphorylases*. Some individual enzymes are likewise named with a view to indicating the type of reaction they catalyze. This results in such names as *carbonic anhydrase*, *adenosine triphosphatase*, and *nitrite reductase* for the factors which catalyze respectively the decomposition of carbonic acid, the splitting of pyrophosphate from a nucleoside triphosphate, and the reduction of nitrite to nitric oxide. Other class names and most individual names can best be acquired gradually, as the functions of the enzymes themselves are developed.

PROPERTIES OF ENZYMES

Reversibility of Enzyme Action

An important characteristic of enzymes is their ability, which indeed they must have if they are to be considered catalysts, to catalyze both a forward and a back reaction. The classical example of such a catalysis is the effect of acid upon the rate of saponification or esterification. Whether the starting materials are ester and water or acid and alcohol, the catalysis consists in hastening the rate at which the identical equilibrium is achieved. With many biological reactions, it is true, the equilibrium point is such that the reaction appears to go to completion in one direction. This results largely from the fact that in the normal setting in the cell, the product of one enzymic reaction becomes the substrate of the next, hence each intermediate is promptly removed, and the reaction has no opportunity to reverse. When this is prevented by using single, pure enzymes, nearly every known biochemical reaction proves to be reversible and to be catalyzed in both directions by the same enzyme. So true is this that until quite recently biochemists assumed that the many syntheses carried out in the cells were catalyzed by the same enzymes which brought about the breakdown of the synthetic end products. This proved not to be generally true, but there are still some reaction sequences which are believed to proceed under different conditions in the cell either forward or back.

Specificity of Enzymes

One of the most striking characteristics of enzymes is their specificity. In the field of inorganic catalysis some substances, such as finely divided metals, are known to hasten a wide variety of different reactions. Platinum as foil or as "platinum black" is such a general catalyst, and some of the metal oxides are also quite versatile. All the enzymes, on the other hand, require very specific substrates and although their specificities differ in degree, it is this property which chiefly accounts for the role they play in the cell. Because of their specificity, they determine which substances will be acted upon and what changes they will undergo. This means that in the final analysis they organize and direct all the chemical events within the cell.

Some enzymes exhibit a rather broad specificity. The *lipases*, for example, normally catalyze the hydrolytic cleavage of the lipid ester bonds, and so may be said to have two substrates, water and the ester. For the water the specificity is unique, but the ester may have a high molecular weight as in the natural substrates, or it may be a small molecule such as methyl acetate or butyrate. The group of *phosphatases* has a similar broad specificity, bringing about the hydrolytic removal of phosphate from a large group of phosphate esters. This is a slightly more restricted specificity than that of the lipases, since the enzymes act only upon phosphoric acid esters, but the alcohol residue may be furnished by a sugar or by glycerol or by any of a number of other hydroxyl compounds.

Among the *phosphokinases* the specificity is still narrower. These are the enzymes which catalyze the transfer of a phosphate group from ATP (or occasionally another nucleoside triphosphate) to one of a great number of acceptors. The name hexokinase for one of these indicates that it can bring about phosphorylation of several different hexoses by ATP, while galacto-kinase acts only with galactose or galactosamine. About fifty different phosphokinases are known, some acting to phosphorylate three or four related compounds, but many acting to transfer a phosphate group to a single substrate. Most are completely specific for ATP as the donor molecule.

At the other end of the scale entirely are the enzymes like urease and argi-nase which bring about hydrolysis of just one compound, urease catalyzing the splitting of urea to ammonia and carbon dioxide, and arginase freeing urea from arginine. It should be noted, however, that it is never safe to deduce from a name that an enzyme has only one substrate. Sucrase for example, splits not only sucrose but various other fructosides. Maltase is particularly confusing. If it is extracted from yeast or from the digestive tract, it is merely an α-glucosidase, but the maltase from malt is truly named, since it acts only upon maltose. Catalase, on the other hand, gives no inkling in its name that it acts uniquely upon hydrogen peroxide.

A final degree of specificity may coexist with other specificities when the enzyme in question requires a definite stereochemical configuration in its substrate. This type of requirement was foreshadowed in early metabolic experiments with animal tissues and with bacteria. If L-glucose was injected into a rat, 85 per cent of this unnatural sugar was excreted within 24 hours, showing that the rat does not use the L form. Bacteria which need glucose in the nutrient medium fail to grow if L-glucose is used instead of the D form. Brain slices, which take up oxygen steadily if supplied with D-glucose, are unable to oxidize the L isomer at all. When we turn from experiments of this sort, in which many unknown enzyme systems are involved, to work with purified enzymes, we find that many enzymes can act with only one particular stereochemical or geometrical isomer. The use of maltase and emulsin to distinguish between an α- and a β-glucoside was a familiar procedure in the early days of sugar chemistry. The digestive protein-splitting enzymes also exhibit stereochemical specificity: they act only upon peptide bonds between α-amino acids of the natural, or L series. In all these examples stereochemical specificity is added to a fairly broad specificity. In others, it further defines an already absolute specificity. Arginase hydrolyzes only L-arginine, and lactic dehydrogenase from muscle oxidizes only L-lactic acid.

Enzymes not only require specific substrates but also form specific products. If the product of an enzymic transformation exhibits stereochemical or geometrical isomerism, even though the substrate has no isomeric forms, only one of the possible products will form. For example, phosphorylation of the symmetrical glycerol molecule by ATP in the presence of glycerol kinase yields only L-α-phosphoglycerol.

$$CH_2OH$$
$$|$$
$$HOCH$$
$$|$$
$$CH_2O \cdot PO_3H_2$$

L-α-Phosphoglycerol

Of recent years a strange variety of *dual* specificity has been noted with certain enzymes. The first example was that of xanthine oxidase. As its name indicates, this enzyme which is found in milk and in some animal tissues, catalyzes the oxidation to uric acid of xanthine or hypoxanthine, but not of other purines. This same enzyme in highly purified form proves to catalyze the oxidation of a number of simple aldehydes to the corresponding acids. Some of the digestive proteinases, which normally act upon peptide bonds, also act as esterases and in addition split hydrazide and hydroxyamide links. A highly purified L-amino acid oxidase has this same type of dual specificity. It catalyzes the oxidation of thirteen different amino acids of the L series on the one hand, and on the other, brings about oxidation of several α-hydroxy acids, also of the L series. This enzyme has been crystallized, and in the course of its purification it was found that any increase in activity toward one type of substrate was exactly paralleled by a corresponding increase in its activity toward the other. There are a few other examples of dual specificity, but as yet no explanation. This will probably have to await a clearer understanding of the nature of the active sites and of enzymic catalysis itself.

Kinetics of Enzyme Action

Much of our present information about the nature of enzymes has been deduced from a study of the rates of enzymic reactions and of the factors which influence those rates. Theoretically, reaction rate may be measured either (*a*) in terms of the amount of change occurring in unit time, or (*b*) in terms of the length of time required to bring about some fixed amount of chemical change. The actual experiments, however, are nearly always carried out by following the change at fixed time intervals, i.e., working in accordance with plan (*a*). If the amount of chemical change measured is then plotted against time, it is of course possible to read from the curve the time required for any fixed amount of change to take place.

The way in which the experiment is set up, as well as the method used to measure the change, depends upon the nature of the catalyzed reaction. In some experiments, enzyme is added to a rather large amount of substrate, and from time to time small aliquot portions are removed to determine how far the reaction has progressed. Other reactions are best followed by setting up a number of small separate flasks and allowing the reaction to proceed for a different length of time in each. If a gas is used or evolved in the course

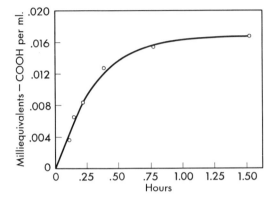

Fig. 7.1. The rate of hydrolysis of a 5 per cent casein solution by crystalline trypsin. The increasing concentration of free amino acid was measured by the formol titration. [From J. H. Northrop, *J. Gen. Physiol.*, **16**, 339 (1932–1933).]

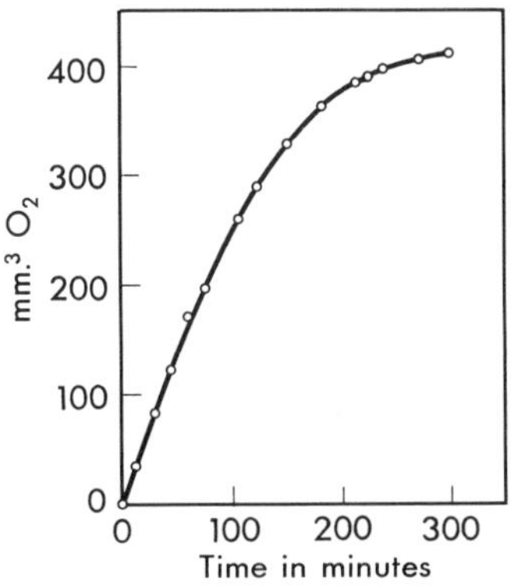

Fig. 7.2. Time-activity curve of glycine oxidase. The reaction rate is plotted in terms of the volume of oxygen used. Note that with this enzyme the rate is linear for more than an hour. [From S. Ratner, V. Nocito, and D. E. Green, *J. Biol. Chem.*, **152**, 119 (1944).]

of the enzymic reaction, the experiment may be carried out in an apparatus designed so that changes in gas volume may be measured directly from time to time. Figures 7.1 and 7.2 show typical enzyme curves obtained by measuring reaction rate in two different ways. The reaction represented in Fig. 7.1 is hydrolysis of casein, catalyzed by crystalline trypsin. Since hydrolysis of a protein ruptures peptide bonds and sets free both carboxyl and amino groups, the extent of the reaction could be measured by determining from time to time the increase in the number of either of these groups. For the curve reproduced, aliquot portions of the digest were submitted to a formol titration, and the number of milliequivalents of new carboxyl groups per milliliter of solution thus determined. The second curve expresses the rate of oxidation of glycine in terms of the cubic millimeters (microliters, μl) of oxygen used by a definite weight of glycine in presence of its specific oxidizing enzyme.

Influence of activity

It will be noted that the two time–activity curves are of the same general type. They indicate that for only short periods, just after an enzyme has been added to its substrate, is the reaction rate constant, or linear. After that it falls off more or less rapidly until finally the enzyme is completely inactivated. There is probably no single reason for this. Some enzymes are extremely labile, and others maintain a linear rate for quite long periods. This suggests

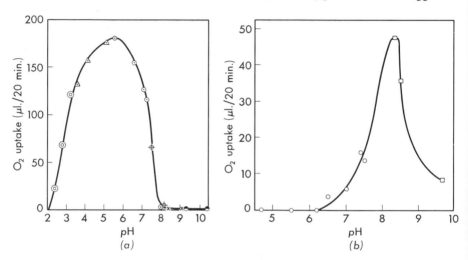

Fig. 7.3. The relation between pH and enzyme activity. (*a*) The effect of pH on the activity of glucose oxidase, reported in terms of the oxygen uptake in the first 20 mins. The different symbols marking the points on the curves indicate the use of several different buffers. [From D. Keilin and E. F. Hartree, *Biochem. J.*, **42**, 221 (1948).] (*b*) The rate of oxygen uptake in the presence of glycine oxidase as a function of pH. [From S. Ratner, V. Nocito, and D. E. Green, *J. Biol. Chem.*, **152**, 119 (1944).]

that different factors are involved with different enzymes. It has been found that some enzymes are inhibited by a product of their own activity. In the next few sections we shall consider some factors other than activity which influence the rate of all enzymic reactions. These must be taken into account in any explanation of the shape of the time–activity curves. It is because of the shape of this type of curve that in many experiments with enzymes only the initial, maximum rates are considered.

Influence of pH

All enzymes are sensitive to changes in the acidity of their environment. Furthermore, most enzymes exert their maximum catalytic effect over a rather narrow pH range, and lose activity rapidly on either side of this optimum. Figure 7.3 shows the effect of a changing pH on the activity of two oxidases in terms of the oxygen uptake in the first twenty minutes. For the glucose oxidase the optimum *p*H is 5.6; it is relatively inactive at *p*H 3 and completely so above *p*H 8. The glycine oxidase, on the other hand, is completely inactive below *p*H 6, surprisingly inactive at *p*H 7, and has an optimum at about 8.3. Many enzymes have *p*H optima close to neutrality; on the other hand, pepsin acts at a strongly acid *p*H while some of the phosphatases, which split phosphoric acid from its esters, require a *p*H as high as 9 or 10. To achieve

TABLE 7.I. Optimal *p*H of a Few Representative Enzymes

Enzyme	Substrate	*p*H
Pepsin	Native proteins	1.5–2.2
α-Glucosidase	Methyl α-glucoside	5.4
Maltase	Maltose	7.0
Lactase	Lactose	5.7
"Zymase"	Glucose	6.2
Amylase	Starch	6.2
Urease	Urea	6.6
Catalase	Hydrogen peroxide	7.0
Trypsin	Proteins	7.8
D-Amino acid oxidase	D-Amino acids	9.0
β-Glycerophosphatase	β-Glycerophosphate	9.5–9.9

and maintain the desired *p*H, enzyme experiments are always conducted in a buffered medium. The optimal *p*H values for a few enzymes are indicated in Table 7.1.

This sensitivity to *p*H changes may reflect a true effect on the velocity of the reaction catalyzed, or it may depend upon changes in the enzyme protein itself. It will be remembered that on the alkaline side of the isoelectric point, proteins exist as anions and react with metal and other cations, but they react with such an anion as bromide ion only on the acid side. At the isoelectric point various physical properties such as swelling, solubility, and conductivity are at a minimum, and rise rapidly on either side of this *p*H. This indicates that the molecular architecture of the ampholyte, the shape of its surface, and the charges upon it depend upon the acidity of the medium. Changes in any of these properties might alter the stability of the enzyme itself or influence its ability to bind its substrate. For example, if its catalytic activity depends upon its attachment to a charged group in the substrate, this would be facilitated by a *p*H which favored formation of an oppositely charged group at the active site of the enzyme itself. The optimal *p*H would then depend on the balance between the effect of *p*H on reaction velocity and its effect, adverse or favorable, upon the structure of the enzyme protein.

Since some enzymes are activated specifically by certain anions, it is also necessary to be sure that the effect measured is a true *p*H effect and is not due merely to the base chosen for the buffer.

Influence of temperature

The influence of increased temperature upon an enzymic reaction is two-fold. Other things being equal, increasing the temperature increases the rate

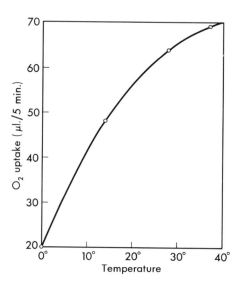

Fig. 7.4. Effect of temperature on the activity of glucose oxidase. Note that the temperature coefficient of the enzyme *activity* falls off with rising temperature, which means that temperature *inactivation* of the enzyme accelerates as the temperature rises. [From D. Keilin and E. F. Hartree, *Biochem. J.*, **42**, 221 (1948).]

at which any chemical reaction takes place. But if the reaction is catalyzed by an enzyme, other things are far from equal. Most enzymes function *in vivo* at moderate temperatures, and are inactivated to a greater or less degree when the temperature is raised. All enzymes are destroyed by boiling, and most are destroyed when the temperature rises to 70°. The extent of the inactivation depends upon the temperature and upon the time during which the enzyme is exposed to its influence. For this reason the optimum temperature for an enzyme cannot be stated definitely as if it were a fixed property of that enzyme. If the activity of an enzyme is to be used over a brief time, it may well be that the increase in reaction rate at a higher temperature will more than compensate for the gradual inactivation of the catalyst. If, however, the reaction is to be of longer duration, it is probable that a greater amount of substrate will ultimately be acted upon if the temperature is not high enough to inactivate the enzyme rapidly. In general, enzymes from the tissues of warm-blooded animals act best at about 37°C, while plant enzymes have an optimum temperature in the neighborhood of 25°C. Figure 7.4 illustrates the effect of rising temperature upon an oxidizing enzyme from the mold *Penicillium notatum*.

This property of heat sensitivity of enzymes is of course referable to the effect of heat upon protein secondary and tertiary structure. This is indicated in the first place by the resemblances between heat inactivation of enzymes and heat denaturation of proteins. Both have temperature coefficients which are higher than those of most chemical reactions. The temperature coefficient of a reaction is defined as the ratio of the rate at $(T + 10)°$ to the rate at $T°$. When we say that for most chemical reactions the temperature coefficient is 2, we mean that for each $10°$ rise in temperature the reaction rate is doubled. The two conspicuous exceptions to this are heat denaturation of proteins and heat inactivation of enzymes, both of which have temperature coefficients enormously greater than 2. Both these processes are alike also in the fact that if the increased temperature is not extreme, and is not too long continued, its effect is reversible. The inactivation of an enzyme protein by heat may then be explained as such a disorientation of the protein, and specifically of the active site, that it can no longer bind its substrate. When the change in the protein is limited, its structure can be reestablished if the temperature is lowered, and under these conditions the enzyme is reactivated.

Influence of enzyme concentration

The rate of an enzyme reaction, when pH and temperature are fixed and when excess of substrate is available, is directly proportional to the enzyme

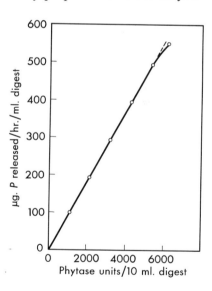

Fig. 7.5. Relation between enzyme concentration and activity in the presence of a purified phytase from wheat. The enzyme hydrolyzes phytic acid (inositol hexaphosphoric acid) and sets free inorganic phosphate. Note that the rate is linear over very nearly the entire concentration range which is plotted. [From F. G. Peers, *Biochem. J.*, **53**, 104 (1953).]

concentration. Figure 7.5 illustrates this relationship in the hydrolysis of phytic acid by a phytase derived from wheat. In this experiment the initial rate is linear over a wide range of enzyme concentrations.

Influence of substrate concentration

In a series of experiments in which the *p*H, temperature, and enzyme concentration are all held constant, the rate of the initial reaction will depend upon the substrate concentration, up to a definite limiting value. Beyond this, any further increase in substrate concentration brings about no further increase in reaction rate. This is shown in Fig. 7.6, which shows graphically how the rate of oxidation of glycine varies with the concentration of the substrate. Substrate concentration is plotted against the initial reaction rate measured

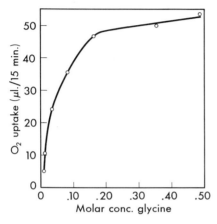

Fig. 7.6. Rate of oxygen uptake in the presence of glycine oxidase as a function of the concentration of the substrate, glycine. [From S. Ratner, V. Nocito, and D. E. Green, *J. Biol. Chem.*, **152,** 119 (1944).]

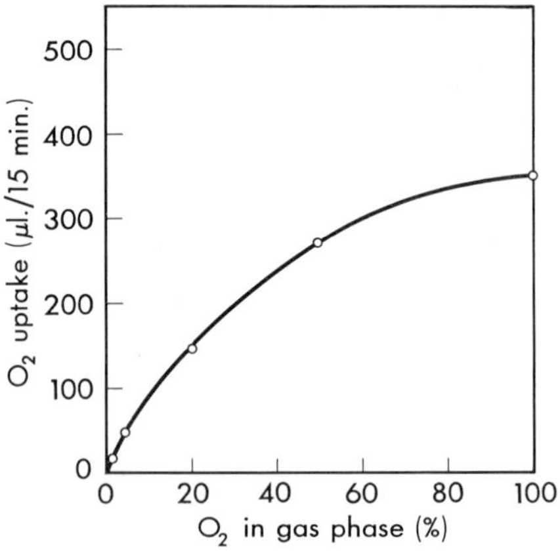

Fig. 7.7. Effect of oxygen tension on the activity of glucose oxidase. [From D. Keilin and E. F. Hartree, *Biochem. J.*, **42,** 221 (1944).]

in terms of the volume of oxygen consumed in a fixed time interval. The flattened curve indicates that with the amount of enzyme used, about 0.5*M* glycine reacts at a maximum rate.

Where a reaction involves two substances, we should perhaps speak of two substrates. This is true, of course, in any hydrolysis. But since the concentration of water is very nearly constant in any reaction mixture using dilute solutions, we seldom think of water as a possible substrate, and in any case cannot study the effect of changes in its concentration. But in reactions in which a substrate is oxidized by molecular oxygen, there are clearly two reactants, and the concentration of either may be varied. In such reactions the rate varies directly with the concentration of either substrate. In Fig. 7.7 are shown data from an experiment with glucose oxidase, in which the oxygen tension was varied while the glucose concentration was constant. The curve is of the same general type as the previous one, showing an enzyme activity in pure oxygen nearly two and a half times that in air.

The Michaelis theory[6]

It has been stated repeatedly that an enzyme binds its substrate, forming some sort of compound or complex, in order to exert its catalytic effect. The earliest attempt to check with the facts what was then only a theory, was made in 1913 by Michaelis and Menten. They assumed that such a compound does form, and worked out an equation relating the velocity of enzyme action to substrate concentration under these assumed conditions. When it was found, as shown below, that their equation did in fact correspond closely with the experimentally determined curves relating these two factors, belief in the reality of an enzyme-substrate compound was greatly strengthened. Since then unequivocal evidence for the existence of such compounds has been obtained, but the Michaelis constant is a fundamental one in enzyme kinetics, and so its derivation is given here.

If E stands for a hydrolytic enzyme, S for its substrate and F and G for the products of an enzymic hydrolysis, the complete reaction would involve the following two steps if an enzyme-substrate compound (ES) is an obligatory intermediate:

$$\text{E} + \text{S} \rightleftharpoons \text{ES} \qquad (a)$$
$$(e - p) \quad (s) \quad (p)$$
$$\text{ES} + \text{H}_2\text{O} \rightarrow \text{E} + \text{F} + \text{G} \qquad (b)$$
$$(p)$$

Now let e stand for the molar concentration of the enzyme, s for that of substrate, and p for that of the ES compound. If it is assumed that the molar concentration of the substrate is, as is usually true, very much larger than that of the enzyme, the formation of the compound would not appreciably decrease the concentration of the substrate. It would, however, have a significant effect on the concentration of the enzyme. For this reason the equilibrium concentration of the enzyme is $e - p$, but that of the substrate may still be considered equal to s.

Applying the law of mass action to reaction (a), and allowing K_m to stand for the dissociation constant of the ES compound, we have

$$K_m = \frac{s(e - p)}{p} \quad \text{or} \quad p = \frac{se}{K_m + s} \qquad (1)$$

K_m is known as the Michaelis constant. In actual practice it is seldom possible to evaluate either e or p, and these terms must therefore be eliminated from the equation before we can compare it with experimental results.

---

[6] Leonor Michaelis (1875–1949) was born in Germany and practiced medicine there until 1922. He was Professor of Medicine at Nagoya University, 1922–1926, and Member of the Rockefeller Institute for Medical Research in New York from 1929 until he became Emeritus in 1941. He is chiefly known for the application of physical chemistry to biology and medicine.

The rate at which the ES compound hydrolyzes will depend on its concentration in the solution, and on the concentration of the other reactant, water. Since the concentration of water is approximately constant we may write

$$v = kp \tag{2}$$

where v is the velocity of reaction (b) and k its velocity constant. Substituting in this equation the value of p from equation (1) we have

$$v = \frac{kes}{K_m + s} \tag{3}$$

This still includes the term expressing the enzyme concentration, and so requires further modification.

Obviously if the concentration of the substrate is large enough, all the enzyme will be in the ES compound, and e will be equal to p. The reaction velocity under these conditions will be at a maximum for a given amount of enzyme, since all of it is saturated with substrate. If V stands for this maximum velocity,

$$V = ke \tag{4}$$

when the substrate is in large excess. Substituting V for ke in equation (3) we have:

$$v = \frac{Vs}{K_m + s} \tag{5}$$

as an expression of the velocity of the reaction in terms of (a), the maximum velocity possible for a given amount of enzyme, (b) the concentration of substrate, and (c) the dissociation constant for the ES compound. How well does this theoretical equation agree with the facts?

The Michaelis equation (equation 5) may be transformed to read:[7]

$$(K_m + s)(v - V) = -K_m V$$

Since K_m and V are both constants for any given amount of enzyme, this equation becomes $(s + k_1)(v - k_2) = -K$. The theoretical curve for such an equation is plotted in Fig. 7.8 in which $X = s$ and $Y = v$ and is seen to be a section of a rectangular hyperbola. But we have already considered some experimental data relating the rate of reaction (v) to substrate concentration (s). This was plotted in Fig. 7.6, which is clearly a curve of the same general shape as the theoretical one.

Other assumptions made by Michaelis are borne out by the experimental facts. According to his equations, the reaction velocity in the presence of a large excess of substrate depends only upon the enzyme concentration

---

[7] (1) $vK_m + vs = Vs$
(2) $vK_m + s(v - V) = 0$
Subtract $K_m V$ from both sides:
(3) $K_m(v - V) + s(v - V) = -K_m V$
(4) $(K_m + s)(v - V) = -K_m V$

($V = ke$). This is shown to be true in Fig. 7.5. Furthermore, if a constant amount of enzyme is considered, all the factors on the right of equation (3) are constants except s, which represents substrate concentration. In other words, the velocity of the reaction in the presence of a fixed amount of

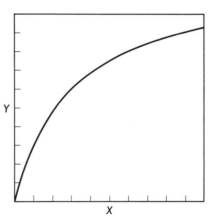

Fig. 7.8. Theoretical curve for the equation $(x + k_1)(y - k_2) = K$. The values were obtained by assigning arbitrary values to k_1 and k_2 and then calculating the values of y which corresponded with a series of possible values of x.

enzyme is dependent only upon substrate concentration, so long as that is the limiting value, so long, in other words, as the concentration of the ES compound (p) is less than that of the enzyme (e). This also fits the experimental facts. In Fig. 7.6 it is apparent that the velocity of the initial reaction is proportional to the substrate concentration only up to a definite limiting value. This limiting value is that concentration of the substrate at which all the enzyme is saturated with substrate.

The curves shown in Figs. 7.5 and 7.6 are representative of many uncomplicated enzyme reactions. From such curves, or others plotted from the same experimental data, the value of the Michaelis constant can be obtained graphically in various ways. For example, equation (5) can be rearranged to read

$$v = \frac{V}{1 + \dfrac{K_m}{s}}$$

When v is plotted against s, as in Fig. 7.6, the value of V can be read from the curve as the maximum velocity recorded when the substrate concentration is great enough to saturate the enzyme during the measurement of the initial velocities. Consider then the situation when the actual velocity is half the maximum. Substituting $V/2$ for v gives

$$\frac{V}{2} = \frac{V}{1 + \dfrac{K_m}{s}}$$

Then
$$2 = 1 + \frac{K_m}{s} \quad \text{and} \quad K_m = s$$

This means that the concentration of substrate in moles per liter at that point on the curve at which the actual velocity is half the maximum velocity gives the value of K_m.

There are other methods for obtaining the value of K_m. These are discussed at length in books dealing with the techniques of enzyme research. One of the most commonly used is that suggested by Lineweaver and Burk in the reference given at the end of the chapter.

The first direct proof of the existence of an ES compound was obtained in 1943 in experiments with the oxidizing enzyme, peroxidase. When this enzyme activates its substrate, hydrogen peroxide, the formation of the ES compound is signalized by the appearance of a new absorption band. More recently with other enzymes it has been found that binding of the enzyme by a substrate results in a change in fluorescent spectrum. These evidences of compound formation are now being actively exploited in studies of the nature and number of active sites on various enzymes.

Activation of Enzymes

It frequently happens that in the course of purification of an enzyme it is separated from some substance, present in the original tissue and essential to its activity. These essential substances have been said to "activate" the enzyme, though the word refers to more than one type of effect. Some activations transform an inactive protein into an active enzyme; others may facilitate formation of the ES compound; still a third type of activation depends upon furnishing a substance which itself takes part in the enzyme action.

Proenzymes

It has long been known that the proteolytic digestive enzymes are secreted in an inactive form. Pepsin, for example, is secreted by special cells in the gastric mucosa and was first identified as a proteolytic enzyme in the gastric juice. However, attempts to obtain the same enzyme by extraction of the secreting mucosa itself yielded only an inactive precursor of pepsin. Such inactive molecules are known as *proenzymes* or *zymogens*, and their nature is indicated in their names by the use of the prefix pro- or the suffix -ogen. Pepsinogen and trypsinogen are the precursors of pepsin and trypsin respectively; prorennin and procarboxypeptidase are the inactive forms of rennin and carboxypeptidase. Precursors as well as active enzymes are simple proteins.

The nature of this type of activation is clearly not identical with all enzymes, though it always seems to consist in a breaking of peptide bonds. This may be brought about through the catalytic effect either of a proteolytic enzyme or of hydrogen ion. Prorennin, for example, is activated by hydrogen ion, pepsinogen by either hydrogen ion or pepsin, and the proenzymes found in pancreatic juice are activated by trypsin or by enterokinase, both of which are protein-splitting enzymes. In some cases the activation splits peptide bonds but does not seem to remove any peptides; in others there is a definite drop in molecular weight. Crystalline pepsinogen, for example, has a molecular weight of 42,500, while the molecular weight of crystalline pepsin is only 34,500. Procarboxypeptidase, with a molecular weight of 96,000 loses two-thirds of the molecule on activation. The molecular weight of the active enzyme is only 34,300. In contrast, trypsinogen and chymotrypsinogen are activated without appreciable drop in molecular weight, though analysis of the end groups in the activated enzymes shows that one or two peptide bonds have been split. Whatever the actual process in each individual case, it results in uncovering or freeing the active site, after which the enzyme can exert its catalytic effect. This could result from hydrolytic removal of some blocking group, but might require only a minor change in the tertiary structure of the protein to bring essential groups into juxtaposition in the active center. One such activation is represented graphically in Fig. 7.10, on page 313.

The function of the proenzymes is of course a protective one, the organism thus making certain that proteolytic hydrolysis will not begin by destroying *in situ* the very cells that secrete the enzymes.

Activation by inorganic ions

It has long been known that salivary amylase which begins the hydrolysis of starch in the mouth, may be inactivated by removal of small inorganic molecules by dialysis. Addition of various anions causes a reactivation, though chloride ion, which occurs naturally in saliva, is far the most effective. This seems to be a relatively unspecific activation, as indeed are most of the known activations by anions. In contrast, the requirements of some enzymes for cations are often highly specific. The cation in question may be so firmly bound to the enzyme that it appears with it in the final crystalline product, and the enzyme is then a true metalloenzyme. With other enzymes the metal is lost in the course of purification, but it must be added to activate the purified protein.

The actual specificity of the cation requirement varies greatly from one enzyme to another. For example, glycylglycine dipeptidase specifically requires Co^{++} ion for its activity, but while carboxypeptidase as isolated contains zinc, the zinc-free protein can be reactivated not only by zinc but by a number of other divalent cations two of which (Co^{++} and Ni^{++}) are more effective than zinc itself.

The mechanism of such metal ion activations is not clear, and undoubtedly differs from one enzyme to another. Essential ions certainly form part of the active center and may there actually participate in the enzymic reaction. For example such ions as cupric or ferric ions may be involved in oxidation of a substrate by accepting electrons and being themselves reduced to a lower valence. Alternatively an ion at the active site of an enzyme may help to bind the substrate by forming links with both. Such a combination is represented in Fig. 7.11, on page 314, where enzymic mechanisms are being considered.

Coenzymes

When a crude enzyme solution is dialyzed there pass into the dialyzing fluid not only inorganic ions, but many small organic molecules. Some of these organic substances have proved to be essential to the activity of the enzymes with which they were extracted. This was first discovered in work with the yeast enzymes known collectively as "zymase." The unknown essential factor in the dialyzate was then called "cozymase." Since then it has been found that many enzymes occur in tissue as conjugated proteins. The prosthetic groups of most such enzymes can be removed, leaving a protein part or *apoenzyme* which is inactive, but can be reactivated by replacing the prosthetic group. When separated from their respective proteins these small organic molecules are known collectively as *coenzymes*. The complete, active conjugated protein is then a *holoenzyme*. The function of the coenzyme is not to induce a change in the enzyme. Coenzymes participate in a quite characteristic way in the catalyzed reaction. Typical of such reactions are those catalyzed by most of the enzymes concerned with physiological oxidations. One such oxidation is described in the following section as an example of an enzyme action in which a coenzyme is involved.

Enzyme Actions in Which Coenzymes Are Involved

A typical example of a reaction catalyzed by a conjugated protein is the oxidation brought about by D-amino acid oxidase. This enzyme is found in various animal tissues and in some microorganisms, it has been prepared in a highly purified form and the reaction it catalyzes is relatively simple.

If D-amino acid oxidase, that is, the complete conjugated protein, is added to alanine, oxygen is absorbed and the following reaction takes place:

$$\text{Alanine} + \text{Water} + O_2 \rightarrow \text{Pyruvic acid} + \text{Ammonia} + H_2O_2$$

If the solution of the purified enzyme is made slightly alkaline the conjugated protein dissociates into a protein part which is inactive as an enzyme, and a coenzyme which has been identified as a complex flavin adenine dinucleotide, the name of which is commonly abbreviated to FAD. Though neither part alone has any oxidizing action, when they are both added to alanine oxygen is again absorbed. This indicates that the two parts have united to form the complete conjugated enzyme again. If, instead of adding a large amount of dinucleotide, graded small amounts are added to separate, identical samples of the enzyme protein, the activity of each mixture is strictly proportional to the concentration of the dinucleotide. This is shown in Fig. 7.9 in which the rate of oxygen uptake is plotted against the dinucleotide concentration. When enough dinucleotide has been added to provide a

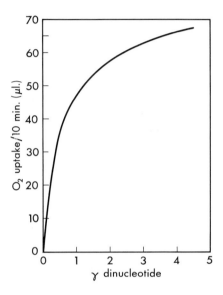

Fig. 7.9. Relationship between rate of oxidation by D-amino acid oxidase and concentration of the coenzyme (FAD). The linear portion of the curve indicates that the coenzyme forms a compound with the enzyme protein in a definite stoichiometric ratio. [Data from O. Warburg and W. Christian, *Biochem. Z.*, **298**, 150 (1938).]

prosthetic group for each molecule of enzyme protein, further increases in the concentration of dinucleotide have no further accelerating effect. This is indicated by the plateau in the curve.

The structure of flavin adenine dinucleotide is given in Chapter 11. For present purposes the only property with which we are concerned is a reversible reaction which takes place entirely in the flavin part of the molecule. This part of the dinucleotide is capable of undergoing reversible oxidation-reduction. In the oxidized form the substance is yellow. When it is reduced it adds two hydrogens and the leuco compound so formed is colorless. When the complete oxidase, composed of colorless protein and yellow dinucleotide, is added to alanine, the yellow color is bleached. If the solution is then aerated by vigorous shaking, the color is restored. Since the dinucleotide is the only colored substance present, this indicates that the alanine reduces it to the leuco form, and the oxygen of the air reoxidizes the leuco form to the original yellow molecule. Clearly then the reaction indicated above in a single equation takes place in steps, and a transfer of hydrogens from the alanine to the flavin compound is the first of these. This may be indicated schematically:

$$FAD + CH_3 \cdot CH \cdot COOH \rightarrow FADH_2 + CH_3 \cdot C \cdot COOH$$

$$\underset{\textbf{Alanine}}{\overset{|}{NH_2}} \qquad\qquad\qquad \underset{\textbf{Imino acid}}{\overset{\|}{NH}}$$

Since molecular oxygen restores the color of the leuco-$FADH_2$, it must react, not with alanine directly, but with the reduced coenzyme. Substances which react in this way with molecular oxygen are said to be *autoxidizable*.

$$FADH_2 + O_2 \rightarrow FAD + H_2O_2$$

Reduced coenzyme	Oxidized coenzyme

Since other reduced flavin compounds may be oxidized by molecular oxygen without the intervention of an enzyme, this reaction is probably spontaneous. Likewise, the third step by which pyruvic acid is formed is believed to be non-enzymic.

$$CH_3 \cdot C \cdot COOH + HOH \rightarrow CH_3 \cdot C \cdot COOH + NH_3$$

$$\underset{\textbf{Imino acid}}{\overset{\|}{NH}} \qquad\qquad\qquad \underset{\textbf{Pyruvic acid}}{\overset{\|}{O}}$$

The coenzyme is thus seen to go through a cycle, beginning and ending with the yellow oxidized form. One molecule can therefore bring about the oxidation of a great number of molecules of alanine, by accepting hydrogens from the activated substrate and passing them on to molecular oxygen.

For the oxidation of alanine both parts of this enzyme are required. The activated substrate cannot hand on its hydrogens to any readily reducible substance which happens to be present. It is not "activated" in general, but activated to give up hydrogen to just the particular dinucleotide which is the coenzyme for its oxidation. Nor should it be assumed, from the fact that the actual reaction involves only the dinucleotide, that the specific protein is unimportant. It is only in the presence of the protein that the hydrogen transfer can take place. If this same flavin adenine dinucleotide is associated with a different enzyme protein, alanine is not oxidized, but D-glucose is. In fact there are many different enzymes for which the same dinucleotide acts as coenzyme. The substrate specificity of each must then reside in the protein part of the conjugated molecule.

Flavin adenine dinucleotide is one of a number of coenzymes all of which form triple complexes with enzyme and substrate. While in this position, they can take part in the enzymic reaction by undergoing some sort of reversible change through which one molecule of coenzyme is able to bring about a transformation in many molecules of substrate.

Enzyme Inhibitors

It has already been noted that enzymes are inactivated by even slightly raised temperatures, and that they are completely destroyed by boiling. There are a number of chemical agents which also destroy them completely. Some of these are protein precipitants, including such substances as trichloroacetic acid and phosphotungstic acid, or toxic cations such as silver, mercuric mercury, or lead. Substances in this group are often used in enzyme studies to stop a reaction at a specified time by suddenly poisoning the enzyme.

Other enzyme inhibitors or poisons act more selectively. Many respiratory enzymes are inhibited by very low concentrations of cyanide. This is interpreted to mean that a metal, usually iron, forms an essential part of the enzyme or coenzyme. When this metal is blocked by being engaged in a cyanide complex, the enzyme can no longer exert its catalytic function. Other enzymes, to the activity of which a metallic ion is not essential, are unaffected by cyanide. These include most of the hydrolytic enzymes. Many of these, however, are inactivated by oxidizing agents, and can be restored to activity by such a reducing agent as reduced glutathione. Other common inhibitors are sodium fluoride, sodium azide (Na_3N), and monoiodoacetate. Any detailed study of the phenomenon of inhibition, and of the conclusions which may be drawn from the sensitivity of an enzyme to specific inhibitors, is beyond the scope of this book. One very important use of inhibitors, however, can suitably be considered at this point.

It was noted earlier that the fermentation of glucose involves many different enzymes, all of which are present in a yeast press juice or extract. This means that a series of separate transformations is involved, with a number of different intermediate products, although the overall reaction may be expressed:

$$C_6H_{12}O_6 \rightarrow 2C_2H_5OH + 2CO_2$$

$$A \quad \rightarrow \quad 2F \quad + \quad 2G$$

This may be indicated schematically as follows, the capital letters standing for different substances, and the small letters for the corresponding enzymes.

When the tissue extract which contains enzymes a, b, d, and e and their essential coenzymes is added to a solution of A, the reaction may appear to be a simple transformation of A into F and G, but this is not so. To follow the actual course of such a reaction the intermediate substances must be identified. Since B is immediately transformed into D, and D in turn is acted upon by its enzyme to form E, etc., it is impossible under ordinary conditions to isolate any except the end products. But if an enzyme poison is added which selectively inactivates enzyme d, the transformation of substance D will not take place. If enzymes a and b are unaffected by the poison, D may well accumulate in such quantity that it can be separated from the mixture and identified. By such methods many apparently simple enzymic transformations have been shown to consist of a series of interlocking reactions. The unraveling of the complex cycle of reactions involved, for example, in the use of glycogen by muscle was facilitated by the use of selective inhibition.

Competitive inhibition

The facts of competitive inhibition early offered indirect evidence for the formation of a compound of enzyme and substrate. Some enzyme inhibitors are equally active whether the substrate concentration is high or low. But others bring about a conspicuous degree of inhibition only in the presence of a low substrate concentration. With these inhibitors the percentage depression of activity decreases regularly as the concentration of substrate is increased. Such inhibitions are spoken of as competitive. Malonate, for example, inhibits in this way the dehydrogenation of succinate by succinate dehydrogenase. This is explained by the close structural relationship between malonic and succinic acids. When the concentration of the normal substrate succinate, is low, malonate, by virtue of its similar structure, attaches itself to the active site and thus blocks the formation of an enzyme-succinate complex. The inhibitor, however, is not acted upon catalytically, and so remains attached to the enzyme and effectively removes it from the sphere of action. But when there is present a high concentration of succinate, the normal substrate competes successfully with the malonate for the enzyme centers. Under these conditions the inhibition by malonate is small. Study of competitive inhibitors has added much to our knowledge of the nature of enzyme-substrate compounds and of the groups involved in their formation.

The Mechanism of Enzyme Action

It was Emil Fischer who first suggested that the specificity of enzymes must depend upon a relation between enzyme and substrate like that between a lock and its key. We now recognize that this fit is necessary in order that a specific substrate molecule may find a point of attachment at the active site of the enzyme, which must at the same time be inhospitable to other molecules. Because enzymes exhibit stereospecificity both in their choice of substrates and in the nature of the products formed, it is generally accepted that there must be at least two points of attachment, and probably more often there are three.

The importance of the intact polypeptide chain of an enzyme protein varies from one enzyme to another. For example, an inactivated mercury derivative of the plant proteolytic enzyme, papain, can be degraded stepwise from the amino end until two-thirds of the original molecule has been digested away. Removal of the mercury from the remaining polypeptide restores activity completely, showing that of the original 180 amino acid residues, only about 60 at the carboxyl end of the chain are essential to its activity. On the other hand, many enzymes are inactivated by removal of only 3 or 4 amino acids from the polypeptide.

The fact that most enzymes are inactivated by denaturation points to the importance of the secondary and tertiary structure of the proteins. This can be understood if the active center, which is limited in area by the size of its substrate, is to include functional groups from two or more chains or from different parts of the same chain. Breaking of hydrogen bonds by denaturing agents would disarrange the orderly protein structure and allow the essential groups to move apart, even though the amino acid chain remained intact.

From the early years of enzyme chemistry, attempts have been made to implicate specific groups as essential factors in enzyme activity. There is now a considerable body of evidence that for a number of different enzymes some of their free sulfhydryl groups are part of the active sites. This is indicated by the fact that destruction of all such groups by oxidation, or by alkylation, or by mercaptide formation inactivates these enzymes. When, in addition, this destruction is prevented by the presence of substrate, it appears that the attachment of substrate to the active site has kept the reagent from reaching and attacking some essential group. Furthermore, it is frequently found that enzymes which are inactivated by oxidation of their sulfhydryl groups can be reactivated by reduction. The list of enzymes which require intact free sulfhydryl groups for activity is now quite a long one, and for some of them it has been possible to determine the number of such groups per molecule. This is usually only a small fraction of the total sulfhydryl groups.

Another group which often seems to be involved in the formation of the ES compound is the imidazole group of histidine. In experiments with lysozyme, an enzyme which hydrolyzes certain polysaccharides, it was found that an oxidation which destroys histidine and tryptophan inactivated the enzyme to the extent of 70 per cent when 1 histidine and 1.2 tryptophan residues per molecule had been destroyed. In another type of experiment it was shown that with some enzymes a group with a pK_a of 6 to 7 shows an appreciable change in pK value when the enzyme binds its substrate. Of all the amino acids, histidine is the only one with the requisite pK value.

A reagent which has come into use quite recently and is yielding information about the chemistry of the active sites is di*iso*propylfluorophosphate (DFP). This compound reacts specifically with enzymes which hydrolyze carboxylic esters, transferring the substituted phosphoryl group to the enzyme protein, with a splitting out of hydrogen fluoride. Allowing EH to stand for the enzyme and R for the isopropyl groups, we may indicate the reaction:

$$\begin{array}{ccc} RO & O & \\ & \diagdown \nearrow & \\ & P & + EH \rightarrow \\ & \diagup \diagdown & \\ RO & F & \end{array} \qquad \begin{array}{ccc} RO & O & \\ & \diagdown \nearrow & \\ & P & + HF \\ & \diagup \diagdown & \\ RO & E & \end{array}$$

It should be emphasized that the reagent does not react with free amino acids nor with proteins in general. It is specific for the special group of esterases which it inactivates irreversibly. It is believed that the inhibitor acts by transfer of the phosphoryl group to the active site where it remains fixed on the enzyme surface, and consequently measurement of the number of groups transferred per molecule is a measure of the number of active sites. This measurement is conveniently made by using reagent labeled with the radioactive P^{32}. In every enzyme so far examined it has been found that a single phosphoryl residue has been attached to the hydroxyl group of a serine in the enzyme protein. The fact that there are many more such residues in the molecule indicates that it is only a serine in a special setting which can bind the reagent. Recent work suggests that part of this special setting is the close juxtaposition of a histidine residue. Figure 7.10 shows schematically how an active site might include a histidine (H), and a serine (SE) from two portions of the polypeptide chain of trypsin, which is one of the enzymes which is inactivated by the fluorophosphate reagent. The X in the drawing represents that part of the active site which confers specificity upon it. The (V) and (I) stand for the two amino acids at the N-terminal end of the polypeptide, valine and isoleucine.

In view of the number of known enzymes and the paucity of information now available, it is obviously impossible to give any general description of the mechanism of enzyme catalysis. With some enzymes it has been suggested that the activation of the substrate consists of transfer of electrons in the substrate from one place to another, in response to charges on the enzyme surface. Sometimes it is thought that at the active site there is a large ring or potential ring formed when two or three points of contact are established between enzyme and substrate. The displacement of electrons around such a ring could bring about a breaking of some bonds and formation of new ones, with ultimate reconstitution of the enzyme and breaking away of the products. In both of these mechanisms it is assumed that after the electronic changes have taken place the activated substrate is attacked by water or phosphoric acid, or whatever substance takes part in the catalyzed reaction.

Another way of explaining the part played by an enzyme is the following, which can be used with many enzymes that bring about transfer of a group from one compound to another. Many reactions which we do not normally think of as transfers can be looked at in this light. In hydrolysis of an ester,

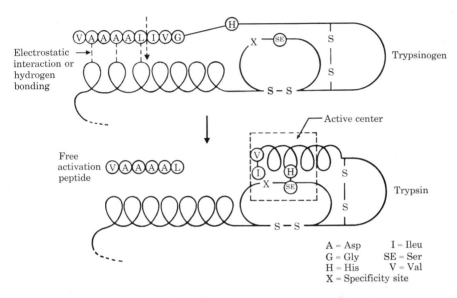

Fig. 7.10. Schematic representation of the structural changes involved in the tryptic activation of trypsinogen. Rupture of the lysyl-isoleucine bond in the N-terminal region (dotted arrow) leads to the liberation of the activation peptide and causes the newly formed N-terminal region of the polypeptide chain to assume a more nearly helical configuration. This in turn permits a histidine and serine side chain to come into juxtaposition so that they can form the active site. The specificity site of the protein (X) is believed to be preexistent in the zymogen molecule. [From H. Neurath, "Protein Structure and Enzyme Action," in *Biophysical Science*, J. L. Oncley (ed.-in-chief), Wiley, New York, 1959.]

for example, the acyl group is actually transferred from the ester to the hydroxyl group of water. It has been suggested for such a reaction, that in which acetyl choline is hydrolyzed, that the sequence involves a preliminary transfer of the acyl group to the enzyme (EH), followed by its transfer to the water as shown below:

$$\text{RCOOR}' + \text{EH} \rightarrow \text{RCO—E} + \text{R}'\text{OH}$$
$$\text{RCO—E} + \text{H}_2\text{O} \rightarrow \text{RCOOH} + \text{EH}$$

There are now quite a number of reactions which are believed to begin in this way, with transfer of part of the substrate to the enzyme which then passes it on to some other reactant.

The function of coenzymes

The discussion in the preceding paragraphs has been concerned with enzymes which are simple proteins. The picture becomes a little more complicated when the enzymes which require coenzymes are considered.

In Fig. 7.11 is shown a formulation of the relation between an enzyme, its substrate, and its coenzyme. The enzyme is the metalloenzyme, alcohol dehydrogenase, and its substrate is ethyl alcohol. On the right, the shaded portion represents the enzyme, with its active site indicated by the depression in the molecular surface. The substrate alcohol molecule is shown attached

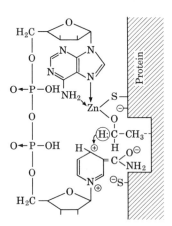

Fig. 7.11. Formulation of the relation between enzyme, coenzyme, substrate, and cation in the complex formed by alcohol dehydrogenase. [From K. Wallenfels and H. Sund, *Biochem. Z.*, **329**, 59 (1957).]

to this site by a dotted bond, and by a covalent bond to zinc. The compound written on the left is a coenzyme of the general type of FAD, with adenine as one base and with nicotinamide as the other. The zinc is shown bound to adenine by two dative bonds, to a sulfhydryl group of the enzyme protein as well as to the hydroxyl group of the substrate. This then constitutes a quadruple complex of enzyme, coenzyme, substrate, and essential cation, and may be considered typical of the sort of compound formed by those enzymes which require a coenzyme.

As indicated in the figure, the reaction catalyzed is the transfer of a hydrogen from the alcohol to position 4 of the pyridine ring of nicotinamide. As with $FADH_2$, this hydrogen is then passed on to some other substance, either directly to oxygen or through another enzymic transfer. The latter type of transfer is considered in some detail in Chapter 11.

If it is assumed then that the hydrogen is removed and that the aldehyde is also released, the reaction will proceed when a new alcohol molecule fits into its place on the active site.

This is not to be construed as a literal and final picture of the course of all enzymic reactions which require coenzymes, nor even surely of the one particular enzymic reaction which is represented. It does, however, indicate the way in which modern enzyme chemists are attempting to draw a coherent picture which will include what is presently known about enzymes and their action.

Integrated Enzyme Activity

In order to study the properties of a given enzyme it has been necessary to separate it not only from the cytoplasmic fabric of the cell, but from other enzymes. It might have been argued, and indeed it was, that the properties which were discovered under such unnatural conditions would bear no relation to those exhibited by the catalyst in its normal environment in the cell. Fortunately this has proved not to be true. It was noted in Chapter 3 that ultracentrifugation of disrupted cells yielded among other particles some relatively heavy ones known as mitochondria. It has been found that the oxidative mechanism of the cell is concentrated in these small organelles. There several transfers such as the one outlined just above take place in orderly sequence until the hydrogen is finally passed on to oxygen. This must involve an arrangement in which the same coenzyme can act in cooperation with two different specific proteins. This may require a movement of the coenzyme from one protein to another, but in very recent years two or three enzymes have been isolated in which there seem to be two coenzymes attached to a single catalytic protein. This may mean that a relatively small shift in binding site would enable a coenzyme which had just acquired a hydrogen to pass it on to a new acceptor. If there really are separate specific proteins for each transfer, they must at least lie very close together. It will be remembered that the interior of the mitochondrion is filled with a series of cristae or membrane projections, almost like shelves one above the other. It is believed that the proteins are arranged in order on or in these lipoprotein shelves, so that hydrogens can be transferred quickly and efficiently from the metabolite through a series of intermediate carriers to the ultimate acceptor, oxygen. As this elaborately organized procedure was unraveled, it proved to consist, not of new and strange reactions, but of reactions already well known. That this orderly sequence of events follows a pattern previously deduced from work with isolated enzymes has been one of the very real triumphs of modern biochemistry.

SUGGESTIONS FOR FURTHER READING

Papers of Historical Interest
Buchner, E., Alcoholic fermentation without yeast cells, *Ber.*, *30*, 117, 1110 (1897).
Liebig, J. von, *Chemische Briefe*, 6th ed., Leipzig and Heidelberg, 1878.
Pasteur, L., *Studies on Fermentation*, Macmillan, London, 1879.

Robiquet, P. J., and A. F. Boutron-Charlard, New experiments with bitter almonds and the volatile oil which they contain, *Ann. chim. phys.*, 2nd series, *44*, 352 (1830).
Sumner, J. B., Isolation and crystallization of the enzyme urease, *J. Biol. Chem.*, *69*, 435 (1926).
Wöhler, F., and J. Liebig, Note on the formation of oil of bitter almonds, *Ann.*, *22*, 1 (1837).

General

Boyer, P. D., H. Lardy, and K. Myrbäck (eds.), *The Enzymes*, 2nd ed., 5 vols., Academic, New York, 1959–1961. Two further volumes are projected.
Dixon, M., and E. C. Webb, *Enzymes*, Longmans Green, London, 1958.

Reversibility of Enzyme Action

Hehre, E. J., Synthesis of a polysaccharide of the starch-glycogen class from sucrose by a . . . bacterial enzyme system, *J. Biol. Chem.*, *177*, 267 (1949).
Tauber, H., Synthesis of protein-like substances by chymotrypsin from dilute peptic digests, *J. Am. Chem. Soc.*, *73*, 4965 (1951).
Waldschmidt-Leitz, E., and K. Kühn, A method for the enzymic synthesis of peptides, *Ber.*, *84*, 381 (1951).

The Michaelis Constant

Michaelis, L., and M. L. Menten, The kinetics of invertase action, *Biochem. Z.*, *49*, 333 (1913).
Lineweaver, H., and D. Burk, Determination of enzyme dissociation constants, *J. Am. Chem. Soc.*, *56*, 658 (1934).
There is a good discussion of the Michaelis constant and its use in various types of enzyme studies in Dixon and Webb, *loc. cit.*

The Active Site and the Mechanism of Enzyme Action

Barnard, E. A., and W. D. Stein, The roles of imidazole in biological systems, *Advances in Enzymol.*, *20*, 51 (1958).
Boyer, P. D., Mechanism of enzyme action, *Ann. Rev. Biochem.*, *29*, 15 (1960).
Boyer, P. D., Sulfhydryl and disulfide groups in enzymes, in *The Enzymes, op. cit.*, Vol. I, p. 511.
Coleman, J. E., and B. L. Vallee, Metallocarboxypeptidases, *J. Biol. Chem.*, *235*, 390 (1960).
Fraenkel-Conrat, H., Reactive groups of enzymes, in *The Enzymes, op. cit.*, Vol. I, p. 589.
Hellerman, L., *et al.*, Role of enzyme sulfhydryl groups, *J. Biol. Chem.*, *233*, 1468 (1958).
Koshland, D. E., Jr., The active site and enzyme action, *Advances in Enzymol.*, *22*, 45 (1960).
Malmstrom, B. G., and A. Rosenberg, Mechanism of metal ion activation of enzymes, *Advances in Enzymol.*, *21*, 131 (1959).
Neurath, H., Protein structure and enzyme action, in *Biophysical Science*, J. L. Oncley (ed.-in-chief), Wiley, New York, 1959.

Ogston, A. G., Interpretation of experiments on metabolic processes, using isotopic tracer elements, *Nature*, *162*, 963 (1948).

Porter, R. R., Relation of chemical structure to the biological activity of proteins, in *The Proteins*, H. Neurath and K. Bailey (eds.), Vol. IB, Academic, New York, 1953–1954.

Shifrin, S., and N. O. Kaplan, Coenzyme binding, *Advances in Enzymol.*, *22*, 337 (1960).

Snodgrass, P. J., *et al.*, Effects of silver and mercurials on yeast alcohol dehydrogenase, *J. Biol. Chem.*, *235*, 504 (1960).

Steyn-Parvé, E. P., and H. Beinert, Isolation and properties of stable enzyme-substrate complexes, *J. Biol. Chem.*, *233*, 843 (1958).

Vallee, B. L., *et al.*, The "active site" of bovine pancreatic carboxypeptidase A, *J. Biol. Chem.*, *235*, PC45 (1960).

Vallee, B. L., *et al.*, Role of zinc in carboxypeptidase, *J. Biol. Chem.*, *235*, 64 (1960).

Part III

INTERMEDIARY METABOLISM

*In the study of the intermediate processes of metabolism we
have to deal, not with complex substances which elude ordinary
chemical methods, but with simple substances undergoing com-
prehensible reactions.*

F. G. HOPKINS: *The Dynamic Side of Biochemistry* (1913)

The methods used in the study of intermediary metabolism

8

IN THE CELLS OF LIVING ORGANISMS the foodstuffs undergo profound chemical changes. They may be degraded to carbon dioxide and water and other excretory compounds or the products of their partial breakdown may be used synthetically. All these changes taken together constitute the *intermediary metabolism* of the cell. Since the transformations follow each other in quick succession, few of the intermediates ever appear in the normal organism in such concentrations as to be measurable. This has made it necessary to approach the problem in all sorts of indirect ways, and for this purpose many different methods have been evolved through the years. Before going on to consider the results of experiments on intermediary metabolism it will be helpful to review briefly some of the more important of these methods, and to learn their terminology.

EXPERIMENTS WITH WHOLE ORGANISMS

The earliest studies of metabolic relationships in animals consisted merely of analyses of food, excreta, and blood. A short time after ingestion of a meal high in starch, the concentration of glucose in the blood was found to rise far above its fasting level, indicating preabsorptive hydrolysis of the polysaccharide. Urine collected during the twenty-four hours following a

321

meal of liver, which is rich in nucleoproteins, proved to contain a higher concentration of uric acid than usual. This pointed to the limited oxidation of the purine bases to the closely related uric acid (see page 514), rather than to their complete oxidation to such small molecules as carbon dioxide and urea. Such experiments as these, carried out with normal organisms, normally nourished, give at best only the beginning and the end of the metabolic story. To elucidate the intervening chemical steps it was necessary to devise other methods.

Experiments with Abnormal Organisms

Probably no single abnormality has contributed more to our knowledge of the intermediary metabolism of animals than has the disease known as diabetes. It usually arises in human patients from the inability of certain cells in the pancreas to secrete insulin. Lack of insulin makes it impossible for the diabetic to metabolize glucose, and as a result any glucose which is ingested or which is formed in the body from other molecules is promptly excreted in the urine. It is possible to induce an experimental diabetes in animals by removal of the pancreas or by injection of alloxan or of phlorizin. When such an animal is given a diet consisting only of protein, it continues to excrete large quantities of glucose in the urine, indicating that the body is transforming protein into carbohydrate. Similar experiments have been carried out with individual pure amino acids replacing protein in the diet of the diabetic animal. They have shown that while certain of the amino acids can be transformed into glucose, others apparently are not so transformed, since their ingestion does not give rise to excretion of glucose in the diabetic.

Several other abnormalities have been exploited in the study of intermediary metabolism. For example, the two diseases known as phenylketonuria and alcaptonuria are characterized by the appearance in the urine of various aromatic compounds which are either not normally found there or are found there in much smaller amounts. These compounds include phenylpyruvate

Homogentisic acid

and phenyllactate, which are excreted by patients with phenylketonuria, and homogentisic acid, which is found in the urine of alcaptonurics. The close relation between these compounds and the two aromatic amino acids, phenylalanine and tyrosine, is obvious. A study of these so-called inborn errors of metabolism has yielded much information on the normal intermediary metabolism of these acids as well as on the abnormalities connected with the diseases.

Other organs than the pancreas may be removed, with more or less profound effects on the animal. Various glands, such as the thyroid, the pituitary, or the adrenals have been removed in attempts to determine the parts played in metabolism by their respective secretions. Hepatectomy, or removal of the liver, though a difficult and drastic operation, has been accomplished in such a way that the animals have survived for a few days. Under such circumstances, substances which are normally transformed in the liver cannot be dealt with and either pile up in the blood or appear as abnormal constituents of the urine. This is true, for example, of ammonia which arises from metabolism of the amino acids. Its concentration in blood and urine is normally very low, but following hepatectomy both blood and urine contain increasing amounts of ammonia. Other substances normally formed in the liver cannot be synthesized, and the urine of the hepatectomized animal therefore lacks such normal constituents. Urea, for example, is normally synthesized in the liver from the ammonia referred to above, but an animal which lacks its liver soon ceases entirely to excrete urea.

Use of Abnormal Diets and Culture Solutions

Another method of attacking the metabolic problem is to make use of normal organisms but to furnish them a diet which is abnormal in one way or another. It may be unduly enriched in some test substance, as when fats are fed exclusively or in great excess, to determine how the body deals with them. Or the diet may include some unnatural substance closely related to a natural one. One of the most fruitful experiments of this kind was performed early in the century by Knoop.[1] He fed fatty acids in which a phenyl group had been introduced at the end of the carbon chain, as in γ-phenylbutyric acid, $C_6H_5 \cdot CH_2 \cdot CH_2 \cdot CH_2 \cdot COOH$. Such a substance might be expected to react in the body more or less as do other fatty acids, but since cells do not usually oxidize aromatic substituents, it would yield a recognizable aromatic excretory product. After feeding a whole series of such substituted acids, Knoop recovered from the urine a corresponding series of detoxication products clearly related to the original acids. These results will be considered in detail in the chapter on lipid metabolism.

---

[1] Dr. Franz Knoop (1875–1946) published his early papers from the University of Freiburg, but after 1928 he was Professor of Physiological Chemistry and Director of the Institute of Physiological Chemistry at the University of Tübingen.

EXPERIMENTS WITH INDIVIDUAL ORGANS

Because the intact animal or plant is so complex a mechanism with so many interacting nervous and chemical controls, it has been fruitful to study the metabolism of isolated organs and tissues. One method of doing this with animal tissue is known as *perfusion* of the organ. This consists in furnishing an organ with an experimental, independent circulation by pumping some suitable fluid repeatedly through the blood vessels. This may be done with a minimum of injury if the organ is left in place in the anesthetized animal, but it is also done after complete removal of the organ from the body. An isolated frog heart has been kept beating for as long as thirty-three days when perfused with a fluid containing only glucose, oxygen, and inorganic salts. To such a solution various substances under investigation may be added. After a time, analysis of a small sample of the perfusion fluid will tell whether or not the organ is using the added substance and may show the presence of some new constituent derived from the added one. Thus, for example, it is clear that an isolated heart makes use of glucose because this substance slowly disappears from the perfusion fluid. When a liver is perfused with a solution containing pyruvic acid, alanine appears as the pyruvic acid disappears, indicating a transformation of the keto acid to the corresponding amino acid. Similarly it has been shown that a perfused kidney forms ammonia from amino acids.

The fluid used for perfusion may be blood from a similar animal to which an anticoagulant has been added, or it may be one or another of the physiological saline solutions. A solution of the chlorides of sodium, potassium, and calcium is known as Ringer's[2] solution in honor of the man who first discovered that perfusion with this simple solution keeps an isolated heart beating. Various adaptations of his original formula have been made to render the fluids suitable for use with organs from animals of different species. They have found a wide use not only in perfusion experiments, but in those with tissue slices which will be considered presently.

One animal tissue which lends itself particularly well to experimentation outside the body is striated muscle. A leg muscle, for example, suspended in a damp atmosphere can be stimulated electrically to contract until it is fatigued. It gains the energy for contraction by metabolizing its store of glycogen, and much of our present understanding of carbohydrate metabolism is based upon the fundamental studies made by Fletcher and Hopkins using isolated frog muscles.

---

[2] Sydney Ringer (1835–1910) was an English physician with an active practice who yet managed to carry out a good deal of physiological research. His medical teaching was done at University College, London.

In plant experiments isolated leaves are often used as experimental material, as in those studies which proved that, although nicotine may make up as much as 8 per cent of the dry weight of the tobacco leaf, it is synthesized exclusively in the roots. When leaves which were accumulating nicotine were detached from the plant, the accumulation ceased abruptly, but began again when the leaves were cultured in sand and allowed to form roots. Similar experiments with excised tobacco roots have indicated some of the intermediates in biosynthesis of nicotine by furnishing in a nutrient solution some supposed precursor and determining whether or not it leads to nicotine synthesis.

TISSUE SLICE EXPERIMENTS

The great disadvantages of the perfusion method are that it requires the use of fairly large animals, and that a single organ can be used for only a comparatively short time, and so for a limited number of observations. However, since about 1925, the development of manometric micro methods has made it possible to carry out with either plant or animal tissues experiments of similar import using only a few milligrams of material. These methods were first extensively used and adapted by Warburg[3] in Berlin, and by Dixon[4] at Cambridge.

If a slice of tissue is cut not more than 0.3 mm in thickness, the cells inside the outermost layers are undamaged and constitute the greater part of the slice. Such a thickness permits ready diffusion inward of oxygen and foodstuffs if the tissue is immersed in a fluid containing these substances. Under these conditions the undamaged cells of a tissue slice will carry on their normal metabolic processes for several hours, respiring, and evolving carbon dioxide. Liver slices, for example, will transform added ammonia into urea; kidney slices will form ammonia from amino acids.

As with perfusion experiments, the fluid used to bathe the slices must contain a carefully balanced concentration of inorganic ions. In particular, it is essential that the osmotic pressure as well as the ratio of calcium, magnesium, sodium, and potassium correspond to that in the blood of the

---

[3] Otto Warburg (1883–   ) is one of the outstanding biochemists of the present day. As Director of the Kaiser Wilhelm Institute for Cellular Physiology in Berlin he has taken a leading part in the development of many phases of biochemistry, including biological oxidation, photosynthesis, and tumor metabolism. He received the Nobel Prize in Medicine in 1931.

[4] Malcolm Dixon (1899–   ) is Reader in Enzyme Biochemistry at Cambridge University. He is particularly known for his applications of physical chemistry to the study of enzymes. Two small books, one on *Manometric Methods* and the other on *Multi-Enzyme Systems*, were followed in 1958 by the exhaustive treatise, titled *Enzymes*, which he wrote in collaboration with E. C. Webb.

animal whose tissues are used. Sometimes the solution is buffered with bicarbonate, sometimes with phosphate, sometimes with other buffers. In Table 8.1 are given the ionic compositions of several common saline solutions. As the table shows, the salt solution of Krebs[5] and Henseleit corresponds closely with mammalian serum, and is consequently an excellent medium for metabolism of mammalian tissues. The directions for making up the various

TABLE 8.I. Composition of Various Physiological Saline Solutions

Constituents	Normal Mammalian Serum, mg %[a]	Phosphate Ringer, mg %	Bicarbonate Ringer, mg %	Krebs-Henseleit Solution, mg %
Na^+	320	314	355	327
K^+	22	10.3	10.5	23
Ca^{++}	10	7.5	8.8	10
Mg^{++}	2.5	—	—	2.9
Cl^-	370	485	466	454
$PO_4^{=}$	10	10	—	11
$SO_4^{=}$	11	—	—	11.4
HCO_3^-	152	—	152	152
CO_2	2.5 vol. %[b]	—	2.5 vol. %	2.5 vol. %
Glucose	ca. 100	—	200	200

[a] Mg% means the number of milligrams of the constituent per 100 ml of solution.
[b] Vol % means milliliters of gas at STP dissolved per 100 ml of solution.

nutrient solutions usually give the volumes of "isotonic" salt solutions which are to be mixed to give the desired ionic concentrations. The word isotonic in this context means isotonic with mammalian serum. An isotonic solution of sodium chloride is therefore often referred to as *physiological saline*. For sodium chloride, potassium chloride, potassiumdihydrogen phosphate, magnesium sulfate, and sodium bicarbonate, $0.154M$ solutions are isotonic; for calcium chloride the proper concentration is $0.11M$.

The tissue slice technique was first used to study respiration and gas exchange, and for this purpose special manometric apparatus was developed. One of the most widely used of these is the Warburg apparatus which can be used to follow the rate of any reaction which either uses or evolves a gas. Figure 8.1 shows the Warburg constant temperature bath with the movable stands (A) which hold reaction vessels and manometers in place during an

[5] Hans Krebs (now Sir Hans) (1900—) is Professor of Biochemistry at Oxford. He began his research career in Germany and published from the University of Freiburg. About 1935 he went to England and was Professor of Biochemistry at Sheffield from 1945 to 1954. In 1953 he shared with Fritz Lipmann the Nobel Prize in Medicine.

Fig. 8.1. The Warburg bath with manometer stands. The reaction vessels containing the tissue or other reaction mixture are suspended inside the constant temperature bath, and changes in pressure are read on the manometers affixed to the stands on the outside of the bath. [Photograph courtesy of Precision Scientific Company, Chicago.]

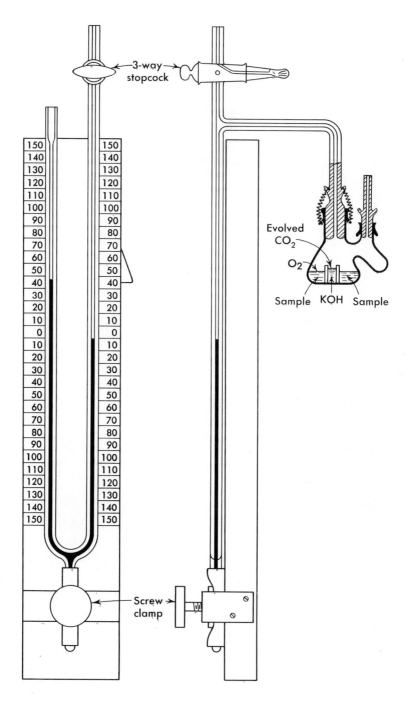

Fig. 8.2. Two views of the Warburg manometer and reaction vessel.

experiment. Figure 8.2 shows two views, taken at right angles to each other, of a single manometer with its attached reaction vessel. These are so designed that when they are set in place on the stands the reaction vessels are in the bath and the manometers, on which changes in gas pressure are to be read, are held parallel to the outside of the bath.

A manometer with its attached vessel forms a closed system when the stopcocks are suitably adjusted, the only gas available to the tissue being that enclosed in the vessel and in the top of the manometer down to the liquid level. When the vessels and manometers are in place on the stands, the whole assembly moves on a rack in such a way that the tissue and fluid in the vessel are shaken gently and continuously, thus facilitating diffusion of gases and other solutes. The manometer is filled, not with mercury, but with a salt solution known as Brodie's solution. This is of such a density that one atmosphere pressure corresponds to a column 10,000 mm high. This makes it possible to measure accurately the small pressure changes involved in the metabolism of 100 mg or less of tissue.

The tissue slice method may of course be used either with or without the Warburg manometric apparatus. Slices may be shaken in suitably buffered saline solutions, to which various possible metabolites have been added, and after a certain length of time the fluid may be examined for derivatives of the added substance. Slices of bird liver, for example, have been shown to synthesize uric acid from added ammonia. At the same time, of course, the living liver cells were carrying on other metabolic activities, using up oxygen to oxidize glucose provided in the nutrient medium, and giving off to the medium carbon dioxide and water. If then such an experiment is carried out in the manometric apparatus, the oxygen uptake of the tissues may be measured at the same time if the central cup in the reaction vessel contains strong potassium hydroxide to absorb any carbon dioxide which is evolved. In this case the progressive loss of oxygen, as it is used by the tissue, is reflected in a gradually decreasing pressure inside the vessel. Some tissues and micro-organisms are able to exist without oxygen, and their anaerobic metabolism may be followed by replacing the oxygen in the reaction vessel with nitrogen or some other inert gas. Specific examples of various uses of this technique will be referred to from time to time as the results become pertinent in the chapters which follow.

Terminology

To express the results of experiments with tissue slices a special terminology has developed. Suppose, for example, the slices of kidney tissue in a single vessel had, in the course of three hours, used up 250 cu mm or microliters (μl) of oxygen, corrected to standard temperature and pressure. At the end of the experiment the tissue would be washed and carefully dried to constant weight. The volume of oxygen used, divided by three times the dry weight of tissue in milligrams, would give the volume of oxygen consumed per milligram of dry tissue per hour. If this volume proved to be 23 μl, the result would be expressed: $Q_{O_2} = -23$, the minus sign indicating that the oxygen was used up. In Table 8.2 are given figures for the oxygen consumption of a number of representative tissues as measured by the Warburg technique.

TABLE 8.2. Aerobic and Anaerobic Metabolism of Rat Tissues

Tissue	Q_{O_2}	$Q^{N_2}_{CO_2}$
Liver	−11.6	+3.3
Kidney	−21	+3.2
Brain (gray matter)	−10.7	+19.1
Retina	−30.7	+88

SOURCE: Figures from O. Warburg, *Tumor Metabolism*, translated by F. Dickens, Constable, London, 1930.

As indicated above, experiments are sometimes conducted in an atmosphere of inert gas and in that case the nature of the gas is indicated by a superscript. For example, many tissues form lactic acid from glucose or glycogen if no oxygen is available to them. If this lactic acid forms in a solution buffered with bicarbonate, carbon dioxide will be set free, equivalent in amount to the lactic acid formed. The direct result of such an experiment might be expressed: $Q^{N_2}_{CO_2} = +19.1$. This means that, per milligram of dry tissue, per hour, 19.1 cu mm of carbon dioxide was set free in an experiment conducted in an atmosphere of nitrogen. The second column of Table 8.2 gives representative figures for the carbon dioxide evolved by a number of different tissues under these conditions. These figures can be simply transformed into milligrams of lactic acid as follows:

1 mole of carbon dioxide is freed by each mole of lactic acid

22.4 l of CO_2 at STP corresponds to 90 g lactic acid

22.4 ml of CO_2 at STP corresponds to 90 mg lactic acid

$\dfrac{90}{22.4} = 4$ mg lactic acid corresponds to 1 ml CO_2

1 μl of CO_2 is equivalent to 0.004 mg lactic acid

19.1 × 0.004 = 0.0764 mg lactic acid formed per hour, per mg dry weight of tissue in the example given above.

This is often expressed $Q^{N_2}_L = +0.08$, or $Q^{N_2}_M = +0.08$, the M standing for *Milchsäure*, the German word for lactic acid.

It should be noted that in all these experiments in which gases are involved, the quantity actually measured is the change in gas *pressure*. This is transformed arithmetically into gas volume by means of a "constant" for each vessel. The derivation of this constant is given in laboratory manuals.

EXPERIMENTS WITH CELLULAR PARTICLES

Since it became possible to fractionate the cell contents in the ultracentrifuge, many experiments have been done with the particles or organelles which this process isolates. It has been shown, for example, that the enzymes for the oxidative reactions of the cell are concentrated in the mitochondria, while other processes, such as protein synthesis, are associated with the microsomal fraction. Work of this sort is gradually yielding a picture of the internal geography of the cell, and showing that whole groups of enzymes which must act together in sequence, are arranged in one or the other of the small particles which dot the cytoplasm. In recent years it has even been possible to rupture the mitochondria in an effort to estimate the structure and contents of the minimal unit structure. One such experiment is discussed in Chapter 11.

CELL-FREE ENZYME SYSTEMS

Even a single thin slice of tissue contains a complex system of enzymes whose activities interlock. It is sometimes possible to analyze such a system by separating it from the cells. With some tissues only part of a group of enzymes is extracted when the cell is chopped or ground with physiological saline or buffer. In others, a tissue so finely ground that cell membranes are ruptured yields a cell-free *brei* or mash which yet contains many enzymes whose activities throw light on the metabolic functions of the tissue itself. Simple extraction of ground muscle with physiological saline dissolves the enzymes responsible for anaerobic formation of lactic acid, leaving behind in the tissue residue those others which bring about oxidation of carbohydrate. Discovery of this simple separation made possible a detailed study of the anaerobic function, uncomplicated by oxidation. With extracts or breis, enzyme inhibitors may be used to inactivate part of the system, and thus allow some intermediates to accumulate. Or intermediate products may be isolated if the enzyme action takes place in the presence of a reagent which will "trap" them, and so prevent their being destroyed by further metabolic changes. The presence of acetaldehyde as an intermediate in alcoholic fermentation was proved by Neuberg when he added bisulfite to the fermenting press juice from yeast. As fast as aldehyde formed, it was caught and held as its bisulfite addition product, which was finally present in sufficient quantity to be isolated.

Finally, from one point of view the most satisfactory metabolic experiment is the one which makes use of a single pure enzyme. Here the product of a single reaction accumulates because any enzymes involved in its further metabolism are absent. In such a system single pure substrates may be tested, one by one, and the specific requirements of the enzyme outlined. In some cases it is discovered that an enzyme cannot perform its function except in conjunction with another enzyme action. This happens when an enzyme catalyzes a reaction which uses up energy. Such an endergonic reaction can only proceed if another one, yielding energy, is going on in the immediate vicinity. Such actions are said to be *coupled* and they are most easily discovered in work with pure enzymes. In other words, having carefully analyzed the activities of a tissue into its constituent enzyme actions, we must often perforce put the parts together again to see how they interlock in the cell!

USE OF ISOTOPES

All the experiments outlined in the preceding paragraphs have suffered from one disadvantage or another. If normal organisms and normal nutrients are used, it is impossible to identify the intermediate products in the smooth sequence of reactions. If either the organism or its nutriment is abnormal it is hard to reason from the results obtained to the events to be expected under normal conditions. These disadvantages are of course magnified if an organ is entirely removed from its normal situation or if the whole cellular structure is disrupted as in experiments with extracts, breis, or purified enzymes. In spite of which, many experiments of fundamental importance have been carried out by these very methods, and many just conclusions have been reached.

A new era in metabolic experimentation was inaugurated in 1932 when Urey[6] and his colleagues first concentrated deuterium, or heavy hydrogen. Ordinary hydrogen as it occurs in nature consists of a mixture of three isotopes, each having a single charge on the nucleus, but having atomic weights of 1, 2, or 3. These are distinguished as $_1H^1$, $_1H^2$, $_1H^3$. The ratio in which they are found is constant, $_1H^1$ making up 99.99 per cent of the total number of atoms; $_1H^2$, or deuterium, 0.01 per cent; while $_1H^3$, or tritium,

[6] Harold C. Urey (1893–   ) was Professor of Chemistry at Columbia University when he made his famous separation of deuterium from ordinary hydrogen. For this work he was awarded the Nobel Prize in Chemistry in 1934. Following a period as Director of War Research, he went in 1945 to the University of Chicago as a Distinguished Service Professor and remained there until 1958. Since then he has been Professor-at-Large of Chemistry at the University of California at LaJolla.

occurs naturally only to the extent of about 7 parts in 10^{10}. Whether a sample of hydrogen is free, or is combined in an inorganic or an organic compound, its deuterium content is always found to be 0.01 atom per cent. This means that 1 of every 10,000 molecules of hydrogen chloride is really deuterium chloride; 1 of every 10,000 hydrogen atoms in a fat is heavy hydrogen. Similarly, ordinary oxygen wherever found consists of 99.76 atom per cent of O^{16}, 0.04 atom per cent of O^{17}, and 0.20 atom per cent of O^{18}. Nitrogen occurs, free or in compounds, as a mixture containing besides N^{14}, 0.37 atom per cent of the heavier isotope, N^{15}. The only common elements which do not occur as isotopic mixtures are phosphorus, iodine, and sodium.

In various ways it has been possible to increase greatly the concentration of the less plentiful isotopes, either in a sample of the element or of some compound. For example, when water is electrolyzed, the lighter isotope of hydrogen is freed preferentially, and the remaining water becomes progressively richer in water containing deuterium (D_2O, or heavy water). In one experiment, 20 liters of water from electrolytic cells was further electrolyzed until only 0.5 ml remained. This water proved to have a deuterium content of 66 atom per cent in contrast with 0.01 atom per cent in ordinary water. Such a sample of heavy water was one of the earliest isotopic compounds used in a biochemical experiment. Its hydrogen is clearly labeled and can be identified wherever it may be found by its abnormal density. The very fact that hydrogen obtained from any part of an animal body contains the normal ratio of isotopes proves that living cells do not distinguish between them, neither rejecting nor preferring any one. Indeed living organisms can use heavy water in reasonable amounts (up to 25 per cent of the total water intake) as they would use ordinary water. When an animal in whose diet heavy water has been included proves to have an abnormal concentration of deuterium in its body fats, the use of body water in fat synthesis is clearly indicated. Heretofore no such relationship could have been proved, because dietary water as soon as it had been absorbed was inextricably mixed with body fluids, and its hydrogens thus rendered indistinguishable from any others.

Since 1932 natural stable isotopes of many elements have been concentrated and obtained in more or less pure form. During the same years the physicists have prepared artificially radioactive isotopes of nearly every element. This has made it possible to synthesize many different compounds of biochemical importance, each labeled with an abnormal concentration of one isotope or another. Such compounds may be fed or injected into animals, or added to nutrient media of plants or bacteria, and their metabolic processes followed by suitable isotope analysis. Table 8.3 lists a few isotopes which have been used in biochemical experiments, with the natural abundance of the stable ones, and the half-life time of the radioactive ones.

TABLE 8.3. Natural and Radioactive Isotopes of Biochemical Interest

Element	Mass	Abundance, Atom %	Half life
Hydrogen	1	99.99	
	2	0.01	
	3		12.5 yrs
Carbon	11		20 min
	12	98.9	
	13	1.1	
	14		5740 yrs
Nitrogen	14	99.63	
	15	0.37	
	16		8 sec
Oxygen	15		126 sec
	16	99.76	
	17	0.04	
	18	0.20	
Sodium	22		2.6 yrs
	23	100	
	24		14.9 hrs
Phosphorus	31	100	
	32		14.3 days
	33		25 days
Sulfur	32	95.1	
	33	0.7	
	34	4.2	
	35		87 days
Potassium	39	93.3	
	40	0.01	
	41	6.7	
	42		12.4 hrs
Calcium	40	96.96	
	42	0.64	
	43	0.15	
	44	2.06	
	45		164 days
	46	0.003	
	48	0.19	
Cobalt	56		77 days
	58		71 days
	59	100	
	60		5.3 yrs
Iron	54	5.81	
	55		2.6 yrs
	56	91.64	
	57	2.21	
	58	0.34	
	59		46 days
Iodine	126		13 days
	127	100	
	130		12.6 hrs
	131		8 days

Choice of Isotopes

Various factors will determine whether an experiment can best be carried out with a stable or with a radioactive isotope. The radioactive ones have some special advantages, and some disadvantages for biological work. One great advantage is the simplicity with which their presence may be detected, either photographically, or by means of a Geiger counter. Figure 8.3 shows how readily the presence of a radioactive isotope in tissue may be detected photographically. Radioactive iodine was injected as potassium iodide into a pregnant cow. After twenty-four hours the animal was killed and "radio-autographs" were made by placing on an x-ray film slices of the thyroids of mother and fetus. The left-hand photographs are ordinary photomicrographs of two thyroid slices, the maternal one in the upper left (*A*) and that of the fetus below (*C*). Beside each slice is the picture which resulted when these same slices were allowed to take their own pictures on photographic film. The radiations from the iodine which had largely concentrated in the two thyroid glands caused a blackening of the film, the depth of the darkening being a rough measure of the iodine concentration in different parts of the tissue. Incidentally these pictures illustrate strikingly the extent to which a fetus may drain the maternal iodine stores to build up its own supply of thyroxin.

The Geiger counter is an electronic instrument for detecting directly any ionizing radiation such as is given off by radioactive elements. One form of the apparatus indicates the presence of radiations by flashes of light; another records graphically the amount of radiation received while a third type signals its presence by a clicking sound. An instrument of this latter type can be used with great effect to show how rapidly the food of a nursing mother is transferred to the offspring. A mother mouse is given salt containing radioactive sodium (Na^{24}). After a few hours, if one of the babies is brought near a Geiger counter, it sets up a veritable fusillade of clicks, indicating unmistakably the transfer of the radioactive isotope from the mother to the offspring through the milk.

In spite of ease of detection, not all radioactive isotopes are suitable for biochemical investigation. With some elements the half life of the isotope is too short to allow time for synthesis of a compound in the laboratory, or for a normal metabolic transformation in living cells. The usefulness of C^{11} is greatly limited by its having a half life of only 20 minutes, and O^{15} with a half life of 126 seconds is too unstable to be used at all. The character of the radiation emitted may also be a determining factor. Tritium (H^{3}) is radioactive and has a half life of 12.5 years, but its use has been limited by the fact that its radiation is so soft that it is difficult to detect. The elements whose radioactive isotopes have so far been most widely used to study the metabolism of organic compounds are radioactive carbon (C^{14}), phosphorus (P^{32}), sulfur (S^{35}), and iodine (I^{126}). These are all relatively simple to prepare, they

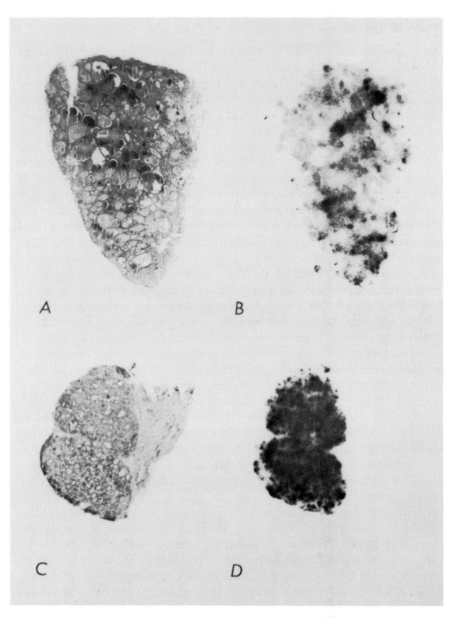

Fig. 8.3. Deposition of radioiodine in the thyroids of mother and fetus following injection of radioactive potassium iodide. *A.* Photomicrograph of the maternal thyroid. *B.* Radioautograph of the same slice of tissue as is shown in *A*. *C.* Photomicrograph of a slice of thyroid from the fetus. *D.* Radioautograph of the tissue shown in *C*. [From A. Gorbman *et al., J. Endocrinol.*, **51**, 546 (1952).]

have convenient half-life times, and they emit radiations which are easy to measure.

Of the elements which make up the major part of the foodstuffs, carbon, hydrogen, nitrogen, and oxygen, it was the stable isotopes which were the first to be used. More recently the available supply of radioactive C^{14} has made it possible to use this long-lived isotope to trace the fate of specific carbon atoms in both plant and animal metabolism. But the radioactive isotopes of nitrogen and oxygen are too short lived to compete with N^{15} and O^{18} and, as already noted, it is easier to determine the concentration of stable deuterium than to detect the soft radiation of tritium.

Representative Isotope Experiments

The usual biochemical isotope technique involves furnishing a plant or animal with a compound having an abnormally high concentration of one or more isotopes, with a view to determining what chemical transformations the compound undergoes in the living cells. It is not normally possible nor desirable to use a compound which contains only the less abundant isotope. Pure heavy water, for example, is toxic to living organisms. Furthermore, it has been shown that at ordinary temperatures pure elementary deuterium reacts much more slowly than hydrogen, and that compounds containing very high percentages of the heavy isotope are oxidized enzymically at about half the ordinary rate. It is therefore customary to use compounds only moderately enriched in the less usual isotope, and actually this is all that is needed. For example, it has been noted that nitrogen normally contains 0.368 atom per cent of N^{15}. The methods for detection of this isotope are so sensitive that if this percentage is increased to only 0.371 atom per cent, it is possible to detect the difference, even if the amount of nitrogen available for analysis is less than 1 mg!

Before using a labeled compound to study its fate in metabolism, it is necessary to make sure that the isotope is stably bound so that it will not exchange in solution. This fortunately is true of nitrogen linked to carbon as in the amino acids, and so N^{15} has been incorporated into many amino acids and its metabolic fate determined. For example, labeled glycine was fed to human beings, and the exact rate at which that particular nitrogen was excreted was followed by estimating the isotopic ratio in the urinary urea. In another experiment, serine $[CH_2OH \cdot CH(NH_2)COOH]$ was labeled with N^{15} and also with C^{13} in the carboxyl group. This was fed to rats, together with some sodium benzoate. It will be recalled that benzoate is detoxicated by conjugation with glycine, and thus gives rise in the urine to benzoyl glycine, or hippuric acid. In the experiment in question the hippuric acid proved to contain both N^{15} and C^{13} in abnormal amounts, thus proving the conversion of serine to glycine in the animal body.

But when the isotope in question is deuterium, its position in a compound must be carefully chosen, for in many positions hydrogen is very unstably held. Most obviously, an acidic hydrogen, ionizing in an aqueous medium, ceases to label the acid from which it came. But other hydrogens are also labile. It has been shown that organic hydrogen bonds may be grouped into three classes. In the first, hydrogen is *labile* and exchanges freely with the aqueous medium. This class includes the hydrogen of carboxyl, hydroxyl, primary amino, or aldehyde groups, as well as hydrogen attached to a carbon which itself holds a carbonyl group. Deuterium in any of these positions would be no label at all. Hydrogen forms a few *semilabile* bonds which exchange only on prolonged boiling in acid. This is true of all the hydrogens of glycine, and of those *ortho* to the hydroxyl group in tyrosine. Finally, hydrogen bound directly to carbon is usually stable. As noted above, this is not true of hydrogen adjacent to a carbonyl group, nor of any hydrogen in glycine. But these exceptions leave a large field for experimentation. Deuterium has been added to double bonds in fat acids, for example, to give saturated compounds which can be used to investigate the fate of such compounds in metabolism. If the deuterium is found later in other acids in the animal's body fats, it is safe to conclude that it has come there as a result of the metabolic transformation of the original fatty acid. In another type of experiment, phenylalanine was labeled by introducing deuterium into the ring. This acid was fed to rats and later it was proved that the tyrosine [HO · $C_6H_4CH_2CH(NH_2)COOH$] in the body proteins of those animals was high in deuterium. This established the metabolic transformation of phenylalanine to tyrosine.

Isotope experiments are also being used in studies of plant metabolism. For example, when green algae metabolize in an atmosphere which contains $C^{14}O_2$, the compounds which they form in the course of photosynthesis are all labeled with the radioactive isotope. These compounds can then be extracted from the plant and separated by paper chromatography, after which a radioautograph of the chromatogram can be made by placing the sheet of paper on a photographic plate. Dark spots on the plate indicate individual compounds which contain the radioactive carbon. The methods which have been developed make it possible to identify intermediate metabolites when they are present in concentrations of less than $10^{-6}M$ in samples weighing only a few milligrams. It is through such experiments as these that the intermediate steps in the photosynthetic process are gradually being elucidated.

The outstanding advantage of the isotope technique is that it can be used in studies of normal organisms, under normal conditions. It has yielded proof of the truth of some old theories and has completely disproved others. It has yielded answers to some problems which could have been solved by no previously known experimental technique. It is at the moment the most promising method of approach to many other problems which still await solution.

SUGGESTIONS FOR FURTHER READING

Manometric Methods

Dixon, M., *Manometric Methods*, 3rd ed., Cambridge University, Cambridge, 1951.

Krebs, H. A., The use of "CO_2-buffers" in manometric measurements of cell metabolism, in *Carbon Dioxide Fixation and Photosynthesis*, No. V of the Symposia of the Society for Experimental Biology, Academic, New York, 1951.

Perkins, J. J., Barcroft-Warburg manometric apparatus, *Ind. Eng. Chem., Anal. Ed., 15*, 61 (1943).

Umbreit, W. W., R. H. Burris, and J. F. Stauffer, *Manometric Techniques*, Burgess, Minneapolis, 1945.

Isotopic Techniques

Mendel, J. L., and D. W. Visser, Studies on nitrate reduction in higher plants, *Arch. Biochem. Biophys., 32*, 159 (1951).

Rittenberg, D., and D. Shemin, Isotope technique in the study of intermediary metabolism, in *Currents in Biochemical Research*, D. E. Green (ed.), Interscience, New York, 1946.

Schoenheimer, R., and D. Rittenberg, Study of the intermediary metabolism of animals with the aid of isotopes, *Physiol. Revs., 20*, 218 (1940).

The early Schoenheimer papers in the *J. Biol. Chem., 111* and *127*, give a clear discussion of the method, its limitations, and techniques.

Transportation systems 9

ALL THOSE PLANTS AND ANIMALS which are high enough in the evolutionary scale to have special organs dedicated to the performance of specific, limited functions have also, of necessity, some sort of transportation system. This consists of a fluid of greater or less complexity, moving from one part of the organism to another usually through vessels which carry it to all the tissues. In vertebrates the main circulatory system is a closed one in which the blood moves out from the heart and returns to the heart to be dispatched again to the peripheral tissues by way of the lungs. In plants the roughly analogous system is made up of the phloem and the xylem through which the plant saps carry food and other substances from one area of the plant to another.

BLOOD

The circulating fluid in the higher animals is really a tissue composed of cells floating in a complex solution which is largely colloidal. This moving tissue performs a variety of important functions. It carries food and oxygen to all the cells of the organism and removes the waste products of their metabolism; it transports the hormones from the site of their secretion in the endocrine glands to the tissues which use them; it helps to maintain the water balance by controlling the flow of water into the tissue spaces; it plays a large role in the control of the pH of the body and it regulates body temperature by cooling such tissues as the muscles in which heat is produced and warming the surface areas from which heat is lost. Of the various animal circulatory fluids mammalian blood has been most extensively investigated, hence blood chemistry as presented in the following pages is largely the chemistry of human and closely related bloods. The human circulatory system is represented diagrammatically in Fig. 10.5, on page 378.

Composition of Mammalian Blood

If blood is drawn into a tube or syringe containing an anticoagulant, all the cells or *formed elements* may be spun down in the centrifuge, leaving a clear, yellowish supernatant fluid, the blood *plasma*. In the absence of an anti-coagulant, drawn blood sets in a clot, from which there is slowly squeezed out a pale yellow liquid called *serum*. Coagulation is a complicated process which results from a series of reactions in which ionic calcium and several of the plasma enzymes are involved. The chief result is the transformation of the soluble protein fibrinogen into fibrin which gels to form the actual clot. Thus the main difference between serum and plasma is that the latter contains fibrinogen and the former does not. The common anticoagulants, sodium oxalate and sodium citrate, act by precipitating the calcium ion, thus interrupting the train of events which leads to formation of fibrin.

The cells which comprise the formed elements in mammalian blood are of three kinds, the red blood corpuscles, the white blood cells, and the platelets. The platelets have a special function in helping to initiate blood clotting; the white cells, of which there are several different kinds, serve chiefly as a protection against all sorts of invading agents. Since the white cells are nucleated and move about freely, their chemistry is that of any unicellular organism and needs no special comment. Human red cells, on the other hand, have no nuclei and are essentially little passive containers in which hemoglobin is carried through the circulatory system. The chemical processes which they mediate are unique and will be considered shortly.

The plasma is an extremely complex solution containing proteins, amino acids, carbohydrates, lipids combined in lipoprotein complexes, and salts as well as vitamins, hormones, and enzymes. It is probable that it contains trace amounts of many substances which are still undetected, but the concentration range of most of its constituents is now known. Roughly, about 92 per cent of the plasma is water, nearly 7 per cent is protein, less than 1 per cent is salts, and approximately 0.1 per cent is glucose. Other substances which are present in small amounts include the lipids, which occur in widely varying concentrations, organic acids, and several substances which are grouped together as "nonprotein nitrogen compounds." In Table 9.1 are listed the most abundant constituents of human plasma or serum. It should be noted that except for the proteins the concentrations are so low that they are

TABLE 9.1. Composition of Normal Human Plasma[a]

	Average or Representative Value, mg/100 ml	Range, mg/100 ml
Inorganic constituents		
Water	93,600	92,400–94,400
Chloride	365	355–381
Sodium	316	300–330
Bicarbonate (as $NaHCO_3$)[b]	226	205–280
Potassium	17.2	12.1–25.4
Phosphate (as P) (inorganic)[c]	3.2	2.6–5.4
Calcium (serum)	10	8.2–11.6
Silica (as SiO_2) (whole blood)	9.0	
Sulfur, total nonprotein	3.38	2.95–3.75
Magnesium (serum)	2.0	1.7–2.3
Zinc	0.21	0.12–0.48
Copper	0.12	0.086–0.161
Iron	0.105	0.028–0.210
Carbohydrates		
Glucose, fasting capillary whole blood	93	
Pentose, total	2.55	
Polysaccharides (serum) (as hexose)	102	73–101
Nonprotein nitrogen compounds		
Amino acids, total (as N) (ninhydrin method)	4.1	3.4–5.5
Creatine (serum)	1.07	0.76–1.28
Creatinine (serum) (male)		1.05–1.65
Uric acid (serum)	4.0	2.9–6.9
Urea (male)	27.1	
Lipids[d]		
Fatty acids (as stearic acid)		200–450
Fats, neutral		0–150
Cholesterol, free and esterified		150–260
Phospholipids		150–250
Proteins[e]	g/100 ml	
Albumin	4.04	
α_1-Globulin	0.31	
α_2-Globulin	0.48	
β-Globulin	0.81	
γ-Globulin	0.74	
Fibrinogen	0.34	
Total	6.72	

SOURCE: Data in this table are adapted from the full tables given in H. A. Krebs, Chemical composition of blood plasma and serum, *Ann. Rev. Biochem.*, *19*, 409 (1950).

[a] Note that the figures for silica and glucose are for whole blood. Except where indicated all others are for plasma.

[b] All bicarbonate ion present is reported as $NaHCO_3$.

[c] Does not include organic acid-soluble phosphate esters.

[d] It is now believed that all the blood lipids are present in lipoprotein complexes in which the various constituents are found in various ratios.

[e] The six groups listed are the main fractions into which human plasma proteins are separated by electrophoresis.

TABLE 9.2. Some Components of Human Plasma Proteins

Substance	Properties	Assumed Functions	Estimated Conc., g/100 ml plasma	Electrophoretic Fraction
Fibrinogen	Converted to fibrin	Clotting	0.27	
Antihemophilic globulin	Clots hemophilic blood	Clotting	v. little	
Nonclottable protein	Insol. at low temps.		0.01	
Immune γ-globulin	Antibodies	Immunological	0.74	γ-Globulin
Immune euglobulins	Typhoid agglutinins	Immunological	v. little	β- and γ-Globulins
Enzymes		Metabolic	0.001	α- and β-Globulins
β-Pseudoglobulin	Combines with Fe and Cu	Solubilization and transport of serum components	0.17	α- and β-Globulins
Glycoproteins	Combined with carbohydrates		0.08	α- and β-Globulins
Lipoproteins	Combined with lipids and carotenoids	Solubilization and transport	0.04	α- and β-Globulins
Bilirubin-containing proteins			0.003	α-Globulin
Albumin		Osmotic regulation	3.35	Albumin

SOURCE: These data come from a table in H. A. Krebs, Chemical composition of blood plasma and serum, *Ann. Rev. Biochem.*, *19*, 409 (1950). The original figures are from papers by Cohn.

reported as milligrams per cent, that is, milligrams of the constituent per hundred milliliters of fluid.

Cohn[1] and his associates at Harvard separated the complex mixture of plasma proteins into a large number of individual fractions. Quantitative data on some of the fractions are assembled in Table 9.2, which shows how various physiologically active substances are distributed, and lists some of their functions.

Regulation of the water balance of the body is primarily the function of the plasma proteins and especially of the large albumin fraction. Although the greater part of the osmotic pressure of the blood is due to the salts, these substances pass too freely through cell walls to have an appreciable effect on the distribution of water. But as long as the plasma contains the normal complement of the hydrophilic albumin, its small but constant osmotic pressure acts as a check on the capillary pressure which is tending to drive water into the tissue spaces.

Distribution of solutes

Certain of the blood constituents are unequally distributed between cells and plasma, as is shown in Table 9.3. Particularly striking is the fact that nearly all the potassium ion is concentrated in the cells whereas a major

TABLE 9.3. Distribution of Certain Solutes between Cells and Plasma in Normal Human Blood

	Moles per 1000 g H_2O	
Solute	Serum	Cells
Protein	0.002	0.007
Urea	0.007	0.007
Glucose	0.004	0.004
Chloride	0.111	0.074
Inorganic phosphate	0.002	0.002
Calcium	0.003	0
Magnesium	0.001	0.003
Potassium	0.004*	0.135*
Sodium	0.145*	0.027*

SOURCE: Data from J. P. Peters, *Body Waters*, Thomas, Springfield, Ill., 1935. The starred figures are revised values kindly provided by Dr. Peters.

---

[1] Edwin J. Cohn (1892–1953) was Professor of Physical Chemistry at the Harvard Medical School. His chief interest had been in the physical chemistry of the amino acids and later in the elegant methods which he had devised for the isolation of electrophoretically homogeneous proteins from blood serum.

portion of the sodium is found in the serum. This is one of the many examples of distributions which can only be maintained by active transport. The movement of ions against a concentration gradient requires osmotic work, and part of the energy generated by the cells is used to move ions into an environment which they would not otherwise be able to penetrate.

Hemoglobin

The ability of the blood to carry large volumes of oxygen depends almost entirely on the presence inside the red blood cell membrane of the pigment hemoglobin. In solution this compound, which contains iron in the ferrous state, readily forms a loose molecular compound with oxygen without changing the valence of the iron. When the oxygen pressure is lowered, the complex dissociates rapidly and again sets free its oxygen. It is therefore able to acquire oxygen in the lungs where the oxygen pressure is about 100 mm of mercury, and to release it in the tissues where the oxygen pressure averages less than 40 mm. This reversible oxygenation takes place only in the presence of water, which is believed to occupy in the reduced molecule the place held by oxygen in oxyhemoglobin. Allowing HHb to stand for hemoglobin to emphasize its acid nature, the two reactions may be formulated:

$$HHb(H_2O) + O_2 \leftrightharpoons HHbO_2 + H_2O$$
Hemoglobin   **Oxyhemoglobin**

Structure of heme

Hemoglobin is a chromoprotein from which may be obtained a colorless, slightly basic protein, globin, and a colored, iron-containing prosthetic group, *heme*. The protein contains a high proportion of histidine, is soluble in water and in dilute acid and alkali, and resembles the histone proteins. The heme is one of a small group of closely related colored compounds which are of unique importance in the living economy. For example, the structure of chlorophyll is extraordinarily like that of heme, while combinations of heme with various proteins give rise to some of the most fundamental and ubiquitous of the oxidizing enzymes as well as to a large group of vertebrate and invertebrate hemoglobins.

It has long been known that when a small quantity of blood is allowed to evaporate in the presence of acetic acid and a trace of sodium chloride, characteristic brown crystalline rods appear. These consist of a chloride of heme to which the name *hemin* is given. It was the exhaustive examination of this compound by many outstanding organic chemists, especially by Küster,[2]

---

[2] William Küster (1863–1929) was Professor of Physiological Chemistry at the Imperial Technical College at Stuttgart. From his laboratory there came a long series of papers dealing with the chemistry of the blood pigments and related compounds. In these he laid the foundations for later work with these complex substances.

Willstätter,[3] and Hans Fischer,[4] which finally established the structure of heme.

Treatment of hemin with hydriodic acid and acetic acid gives rise as chief products to several differently substituted pyrrole bases. The formulas below, for pyrrole itself and for one of these products of the reductive decomposition of hemin, indicate how the atoms of the pyrrole ring are numbered. In later formulas, in accordance with accepted usage, the carbons and hydrogens of the pyrrole rings are omitted.

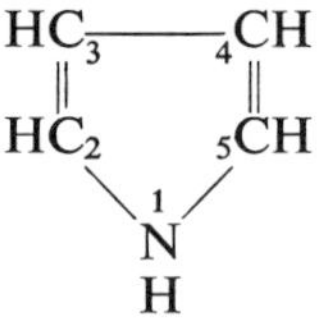

Pyrrole

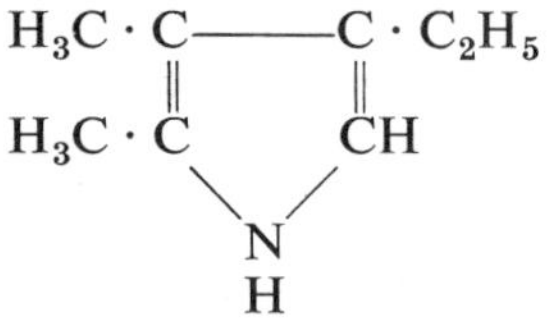

Hemopyrrole, or
α′-Methyl-β′-methyl-β-ethylpyrrole, or
2,3-Dimethyl-4-ethylpyrrole

The molecular weight of hemin indicated that four pyrrole rings were probably involved in its structure, which was finally proved by Hans Fischer's synthesis to be that of an *iron porphyrin*. The large porphyrin ring consists of four pyrrole rings united through methene ($=CH—$) bridges in such a way that eighteen of the inner atoms make up a ring of conjugated double linkages. Obviously the possibilities for resonance are many and the particular distribution of double bonds in the formula simply serves to give a concrete

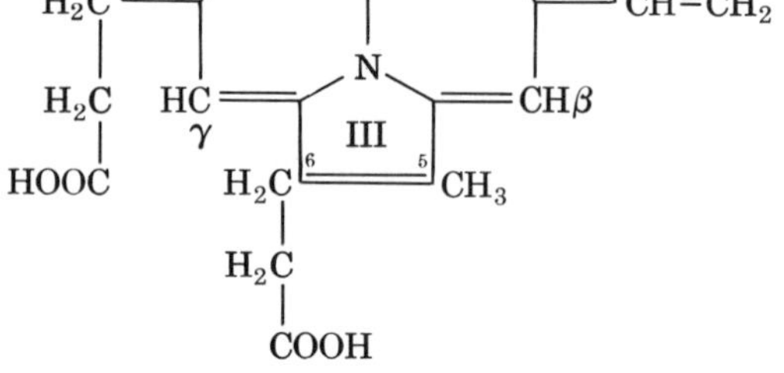

Hemin

[3] Richard Willstätter (1872–1942) was Professor of Chemistry at the University of Munich, and although he became Professor Emeritus in 1925, he continued to publish on a wide range of subjects until shortly before his death. His personality and genius attracted

representation of something for which no single formula can be written. The two types of numbers and the Greek letters are used in differentiating the four rings and the various possible substitution positions.

Plant hemoglobin

Leguminous plants have an almost unique place in nature in that in the presence of certain soil bacteria they are able to fix atmospheric nitrogen and thus to use it in synthesis. This reaction takes place in nodules formed by bacteria on the roots of the plants. In these nodules hemoglobin has been identified, partly by its absorption spectrum, partly by its reversible reaction with oxygen, and partly by the bile pigment-like decomposition products which it forms. Up to the present it has not been possible to prove that it serves a function in symbiotic nitrogen fixation, but its localization in the nodules certainly suggests that either the plant or the bacteria make some use of its ability to store and to release oxygen.

Nomenclature

The nomenclature of the porphyrins is complicated. In the first place many of the compounds were identified spectroscopically long before their structures were known, and the many very similar names were designed to indicate a complex set of interrelationships. Furthermore, there have been recent changes in nomenclature with the result that the same substance appears under more than one name even in current publications. Finally there are still some differences in British and American usage beyond the British use of the diphthong. Although the details of nomenclature in this large group of compounds is beyond the scope of such a book as this, it seems wise to give a few guideposts so that anyone dipping into the literature of heme chemistry may not be hopelessly confused at the outset.

A large ring composed of four unsubstituted pyrrole residues united through methene bridges is considered the parent substance of the tetra-pyrrole compounds and was named *porphin*. Its various substitution products were then called *porphyrins*. This name is most commonly used, but there was an attempt a few years ago to drop the middle syllable and call the derivatives "porphins." In the formula for the parent compound, porphin, a second common representation of the ring tetrapyrrole compounds is used. Removal of the iron from heme leaves a porphyrin with eight substituents, four methyl groups at positions 1, 3, 5, and 8, two vinyl groups at positions 2 and 4,

---

graduate students from all over the world, and his school made fundamental contributions to enzyme purification and action and to the chemistry of the plant pigments. He was awarded the Nobel Prize in Chemistry in 1915.

[4] Hans Fischer (1881–1945) was Professor in the Chemical Institute of the Technical College in Munich. He is best known for his work on the two pigments, heme and chlorophyll, and for his contributions in these fields was awarded the Nobel Prize in 1930. The long strain of the war and the destruction of his Institute led to his tragic death by his own hand.

and propionic acid residues at positions 6 and 7. This compound is known as *protoporphyrin*. If hemin is reduced very gently before removal of the iron, only the two vinyl groups react and the product is therefore identical with

Porphin

protoporphyrin except that the vinyl groups have been replaced by ethyl groups. This compound is known as *mesoporphyrin*. In order to determine the positions occupied by the various substituents in the mesoporphyrin related to heme, Hans Fischer determined to synthesize it. He began by drawing up a table showing that there were fifteen possible arrangements. When later he succeeded in preparing a compound identical with the natural mesoporphyrin it proved to correspond with the ninth one on his list. Hence the mesoporphyrin and the protoporphyrin related to heme are often referred to as mesoporphyrin IX and protoporphyrin IX. The particular variety and arrangement of substituents in protoporphyrin IX seem to be adaptable to many biological purposes, for with only minor variations they are characteristic of all the naturally occurring porphyrins.

Another substance which was important in the elucidation of the structure of heme is *etioporphyrin* which is formed when hemin is vigorously reduced and then subjected to pyrolysis. In these reactions not only are the vinyl groups saturated, yielding ethyl groups, but the propionic acid groups are also transformed into ethyl groups by loss of carbon dioxide. With only two kinds of substituents in the molecule there are but four possible arrangements of the side chains. The one which is present in the etioporphyrin derived from heme proved to correspond with the third one on the original list, hence substances having this arrangement are said to be related to etioporphyrin III.

Complete removal of the unsaturated side chains of hemin can be achieved by bacterial action, giving rise to a *deuteroporphyrin*, unsubstituted at positions 2 and 4. From deuteroporphyrin it is possible to prepare another

TABLE 9.4. Porphyrin Compounds Related to Heme

	Substituents		
	Positions 1,3,5,8	Positions 2,4	Positions 6,7
Protoporphyrin IX	(—CH₃)₄	(—CH=CH₂)₂	(—CH₂—CH₂COOH)₂
Mesoporphyrin IX	(—CH₃)₄	(—C₂H₅)₂	(—CH₂—CH₂COOH)₂
Etioporphyrin III	(—CH₃)₄	(—C₂H₅)₂	(—C₂H₅)₂
Etioporphyrin I	1,3,5(—CH₃)₃	(—C₂H₅)₂	6—C₂H₅
	8—C₂H₅		7—CH₃
Deuteroporphyrin IX	(—CH₃)₄	(—H)₂	(—CH₂—CH₂COOH)₂
Hematoporphyrin	(—CH₃)₄	$\left(-\overset{OH}{\underset{CH_3}{CH}}\right)_2$	(—CH₂—CH₂COOH)₂
Coproporphyrin III	(—CH₃)₄	(—CH₂—CH₂COOH)₂	(—CH₂—CH₂COOH)₂
Coproporphyrin I	1,3,5(—CH₃)₂	(—CH₂—CH₂COOH)₂	6—CH₂—CH₂COOH
	8—CH₂—CH₂COOH		7—CH₃
Uroporphyrin I	1,3,5(—CH₂COOH)₃	(—CH₂—CH₂COOH)₂	6—CH₂—CH₂COOH
	8—CH₂—CH₂COOH		7—CH₂COOH

heme derivative, *hematoporphyrin*, with hydroxyethyl groups at positions 2 and 4.

Besides these substances which have been prepared from heme, there are three porphyrins which occur naturally, coproporphyrin I, coproporphyrin III, and uroporphyrin I. These substances normally occur in trace amounts only and are believed to be by-products of protoporphyrin synthesis in the body. The compounds with the type I structure are related to etioporphyrin I in which the ethyl and methyl groups alternate around the large ring. The composition of these various porphyrins is given in Table 9.4.

It was noted above that the iron both in reduced and in oxygenated hemoglobin is in the ferrous condition. But the valence of the iron can be changed if hemoglobin is treated with an oxidizing agent such as potassium ferricyanide. The prosthetic group is then sometimes known as *hematin*, or the difference in the two types of compound may be indicated by the use of the prefixes ferro- and ferri-. Recently it has been suggested that hem*o*globin be used for the conjugated protein containing ferrous iron and hem*i*globin for the ferric derivative. This latter substance appears in all except the most

TABLE 9.5.   Nomenclature of Heme and Its Derivatives

Substance	Synonyms	Composition
Heme	Haem[a]; ferroheme; protoheme	Ferrous protoporphyrin IX
Hemin	Chlorohemin	Heme chloride
Hemoglobin	Ferrohemoglobin	4 Hemes + globin
Methemoglobin	Hemiglobin; ferrihemoglobin	4 Ferric protoporphyrins + globin
Myoglobin	Muscle hemoglobin	1 Heme + protein
Oxyhemoglobin		Ferrohemoglobin + O_2
Carboxyhemoglobin		Ferrohemoglobin + CO
Hemichrome	Ferric hemochromogen	Ferric protoporphyrin IX + a base
Hemochrome	Ferrous hemochromogen	Heme + a base

[a] In British usage the diphthong is used in all the words related to haemoglobin.

recent literature as *methemoglobin*, which is formed in the body as a result of poisoning by nitrobenzene or other toxic agents. There is some evidence that a very small amount of methemoglobin is normally present in the red cells, but when there is any appreciable amount of this substance the condition is pathological and is referred to as *methemoglobinemia*.

Another hemoglobin derivative which is formed in cases of carbon monoxide poisoning is *carboxyhemoglobin* (HHbCO). In this compound carbon monoxide holds the position normally occupied by oxygen, and as the carbon monoxide is very tenaciously held, the hemoglobin ceases to function in oxygen transport.

Heme unites not only with globin but also with a large number of other proteins and even with such simple basic compounds as pyridine and ammonia. These substances have been known as *hemochromogens*. It is now suggested that the two final syllables be dropped and that the valence of the iron be indicated, giving two types of compound, the *hemochromes* and the *hemi-chromes*. Table 9.5 gives the names which are used for heme and its more important derivatives.

Structure of hemoglobin

Heme as it occurs in hemoglobin is a ferrous derivative of protoporphyrin IX. Because of resonance this is a stable structure which has strong absorption bands in the visible region. This latter fact facilitated the early studies of

Heme
Ferrous protoporphyrin IX

hemoglobin and its derivatives, many of which were known only through their characteristic and easily observed absorption spectra. The molecule of heme is a flat disk, all the resonating atoms lying in the same plane with the iron atom at the center of this ring.

Of the six coordination positions available on the iron, four are used to bind the metal to the four nitrogens of the porphyrin. The two remaining valences are directed, one upward and the other downward, at right angles to the plane of the ring. When heme is linked to globin, one of these valences is involved in addition to links formed through the propionic acid side chains.

The molecular weight of hemoglobin is 68,000, and each molecule carries four heme groups. X-ray studies indicate that the molecule is cylindrical in shape, with dimensions of 55 by 55 by 65 A. Studies reported by Perutz and his colleagues in 1960 show that each of the four polypeptide chains which make up the protein has, like the myoglobin shown in Fig. 5.14 on page 231, certain segments which take the form of an α helix. Beyond this, each twisted rod is folded into tetrahedral form and the four tetrahedra are fitted together to give a molecule of the dimensions noted above. The four heme disks fit into open places on the surface of the protein. One link between heme and protein is, as has long been suspected, a result of coordination of the iron atom with a nitrogen of a histidine side chain in the protein. Other links appear to be made through hydrogen bonds from side chains of the heme. The hemes are tilted at such an angle that the one unused coordination position on each iron faces outward. When the hemoglobin is oxygenated, an oxygen *molecule* displaces the water previously held in each of these four positions. These relationships are indicated below for a single heme, represented by the central iron and the four nitrogens.

$$
\text{Globin—Fe—}H_2O + O_2 \rightleftharpoons \text{Globin—Fe—}O_2 + H_2O
$$

Hemoglobin   **Oxyhemoglobin**

Synthesis and destruction of heme in man

The red corpuscles or *erythrocytes* of the adult are formed in the red bone marrow and after a life span of about 120 days are destroyed. It has been estimated that approximately 10 million of these cells are normally removed from the circulation every second. This figure becomes less startling when it is realized that the total blood volume in the adult is between 5.5 and 6 liters and that every cubic millimeter contains 4.6–5.5 million red cells.

When the red cells are destroyed, the hemoglobin they contain is decomposed. This involves a daily loss of about 25 g of pigment containing 85 mg of iron. The daily excretion of iron, however, is only about 4.5 mg, and this indicates that the body conserves most of the iron and uses it again. Storage iron is found in the spleen, intestinal mucosa, and liver in combination with protein in the compound ferritin. The porphyrin part of the molecule is degraded and excreted, hence normal replacement of red cells involves a daily synthesis of about 1 g of heme.

SYNTHESIS OF HEME. Our present knowledge of the way in which heme is synthesized in the body began with studies made by Shemin and Rittenberg[5] and their colleagues at the College of Physicians and Surgeons. They showed first that in man ingestion of glycine, $H_2N \cdot CH_2 \cdot COOH$, labeled with N^{15} was followed by significant incorporation of the isotope in hemoglobin. In later experiments hemoglobin was synthesized by avian erythrocytes, which are nucleated cells. These confirmed the specific utilization of glycine not only to provide nitrogen for all four pyrrole rings but also to provide eight carbons, two per pyrrole, for the porphyrin. These were the four methene carbons and one α-carbon in each pyrrole. To determine whether both carbons of glycine were used, some of this compound was labeled in the α-carbon and some in the carboxyl carbon with C^{14}. When these were used separately as heme precursors, the distribution of radioactivity in the products proved that it is only the α-carbon of glycine which is incorporated in the porphyrin. The remaining carbons and one-third of the hydrogens are furnished by the methyl group of acetic acid. This was proved by experiments in which the two acetate carbons were labeled separately with C^{14} and the methyl group hydrogens were replaced by deuterium.

The details of the biosynthesis of heme from acetate and glycine will be considered in Chapter 13.

DESTRUCTION OF HEME. It will be found in later chapters that many of the constituents of living cells are astonishingly labile and are replaced with new molecules after quite brief periods. In contrast to such compounds, hemoglobin is extraordinarily stable and remains unchanged during the life span of the erythrocyte. After about four months of being buffeted about in the blood stream, human red blood cells are withdrawn from the circulation by special cells in the spleen and liver. There they are broken up and digested and the hemoglobin is split to protein and prosthetic group. The globin is degraded and its amino acids mingle with those from other sources. The iron is set free and conserved in ferritin. But the porphyrin seems to be of no further use, for it undergoes chemical transformation in the liver and is excreted in the bile. This fluid is an external secretion of the liver; it is formed continuously, stored in the gallbladder, and released from time to time into the upper intestine. Some of the substances which it contains serve to facilitate the digestion and absorption of the lipids (see page 374), but the *bile pigments* are simply excretory products derived from heme. These are,

---

[5] David Rittenberg (1906–   ) is now Professor of Biochemistry and Head of Department at the College of Physicians and Surgeons of Columbia University. It was he who contributed to the original team of Schoenheimer and Rittenberg the specialized knowledge of isotopes which was as important as Schoenheimer's biochemical insight. His major interests lie in the fields of lipid and protein metabolism.

David Shemin (1911–   ) is Professor in the Biochemistry Department at the College of Physicians and Surgeons, and in work with Rittenberg is developing the use of isotopes to trace pathways of synthesis in the body.

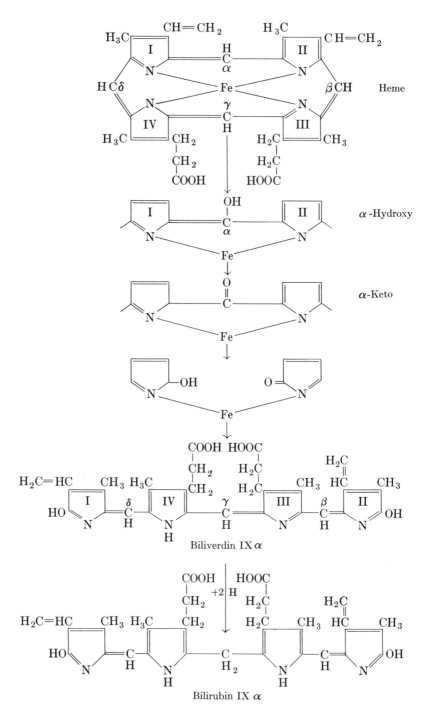

Fig. 9.1. The conversion of heme to bile pigments. The opening of the large ring is believed to be an oxidative process. [From S. Granick and H. Gilder, "Distribution, Structure, and Properties of the Tetrapyrroles," in F. F. Nord (ed.), *Advances in Enzymology*, **7**, 336. Copyright 1947, Interscience Publishers, Inc., New York-London.]

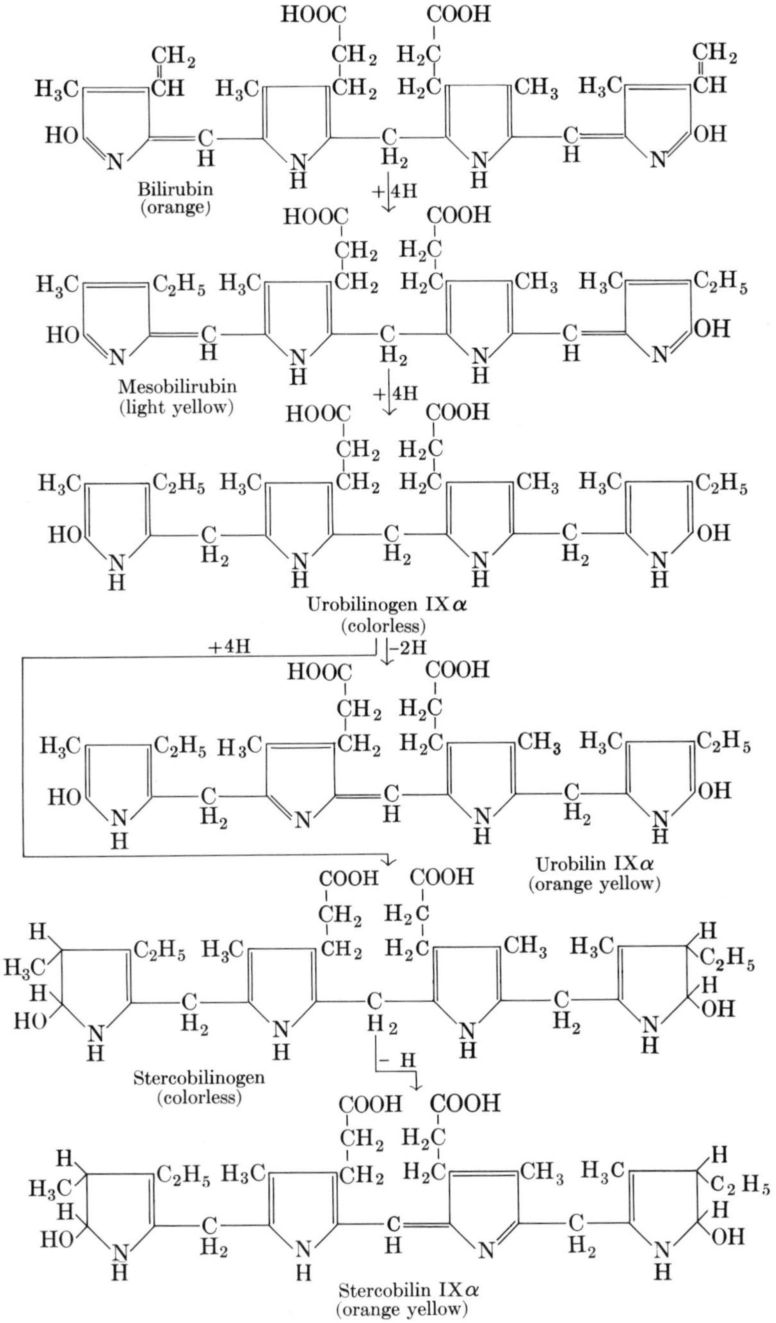

Fig. 9.2. Stages in the transformation of bilirubin to urobilin and stercobilin. [From C. J. Watson, *The Harvey Lectures,* **44,** 44 (1948–1949).]

as the name indicates, colored substances which give the bile its yellowish-green color. As they travel down the gut, they undergo chemical changes which darken them and make them chiefly responsible for the characteristic color of the feces.

The two chief bile pigments, bilirubin and biliverdin, are formed from heme by loss of iron and oxidative opening of the porphyrin ring at the α-methene group. This gives a product which is still a tetrapyrrole, with side chains arranged as in heme, but with its four pyrroles strung together in an open chain.

In Fig. 9.1 is summarized the series of reactions by which the two bile pigments are believed to be formed from heme. The "IXα" following some of the names indicates that the arrangement of side chains is that of meso-porphyrin IX and that the break in the porphyrin ring has been made at the α-methene carbon.

As the bile pigments travel down the intestinal tract they are reduced, probably by intestinal bacteria, yielding among other products two orange-yellow compounds, urobilin and stercobilin. The relation of these compounds to bilirubin is outlined in Fig. 9.2. It is probable that there are still other final products of a deeper color, since these two do not adequately account for the actual color of feces. But so far the other pigments which occur in feces have not been characterized chemically.

Transportation of the Blood Gases

Hemoglobin is involved not only in oxygen transport but also in the ability of the blood to carry carbon dioxide without appreciable disturbance of its *p*H. Although these functions are exercised in much the same way in all bloods which contain hemoglobin, it should be noted that the quantitative data used in the following discussion have nearly all been obtained with human blood.

Transportation of oxygen

The affinity of hemoglobin for oxygen is such that in the short time required for blood to traverse the capillaries of the alveoli the pigment is very nearly saturated with oxygen, while at the oxygen tension which obtains in the tissues nearly half of this oxygen is released. The partial pressure of oxygen in the alveoli is approximately 100 mm and at this pressure each 100 ml of blood holds about 19.6 ml of oxygen. In the tissues the oxygen tension is 35 mm or less, and as a result 7 to 9 ml of oxygen is set free by each 100 ml of blood traversing the capillaries.

The quantitative relationship between oxygen pressure and the dissociation of oxyhemoglobin is shown in Fig. 9.3 in which the oxygenation of whole blood at three different *p*H values is plotted against the oxygen pressure. The

general shape of the curves indicates that the relation is not a simple proportionality which would give a straight line, while the differences between
the three show that the extent of dissociation of oxyhemoglobin is also a
function of the *p*H. Thus at a partial pressure of 40 mm and *p*H 7.24 a
significantly larger volume of oxygen is set free than at a *p*H of 7.44. This is
of importance because of other changes taking place in the blood as it passes
through the tissues. The release of oxygen to the tissues is accompanied by

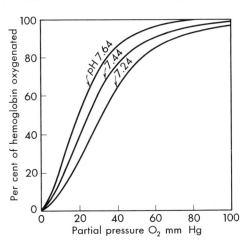

Fig. 9.3. Effect of oxygen pressure
and of acidity on oxygen dissociation
curve of blood. [From J. F. Fulton
(ed.), *Textbook of Physiology*, Saunders, Philadelphia, 1949. After
Peters and Van Slyke.]

a transfer of carbon dioxide from the tissues to the blood stream and this
tends to lower the *p*H slightly just when a lowered *p*H is advantageous. On
the other hand, oxyhemoglobin is a stronger acid than hemoglobin, the pK_1
value for horse hemoglobin being 6.68 for oxyhemoglobin and 7.93 for hemoglobin. This means that the tendency of the entering carbon dioxide to lower
the *p*H of the blood is counterbalanced in part by the transformation of an
acidic compound into a weaker acid. The fact that the curves are steepest
between 20 and 40 mm pressure makes sure that adequate amounts of oxygen
will be made available to the tissues at their normal levels of oxygen tension.

Carbon dioxide transport

A small amount of carbon dioxide is carried in the blood in true solution
but the major part is present as bicarbonate ion with smaller amounts as
carbonic acid and perhaps 10 per cent as a hemoglobin complex known as a
carbamino compound. Although this compound is frequently indicated by
the formula $HHbCO_2$ this does not mean that the carbon dioxide replaces
oxygen and is attached to the iron. It is believed that carbon dioxide reacts
directly with free amino groups in the globin to form carboxyl groups:

$$RNH_2 + CO_2 \rightarrow R \cdot NH \cdot COO^- + H^+$$
Carbamino compound

All the various forms in which carbon dioxide is carried are in equilibrium with each other, and when reference is made to the "volume" of carbon dioxide in blood, it is to be understood that this refers to the sum of all these forms, reported in terms of the volume of gas which would be used in forming them, or which can be released by suitable procedures.

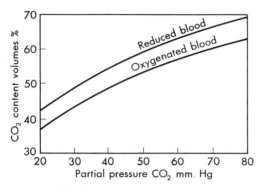

Fig. 9.4. Carbon dioxide content of arterial and venous blood at various carbon dioxide pressures. [From J. F. Fulton (ed.), *Textbook of Physiology*, Saunders, Philadelphia, 1949. After Peters and Van Slyke.]

As might be expected, the volume of carbon dioxide absorbed by the blood depends in part on the partial pressure of the gas itself. This is illustrated in Fig. 9.4 in which the volume of carbon dioxide which can be taken up by arterial and by venous blood is plotted against the carbon dioxide tension.

Fig. 9.5. The effect of different concentrations of carbon dioxide on the dissociation of oxyhemoglobin. [From J. F. Fulton (ed.), *Textbook of Physiology*, Saunders, Philadelphia, 1949. After Barcroft.]

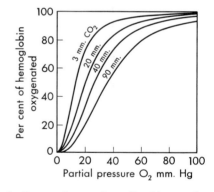

The fact that the two curves are different indicates that carbon dioxide uptake depends also upon the partial pressure of oxygen in the system. Thus arterial blood, in which the oxygen concentration is high, carries less carbon dioxide at a given carbon dioxide tension than does venous blood with its lower oxygen content. Another facet of this relationship is brought out in Fig. 9.5 in which can be seen the effect of different partial pressures of carbon dioxide on the oxygenation of whole blood. A result of this influence is that a high carbon dioxide tension facilitates release of oxygen just as a high partial pressure of oxygen hastens the evolution of carbon dioxide.

A small part of the carbon dioxide which enters the blood stream reacts slowly with water in the plasma to form carbonic acid or bicarbonate ion. But the major part of it diffuses into the red cells where there are two special mechanisms for dealing with it. Inside the red cell but not in the plasma is an enzyme, *carbonic anhydrase*, which acts to speed up the normally rather sluggish hydration of carbon dioxide to carbonic acid. At the same time some of the carbon dioxide which enters the red blood cells reacts there with oxyhemoglobin to form the carbamino compound.

$$CO_2 + HHbO_2 \rightleftharpoons HHbCO_2 + O_2$$

This hastens the release of oxygen, for the carbamino compound has a smaller affinity for oxygen than has hemoglobin itself. As indicated, the reaction is reversible and when the blood reaches the lungs where the oxygen tension is high and the pressure of carbon dioxide is relatively low, the reverse reaction facilitates the expulsion of carbon dioxide and oxygenation of hemoglobin.

The blood buffers

It has been noted many times that in spite of the reactions which have just been outlined the *p*H of the blood is held remarkably constant at about 7.40. This is achieved partly by the change in the strength of the hemoglobin acids, the weaker hemoglobin appearing simultaneously with the influx of acidic carbon dioxide, and the stronger oxyhemoglobin at the time when carbon dioxide is leaving the blood. But the main defense against changes in acidity is the series of buffer pairs listed below:

$$\frac{HProteinate}{NaProteinate} \qquad \frac{NaH_2PO_4}{Na_2HPO_4} \qquad \frac{H_2CO_3}{NaHCO_3}$$

Of these the proteins, and especially the two hemoglobin pairs, those of reduced and of oxyhemoglobin, are quantitatively most important.

Examination of the titration curves for the inorganic buffer pairs, the carbonates and orthophosphates (Fig. 9.6), shows that at the *p*H of blood neither pair is present in optimum buffering ratio. At *p*H 7.4 the ratio of NaH_2PO_4 to Na_2HPO_4 is about 1:4, which does not give a wide buffering capacity but does provide effective resistance to a small increase in acidity. Since normal metabolic changes are more likely to give rise to acidic than to basic products this is a useful provision.

At the same *p*H, the ratio of carbonic acid to its salt seems even less effective, being approximately 1:20. In spite of this low ratio, the carbonate pair constitutes a good physiological buffer because respiratory removal of carbon dioxide keeps this ratio nearly constant. When acid enters the blood, it is neutralized by the bicarbonate present and such a reaction in a solution would change the buffer ratio by decreasing the salt concentration and increasing that of the acid. But in the body the extra carbon dioxide is eliminated promptly, and as long as the bicarbonate is not entirely exhausted, a buffer ratio close to the normal 1:20 is maintained. Because of its function in neutralizing acids the bicarbonate in the blood has been called the "alkaline

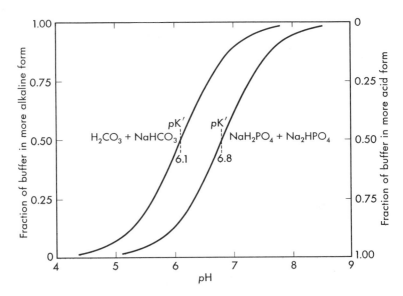

Fig. 9.6. Dissociation curves of the blood buffer acids, H_2CO_3 and $H_2PO_4^-$. [From J. F. Fulton (ed.), *Textbook of Physiology*, Saunders, Philadelphia, 1949.]

reserve" of the body. Actually the total alkaline reserve consists of bicarbonate ion, secondary phosphate ion, HPO_4^{--}, and all the anionic proteins which can accept hydrogen ion and go over into un-ionized form.

$$H^+ + Proteinate^- \rightleftharpoons H—Protein$$

As a result of all the adjustments which take place when acidic substances enter the blood stream the pH of venous blood is only about 0.02 pH unit lower than that of arterial blood.

Summary

Figures 9.7 and 9.8 indicate diagrammatically the important events which take place as blood traverses the capillaries of the alveoli and the capillaries of the tissues. It should be remembered that although the reactions are represented with single arrows they are all reversible.

Blood reaches the alveolar capillaries carrying carbon dioxide as bicarbonate ion in cells and plasma and as hemoglobin carbamino compound

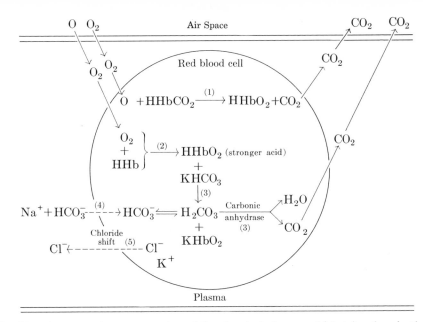

Fig. 9.7. Diagrammatic representation of the chemical changes which take place in the capillaries as the blood moves through the lining of the alveoli. The passage of oxygen into the blood is a result of the high oxygen tension in the alveoli, while the carbon dioxide is driven out of the blood by its higher pressure there. [From J. F. Fulton (ed.), *Textbook of Physiology*, Saunders, Philadelphia, 1949.]

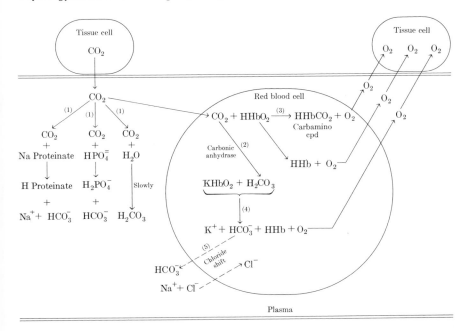

Fig. 9.8. Diagrammatic representation of the chemical changes which take place as the blood moves through the capillaries of the tissues. Here the carbon dioxide tension of the tissue cells is higher than that of the plasma, and the oxygen tension is lower. This leads to a movement of carbon dioxide into the blood and a movement of oxygen into the cells.

inside the erythrocytes. It should be noted that even in very active tissues where the need for oxygen is urgent, only part of the oxyhemoglobin dissociates in the tissues, and so the cells of the venous blood always contain both reduced and oxygenated hemoglobin. As the blood flows through the capillaries of the alveoli, oxygen diffuses across the capillary wall into the plasma and thence into the erythrocytes. The chemical changes which take place may be summarized as follows:

1. Oxygen reacts with the carbamino compound, releasing its carbon dioxide.
2. Oxygenation of the reduced hemoglobin gives rise to an acid, $HHbO_2$, which is a stronger acid than HHb.
3. This increased acidity is neutralized by the $KHCO_3$ in the cell, thus freeing more carbon dioxide. The rate of this reaction is high because of the presence in the cells of carbonic anhydrase which greatly hastens the decomposition of carbonic acid as it forms.
4. Escape of carbon dioxide lowers the concentration of bicarbonate ion in equilibrium with carbonic acid inside the cells, and this allows more bicarbonate ion to move into the cells from the plasma.
5. The increased concentration of bicarbonate ion in the cells is balanced by a simultaneous migration of chloride ions out into the plasma. This reciprocal change in the ratio of chloride ion to bicarbonate ion in cells and plasma is known as the *chloride shift*.

As a result of this series of reactions blood leaves the lungs with a diminished load of carbon dioxide and carrying about 95 per cent of its hemoglobin in the oxygenated form.

In the tissues the oxygen tension may be as low as 30 mm and the pressure of carbon dioxide is 50 mm or more. The reactions which ensue when the oxygenated blood reaches the tissue capillaries are as follows:

1. Carbon dioxide moves into the plasma and there reacts slowly with water and with buffers, including the plasma proteins, to form bicarbonate ion and a small amount of carbonic acid.
2. Most of the carbon dioxide enters the cells and there reacts rapidly with water, under the influence of carbonic anhydrase.
3. Another part of the carbon dioxide which diffuses into the cells reacts with oxyhemoglobin to form carbamino compound and to release oxygen to the tissues.
4. Part of the oxyhemoglobin dissociates, its oxygen diffuses away, and the hemoglobin which remains is a weaker acid than was the oxygenated acid. This means in effect that the oxyhemoglobin in giving up its oxygen is enabled to accept part of the hydrogen ion formed in step 2, when carbon dioxide reacts with water.

$$H^+ + HbO_2^- \rightarrow HHb + O_2$$

5. The increased concentration of bicarbonate ion in the cells drives it into the plasma and this in turn causes chloride ions to invade the cells. Thus in the tissues there is a chloride shift which is the reverse of that which occurs in the lungs.

Leaving the tissue capillaries the blood returns to the heart whence it is sent to the lungs to dispose of its carbon dioxide and to be recharged with oxygen.

Respiratory Pigments

In the preceding discussion of the respiratory functions of human blood, the word hemoglobin has been used as if it referred to a definite chemical entity. Actually many different "hemoglobins" occur, not only in the vertebrates but in some species of invertebrates, and even in at least one place in the plant world (see page 347). These compounds are called by a single name because they are all conjugated proteins which react reversibly with oxygen and have heme as prosthetic group. But they differ among themselves in physical and chemical properties, including solubility, crystalline form, absorption spectra, and quantitative response to changing oxygen tension. In explanation of these differences it has been noted that the protein parts of the various hemoglobins differ widely in molecular weights and in amino acid composition.

The hemoglobins of vertebrate bloods, while they show some species differences, have a uniform molecular weight of approximately 67,000, and consist of a globin united with four heme residues. But the hemoglobin of vertebrate muscles, myoglobin, with a molecular weight of only 17,000 and but one heme group per molecule, seems to be one-fourth of a blood hemoglobin molecule. Contrasted with both of these are the invertebrate hemoglobins, some of which contain over 100 heme groups and have been isolated with molecular weights as high as 3,000,000. These very high molecular weights are usually found in organisms in which the hemoglobin is in solution in the plasma instead of being confined inside a cell membrane. This may reflect the need to provide a good many heme groups for oxygen transport without increasing too greatly the osmotic pressure of the plasma.

Another property which varies greatly from one hemoglobin to another is the affinity for oxygen, usually measured in terms of the oxygen tension required to cause half saturation. This depends, as we have seen, upon the pH and also upon the temperature, but when these are allowed for, it is found that some hemoglobins hold oxygen so tenaciously that they do not release it even to a vacuum, while others give it up at relatively high partial pressures of oxygen. In most cases these differences prove to reflect the differing conditions under which the pigment must function. We have already seen how well human hemoglobin is adapted to the conditions it meets in human tissues. In the same way, organisms which live where the oxygen tension is low are equipped with a hemoglobin which can be saturated at low pressures. Others which normally obtain their oxygen by simple diffusion carry in their body fluids a variety of hemoglobin which does not give up its oxygen until the oxygen tension in their environment has fallen too low to meet their needs by diffusion. Then the reserve of oxygen in hemoglobin is released to carry them past the time of crisis. In Table 9.6 the affinities of several different hemoglobins for oxygen are listed in terms of oxygen tensions required for half saturation. Obviously the lower the pressure recorded the greater the oxygen affinity of the hemoglobin.

TABLE 9.6. Oxygen Affinities of Various Hemoglobins

Hemoglobins	Temp., °C	Oxygen Tension for Half Saturation, mm
Human	35	7.5
Frog	35	42
Human	15	0.3
Planorbis (snail)	15	2
Chironomus riparius (midge)	17	0.6
Daphnia magna (water flea)	17	3.1
Root nodules of leguminous plants	15	>0.1
Nematode (roundworm)	19	>0.1

Besides the hemoglobins there are at least three other animal pigments or groups of pigments which are used in oxygen transport. These are the *chlorocruorins*, the *hemocyanins*, and the *hemerythrins*.

Chlorocruorin is a dichroic substance, red in concentrated and green in dilute solution. It is found in solution in the plasma of certain marine worms, and is closely related to hemoglobin. Its prosthetic group is a ferrous tetrapyrrole which differs from heme only in having an aldehyde group in place of the vinyl group at position 2. But the protein part of the pigment is very different from globin since the molecular weight of chlorocruorin as isolated is in the neighborhood of 2,500,000. It differs from hemoglobin also in having a much lower affinity for oxygen than have most hemoglobins.

The other two pigments have been less completely characterized. Hemocyanin, which is blue in the oxidized form, has an apparently random distribution in the blood of some molluscs and arthropods. It is a copper protein. When the pigment reacts with oxygen it is in a ratio of two atoms of copper to each molecule of the gas. The molecular weights of the hemocyanins are very high, and this again is to be correlated with their occurrence in solution in the body fluids rather than in cells.

Hemerythrin is a rare pigment which occurs only in the cells of sipunculid worms. Almost nothing is known of its chemistry except that its prosthetic

TABLE 9.7. Respiratory Pigments

	Hemoglobins		Chlorocruorin	Hemocyanin	Hemerythrin
Source	Vertebrates	Invertebrates[a]	Marine Polychaete Worms	Arthropods and Molluscs	Sipunculid Worms
Mol. wt. range[b]	67,000	17,000–3,400,000	2,750,000	400,000–10,000,000	66,000
Metal	Fe—0.34%		Fe—1.20%	Cu—1.25%	Fe—1.01%
Prosthetic group	Heme		Ferrous protoporphyrin	—	?
Molecules O_2 per atom metal	1:1		1:1	1:2	1:3
Occurrence	Cells or plasma		Plasma	Plasma	Cells
Colors	Red		Green $\rightleftharpoons$ Red	Blue	Red

SOURCE: Most of the data from T. Svedberg, *Biol. Bull.*, 71, 489 (1936).
[a] The invertebrate hemoglobins have also been called erythrocruorins.
[b] Molecular weights are given in round numbers.

group is not a porphyrin though it does contain iron. The molecular weight of the compound is about 67,000 of which just over 1 per cent is iron, which means that it contains three times as much iron per molecule as does hemoglobin. Since, however, it unites with oxygen in the ratio of three atoms of iron to one molecule of oxygen, each molecule carries the same amount of oxygen as does a molecule of hemoglobin. The known properties of the respiratory pigments are collected in Table 9.7.

TRANSPORT IN PLANTS

Although the transportation systems of plants are apparently less complex than those of animals, much less is known of the actual mechanism by which substances move from one area of the plant to another. Multicellular plants like multicellular animals have to make provision for many cells which are not in immediate contact with essential nutrients or raw materials. Thus the roots, while they do have effective contact with the salt solutions of the soil, must be furnished with organic foodstuffs. The leaf cells, on the other hand, synthesize their own organic foods from carbon dioxide and water, but in order to build such compounds as phospholipids and proteins must acquire from the soil the nitrogen, phosphorus, and sulfur which occur there in inorganic ions.

Absorption of Water

The root hairs, each of which consists of a single surface cell with a fine, threadlike extension, are formed just behind growing root apices and usually occupy only a few centimeters of root. As the root grows through the soil, the old hairs die and are replaced by others nearer the tip, so that the root progressively draws upon new layers of soil. Here the root hairs are in close contact with the soil water which holds in solution not only inorganic ions but also some oxygen and perhaps small amounts of carbon dioxide in the form of carbonates. The solute concentration in ordinary agricultural soils is low, so that the osmotic pressure is usually less than an atmosphere. In the root hairs, on the other hand, the osmotic pressure may be 5 atmospheres or more. This osmotic gradient is undoubtedly one factor in the movement of solution into the root cells.

There is abundant evidence, however, that the process is not simply a passive response to osmotic differences. For example, when carrot root tissue is immersed in isosmotic solutions of sucrose, calcium chloride, and potassium sulfate, considerably less water is absorbed from the calcium chloride solution than from the others. What this undoubtedly means is that the flow of water and solutes into plants is an active process, meticulously controlled by the cells themselves. Only in this way can the selective absorption found in all types of living cells be accounted for. The fact that water absorption is reduced when the respiration of root cells is curtailed by poor aeration of the soil certainly points toward some such explanation. Lack of oxygen inhibits the exergonic reactions in the cell and so limits the amount of energy at its disposal for carrying out all sorts of work, whether osmotic work or the lifting of water into the leaves.

Ascent of Water and Solutes

As a result then of factors which still need to be clarified, a dilute aqueous solution enters the root hairs from the soil and passes through the living root cells into the xylem tissue. This is made up predominantly of dead cells, some of which are joined end to end to form the long vessels known as *tracheae*. Other cells, the *tracheids*, have pitted walls through which water passes from cell to cell. If a well-watered plant is cut off just above the soil, liquid often exudes for some time from the cut surface, showing that a pressure has developed which tends to force water from the root cells into the xylem. This is known as *root pressure*, and it is believed to result in part from the osmotic gradient between the root cells and the more concentrated solution in the xylem tissue.

The aqueous solution which enters the xylem in the roots is carried upward to the leaves where the salts are used and most of the water evaporates. This *transpiration stream* may rise several hundred feet, moving at a rate which is too rapid to be entirely dependent on osmosis, and reaching heights too great to be accounted for by capillarity or by root pressure. Here again energy is undoubtedly being used by the cell to bring about this essential movement of water and solutes. As water evaporates from the leaf surface, the salt concentration of the remaining solution increases. The resulting elevation of osmotic pressure in the leaf cells tends to draw water out of the upper ends of the xylem columns.

Transport of Photosynthetic Products

Of the compounds formed during photosynthesis only a small fraction is needed to maintain the leaf tissue itself. The greater part of this material is translocated either to actively growing parts of the plant where it is used immediately in building or nourishing tissue, or to places where it is stored for future use. This movement of nutrients away from the leaves takes place through the phloem. Here the actual conducting tissue consists largely of *sieve cells* which, with perforated end walls, form a continuous conducting system from the living cells of the leaves to the roots, to the apices of growing shoots, and to the varied places of storage in the plant. Through the phloem are transported not only soluble sugars but probably also various other small molecules such as amino acids and organic phosphates. These compounds may be oxidized or they may be used synthetically by the cells to which they are carried. If they are to be stored, they are transformed into large or otherwise insoluble molecules and stored as starch or protein or fat.

In plants other than annuals the process of translocation just outlined is reversed in the spring. Starch or protein reserves are hydrolyzed to yield small soluble molecules and these move, again through the phloem cells, but now often in the opposite direction, to the growing parts of the plant. Here they furnish substrates for oxidation and for synthesis until photosynthesis begins.

There is in plants no need for an elaborate system of oxygen transport, for the energy requirements of most plant cells are low compared with the requirements of many cells. A large part of the living tissue of the plant consists of thin, porous leaves the cells of which are in direct contact with air through the stomata, and the oxygen needs of other cells are adequately met by the small amounts of oxygen dissolved in soil water, or by simple gas diffusion into the intercellular spaces.

SUGGESTIONS FOR FURTHER READING

Any good modern textbook of physiology or plant physiology would be helpful in studying the material in this chapter.

Respiratory Pigments

Conant, J. B., *et al.*, The prosthetic group of limulus hemocyanin, *J. Biol. Chem.*, *107*, 755 (1934).

Fox, H. M., On chlorocruorin and haemoglobin, *Proc. Roy. Soc. (London)*, *B136*, 378 (1949–1950).

Granick, S., The structural and functional relationships between heme and chlorophyll, *The Harvey Lectures*, *44*, 220 (1948–1949).

Haurowitz, F., and R. L. Hardin, Respiratory proteins, in *The Proteins*, H. Neurath and K. Bailey (eds.), Academic, New York, 1954.

Keilin, D., and Y. L. Wang, Hemoglobin in the root nodules of leguminous plants, *Nature*, *155*, 227 (1945).

Klotz, I. M., and T. A. Klotz, Oxygen-carrying proteins: A comparison of the oxygenation reaction in hemocyanin and hemerythrin with that in hemoglobin, *Science*, *121*, 477 (1955).

Plasma Proteins

Krebs, H. A., Chemical composition of blood plasma and serum, *Ann. Rev. Biochem.*, *19*, 409 (1950).

Putnam, F. W. (ed.), *The Plasma Proteins*, 2 vols., Academic, New York, 1960.

Plant Transport

Kursanov, A. L., Transport of organic substances in plants, *Endeavor*, *20*, 19 (1961).

The fundamental problem of biology, viewed as the science of
living things, is undoubtedly that of assimilation and growth.

W. P. D. WIGHTMAN: *The Growth of Scientific Ideas* (1951)

Digestion and absorption 10

NEARLY ALL LIVING ORGANISMS carry on digestive processes of greater or less complexity. This is enforced by the fact that most foodstuffs are ingested or stored in the form of large, insoluble molecules. Proteins and polysaccharides must be hydrolyzed to simpler compounds in order that they may pass through cell membranes for transportation and use. Even the comparatively simple fats are not absorbed until at least part of them have been hydrolyzed. Furthermore, although the heterotrophic organisms require some degree of complexity in their foodstuffs, the prescribed substrates for cellular oxidation and synthesis are not proteins and polysaccharides but simple monosaccharides, amino acids, fatty acids, and similar small molecules. Therefore for the most part the digested foodstuffs are absorbed and transported in these forms.

In plants the digestive demands are relatively simple. Yet plants elaborate and presumably use many enzymes which are entirely analogous to the animal proteases, carbohydrases, and lipases. Since excess carbohydrate is stored in the plant largely as starch, even actively growing green plants must be able to digest this compound when it is mobilized for use. There is an even clearer case for digestion in the seeds. Until they reach the light and begin to photosynthesize for themselves, young seedlings are entirely dependent on the foodstuffs stored for their use in the seeds. These include proteins which are needed for synthesis of cell proteins, and varying mixtures of oil and starch. Very little is known about the actual course of plant digestion, but the seeds and seedlings contain the enzymes necessary for digestion of

369

all three types of compounds. In those seeds which store large amounts of oil the lipases are especially abundant; where starch is the chief reserve foodstuff the amylases predominate.

Animal digestion, as was noted in Chapter 3, may be extracellular or intracellular. The latter is not only characteristic of unicellular organisms which customarily engulf their food and then secrete digestive juices into a food vacuole. This type of digestion is also found in some of the lower multicellular forms, in which the activities of a primitive gut are supplemented by some degree of intracellular digestion. But with the evolution of higher animals the preparation of the foodstuffs for absorption and use became confined to a special set of organs. Obviously the details and the complexity of this digestive system vary from species to species. For example, the compound stomach and the long intestine of the herbivores are especially adapted to their bulky diet and are not found in carnivorous forms. But on the whole the digestive process is the same in all kinds of animals, using the same or very similar enzymes and giving rise to the same split products. For obvious reasons, these reactions have been most extensively investigated in man and other mammals, hence the following description of the organs and enzymes concerned with digestion refers specifically to the human system except where otherwise indicated.

THE DIGESTIVE SYSTEM

The relation between the various digestive glands and organs in man was shown in Fig. 3.12 (page 108). With minor variations this arrangement may be considered typical of the vertebrates. While a detailed discussion of the physiology of secretion and enzyme activation is outside the scope of this book, it will perhaps be helpful to outline briefly the various digestive fluids and the enzymes which they furnish.

Saliva

Saliva is secreted into the mouth from numerous glands but chiefly from the submaxillary, sublingual, and parotid glands. It consists of a dilute solution having a solid content of only about 1.0 per cent, of which a high proportion is the slimy glucoprotein, mucin. This substance contributes to one of the main functions of saliva, that of lubricating both the tissues of the mouth and throat and the food mass, which is thus rendered easier to swallow. The only digestive enzyme in saliva was originally named "ptyalin;" it is an *amylase* which acts upon boiled starch over a wide range of pH values. The pH of saliva itself varies between 6.2 and 7.6.

Gastric Juice

In the lining of the stomach two types of cells contribute to the mixed gastric juice. This is a dilute secretion, containing a mucin-like protein, and also hydrochloric acid, some inorganic salts and several enzymes or pro-enzymes. A conspicuous property of the gastric juice is its acidity. The concentration of hydrochloric acid is approximately $0.12N$, corresponding to a pH of about 1.0. After the food enters the stomach, it is slowly mixed by peristaltic motion with this strongly acid solution until the pH of the mass is sufficiently low for the gastric proteinases to act.

The chief enzymes of the gastric juice are two which act on proteins. These are pepsin and rennin, both of which are secreted as zymogens. Pepsinogen becomes the active pepsin when the pH falls to 6 or below. As outlined on page 305 this results from a splitting of peptide bonds in the course of which the molecular weight of the protein drops from 42,500 to 34,500. Both zymogen and enzyme consist of a single peptide chain, and the activation results from the removal of several peptide fractions from the N-terminal end. In Fig. 10.1 are shown crystals of the active and the inactive forms of pepsin. The optimum pH for the enzyme is close to 2, and thus the high acidity of the gastric juice serves both to activate the zymogen and to furnish a medium in which the enzyme can attack the proteins which serve it as substrates. Prorennin is activated by acidity also, but its optimum pH is about 4. Nothing is known of the process of activation.

Rennin brings about the coagulation of milk, apparently by causing a partial hydrolysis of its principal protein, casein. One of the products of this hydrolysis is the soluble "paracasein," which forms an insoluble calcium salt. This precipitate makes up the "curd."

There is some evidence that the gastric juice also contains a lipase, but the acidity of the medium is not favorable for lipolytic action. Certainly no extensive hydrolysis of fats takes place in the stomach.

When the food has been thoroughly mixed with the gastric juice, it forms a thick liquid mass, partly solution, partly emulsion, partly suspension, known as *chyme*. After a time, which varies with the individual and with the nature of the meal, a small portion of the chyme is ejected through the pyloric valve into the upper small intestine or *duodenum*. This process is repeated at more and more frequent intervals until the stomach is empty.

Intestinal Digestive Juices

The acid chyme at first lies in the curve of the duodenum while digestive juices pour upon it; somewhat later, constrictions of the intestinal wall begin to mix food and secretions. These secretions arise in three different places, and consist of *intestinal juice*, secreted by glands in the lining of the intestine;

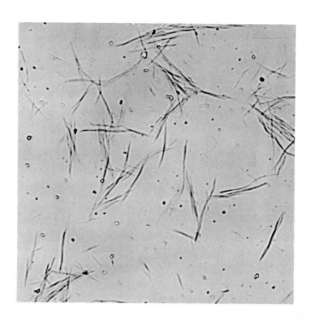

Fig. 10.1. Crystals (above) of pepsinogen (×340) and (below) of pepsin (×90). [From R. M. Herriott, *J. Gen. Physiol.*, **21**, 501 (1937–1938); and R. M. Herriott and J. H. Northrop, *J. Gen. Physiol.*, **18**, 39 (1934–1935).]

pancreatic juice, the external secretion of the pancreas; and *bile*, which is secreted by the liver and stored in the gallbladder until needed. All three of these fluids are alkaline in reaction and ultimately bring about neutralization of the acid chyme.

Intestinal digestive enzymes are secreted throughout the length of the small intestine, but by far the largest volume of the intestinal juice is formed in the duodenum. It contains numerous hydrolytic enzymes, including *maltase*, *sucrase*, *lactase*, and *amylase*, several enzymes concerned with the hydrolysis of peptones and proteoses, and others which together bring about the digestion of nucleic acids. *Enterokinase* is the name given to the component of intestinal juice responsible for activation of the proenzyme, trypsinogen, which is secreted as the inactive proenzyme in pancreatic juice.

Opening into the duodenum just below the pyloric valve is a duct formed by the fusing of two separate ducts from gallbladder and pancreas (see Fig. 3.12). Through this passage there is poured over the food mass lying in the duodenum a mixture of bile and pancreatic juice. The latter contains an amylase, known in the past as "amylopsin;" a lipase, originally called "steapsin," and several different zymogens concerned with protein digestion. One of these, trypsinogen, is activated when it comes in contact with the protein-splitting enzyme of the intestinal juice, enterokinase. This is one of the activations which were referred to in Chapter 7. The active site shown in Fig. 7.10 on page 313 was in some way freed or unmasked by removal of the hexapeptide which had previously been attached to the isoleucine residue of the active site.

Activation of chymotrypsinogen is more complicated. It is brought about by the newly generated trypsin, it includes rupture of nine peptide bonds, and it gives rise to a number of different activated enzymes known as α-, β-, γ-, δ-, ϵ-, and π-chymotrypsins. Figure 10.2 suggests a probable structure for the commonly isolated pancreatic chymotrypsinogen A, and gives structures for three of the active enzymes. None of these is actually proved, but they take account of the available data and may be taken as highly probable. The numbers of course indicate the presence of amino acid residues which are not specified.

Two different procarboxypeptidases are also activated by trypsin. One of these was the enzyme referred to on page 305 which in the course of activation loses two-thirds of its molecule. When all these proenzymes are being acted upon in the gut the various activations are mutually interdependent. When the enterokinase concentration becomes high enough to begin activation of trypsinogen the whole process moves with gradually increasing speed as the newly formed trypsin not only acts upon chymotrypsinogen and the pro-carboxypeptidases, but also acts autocatalytically to hasten the activation of more trypsinogen. Figures 10.3 and 10.4 show crystals of the two active proteinases.

Bile has already been discussed in connection with the destruction of hemoglobin (see page 353). Mammalian bile contains in addition to the pigments, sodium salts of the two bile acids, *taurocholic acid* and *glycocholic acid*. These are known as the bile salts, and have the property of lowering markedly the surface tension between water and oils. This facilitates the formation from fats of a fine emulsion, which in turn provides a very large

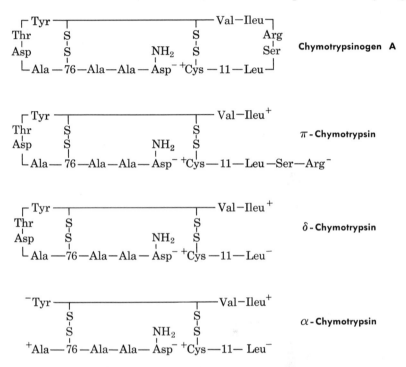

Fig. 10.2. Possible structures of chymotrypsins. It should be noted that a consequence of writing the structure in a cyclic form is that the top line, contrary to the usual convention, has the N-terminal end on the right. [From M. Dixon and E. C. Webb, *Enzymes*, Longmans Green, London, 1958. Revised by Dr. Dixon.]

surface on which the lipases can act. Furthermore, the presence of these salts causes fatty acids and various otherwise insoluble steroids to go into solution, thus furthering their absorption from the intestine.

The bile acids are conjugated compounds which are hydrolyzed by heating in acid solution. Glycocholic acid yields glycine and a compound related to the sterols which is known as *cholic acid*; taurocholic acid gives rise to the same cholic acid and to the amino sulfonic acid, taurine, $HO_3S \cdot CH_2CH_2NH_2$. The formulas of the bile acids show the close relationship of cholic acid to cholesterol.

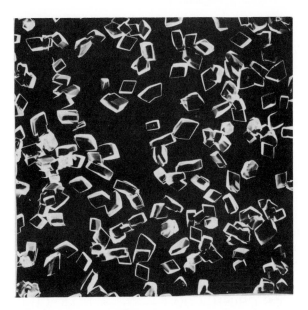

Fig. 10.3. Crystals of chymotrypsin (×120). [From M. Kunitz and J. H. Northrop, *J. Gen. Physiol.*, **18**, 446 (1934–1935).]

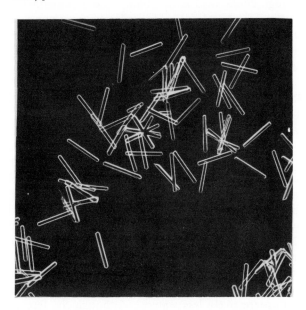

Fig. 10.4. Crystalline trypsin (×202). [From M. Kunitz and J. H. Northrop, *J. Gen. Physiol.*, **19**, 994 (1935–1936)].

Glycocholic acid

Taurocholic acid

Cholic acid is synthesized in the liver from cholesterol. Glycine is usually available from protein digestion, and in any case is one of the amino acids which can be synthesized by living cells. Taurine arises from cysteine. The experimental evidence for this was obtained in an experiment in which methionine containing radioactive sulfur was administered to animals. Subsequent analysis of the tissues discovered radioactivity in taurine as well as in the more closely related cystine and cysteine.

$$SH \cdot CH_2CH(NH_2)COOH \xrightarrow[\text{decarboxylation}]{\text{Oxidation and}} HO_3S \cdot CH_2CH_2NH_2 + CO_2$$

Cysteine   **Taurine**

Although cholic acid is the main steroid component of mammalian bile acids, other closely related acids are known to occur conjugated with taurine or glycine. These acids, like cholic acid, are all hydroxy derivatives of the 24-carbon cholanic acid and differ from cholic acid in the number or positions of the hydroxyl groups. Several of these compounds have been found in small amounts in human bile while others seem to be confined to small groups of related species. A few of the more common acids are listed in Table 10.1.

After being thoroughly mixed with the bile and with the digestive juices of the intestinal tract, the food mass moves slowly along the small intestine. In its passage it meets more enzymes secreted by the mucosa, and these join those already present in splitting the foodstuffs into small soluble molecules. In the ruminants there is an interesting provision for making cellulose available as a foodstuff, though the animals themselves elaborate no cellulose-splitting enzymes. Some of the hordes of bacteria which inhabit the long gut degrade the cellulose to compounds which can be utilized by the host, thus affording an excellent example of the beneficent cooperation of two organisms which is known as *symbiosis*.

In the large intestine there are few if any new enzymes. Some mucus is secreted, but much water is absorbed, so that the contents of the colon become progressively less watery. Although the feces do finally contain a certain amount of undigested food, this makes up far less of the total mass than is commonly supposed. They consist largely of residues from the digestive fluids, together with excretory sterols and pigments secreted in the bile, to which is added a staggering number of bacteria, living and dead. The latter may provide as much as one-third of the total dry weight of the feces!

After this brief examination of the topography of the digestive tract, the rest of this chapter will be devoted to a summary of the course of digestion and absorption of the different classes of foodstuffs. It is most convenient

TABLE 10.1. Steroid Components of Bile Acids in Various Species

Acid	Formula	Position of Hydroxyl Groups	Occurrence
Cholic acid	$C_{24}H_{40}O_5$	3, 7, 12	Man, kangaroo, monkey, mouse, whale, dog, fox, cat, lion, otter, walrus, horse, etc. Many fish and reptiles
Deoxycholic acid	$C_{24}H_{40}O_4$	3, 12	Many vertebrates
Hyodeoxycholic acid (Gr. *hyo-*, swine)	$C_{24}H_{40}O_4$	3, 6	Hog
Chenodeoxycholic acid (Gr. *cheno-*, goose)	$C_{24}H_{40}O_4$	3, 7	Many vertebrates including fish
Lithocholic acid	$C_{24}H_{40}O_3$	3	Man, ox, rabbit
Pythocholic acid	$C_{24}H_{40}O_5$	3, 12 and 16	Python and other members of its species

to treat each group separately, and within the group to discuss separately the action of individual enzymes. But it must be emphasized that digestion of all the foods goes forward at once except when one enzyme can act only upon the product of another's activity.

Figure 10.5 shows diagrammatically the relation of the blood circulatory paths to the organs of the body and indicates also the course of the main lymphatic ducts. It will be remembered that the lymph system begins in the tissues as blind tubes which fuse to form larger and larger vessels and finally empty their contents into the blood stream. The lymph capillaries in the intestinal mucosa are known as *lacteals*, one of which is found in each of the thousands of tiny villi which jut into the lumen of the gut. Figure 10.6 shows the relation of the blood capillaries of a villus to the central lacteal with its closed end. When the food molecules are ready for absorption they diffuse into the villi, entering either the blood capillaries or the lacteals. Those which enter the blood are carried directly to the liver by way of the portal vein.

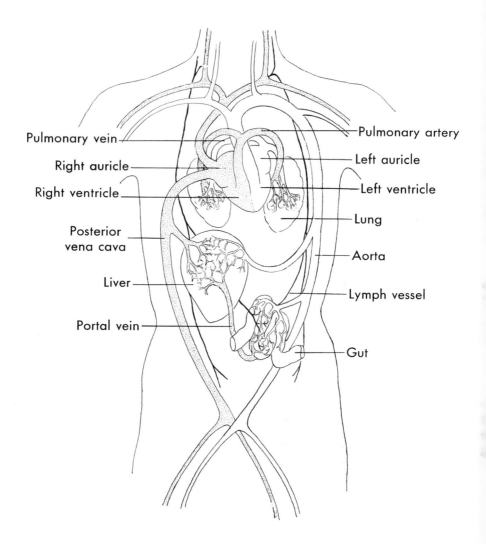

Pulmonary vein

Right auricle

Right ventricle

Posterior
vena cava

Liver

Portal vein

Pulmonary artery

Left auricle

Left ventricle

Lung

Aorta

Lymph vessel

Gut

Fig. 10.5. Diagram of the blood circulatory system and of the main lymph vessels. The latter are represented by the solid black lines which originate in the tissues and empty finally into the right and left subclavian veins.

Those which enter the lacteals move much more slowly through the lymphatics and are finally transferred to the general or systemic circulation by way of the main thoracic duct. Thus the liver has first call upon any molecules

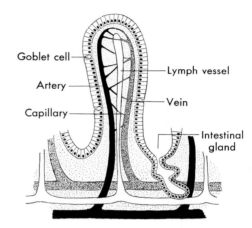

Goblet cell

Artery

Capillary

Lymph vessel

Vein

Intestinal gland

Fig. 10.6. Diagram of a villus, showing the blood capillaries and the single lacteal or lymph vessel.

which enter the capillaries, but those which enter the lacteals reach the liver only indirectly and slowly.

DIGESTION AND ABSORPTION OF PROTEINS

The Protein-Splitting Enzymes

In the early years it was believed that two distinct types of enzymes collaborate to bring about the complete hydrolysis of proteins. Pepsin, trypsin, and chymotrypsin represent the group once thought to have the unique ability to attack native protein molecules and to degrade them to proteoses and peptones. The further hydrolysis of these derived proteins, or of the polypeptides derived from them, was supposed to be the function of a single enzyme, called erepsin, found in the intestinal secretion. When later it became evident that several enzymes were involved in the later stages of protein digestion, these were referred to collectively as "erepsins."

A radical revision of this old classification was made necessary by the work of Bergmann and his collaborators. Reference has already been made to the Bergmann method for protecting amino groups, which made possible for the first time the synthesis of a wide variety of peptides (see page 203). With these synthetic substrates available, Bergmann addressed himself to the problem of the specific requirements of the various protein-splitting enzymes. From his work has come not only an understanding of the specificities of the individual enzymes but also a completely new classification of the enzymes themselves.

Exopeptidases

It is now clear that certain of the digestive proteases attack only those peptide bonds which hold a terminal acid. If such an enzyme splits an amino acid from that end of the polypeptide chain which has a free carboxyl group, it is known as a *carboxypeptidase*; if it frees from the other end of the chain an acid whose carboxyl group is involved in linkage, but whose amino group is free, it is called an *aminopeptidase*. These enzymes are known collectively as *exopeptidases*, since they attack only external bonds, and they include all those agents originally designated as erepsins. At one time it was believed that when a polypeptide chain had been degraded to the dipeptide stage a special enzyme concerned itself with the final hydrolysis. This is now somewhat uncertain. It seems more likely from what is known of the specificity of proteolytic enzymes in general that there exist a great number of exopeptidases, each adapted to hydrolysis of bonds between more or less rigidly specified amino acids. Requirements which have to do with that part of the amino acid which is not involved directly in peptide bonds, Bergmann calls "side group specificity." If all the demands of a particular enzyme are fulfilled, it can probably free a particular terminal acid, whether it is attached to a polypeptide or a dipeptide.

Endopeptidases

Pepsin, trypsin, and chymotrypsin differ from the exopeptidases in that they are capable of attacking peptide bonds which are centrally located in the protein molecule. Bergmann classifies these enzymes as *endopeptidases*. Their positional requirements are extremely specific, including both backbone and side chain specificities. Pepsin cannot act if either of the two acids involved in the peptide bond has a free amino group. Trypsin requires such a free group. Pepsin and chymotrypsin attack only bonds which bind an aromatic acid in the chain. For pepsin to act, the aromatic acid must be the one which furnishes the —NH— of the peptide bond; for chymotrypsin the aromatic acid must supply the peptide carboxyl. In the formula below are indicated the points at which pepsin, trypsin, and chymotrypsin might attack a protein, setting free the central tyrosine and lysine molecules. As the diagram shows, for trypsin to act, the bond must be formed through the carboxyl group of one of the basic acids, arginine or lysine. Bergmann's work has shown that the original classification, which limited these enzymes to action upon the intact protein molecule, has no basis in fact. Each will attack any bond which meets its specifications, whether it occurs in a protein or in a much smaller molecule. The property which distinguishes this group is the ability to attack bonds other than terminal ones.

Digestion of Proteins

In the stomach pepsin begins the hydrolysis of proteins as soon as the required acidity is reached. This process gives rise to polypeptides of different molecular weights, depending upon where the aromatic acids appear in the chain. Peptic digestion continues as long as food remains in the stomach, and probably goes on locally for varying lengths of time in the upper intestine. The neutralization of the acid chyme is a slow process, and even after peristalsis has begun, there are undoubtedly many places in the food mass in which the acidity is sufficiently high for pepsin to act.

Wherever the acidity of the chyme is neutralized, or nearly so, by the alkaline fluids in the upper intestine, trypsin and chymotrypsin take up the hydrolysis of internal bonds. Simultaneously the various exopeptidases of the pancreatic and intestinal fluids are at work, splitting terminal amino acids from the peptide chains. Ultimately all these overlapping hydrolyses result in the complete degradation of the food proteins to a mixture of amino acids. See Table 10.2 for a summary of the digestive enzymes which act on proteins.

Absorption of Proteins

Absorption, except for a very few substances, begins in the duodenum and is largely confined to the small intestine. When the food mass has been acted upon by the digestive juices of pancreas and intestine, the proteins have been reduced to a mixture of peptones and smaller peptides with some free amino acids. Since all of these are water-soluble, there is no obvious reason why they should not all diffuse through the capillary walls and thus enter the portal circulation. But, though there have been some apparent exceptions, the weight of evidence points to the conclusion that proteins are completely hydrolyzed to amino acids before being absorbed. In the early stages of digestion the concentration of peptones and peptides in the intestine is high, but there is no satisfactory evidence that such products pass into the blood stream. During this same time the concentration of amino acids in the blood rises steadily for two and a half to three hours, then gradually falls to the preabsorptive level. This rise in amino acid concentration in the blood runs

TABLE 10.2. Enzymes Concerned in Protein Digestion

Substance Secreted	Source	Activating Agent	Active Enzyme	Substrate	Activity Range (pH)	Product
Pepsinogen	Gastric juice	Hydrogen ion	Pepsin	Internal peptide bonds	Varies with substrate 1.5–2.5	Polypeptides
Prorennin	Gastric juice	Hydrogen ion	Rennin	Casein	4.0–6.0	Caseinogen
Trypsinogen	Pancreatic juice	Enterokinase	Trypsin	Internal peptide bonds	7.8	Polypeptides
Chymotrypsinogen	Pancreatic juice	Trypsin	Chymotrypsin	Internal peptide bonds	7.6	Polypeptides
	Intestinal juice		Amino-peptidases	Terminal peptide bonds		Terminal amino acids
	Pancreatic juice		Carboxy-peptidases	Terminal peptide bonds		Terminal amino acids

parallel with a corresponding loss of nitrogen from the gut. As early as 1913 Abel[1] attempted to obtain direct evidence on this point by an experimental method which he named *vividiffusion*. The arterial blood of a living anesthetized animal was deflected through a series of collodion tubes immersed in saline, before being returned to the animal's own system by way of a vein. Among the substances which diffused into the surrounding saline solution several amino acids were identified, but no more complex nitrogenous molecules were found. A further strong argument against the absorption of peptones is the fact that direct injection of such a mixture into the blood stream gives rise to "peptone shock," a reaction which is absent during normal absorption of a protein meal.

More recently, making use of new micro methods for the quantitative estimation of amino acids, this whole question has been reexamined. Dogs were fed various kinds of proteins, and the amino acid content of both portal and systemic blood was followed. The amino acid concentration was found to increase in the portal blood even more rapidly than in the general circulation, as would be expected if the acids were pouring into the capillaries of the villi. There were found also very slight increases in the concentration of "bound amino nitrogen" in the blood. That is, the number of free amino groups in the serum increased slightly after hydrolysis, as would happen if there were present a small concentration of peptides. However, it was found that this same rise in bound amino nitrogen also followed ingestion of glutamic acid alone. This points to the possibility that the compounds involved arise, not from absorption at all, but from tissue breakdown. In any case, "the results indicate that at most a minor part of the protein was absorbed in peptide form." In this connection it should be noted that this process of absorption is not at all a passive one. This is shown by the fact that the L-amino acids, that is the natural isomers, are absorbed more rapidly than their D isomers, indicating the existence of that mechanism for active transport to which reference has so often been made.

As indicated in the diagram on page 378, the absorbed amino acids are carried directly to the liver via the portal vein. Their fate in this organ and elsewhere in the body is considered in Chapter 13.

DIGESTION AND ABSORPTION OF FATS

Although a lipase is present in gastric juice, the acidity of the stomach makes it unlikely that there is any gastric digestion of fats in the adult.

---

[1] Dr. John Jacob Abel (1857–1938) was one of the brilliant group of pioneers who contributed so significantly to the early years of the Johns Hopkins Medical College. It was in his laboratory that adrenaline was first isolated and insulin first crystallized. When he retired in 1932 as Professor of Pharmacology, a special department was created in which he continued his scientific investigations until very shortly before his death.

However, during the time that the food mass remains in the stomach the churning motions by which it is mixed with the gastric secretions probably begin the emulsification of fats. Then in the intestine emulsification is greatly facilitated by the presence of the bile salts. Here also the acidity of the chyme is slowly neutralized so that the lipases of the pancreatic and intestinal juices can act. Under these conditions the fats are hydrolyzed, though not completely. It has recently been estimated that approximately 40 per cent of the triglycerides are completely hydrolyzed, and the remaining 60 per cent are partially hydrolyzed to yield a mixture of mono- and diglycerides.

Fat Absorption

Fat absorption has been a puzzling phenomenon because of the fact that although the enzymes for fat hydrolysis were present in the intestine, there was no evidence that free fatty acids or glycerol found their way into the blood stream. Over the years many different theories have been advanced to account for this apparent discrepancy, but only recently has it become possible to trace the fate of the hydrolyzed fragments with any certainty. These fragments, accompanied perhaps by sterols and various other fatty substances, are absorbed into the epithelial cells of the intestinal mucosa where they are resynthesized into triglycerides. These triglycerides, with small amounts of other lipids then associate with protein to form the *chylomicrons*. These lipoprotein macromolecules are then extruded into the lacteals and are carried in the lymph until they are emptied into the blood stream. It is these relatively insoluble particles which give to serum from blood drawn soon after a fatty meal its milky appearance. They are normally removed from the blood quite rapidly, and isotopic labels indicate that much of the fat goes to the liver, the muscles, and the adipose tissues. It is now believed that when some of this is later mobilized to serve as an oxidative substrate for the cells it is transported not as free lipid, but as a lipoprotein complex. In the chylomicrons the major lipid is triglycerides, but other serum lipoproteins include higher percentages of sterols and compound lipids.

Role of the bile salts

The bile salts in the course of a short journey through part of the gut have several functions. Their emulsifying action certainly facilitates the digestion of fats and may well play a part in the absorption of some undigested ones. They also exert what is known as a *hydrotropic* effect on free fatty acids and sterols, causing these substances, normally insoluble in water, to dissolve freely in an aqueous solution of bile salts. This effect depends upon the formation of soluble molecular complexes made up of fatty acid and bile salt in varying ratios. In this form the acids are able to cross cell membranes readily. Those bile salts which are not removed from the intestine in this way are reabsorbed into the circulation and carried back to the liver. Here they are again secreted in the bile and thus launched upon another cycle of activity.

DIGESTION AND ABSORPTION OF CARBOHYDRATES

Compared with fats and proteins, the fate of the carbohydrates in digestion is a simple, straightforward one. They are subjected to a series of hydrolytic enzymes beginning with the amylase of the saliva which acts upon boiled but not upon raw starch. The common food polysaccharides, amylose and amylopectin, are degraded by various enzymes called amylases, some of which are endo- and other exoamylases. All split glycosidic links, but the one called α-amylase attacks only centrally located links while others act at the non-reducing end of chains and split out successive maltose units. This goes on until a branching point is reached, where amylo-1,6-α-glucosidases open the $1 \rightarrow 6$ links and make it possible for an exoamylase to reach a new nonreducing end. Enzymes are known which attack a variety of other glycosidic links, such as those in which the monose unit is another sugar than glucose, and those in which the link is a $1 \rightarrow 2$ or a $1 \rightarrow 3$ link. Special enzymes are present in digestive juices for hydrolysis of maltose, sucrose, and lactose, so that at the end glucose, fructose, and galactose, constitute the major part of the absorbed carbohydrate, to which must be added varying small amounts of pentoses from digestion of nucleic acids. There is no evidence that the disaccharides, soluble though they are, can be absorbed without hydrolysis. In fact if a disaccharide is injected into a vein, it is promptly excreted in the urine, showing that it is of no use to the cells in that form.

Beyond the fact that disaccharides do not diffuse into the blood, there is further excellent evidence that the passage of carbohydrates into the portal circulation is not simply a passive process, governed by the laws of diffusion. For example, it has been found that hexoses in general are absorbed more rapidly than pentoses, though the smaller size of the pentose molecule would lead to just the opposite expectation. Furthermore, the different hexoses are themselves absorbed at widely different rates. In one experiment Cori showed that if the rate at which 50 per cent glucose disappears from the gut is taken as 100, the absorption rates for some other hexoses are as follows: D-galactose 110, D-fructose 43, D-mannose 19. But if these same sugars are injected into the peritoneum, from which they diffuse into the blood without passing through the intestinal mucosa, they all enter the blood at the same rate. This is true also if they are enclosed in a loop of dead intestine and allowed to diffuse *in vitro*. Clearly then the normal diffusion into the villi is an active process governed in some way by the living cells of the intestinal mucosa.

It is interesting that there appear to be very definite structural specifications which must be met by a sugar if it is to be absorbed against a concentration gradient, and that entry of sugar into a cell takes place only while sodium ion is moving out. This last phenomenon is sometimes referred to as the "Na^+ pump."

SUMMARY

As a result of the action of the digestive enzymes and of absorptive processes which are still poorly understood, the foodstuffs are transferred to the blood as relatively simple molecules. The proteins appear as α-amino acids and the carbohydrates as hexoses and pentoses. The chylomicrons consist largely of triglycerides which are, however, closely associated in macromolecules with other lipids and with protein. There is a special fat-splitting enzyme known as lipoprotein lipase which hydrolyzes fat which is part of a lipoprotein complex. The chemical reactions which these various compounds undergo in the cells together constitute their metabolism. The remaining chapters of this book will trace, as far as it is known, the story of these many reactions and their relation to the energy needs of the cell.

SUGGESTIONS FOR FURTHER READING

Bergmann, M., Classification of proteolytic enzymes, *Advances in Enzymol.*, *2*, 49 (1942).

Bergmann, M., and J. S. Fruton, Specificity of the proteinases, *Advances in Enzymol.*, *1*, 63 (1941).

Crane, R. K., Intestinal absorption of sugars, *Physiol. Revs.*, *40*, 789 (1960).

Dent, C. E., and J. A. Schilling, Studies on the absorption of proteins, *Biochem. J.*, *44*, 318 (1949).

Dixon, M., and E. C. Webb, *Enzymes*, Longmans, Green, London, 1958.
   This book carries a very good discussion of the specificities of the protein splitting enzymes, and of their activation.

Fredrickson, D. S., and R. S. Gordon, Jr., Transport of fatty acids, *Physiol. Revs.*, *38*, 585 (1958).

Olson, R. E., and J. W. Vester, . . . Control of fat transport in man, *Physiol. Revs.*, *40*, 677 (1960).

In periods of transition, dogmatic treatises are understandably difficult [to write] because a work is obsolete before it is finished and there is the risk of a doctrine's being overthrown before it has been completely formulated.

CLAUDE BERNARD: *Leçons de Physiologie* (1855)

Biological oxidations 11

THE ENERGY WHICH EVERY CELL USES in synthesis and in the performance of work is obtained by oxidation of the metabolites, with water and carbon dioxide as the chief products. As later chapters will show, these products are obtained from carbohydrates, fats, and proteins through a complicated series of metabolic changes of which the oxidations are the final steps. Two facts, however, make it possible to consider the oxidations first, and for the later understanding of the complete sequences it will be useful to have this information available. In the first place, formation of water begins with the removal of hydrogens from a wide variety of metabolites, and the subsequent transformations by which these are carried to their combination with oxygen are very nearly identical, whatever their source. In the second place, it will be found that many metabolic sequences converge upon one key substance, pyruvic acid, and formation of carbon dioxide for all the substances which are so transformed takes place through oxidation of pyruvate. This chapter will then consider these two fundamental procedures, the formation of water in oxidation and the formation of both water and carbon dioxide from pyruvate.

FORMATION OF WATER

Early Theories

In the early years of the present century work with enzymes of plants, of animals, and of bacteria led to the formulation of a number of theories designed to explain oxidation in living tissue as a single, specific "activation." Of these theories two have survived and been incorporated in modified form in modern theories of biological oxidation. The first relates biological oxidation to the activation of oxygen; the other postulates an activation of the hydrogen of the metabolites.

Activation of oxygen

Many of the earliest attempts to explain oxidation assumed a transformation of molecular oxygen into some more active substance such as ozone or atomic oxygen. Beginning about 1920 Warburg elaborated and vigorously defended the rather similar idea that physiological oxidations depend upon a specific catalytic activation of molecular oxygen by iron or an iron compound. His evidence was perforce indirect, but he presented a telling case. He showed that living cells all contain small amounts of iron and that various substances such as hydrogen sulfide and potassium cyanide, known to react with iron or to break up its organic compounds, also inhibit cell respiration. He found that "blood charcoal," that is, the impure carbon made by charring whole blood, catalyzes the oxidation of amino acids, and that its efficacy as a catalyst is roughly proportional to its iron content. Although he did not at first succeed in isolating a "respiratory enzyme" he did carry out a most brilliant study of the properties *in situ* of a substance we now know to be one of a number of enzymes concerned with cellular oxidation (see page 399). His conclusion was that "the respiratory ferment is the sum of all the catalytically active iron compounds" in the cells, and that the function of this catalysis is the activation of oxygen.

Activation of hydrogen

Meantime, in 1912 Wieland[1] had suggested, on the basis of a different set of experiments, an entirely different mechanism for the oxidative reactions of living cells. He noted that palladium black as a catalyst brought about the oxidation of moist acetaldehyde to acetic acid even when air was excluded. Under these circumstances some molecular hydrogen was found trapped in the spongy metal. He found further that this hydrogen did not accumulate when oxygen was present, nor in the presence of other easily reducible substances such as benzoquinone or methylene blue. The reaction of acetaldehyde with oxygen was thus formulated as taking place in two steps. In the first "activated hydrogen" is removed from the hydrated aldehyde by the catalyst; in the second this hydrogen is transferred to oxygen with formation of water.

---

[1] Heinrich Wieland (1877–), Professor at the University of Munich, is an outstanding biochemist whose brilliant work in the first quarter of the twentieth century contributed largely to the rapid growth of our understanding of the mechanism of biological oxidations. He was awarded the Nobel Prize in Chemistry in 1927 and retired in 1953.

$$CH_3CHO \xrightarrow{+H_2O} CH_3 \cdot \overset{\displaystyle OH}{\underset{\displaystyle OH}{CH}} + (Pd) \rightarrow CH_3COOH + (Pd\!-\!H_2)$$

$$(Pd\!-\!H_2) + \tfrac{1}{2}O_2 \rightarrow H_2O + (Pd)$$

According to Wieland the essential catalysis is the activation of hydrogen of the hydrated substrate, which then functions as a *hydrogen donor*. The palladium acts as a *hydrogen carrier* and may pass on its hydrogen to oxygen or to such other *hydrogen acceptors* as benzoquinone or methylene blue. The fact that the hydrogen acceptor could be such unnatural substances led Wieland to the view that the role of oxygen is nonspecific, and that the cell catalysts act only upon hydrogen of the metabolites. The work of Thunberg (see following section) lent support to Wieland's theory of hydrogen activation, but gradually it became apparent that the truth was to be sought not in a decision between but in a synthesis of the two conflicting theories. It was Szent-Györgyi who first suggested that both Warburg and Wieland were right and that to explain cellular oxidations we must assume both an activated hydrogen and an activated oxygen.

The Thunberg Technique

The significance of Wieland's experiments with methylene blue was greatly increased by the discovery that living tissue contains a great number of catalysts capable of transferring hydrogen from various organic compounds to this dyestuff. Methylene blue is a complex heterocyclic compound with several resonance forms, but the formulas given will serve to indicate its reversible oxidation–reduction. Of the two hydrogens involved, one attaches itself to the dye, the other becomes a hydrogen ion.

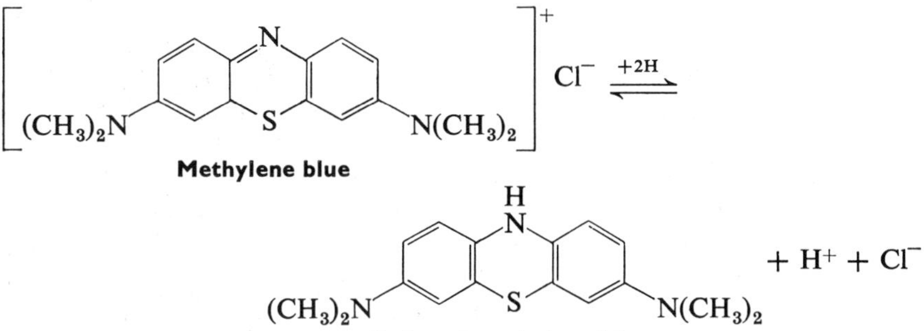

Methylene blue

Reduced methylene blue

$$MB \leftrightharpoons MBH_2$$

The oxidized form of the dye is bright blue, while the reduction product is called a leuco compound, from the Greek *leukos*, meaning white. In the presence of oxygen the leuco form regains its color. It is said to be *autoxidizable*, since this transformation does not require a catalyst.

$$MBH_2 + O_2 \rightarrow MB + H_2O_2$$
Colorless   **Blue**

When methylene blue is added to any one of a wide variety of minced plant or animal tissues, or to suspensions of yeast or bacteria, the dye is rapidly reduced, except perhaps near the surface where autoxidation keeps it in the oxidized form. Since boiled tissue brings about no such bleaching, the reaction must be enzymic. The group of enzymes which thus bring about the transfer of hydrogen to methylene blue are known as *dehydrogenases*. Although methylene blue is not a normal cell constituent it has been convenient to use the color change which it undergoes to detect the presence of hydrogen-activating enzymes. Obviously it was necessary to reason cautiously from such experiments, but in point of fact they have been justified. Normally in the cell other reducible compounds are present which react very much as methylene blue does to accept hydrogens from oxidizable substrate molecules.

In the hands of the Swedish physiologist Torsten Thunberg the methylene blue technique was developed not only to test for the presence of dehydrogenases in tissue, but also to measure their concentration. The reaction is usually carried out in a "Thunberg tube" (Fig. 11.1) so arranged that it can either be evacuated or be flushed out with nitrogen or other inert gas. With autoxidation of the dye thus prevented, it has been found that the length of time required for the bleaching of a given amount of dye under standard conditions is inversely proportional to the amount of dehydrogenase present.

When the minced tissue is washed repeatedly before being tested, it is found to bleach the dye much more slowly. The rate of reduction can then be greatly increased by adding to the system any one of a large number of organic substances, such as lactate or glucose or alcohol. This indicates that the enzymes are intact, but that the washing has removed the soluble cell substrates which previously donated hydrogen to the dye. That an enzyme system is involved becomes clear when the substrates are mixed with methylene blue in the absence of tissue, or in the presence of boiled tissue. Under those conditions no bleaching ensues.

By the use of the Thunberg technique it has been proved that plant and animal tissues as well as yeast and bacteria contain a wide variety of dehydrogenases. As might have been expected, the number of substrates which can be dehydrogenated by bacteria is enormous and includes many for which multicellular organisms have no enzymes. This reflects the wide variety of metabolic types found among bacteria. On the other hand, there are many dehydrogenases which have been found in every type of tissue investigated. Succinate and lactate dehydrogenases, for example, are widely distributed. So also is

triose phosphate dehydrogenase which catalyzes the oxidation of glyceraldehyde phosphate to phosphoglyceric acid. In short, it seems likely that in all
aerobic cells many of the same dehydrogenases function in exactly the same
way to activate the hydrogens of their substrate molecules.

As usually happens when a system of nomenclature grows up with a rapidly
changing branch of science, the naming of the enzymes which activate

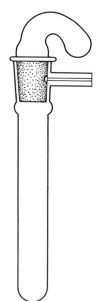

Fig. II.I. A Thunberg vacuum tube. The enzyme source is
placed in the hollow stopper and the methylene blue and substrate in the tube. After evacuation of the tube the enzyme is
tipped in and the time required for decolorization is measured.

hydrogen is in a somewhat confused state. Some of the enzymes are called
dehydrogenases. Some, which were discovered in reactions that are the
reverse of dehydrogenations are known as reductases, and finally a few, which
were named before their nature was clear, are called oxidases. These last
include a group of amino acid "oxidases" which act in exactly the same way
as other dehydrogenases, to remove two hydrogens from a substrate molecule.

Coenzymes

When a sample of tissue is washed exhaustively before being treated with
methylene blue, it may occur that even in the presence of added substrate
the tissue is no longer able to bring about reduction of the dye. This might
mean that the specific enzyme is soluble and has been washed away. But
with most tissues addition of boiled tissue extract restores the catalytic
activity, hence the enzyme protein must still be present. The same loss of
activity results from prolonged dialysis, and again catalytic activity is
restored to the tissue suspension by boiled tissue extract. It has been shown
that the preliminary washing or dialysis separates from the insoluble enzyme

proteins their water-soluble prosthetic groups which are restored to the system when boiled tissue extract is added. Such compounds, essential to the action of an enzyme, are known as coenzymes and are found more or less closely bound to the proteins of the majority of the oxidizing enzymes. It is usually possible by suitable procedures to separate the thermolabile enzyme proteins, or *apoenzymes*, from the thermostable prosthetic groups which serve them as coenzymes. Separation may result for example from a change in *p*H or from selective precipitation with organic solvents. As we have just seen, dialysis sometimes brings about the same result. Once separated, neither the coenzyme nor the protein alone is catalytically active, but usually activity can be restored by putting the two together.

An oxidizing enzyme then consists of a protein part in which resides the substrate specificity, and a coenzyme of low molecular weight which can be reversibly oxidized and reduced. Such a coenzyme is the flavin adenine dinucleotide which was described in Chapter 7 as accepting hydrogen from D-amino acids. The oxidase protein which is needed for that specific oxidation is only one of several oxidizing enzymes which are active in the presence of this particular dinucleotide. Thus the same coenzyme is found to act in conjunction with one protein to oxidize an amino acid, for example, and in the presence of a different protein to oxidize a quite different substrate such as choline. The *holoenzymes* of this group are known as the *flavoproteins*. Another group of dehydrogenases consists of specific proteins combined with somewhat similar prosthetic dinucleotides in which the flavin is replaced by the pyridine derivative, nicotinamide. These enzymes are the *pyridinoproteins*. Still a third class of oxidizing enzymes has as prosthetic group a metalloporphyrin of the heme type. Before attempting to trace the relation of these various oxidation catalysts to each other, it will be necessary to consider separately the chemistry of the three different types of coenzymes.

THE PYRIDINOPROTEIN ENZYMES

The name cozymase was used early in the century to designate the unknown essential factor which was removed from yeast juice by dialysis. This substance was eventually isolated from yeast juice by Hans von Euler of the University of Stockholm. Shortly thereafter Warburg and Christian obtained a similar compound from red blood corpuscles where it takes part in the oxidation of glucose-6-phosphate to 6-phosphogluconic acid. The yeast factor then became "coenzyme I" and the Warburg preparation from blood "coenzyme II." The two compounds proved to be very much alike in chemical composition as both yielded on hydrolysis D-ribose, adenine, nicotinamide, and phosphoric acid. They differed only in their phosphate content, coenzyme II yielding three moles of phosphoric acid per mole, while the yeast factor, coenzyme I, contained only two. The structure of the latter compound proved to be that of a dinucleotide with the two mononucleotides linked through their phosphate groups. Since nicotinamide is a pyridine derivative, and because of the two phosphate groups in the compound, coenzyme I became known as diphosphopyridine nucleotide. This is commonly abbreviated to DPN+, whereas the older name becomes Co I. Coenzyme II (Co II) is then triphosphopyridine nucleotide or TPN+. With the abbreviations, the reduced forms are written CoIH₂ and CoIIH₂, or DPNH and TPNH. When the latter forms are used, the second hydrogens removed from the substrate are written as hydrogen ion, although when the reduced compounds are isolated this hydrogen is attached to the molecules.[2]

The position of the third phosphate group in coenzyme II (TPN+) remained in doubt long after the structure of coenzyme I had been elucidated. It has now been proved that the two molecules are alike except that CoII has a third phosphate group esterified at position 2 of the ribose in the adenosine-5-phosphate of the dinucleotide. In the formula for diphosphopyridine nucleotide the asterisk indicates the point of attachment of the phosphate group in TPN+.

Diphosphopyridine nucleotide
DPN+ or coenzyme I

---

[2] Since this book went to press, the editors of the *Annual Review of Biochemistry* have adopted in the 1961 volume the names and abbreviations for the pyridine coenzymes recommended by the Enzyme Commission of the International Union of Biochemistry. The coenzymes are named *nicotinamide adenine dinucleotide (NAD)* and *nicotinamide adenine dinucleotide phosphate (NADP)*. The reduced forms are designated *NADH₂* and *NADPH₂*. It seems probable that these forms will be adopted by the International Union of Biochemistry and that they will eventually supersede both older designations. Since all three forms will undoubtedly continue to appear in the immediate future, the older forms have been retained in this book, with the new ones occasionally included in parentheses.

The nicotinamide which is the functional part of the two pyridine coenzymes is one of the compounds which are grouped together as the B vitamins. The best-known members of the group are listed on pp. 445–447 with their formulas. Several of them find a use, as does nicotinamide, as the active part of various coenzymes. Indeed this is apparently the reason these compounds, needed in only very small amounts, are essential to the nutrition of many living organisms. The other coenzymes which incorporate vitamins will be taken up later in connection with the enzymes with which they act.

Mechanism of dehydrogenation by pyridine enzymes

Early study of the chemistry of the pyridine coenzymes was facilitated by their having strong absorption bands in the ultraviolet. More recently

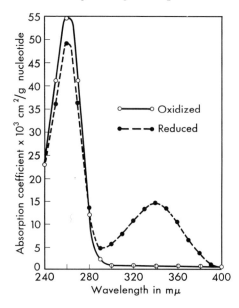

Fig. 11.2. Absorption curves of oxidized and reduced diphosphopyridine nucleotide (*p*H 7.4). [From O. Warburg and W. Christian, *Biochem. Z.*, **287**, 291 (1936).]

Theorell has made use of the fact that reduced coenzyme I (NADH$_2$), but not the oxidized form, fluoresces.

In the oxidized form both pyridine coenzymes show a single absorption band at about 2600 A. When they are reduced, either chemically as with hyposulfite, or enzymatically with a dehydrogenase, a second absorption band appears at 3450 A. Absorption curves for DPN$^+$(NAD) in the oxidized and in the reduced form are shown in Fig. 11.2. Corresponding curves for TPN$^+$(NADP) are almost identical.

The absorption band at 2600 A can be accounted for by the known absorption spectra of the two heterocyclic rings. Therefore when Warburg found that reduction of a simple pyridine derivative caused the appearance of a band at 3600 A he concluded that the reduction of the coenzyme which gives rise to a new band at 3450 A is in reality simply the reduction of the pyridine part of the molecule. For the simple methiodide of nicotinamide he formulated the reduction as follows, two hydrogen atoms yielding to the ring one of the two, and forming in solution a hydrogen ion.

$$\text{(pyridinium methiodide with CONH}_2\text{)} + 2\text{H} \rightleftharpoons \text{(dihydropyridine with CONH}_2\text{)} + \text{H}^+ + \text{I}^-$$

The same reaction is believed to take place when the coenzymes are reduced. In the following formulation R stands for all the dinucleotide except the nicotinamide, the negative charge being associated with one of the phosphate groups in the coenzyme.

$$\text{(oxidized form with CONH}_2,\ \text{R}^-\text{)} + 2\text{H} \rightleftharpoons \text{(reduced form with CONH}_2,\ \text{R}^-\text{)} + \text{H}^+$$

Oxidized coenzyme   **Reduced coenzyme**[3]

The accuracy of Warburg's explanation of the function of the coenzyme has been proved in experiments with alcohol labeled with deuterium. This compound was used as substrate with alcohol dehydrogenase and crystalline diphosphopyridine nucleotide, and the reduced coenzyme was later isolated. The presence of deuterium in the reduced coenzyme proved the actual transfer of hydrogen from substrate to coenzyme, and ruled out the possibility that the hydrogen which attached itself to the coenzyme came from water and not from the substrate at all. The deuterium atoms are indicated by the asterisks.

$$CH_3\overset{*}{C}H_2OH + DPN^+ \xrightarrow[\text{dehydrogenase}]{\text{alcohol}} CH_3\overset{*}{C}HO + H^+ + DPN\overset{*}{H}$$

Oxidized   **Reduced**
coenzyme   **coenzyme**

Recent work is making clear that addition of hydrogen to the pyridine ring is stereospecific, that is, that the hydrogen with a given enzyme goes always to the same side of the ring. Alcohol dehydrogenase and several other dehydrogenases all transfer hydrogen to the same side of the ring, giving what has been designated the α arrangement. With other enzymes the hydrogen goes to the other side of the ring giving a β form. These differences

---

[3] Actually Warburg's original formulations added the hydrogen in the *ortho* position, but as that has since been shown to be incorrect, the hydrogen in the formulas has been put, correctly, in the *para* position.

TABLE 11.1. Some Representative Dehydrogenases

Substrate[a]	Source	Reaction Catalyzed	Coenzyme	Other Required Factors
Alcohol	Liver, yeast, peas	Alcohols → Aldehydes	CoI	Zn^{++}
Alcohol	Bacteria	Alcohols → Aldehydes	CoII	
Choline	Liver	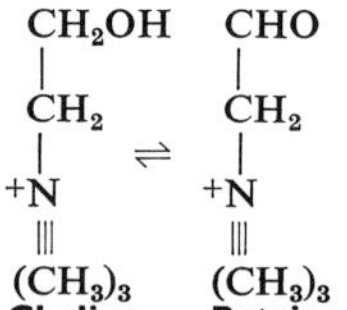 (see structure below)	CoI	
Glucose	Liver	β-D-Glucose $\rightleftharpoons$ D-δ-Gluconolactone	CoI or II	
L-Glutamate	Liver	(see structure below)	CoI or II	Zn^{++}
L-Glutamate	Widely distributed	Amino acid $\rightleftharpoons$ Imino acid	CoI	
L-Glutamate	Yeasts, molds, bacteria	Amino acid $\rightleftharpoons$ Imino acid	CoII	
Hydro-lipoate	Widely distributed	(see structure below)	CoI	

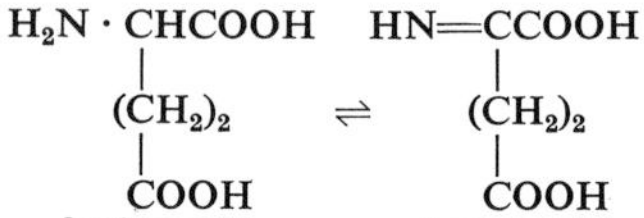

Choline reaction:

$$
\begin{array}{ccc}
CH_2OH & & CHO \\
| & & | \\
CH_2 & & CH_2 \\
| & \rightleftharpoons & | \\
{}^+N & & {}^+N \\
\| & & \| \\
(CH_3)_3 & & (CH_3)_3 \\
\textbf{Choline} & & \textbf{Betaine aldehyde}
\end{array}
$$

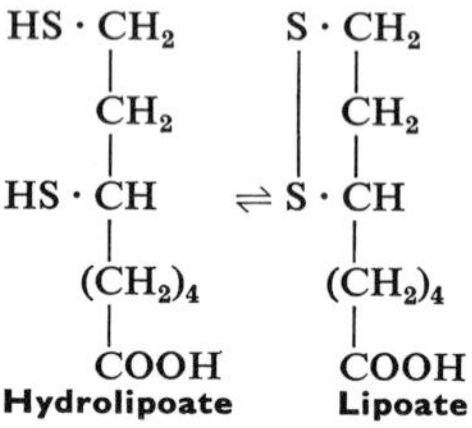

L-Glutamate reaction:

$$
\begin{array}{ccc}
H_2N \cdot CHCOOH & & HN{=}CCOOH \\
| & & | \\
(CH_2)_2 & \rightleftharpoons & (CH_2)_2 \\
| & & | \\
COOH & & COOH \\
\textbf{Amino acid} & & \textbf{Imino acid}
\end{array}
$$

Hydrolipoate reaction:

$$
\begin{array}{ccc}
HS \cdot CH_2 & & S \cdot CH_2 \\
| & & | \\
CH_2 & & CH_2 \\
| & & | \\
HS \cdot CH & \rightleftharpoons & S \cdot CH \\
| & & | \\
(CH_2)_4 & & (CH_2)_4 \\
| & & | \\
COOH & & COOH \\
\textbf{Hydrolipoate} & & \textbf{Lipoate}
\end{array}
$$

[a] The name of the substrate is given so that it also gives the name of the dehydrogenase, although to avoid the use of the negative charge in crowded formulas, the acids have been written with complete carboxyl groups.

are obviously a result of the positions enforced upon the reactants, substrate and coenzyme, when they become attached to the active site on the enzyme.

Although coenzymes I and II both act in conjunction with several different enzymes, they are not usually interchangeable. Those enzymes which use CoI are in general inactive or nearly so in the presence of CoII, and vice versa. The rule about coenzyme specificity is not without exceptions, since a few enzymes can make use of either. This is true, for example, of both glutamate and glucose dehydrogenases. Usually, however, even when an enzyme can use more than one coenzyme, it acts much more rapidly with one.

The importance of the pyridine coenzymes is indicated by the fact that nearly 100 enzymes are known which require one or the other. In Table 11.1 some representative dehydrogenases are listed, with their sources. It will be noted that there are two alcohol dehydrogenases listed, and three glutamate dehydrogenases. This type of apparent duplication means that similar enzymes have been extracted from different types of tissue, and have been

Substrate	Source	Reaction Catalyzed		Coenzyme	Other Required Factors
β-Hydroxy-butyrate	Animal tissues bacteria	CH_3 $\|$ $CHOH$ $\|$ CH_2COOH β-Hydroxybutyrate	$\rightleftharpoons$	CH_3 $\|$ CO $\|$ CH_2COOH Acetoacetate	CoI	
D-Lactate	Animal tissues bacteria	CH_3 $\|$ $CHOH$ $\|$ $COOH$ D-Lactate	$\rightleftharpoons$	CH_3 $\|$ CO $\|$ $COOH$ Pyruvate	CoI	
L-Lactate	Animal tissues	L-Lactate $\rightleftharpoons$ Pyruvate			CoI	Zn^{++}
L-Malate	Animal tissues, plants, bacteria	$COOH$ $\|$ $CHOH$ $\|$ CH_2COOH L-Malate	$\rightleftharpoons$	$COOH$ $\|$ CO $\|$ CH_2COOH Oxaloacetate	CoI	
Phospho-glucose	Widely distributed	Glucose-6-phosphate	$\rightleftharpoons$	Glucono-lactone-6-phosphate	CoII	
Phospho-glycerol	Animal tissues	CH_2OH $\|$ $CHOH$ $\|$ $CH_2O \cdot P$ α-Glycerophosphate	$\rightleftharpoons$	CH_2OH $\|$ CO $\|$ $CH_2O \cdot P$ Dihydroxy-acetone phosphate	CoI	
Phosphogly-ceraldehyde	Green leaves	CHO $\|$ $CHOH$ $\|$ $CH_2O \cdot P$ Glyceraldehyde-3-P		$COOH$ $\|$ $CHOH$ $\|$ $CH_2O \cdot P$ Glyceric acid-3-P	CoII	

shown to be different enough in their properties to indicate that they are separate entities which bring about the same reaction. As a matter of fact, it is incorrect to list as if it were a single substance the "alcohol dehydrogenase" which requires coenzyme I. The enzyme from yeast catalyzes a reaction with an equilibrium point far toward the side of reduction rather than dehydrogenation, while the equilibrium point of the liver enzyme is far to the side of oxidation of alcohol to aldehyde.

It will be remembered that the function of essential metal ions was discussed in Chapter 7, and that Fig. 7.11, on page 314, showed how such an ion can be used to bind enzyme, coenzyme and substrate. The coenzyme for the particular enzyme there represented is $DPN^+(NAD)$ and the enzyme is alcohol dehydrogenase.

The dehydrogenases are named as usual from their substrates. Originally those which acted upon acids were called, for example, lactic dehydrogenase and glutamic dehydrogenase. Many writers still do this, but since acids exist as ions in the physiological pH range it now seems better to refer to lactate or glutamate or malate dehydrogenases.

Work on oxidative mechanisms has been done with mammalian and other animal tissues, with many different types of plant cells and with yeasts and bacteria. Dehydrogenases have been isolated from such different tissues as the very specialized cells of mammalian liver, from green leaves and from many types of unicellular organism. This indicates that transfer of hydrogen from a wide variety of metabolites to a pyridine coenzyme is a fundamental procedure in all aerobic cells.

The reduction potentials for the pyridine coenzymes at pH 7 (E_0') and 25° are -0.320 volt for DPN^+ and -0.324 volt for TPN^+. These will later be compared with similar figures for other respiratory catalysts. In general the oxidized form of a coenzyme will be reduced by substances with lower reduction potentials, and the reduced form will in turn reduce other substances having higher potentials.

Summary

The oxidation of many substrate molecules begins in the presence of a specific dehydrogenase protein with the transfer of hydrogen from a metabolite to a pyridine dinucleotide. This takes place when coenzyme and substrate form a complex at the active site of the enzyme. In order that a molecule of coenzyme may continue to function as a hydrogen acceptor it must be promptly reoxidized by transferring this hydrogen to some other reducible substance. In the artificial systems which include methylene blue, the dye acts as acceptor and is bleached anaerobically to its leuco form. If this type of experiment is carried out aerobically, there is a continuous uptake of oxygen which simulates normal respiration. The reduced methylene blue under these conditions passes on its hydrogen to oxygen and so acts as an intermediate carrier of hydrogen from primary pyridine acceptor to the terminal acceptor, oxygen. Letting TH_2 stand for any oxidizable tissue substance, the process may be represented as taking place in a series of steps:

$$TH_2 + DPN^+ \xrightarrow{\text{dehydro-genase}} T + DPNH + H^+$$

$$DPNH + H^+ + MB \longrightarrow DPN^+ + MBH_2$$

$$MBH_2 + O_2 \longrightarrow MB + H_2O_2$$

In this process both the coenzyme and the dye are repeatedly reduced and then oxidized, each complete cycle leaving them in the oxidized form, ready to accept another pair of hydrogens.

But if a purified dehydrogenase is treated with its substrate in the absence of methylene blue, there is no oxygen uptake. The appearance of the characteristic absorption band at 3450 A proves that the coenzyme has been reduced, but there the reaction stops. This means that the reduced coenzymes are not capable of reacting directly with molecular oxygen. Since tissue slices do take up oxygen, there must be in the intact cell some sort of intermediate carrier which acts as methylene blue does in the artificial system to bridge the gap between the reduced pyridine compound and oxygen. Several such substances have been found among the other groups of oxidizing enzymes. Together they constitute the hydrogen transport system, a sort of bucket brigade in which the pyridine coenzymes usually serve as the first bucket. Of these other intermediate substances, the first to be recognized were those involved in the final stages of the reaction, where activation of oxygen results in formation of water. These are the iron porphyrin enzymes which will be considered in the following section.

The Iron Porphyrin Enzymes

We have already noted that as early as 1920 Warburg was searching for an *Atmungsferment* or respiratory enzyme in which the active agent would be an organic compound of iron. Although he did not isolate such a compound, his early work should be noted at this point because of his fundamental contributions to oxidative theory, and even more because of its brilliant indirect approach to a problem which could not at that time be attacked directly.

Working with enzyme inhibitors, he found that in the dark the respiration (oxygen uptake) of living cells was almost completely abolished by high concentrations of carbon monoxide, and that this inhibition was reversed by light. It was known that carbon monoxide forms complexes, known as metal carbonyls, with many heavy metals including iron, and that these compounds decompose in the light. Furthermore, the iron of hemoglobin was known to react in this way with carbon monoxide. Warburg therefore reasoned that the inhibition of respiration by carbon monoxide resulted from combination of this gas with the iron in a respiratory ferment, and that dissociation of the carbon monoxide complex by light restored the activity of the enzyme.

The effectiveness of light in bringing about reactivation of the oxidizing system proved to depend upon its wavelength. In one experiment illumination of monoxide-poisoned yeast with ultraviolet light resulted in almost no additional oxygen uptake, while blue light (4360 A) brought about a fourfold increase. Since light must be absorbed in order to act upon a compound, this observation indicated that the carbon monoxide complex did not absorb ultraviolet but did absorb blue light. It therefore provided a means of determining the absorption spectrum of a purely hypothetical cell constituent! In Fig. 11.3 the effectiveness of light in reversing the carbon monoxide inhibition of respiration is plotted against its wavelength. On the reasonable assumption that a large reversal of inhibition results from a high absorption of light of that wavelength, this curve then gives the absorption spectrum of the enzyme–carbon monoxide complex. From the point of view of

Warburg's thesis this curve was significant because it proved to resemble so strongly a similar curve obtained with carbon monoxide hemoglobin, in which the carbon monoxide is known to be attached to iron. This similarity was therefore interpreted as evidence that a respiratory enzyme would in all probability prove to be an iron tetrapyrrole compound.

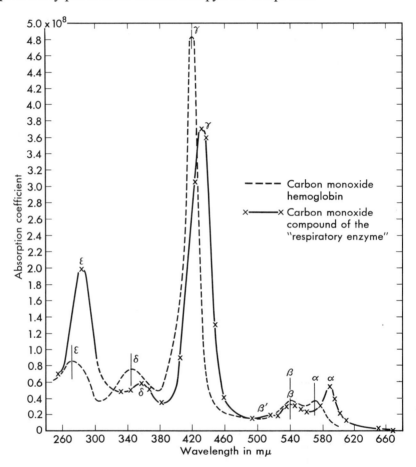

Fig. 11.3. Absorption spectra of carbon monoxide hemoglobin and of the carbon monoxide compound of Warburg's *Atmungsferment*. [From O. Warburg, *Z. Angew. Chem.*, **45**, 1 (1932).]

Discovery of the cytochromes

As early as 1886 it had been reported that a substance present in muscle exhibited four characteristic absorption bands in the visible region. The compound was never isolated and was eventually completely forgotten.

In 1925 Keilin[4] rediscovered this substance, named it "cytochrome" and showed that it was present in every type of aerobic cell or tissue examined. This demonstration is remarkably simple with organisms which do not contain hemoglobin, which also absorbs light in the visible region. For example, a yeast suspension or the thoracic muscles of a honey bee pressed on a micro-

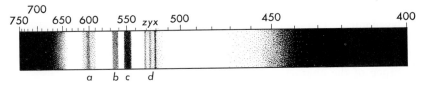

Fig. 11.4. Absorption spectrum of cytochrome in thoracic muscles of a bee. A layer of muscle 0.65 mm thick was examined in a Zeiss microspectroscope. [From D. Keilin, *Proc. Roy. Soc.* (London), **98**, 312 (1925).]

scope slide show readily the four characteristic absorption bands which are represented in Fig. 11.4. However, when oxygen is bubbled through the yeast the bands disappear, to be replaced by a very low, diffuse absorption.

	610 ... 600	a	... 570	b	... 550	c	... 520	d
Bee: wing muscles	6046	a	5665	b	5502	c	5210	d
Dytiscus: wing muscles	6038		5664		5495		5205	
Galleria: wing muscles	6046		5657		5495		5200	
Helix: radula muscles	6035		5650		5495		5200	
Frog: heart muscle	6040		5660		5500		5205	
Guinea pig: heart muscle	6045		5662		5500		5205	
Yeast cells	6035	a	5645	b	5490	c	5190	d

Fig. 11.5. Positions of the four main absorption bands of the cytochromes in various organisms. [From D. Keilin, *Proc. Roy. Soc.* (London), **B98**, 312 (1925).]

If the oxygen is removed by a stream of nitrogen, the four bands reappear. These experiments indicate that the cytochrome can be reversibly oxidized and reduced, and that it is the reduced form to which the sharp absorption bands are due. The positions and relative intensities of these bands differed slightly from tissue to tissue but were remarkably constant for a wide variety of organisms as is indicated in Fig. 11.5. Occasionally one would be absent.

[4] David Keilin, Professor of Biology at Cambridge University until 1952, has been for the past quarter century a distinguished contributor in the field of enzyme chemistry. He is now at the Molteno Institute, Cambridge.

These irregularities proved to be due to the fact that "cytochrome" is really a mixture of several different but very similar components. The four absorption bands represent a summation of two individual bands per component, some of which overlap.

Two simple experiments with respiratory inhibitors clarified the role which the cytochromes play in cellular oxidation. A yeast suspension in which the cytochrome was in the reduced form was treated with potassium cyanide and then oxygenated. The bands of the reduced cytochrome failed to disappear. But if cyanide was added to a suspension in which the pigment was already in the oxidized form an immediate reduction resulted as shown by the appearance of the characteristic bands of reduced cytochrome. These two results indicate that there is in the cells a mechanism for the reduction of oxidized cytochrome which is not influenced by the presence of cyanide, and a second which brings about oxidation of the reduced cytochrome and is inhibited by cyanide. In similar experiments, such narcotic enzyme inhibitors as alcohol or ethyl urethane prevented the reduction of the oxidized form, but did not interfere with the oxidation of reduced cytochrome. Thus cytochrome was shown to take part in an enzymic, cyclical process in the cells, being reduced by hydrogen donors and reoxidized by molecular oxygen. The enzymes responsible for the reduction are inhibited by narcotics but not by cyanide, while the reverse is true of the oxidizing system. This points to a fundamental difference in the catalysts involved and suggests that the one which brings about the reaction with molecular oxygen may contain iron, since it is sensitive to cyanide. Allowing ox. Cy to stand for the oxidized cytochrome and red. Cy to stand for the reduced form, the two reactions in which this compound is involved may be represented:

$$TH_2 + ox.\ Cy \xrightarrow[\text{narcotics}]{\text{inhib. by}} T + red.\ Cy$$

$$red.\ Cy + \tfrac{1}{2}O_2 \xrightarrow[\text{KCN}]{\text{inhib. by}} H_2O + ox.\ Cy$$

Structure of the cytochromes

Keilin recognized the existence of three different components in his preparations, and called them cytochromes *a*, *b* and *c*. Many others have since been identified, and there are now known more than twenty individuals of closely related composition. The only one which yielded readily to extraction and purification was cytochrome *c*, which proved to be a bright red conjugated protein with a prosthetic group closely related to heme. It has the low molecular weight of about 13,000 and one iron porphyrin group per molecule. The porphyrin is firmly linked to the protein through covalent thioether bonds between the reduced vinyl groups at positions 2 and 4 in the heme and two cysteine residues in the protein. Figure 11.6 gives the structure of the porphyrin part of cytochrome *c*, and Fig. 11.7 indicates in two ways the relation of the iron porphyrin to the protein. The heme shown in 11.7(*a*) with its attached peptide, was obtained by subjecting cytochrome *c* to peptic digestion thus removing a large part of the protein, but leaving the porphyrin firmly bound to the fragment shown. Figure 11.7(*b*) is a photograph of a model which was made to show the spatial relation between the flat heme molecule and the part of the protein which is immediately adjacent. The model shows the peptide as a left twisting spiral in which the two sulfhydryl

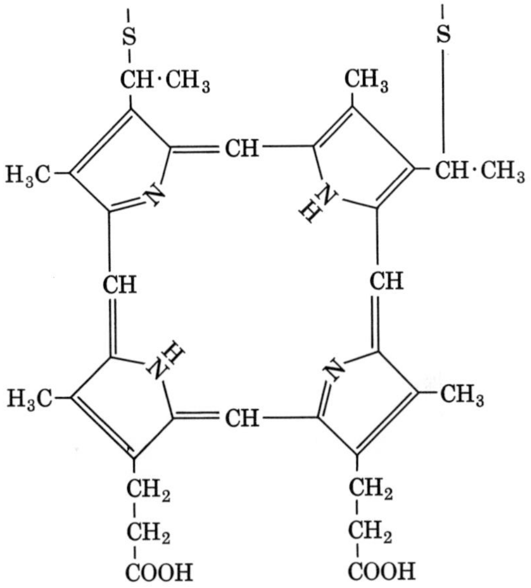

Fig. 11.6. The porphyrin of cyto-chrome *c*. That of the *b* type cytochromes is identical except that vinyl groups, instead of ethyl groups, are at positions 2 and 4. The sulfur atoms are in cysteine residues in the protein to which the cytochrome is bound. Other bonds to the protein are from the central iron atom in the heme, four coordination positions of which are filled by bonds to the four nitrogens, leaving two for binding to the protein.

groups and one imidazole group are in such positions that they easily form links with the porphyrin. Theorell,[5] in whose laboratory the model was made, suggests that in the complete molecule three other such polypeptide helices so surround the heme iron that it is inaccessible to oxygen and hence resistant to autoxidation.

Of the many known cytochromes, none has been as fully characterized as has cytochrome *c*. Many others have been isolated from various sources, partially purified and identified by their activity and by their specific absorption bands. The simple *a*, *b*, and *c* of Keilin's early papers have been joined by c_1 through c_5, b_1 through b_7 or b_8, and a_1 through a_4. There have also been others to which the letters *e*, *f*, *h*, *m*, and *x* were assigned, though most of these have now been given other letters. Among all these related compounds there seem to be three general types, corresponding to the original *a*, *b*, and *c*. They differ either in the structure of the porphyrin or in the way in which the porphyrin is bound to the protein. Both the *b* and the *c* cytochromes have a

---

[5] Professor Hugo Theorell is Head of the Biochemistry Department of the Nobel Institute in Stockholm. He received the Nobel Prize in Medicine in 1955.

1 2 3 4 5 6 7 8 9 10 11 12

Val – Glu – Lys – Cy – Ala – Glu – Cy – His – Thr – Val – Glu – Lys

(4) CH–CH$_3$ (2) CH·CH$_3$

S   S

Fe

(a)

(b)

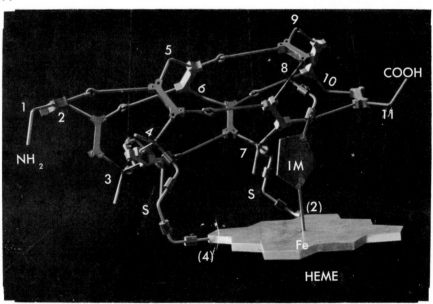

Fig. 11.7. Two representations of the relation between cytochrome *c* and its protein. (*a*) The residue symbols are used to indicate the polypeptide which remains attached to the cytochrome by two cysteine-S-bridges and a histidine-iron link. (*b*) This same polypeptide is shown in a scale model of its helix. The numbers are those of the acids shown in the top illustration and the IM is the imidazole ring of histidine which in the model is seen to be in a position for attachment to iron. The numbers in parentheses are the positions on the porphyrin ring. [From H. Theorell, *Science*, **124**, 467 (1956). Reprinted from *Science* by permission.]

porphyrin part which is essentially a heme, although the vinyl groups are reduced in cytochrome c. These two differ then in the way in which the protein is linked to the prosthetic group. In compounds of the c type the covalent bonds between these units are so firm that when an attempt is made to separate them the porphyrin carries with it, attached through the two thioether bonds, part of the protein chain. In the b compounds, on the other hand, the bonds are weak enough so that the heme can easily be freed without any addendum.

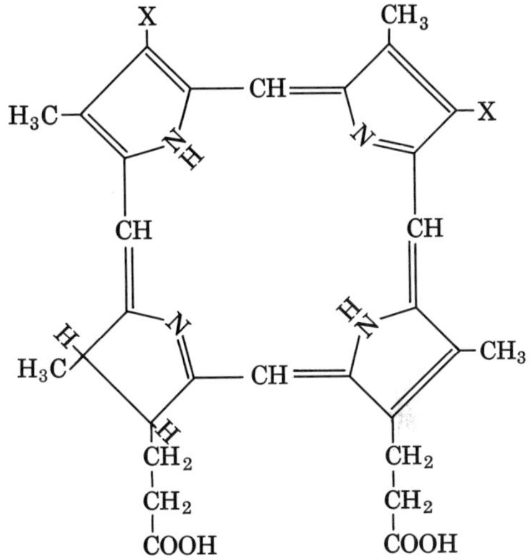

Fig. 11.8. The porphyrin from cytochrome a_2. The X may be vinyl or a combination of hydroxyethyl or ethyl with vinyl. Ring IV is reduced, making the compound a dihydroporphyrin or *chlorin*.

The porphyrins of the a cytochromes differ from those of the other two groups in having a variety of side chains which are not like those of heme. Figure 11.8 gives the structure which has been suggested for the porphyrin of cytochrome a_2, isolated from bacterial sources. Table 11.2 lists some characteristics of the cytochromes, including the reduction potentials, E_0', where they are known. These figures will of course determine the order in which the cytochromes will be reduced, and like similar figures for the pyridine coenzymes are subject to continuous revision.

Oxidation and reduction of the cytochromes

When a cytochrome is oxidized, its iron changes from the ferrous to the ferric condition. The oxidized and reduced modifications are therefore often referred to as ferri- or ferrocytochromes. In their normal activity in the cell, the cytochromes thus differ from hemoglobin, in which the iron remains in the ferrous condition unless it is oxidized chemically.

Purified cytochrome c is readily reduced by mild reducing agents, but the reduced ferrocytochrome cannot be reoxidized by molecular oxygen. Since this same substance in a cell suspension reacts readily with oxygen, there must

TABLE II.2. The Cytochromes

Type	Source	Mol. Wt.	Heme/groups per molecule	E_0'	Comments
a	Widely distributed[a]			+0.29	Always closely associated with a_3
a_1	Bacteria, yeasts				
a_2	Bacteria				Autoxidizable
a_3	Widely distributed				Autoxidizable; is cytochrome c oxidase
a_4	Acetobacter				
b	Widely distributed			+0.077	Involved in nitrate reduction
b_1	Bacteria			+0.25	
b_2[b]	Yeasts	About 150,000		+0.012	Associated with lactate dehydrogenase
b_3	Plants			+0.04	Autoxidizable
b_4	Bacteria				
b_5, also known as m and x	Liver, insects	16,900	1	+0.03	Microsomal cytochrome
b_6	Chloroplasts			−0.06	Autoxidizable; may be concerned with photosynthesis
b_7	Plant mitochondria			−0.03	Autoxidizable
c	Widely distributed	About 13,000	1	+0.25	
$c_1(e)$	Mitochondria of animal and plant cells		5	+0.220	Transfers electrons to c
c_2	Photosynthetic bacteria			+0.34	
c_3	Sulfate-reducing bacteria	About 13,000	2	−0.205	Concerned in sulfate reduction
c_4	Bacteria			+0.30	
c_5	Bacteria			+0.32	
f	Chloroplasts	110,000	2	+0.365	Carrier in photosynthesis?
h	Helix pomatia hepato-pancreas, young roots	18,500	1	+0.02–0.05	

[a] Indicates that it has been found in plants and animals and in some bacteria.
[b] Is also known as lactate dehydrogenase. When crystallized proves to consist of a protein to each molecule of which are attached both a heme and a flavin.

be in the cell some catalyst which mediates the reaction. This catalyst proves to be an enzyme, known as *cytochrome oxidase* which is also an iron pyrrole protein. The cytochrome oxidases are cytochromes of the *a* type, the one from animal tissues being cytochrome a_3 and the one from bacteria a_2.

The cytochrome oxidases are sensitive to cyanide, hydrogen sulfide, and sodium azide. They are, furthermore, inhibited by carbon monoxide and this inhibition is reduced in strong light. These are, of course, the properties of Warburg's *Atmungsferment*. There is in fact much evidence that this enzyme which brings about the oxidation of reduced cytochrome by molecular oxygen is indeed that one which was the object of Warburg's earlier investigations. It is, as he predicted, an iron porphyrin compound, closely related chemically to heme and to the other cytochromes. This is probably the only enzyme for which physical and chemical properties had been determined before there was any certainty that it existed at all! In view of Warburg's identification of oxidation catalysis with the presence of iron, it is of interest that recent very careful measurements indicate that cytochrome oxidase contains copper, and that this metal undergoes reversible oxidation when the enzyme is functioning.

Since the only change in most cytochromes when they are reduced is a change in the valence of the iron, it is not obvious how these catalysts have any part in the formation of water from the hydrogen of a metabolite. This is explained by assuming that each hydrogen reduces the cytochrome by donating an electron and remaining in the vicinity as a hydrogen ion which will be called on finally to unite with oxygen when the electrons have been donated to an oxygen atom. Accepting this picture, we may conclude that identification of cytochrome oxidase clarified the final oxidative step in which hydrogen from a metabolite is transferred from reduced cytochrome to molecular oxygen. But there was still no light on the pathway by which this hydrogen reached and reduced cytochrome, since neither nicotinamide coenzyme donated hydrogen directly to cytochrome. Before the complete sequence could be outlined a third set of hydrogen acceptors, the flavins, had to be discovered and their reactions explored.

Significance of the cytochromes

Keilin's early surveys suggested that the cytochromes were widely distributed. Later work has shown that they do actually occur so universally in plant, animal, and bacterial cells that the conclusion is inevitable that they constitute the chief terminal oxidizing system, that is, the one in which oxygen itself is involved, for every type of aerobic cell.

The Flavoprotein Enzymes

As noted above, work with purified enzymes showed that the reduced pyridinoproteins could donate their hydrogens neither to molecular oxygen nor to cytochrome. Since in living cells hydrogen is finally united to oxygen by way of the cytochromes, there was clearly another link in the hydrogen transport system. The third type of carrier was found in the enzymes known as the flavoproteins. From most of these it is relatively easy to extract a soluble coenzyme which is a phosphorylated derivative of vitamin B_2. Here then is a second coenzyme in which the functional part of the molecule is one of the B vitamins.

The flavin coenzymes

Vitamin B_2 is a derivative of a heterocyclic compound known as iso-alloxazine. The vitamin is a 6,7-dimethyl derivative, with which the sugar

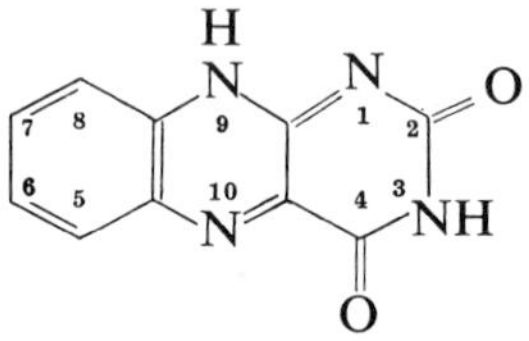

Isoalloxazine

alcohol, ribitol, has been condensed at position 9. When this compound is further modified by phosphorylation at carbon 5' of the ribitol, the resulting substance is one of the two common flavin coenzymes. It is usually referred to as flavin mononucleotide (FMN) in spite of the fact that the sugar component is not a pentose as in a true nucleotide but the related pentahydroxy alcohol.

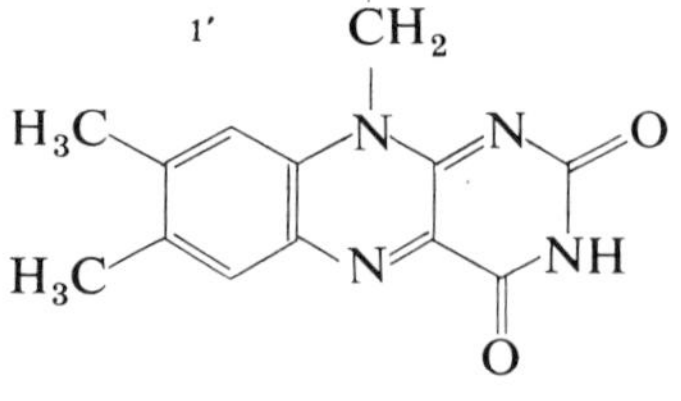

Oxidized flavin
mononucleotide
(FMN)

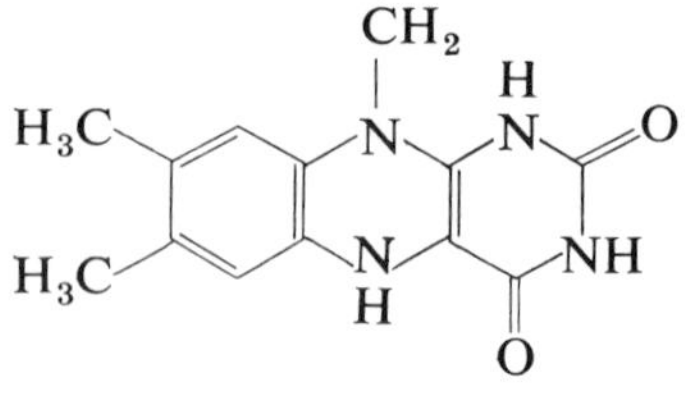

Reduced flavin
mononucleotide
(FMNH₂)

The other type of flavin coenzyme is flavin adenine dinucleotide (FAD), already used as an example of an oxidizing coenzyme, which acts with the specific protein which catalyzes the oxidation of D-amino acids. The molecular pattern of this substance is like that of coenzyme I except that riboflavin replaces the nicotinamide-ribose complex.

Adenine-ribose-phosphate

|

Flavin-ribityl-phosphate

As with the pyridine coenzymes, the activity of the flavin coenzymes depends upon the reversible oxidation-reduction of one of the heterocyclic rings. With these coenzymes a pair of hydrogens become attached to nitrogens in adjacent rings, as indicated in the formulation of the mono-nucleotide, and of the reduced form of the dinucleotide.

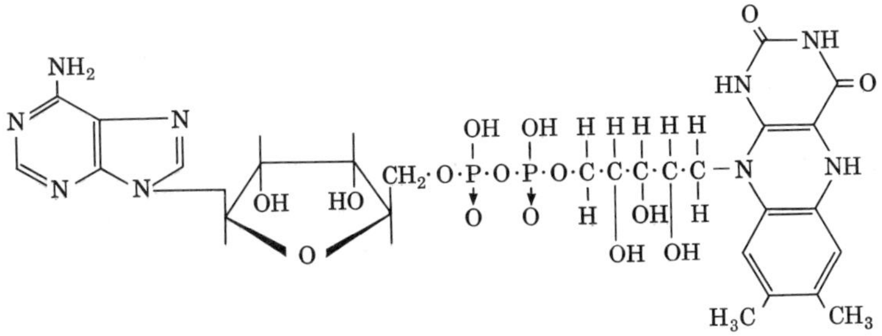

Reduced flavin adenine dinucleotide ($FADH_2$)

In Table 11.3 are listed some of the enzymes, extracted from a wide variety of different cells and tissues, for which a flavin serves as coenzyme. It should be noted that the first on the list are those which catalyze transfer of hydrogen from one of the pyridine coenzymes, and that three of these transfer it to a cytochrome. These are known as cytochrome reductases. Here then is the required link between the primary hydrogen acceptors and the cytochromes, so that the general pattern for hydrogen transfer can be outlined:

Substrate → pyridinoprotein → flavoprotein → cytochromes → oxygen

As Table 11.3 indicates, the hydrogens acquired by the flavins are not always passed on to oxygen through the cytochromes. They may be used to form H_2O_2 or to reduce nitrate or nitrite or a variety of different quinones.

The flavins differ from the iron porphyrin enzymes in the fact that in conjunction with some enzyme proteins they are able to accept hydrogen directly from metabolites. In the two amino acid oxidases, for example, FAD removes two hydrogens from amino acids to form the imino acids, passing on the hydrogens, not to a cytochrome but directly to oxygen with formation of hydrogen peroxide. In some cells the hydrogen peroxide may have a

TABLE II.3. Some Representative Flavoproteins

Name	Source	Prosthetic Group	Hydrogen Donor	Hydrogen Acceptor Reduced Form	Other Factors
DPNH-cyt. c^a reductase	Bacteria		DPNH	Ferrocytochrome	Fe
DPNH-cyt. c reductase	Animal tissue	FMN	DPNH	Ferrocytochrome	
TPNH-cyt. c reductase	Animal tissue, yeast		TPNH	Ferrocytochrome	
Coenzyme-naphtho-quinone reductase^b	Animal tissue, bacteria, plants		DPNH or TPNH (slow)	H_3C — (naphthoquinol structure, OH, OH)	
Nitrate reductase	Plants, molds, bacteria	FAD	TPNH	Nitrite	Mo
Nitrite reductase	Plants, molds, bacteria	FAD	TPNH	Nitric oxide	Cu
GSSG reductase	Widely distributed	FAD	TPNH	GSH	
Xanthine oxidase	Animal tissue, milk, bacteria	FAD	Xanthine, Aldehydes	$H_2O_2{}^c$	Mo, Fe
Succinic dehydrogenase	Animal tissue, bacteria, yeast	FAD-peptide	Succinate	Reduced dye	Fe
D-Amino acid oxidases	Animal tissue, molds, bacteria	FAD	D-Amino acids	H_2O_2	
L-Amino acid^d oxidases	Animal tissue, snake venom, molds, bacteria	FAD or FMN	L-Amino acids	H_2O_2	
Lactate dehydrogenase (cytochrome b_2)	Yeast, bacteria		L-lactic acid	Ferrocytochrome	

^{a} This type of name gives both hydrogen donor and hydrogen acceptor.
^{b} Acts also with other quinones, including vitamin K_1.
^{c} When H_2O_2 is the product, the hydrogen acceptor is oxygen.
^{d} Enzymes from animal tissue also oxidize α-hydroxy acids.

bacteriocidal use, or it may be used as an oxidizing agent in the presence of a suitable peroxidase. In others, it may be decomposed by catalase to yield water and free oxygen.

The requirement of several of the flavin enzymes for metal ions is noted in the table. Succinic dehydrogenase, for example, as isolated contains four atoms of iron for every mole of flavin. This enzyme was a great puzzle for many years because it was impossible to release the flavin prosthetic group by any of the classical methods such as dialysis against dilute acid or treatment with acidified alcohol or acetone. When it was finally freed, it was found

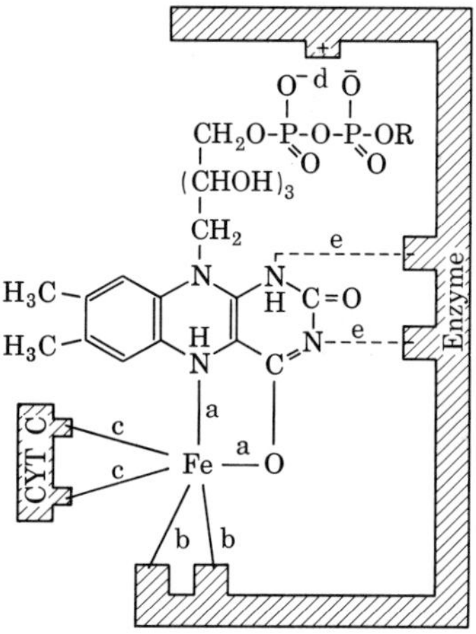

Fig. 11.9. Active enzyme site for cytochrome *c* reduction. The flavin, shown here as substituted riboflavin pyrophosphate, is in the reduced form. The different types of bonds indicated by the letters are explained in the text. [From H. R. Mahler and D. G. Elowe, *J. Biol. Chem.*, **210**, 177 (1954).]

to be still attached to a peptide moiety, and to differ somewhat in its absorption spectrum from the usual FAD, though it yields the same products on hydrolysis. It is impossible to say at present whether this prosthetic group has a unique structure, or whether the absorption spectrum of FAD is modified by its association with peptide and metal. In the oxidation of succinate to fumarate, hydrogens are acquired by the flavin and then transferred to cytochrome. Figure 11.9 shows the way in which this passage of hydrogens from flavin to cytochrome may be pictured in the light of the requirement of cytochrome *c* reductase for iron. The flavin is shown in its reduced form. The six coordination positions of the iron are used: two (marked a) link the iron to two of the rings of the flavin, two (marked b) link it to the enzyme protein and two (marked c) chelate it with cytochrome *c*. The flavin is held to the protein by ionic bonds through the phosphate groups (marked d) and by additional covalent links (marked e). The iron thus contributes to establishing the complex at the active site, and also catalyzes the flow of electrons from the reduced flavin to the cytochrome.

Another example of a flavin which is like succinic dehydrogenase in accepting hydrogens directly from a metabolite is the substance extracted from microorganisms which is sometimes called cytochrome b_2 and sometimes lactate dehydrogenase. This is one of those enzymes, mentioned earlier, which carry two prosthetic groups, one a heme and the other a flavin. In the presence of lactic acid this dehydrogenase brings about reduction of both these groups. But if the flavin is removed, no transfer of hydrogen to the heme takes place. Evidently then the first transfer with the complete system is to the flavin, which then passes on electrons to an adjacent heme.

Respiratory Pathways

It is obvious that with such a multiplicity of cytochromes and such a variety of flavoproteins, there is no one pathway along which hydrogens travel in all types of cells to achieve their union with oxygen. Since some metabolites can be activated by flavoproteins, the pyridinoproteins are sometimes bypassed entirely.

The respiratory pathway has been studied by many different types of experiment. Comparative reaction rates may indicate the order in which coenzymes are reduced. For example, a given cytochrome cannot be in the path between flavin and oxygen if its rate of oxidation is lower than that of the flavin. If in a tissue extract which contains a complete oxidizing system, one cytochrome is reduced in the presence of narcotics, though others including cytochrome c remain in the oxidized form, then the one which is reduced is clearly nearer the substrate than is cytochrome c, the reduction of which is known to be blocked by narcotics. Measurement of reduction potentials, though still fraught with uncertainties, also helps to establish the order in which respiratory catalysts must act. Taking into account all the information available, the respiratory chain in animal tissues has been outlined as follows, fp_1 and fp_2 standing for flavoproteins.

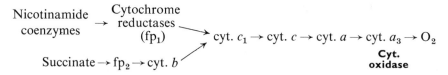

Nicotinamide coenzymes $\rightarrow$ Cytochrome reductases (fp_1)

$\rightarrow$ cyt. c_1 $\rightarrow$ cyt. c $\rightarrow$ cyt. a $\rightarrow$ cyt. a_3 $\rightarrow O_2$
Cyt. oxidase

Succinate $\rightarrow fp_2 \rightarrow$ cyt. b

Table 11.4 lists the approximate reduction potentials at pH 7 and 25° for the main components of the respiratory chain. The series of transfers involved in this chain permits the release of the energy of oxidation in a series of small steps, rather than in a single explosive reaction. The amount of energy released is indicated by the difference in reduction potential which is the driving force of each transfer. Of the six transfers indicated in the table for animal or plant metabolites, three are a result of relatively large differences in reduction potentials, i.e., those from pyridine coenzyme to a flavin, from cytochrome b to c, and from cytochrome a or f to oxygen. In the next chapter the ways in which the cell mobilizes this energy for its own purposes will be considered.

TABLE 11.4. Approximate Reduction Potentials of the Respiratory Carriers at pH 7

Compounds Involved	E_0', v	Difference, v
Substrates	0.0 to −0.45	
DPN$^+$(NAD)	−0.32	
		+0.32
FAD	0.0	
		+0.08
Cyt. *b*	+0.08	
		+0.17
Cyt. *c*	+0.25	+0.04
Cyt. *a*	+0.29	
Cyt. *f* (plant)	+0.37	+0.51
	+0.43	
Oxygen	+0.80	

Plant respiratory paths

As noted above it is now agreed that a large part of the respiration of higher plants is mediated by similar catalysts and the same cofactors as operate in animal tissues. There probably are, however, other systems in plant cells, catalyzed by special enzymes. In barley root tips, for example, the cytochrome system seems to be supplemented by ascorbic acid oxidase. This copper-protein enzyme catalyzes the reversible oxidation-reduction of ascorbic acid, which thus acts as a soluble coenzyme. Both DPNH and TPNH can be reoxidized by way of ascorbic acid, which means that the oxidation of any metabolite from which hydrogen can be transferred to a pyridine coenzyme can take place in some plant cells without using the cytochromes. With this enzyme as with cytochrome oxidase the end product is water. This pathway

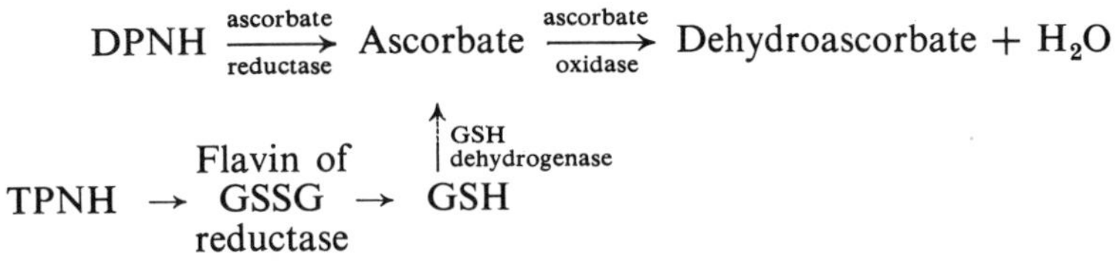

$$\text{DPNH} \xrightarrow[\text{reductase}]{\text{ascorbate}} \text{Ascorbate} \xrightarrow[\text{oxidase}]{\text{ascorbate}} \text{Dehydroascorbate} + H_2O$$

$$\begin{array}{c} \text{Flavin of} \\ \text{TPNH} \rightarrow \text{GSSG} \rightarrow \text{GSH} \\ \text{reductase} \end{array} \quad \begin{array}{c} \uparrow \text{GSH} \\ | \text{dehydrogenase} \end{array}$$

is indicated in the diagram, with the arrows giving the direction of hydrogen transfer. The substance to which hydrogen is transferred from DPNH is of course the oxidized dehydroascorbate, the reversible oxidation-reduction of which is shown in the formulas.

$$\underset{\pm 2H}{\rightleftharpoons}$$

L-Ascorbic acid   **L-Dehydroascorbic acid**

Coupled Reactions

A great advantage of the use of the same coenzyme with a number of different enzymes is that this makes it possible for the cell to carry out simultaneous, coupled oxidations and reductions. This is possible whenever the equilibrium constants for two reactions using the same coenzyme have such values that in one reaction the tendency is toward reduction of the coenzyme and in the other toward its oxidation. We have already noted that there is such a difference in equilibrium constants in the case of the alcohol dehydrogenases. Allowing S_1H_2 to stand for a substrate which tends to be oxidized, and S_2 for the oxidized form of another substrate which tends to be reduced by the same coenzyme, the two reactions may be represented as follows:

$$S_1H_2 + DPN^+ \rightleftharpoons S_1 + DPNH + H^+$$
$$S_2 + DPNH + H^+ \rightleftharpoons DPN^+ + S_2H_2$$

Sum: $$S_1H_2 + S_2 \rightleftharpoons S_1 + S_2H_2$$

In view of the number of enzymes which use the nicotinamide coenzymes, it will be clear that they offer the cell a mechanism for utilizing various cell oxidations to bring about reduction of some other substrate. This same possibility exists, of course, with any coenzyme which acts with more than one enzyme protein.

Other Respiratory Carriers

In addition to the fundamental respiratory coenzymes so far considered, there are others whose place in the oxidative mechanism of the cell is not yet clearly established. One such compound, ascorbic acid, has already been noted as a probable respiratory intermediate in plants. Another is the substance known as *diaphorase*. This is a flavoprotein, obtained from heart muscle, which was originally believed to catalyze the transfer of hydrogen from DPNH to various dyes which were often used in studies of cell oxidation. Quite recently this enzyme has been shown to be identical with lipoate dehydrogenase. It has a relatively negative redox potential and is believed to mediate transfer of hydrogen from reduced lipoate to DPN^+.

A third possible carrier is the substance known as *coenzyme·Q* or ubiquinone. This is one of a number of substances the structures of which include a quinone moiety with a polyisoprenoid side chain. Vitamin K_1 is a related compound, for which some respiratory function has been suggested from time to time. Coenzyme Q is one of a number of homologues differing one from

O
╱CH₃
CH₃   CH₃   CH₃   CH₃
│   │   │   │
╲CH₂·CH=C(CH₂)₃·CH(CH₂)₃·CH(CH₂)₃·CH·CH₃
O
Vitamin K₁

the other in the number of isoprene units in the side chain. These are differentiated by calling the one which has the formula below coenzyme Q_{10}, and indicating by a similar subscript the number of isoprene units in the side chains of the other coenzymes. Coenzyme Q_{10} is the only compound of this type obtained from mammalian tissues, but bacterial preparations have from six to nine isoprene units in their side chains.

These compounds all undergo the typical hydroquinone ⇌ quinone reversible oxidation, and by virtue of this property are proposed as obligatory

O
‖
CH₃O─┌─┐─CH₃   CH₃
      │ │   │
CH₃O─└─┘─(CH₂·CH=C·CH₂)₁₀H
‖
O
Coenzyme Q₁₀

members of the respiratory chain. Specifically it is suggested that coenzyme Q_{10} forms the link between the succinic dehydrogenase flavoprotein and cytochrome, thus replacing the cytochrome *b* which performs this function in the scheme on page 412. For the moment then it seems likely that the various coenzyme Q compounds do play a part in the respiratory sequence, but there is as yet no general agreement either on the importance of this group of compounds or on their exact relation to the other respiratory carriers.

MISCELLANEOUS OXIDIZING ENZYMES

Many enzymes catalyze oxidative reactions other than those of hydrogen transport.

Catalase: An Iron Pyrrole Enzyme

The existence of the enzyme catalase which catalyzes the decomposition of hydrogen peroxide to water and oxygen has long been known. It is widely distributed and has been the subject of many kinetic studies because of the ease with which various enzyme-substrate compounds can be identified. In spite of this there is no general agreement on the course of the reaction. Catalase is a hemoprotein with a molecular weight in the vicinity of 248,000, and with four heme residues per molecule. The iron is in the ferric state.

It was originally believed that the function of the catalases was to destroy the toxic hydrogen peroxide, but it has now been recognized that catalase is not so restricted in its action. It is in fact a special kind of peroxidase which uses hydrogen peroxide to oxidize either hydrogen peroxide itself, in which case water and oxygen are the products, or some few other substances including ethyl alcohol and nitrites. When it functions in the latter way, it is said to be exerting a peroxidase function, because other peroxidases are known which catalyze the oxidation of a wider variety of substrates by hydrogen peroxide.

In whichever of its two functions catalase is engaged, it begins by forming a green enzyme-substrate compound which undergoes intramolecular change before interacting with another molecule. The nature of the change is not known, but it is believed that it is the modified enzyme-H_2O_2 complex which then reacts with either a second molecule of hydrogen peroxide or with some other substance which is to be oxidized. Allowing the noncommittal E-H_2O_2' to stand for the active complex, the two possible reactions may be indicated:

$$\text{E-}H_2O_2' + H_2O_2 \rightarrow E + 2H_2O + O_2$$
$$\text{E-}H_2O_2' + R \cdot CH_2OH \rightarrow E + 2H_2O + R \cdot CHO$$

Peroxidases: Iron Pyrrole Enzymes

A number of enzymes catalyze the oxidation of various substrates by hydrogen peroxide. The possible substrates include phenols and diphenols, tryptophan, some fatty acids, and aminophenols. The peroxidases, like catalase, are iron pyrrole enzymes in which the iron is in the ferric state. Although the intramolecular changes which take place when peroxidase forms a complex with hydrogen peroxide are easy to see, since they involve color changes, the nature of the change which yields the reactive complex is still unknown. The equations given above for catalase action will therefore serve also for the peroxidases, with substitution of a peroxidase substrate for the alcohol shown in the equation.

Copper Protein Enzymes

Just as the iron pyrrole compounds have found a use both in hemoglobins and as oxidative enzymes, so copper compounds occur in nature not only as respiratory pigments in the hemocyanins and in cytochrome a_3 but also as oxidizing enzymes. Such, for example, are the three enzymes ascorbic acid oxidase, phenolase, and laccase.

Ascorbic acid oxidase has already been referred to in connection with plant respiration. This enzyme is not found in animal tissues, where the oxidation of ascorbate is carried out through the cytochromes.

Phenolase

Phenolase is also a plant enzyme which catalyzes the oxidation of a number of mono- and diphenols by molecular oxygen. The enzyme is a copper protein which undergoes reversible oxidation of the copper in the course of its catalytic activity. As obtained from different sources and used with different substrates it has been known as diphenol oxidase, tyrosinase, and polyphenol oxidase as well as phenolase. The last name is used here because the enzyme has a broad specificity and can act upon mono- as well as di-phenols.

When monophenols are acted upon, the first step is addition of oxygen to form an *ortho* diphenol. This compound is then oxidized to the corresponding quinone. When tyrosine is oxidized the resulting quinone may undergo further transformations leading to formation of the dark pigment known as melanin.

As shown in the formulation, the oxidation of the diphenol is reversible, and there is some evidence that in the presence of reducing agents the quinone can act as an intermediate hydrogen carrier, but it now seems unlikely that such a reaction plays any large role in plant respiration.

Laccase

The copper protein laccase is also a phenolase, but one which brings about oxidation of para and not of ortho phenols. It is obtained from the latex of an Indo-Chinese lacquer tree where it acts upon substances present in the latex to form the black, resinous lac. Like the other phenolases, laccase catalyzes formation of a quinone from a diphenol.

Hydroquinone   **p-Benzoquinone**

Laccase, like phenolase, has been suggested as a terminal oxidase in plant tissues, but it now seems more likely that both enzymes are more important to plant cells in their synthesis of flavonoids and tannins than as respiratory carriers.

FORMATION OF CARBON DIOXIDE

The greater part of the carbon dioxide formed by aerobic cells, whether from fats, proteins, or carbohydrates, is formed by way of a series of reactions which together constitute what has been variously called the Krebs cycle or the tricarboxylic acid cycle or the citric acid cycle. This fusing of many oxidative paths is possible because, as later chapters will show, many of the compounds which act as oxidative substrates are transformed in the cell to yield either pyruvic acid or one of the compounds formed from pyruvate in the course of its oxidation. Any of these intermediates can then enter the cycle to complete their oxidation.

The elucidation of the series of chemical events by which the 3-carbon pyruvate molecule is degraded followed lines which are already familiar. Tissue slices or extracts were tested with different substrates which they were known to oxidize, and attempts were made to identify intermediate products. Whenever a compound seemed to be a likely intermediate, it in turn was tested with the same tissue enzymes. If it proved to be oxidized at least as rapidly as the original substrate, its position as an intermediate was strengthened. Gradually it became possible to sketch and then to test a possible sequence of reactions in which the various substrates and their intermediate products could be fitted into a logical pattern. From such studies as these there has evolved the theory that formation of carbon dioxide from pyruvate takes place in the course of a cyclical process in the course of which the pyruvate first reacts with oxaloacetate and is then completely oxidized. In this process the oxaloacetate is reconstituted and so is able to react with another pyruvate and start a new turn of the cycle.

In the course of the early work on oxidation it had been recognized that most cells can bring about oxidation of a number of organic acids all of which are structurally related in some degree. Some of these have been mentioned in the discussion of their dehydrogenases. It was found, furthermore, that the enzymes needed for the interconversion of several of these compounds were present in living tissues. These are the acids which were eventually found to be essential to the oxidation of pyruvate, and which are listed in Table 11.5.

Reactions of the Individual Acids of the Citric Acid Cycle

It is obvious from a glance at Table 11.5 that the acids listed can be derived from each other by simple reactions of types known to take place in living cells, such as hydrogenation or dehydrogenation, removal or addition of the elements of water and carboxylation or decarboxylation. The enzymes which catalyze these reactions have been found in nearly all tissues which have been examined, whether plant, bacterial, or animal. This points to a very wide applicability for the cycle in which these enzymes are used. Some important reactions undergone by the acids in this group are outlined in the following sections.

Citrate

1. Oxidation of citric acid, catalyzed by a dehydrogenase from cucumber seeds, was shown to use only one atom of oxygen per molecule of acid, and to give rise to one molecule of carbon dioxide. It was later shown that the other oxidation product is α-ketoglutarate and that the reaction is catalyzed by animal tissue also. Obviously this reaction involves more than the single step here indicated.

$$
\begin{array}{l}
\text{CH}_2\text{COOH} \\
|\\
\text{HOC} \cdot \text{COOH} \\
|\\
\text{CH}_2\text{COOH} \\
\text{Citric acid}
\end{array}
\quad \xrightarrow{+\frac{1}{2}\text{O}_2} \quad
\begin{array}{l}
\text{CO} \cdot \text{COOH} \\
|\\
\text{CH}_2 \\
|\\
\text{CH}_2\text{COOH} \\
\alpha\text{-Ketoglutaric acid}
\end{array}
\quad + \text{CO}_2 + \text{H}_2\text{O}
$$

2. The other important fact about citric acid is that many tissues contain an enzyme *aconitase* which brings about an equilibrium involving the three

TABLE 11.5. Acids Rapidly Oxidized by Aerobic Cells

Acid	Formula
Citric acid	CH_2COOH | $HOC \cdot COOH$ | CH_2COOH
cis-Aconitic acid	$CH \cdot COOH$ || $C \cdot COOH$ | CH_2COOH
d-Isocitric acid	$HOCH \cdot COOH$ | $CH \cdot COOH$ | CH_2COOH
α-Ketoglutaric acid	$CO \cdot COOH$ | CH_2 | CH_2COOH
Succinic acid	CH_2COOH | CH_2COOH
Fumaric acid	$CH \cdot COOH$ || $HOOC \cdot CH$
Malic acid	CH_2COOH | $HCOH \cdot COOH$
Oxaloacetic acid	$CO \cdot COOH$ | CH_2COOH
Pyruvic acid	$CH_3 \cdot CO \cdot COOH$

tricarboxylic acids, citric acid, isocitric acid and *cis*-aconitic acid. This was until very recently believed to come about through removal and later addition of water as shown in the formulas. It has recently been shown that *cis*-aconitic

$$
\begin{array}{ccc}
CH_2COOH & CH \cdot COOH & CHOH \cdot COOH \\
| & \| & | \\
HOC \cdot COOH \;\overset{\pm H_2O}{\rightleftharpoons}\; & C \cdot COOH \;\overset{\pm H_2O}{\rightleftharpoons}\; & CH \cdot COOH \\
| & | & | \\
CH_2COOH & CH_2COOH & CH_2COOH \\
\textbf{Citric acid} & \textit{\textbf{cis}}\textbf{-Aconitic acid} & \textbf{Isocitric acid}
\end{array}
$$

acid is not an obligatory intermediate, but that all three acids come into equilibrium with a common intermediate. The proposed structure for this intermediate is given on page 428.

α-Ketoglutarate

Decarboxylation is an enzymic reaction which is characteristic of α-ketonic acids, and it therefore might be expected that α-ketoglutarate would be converted oxidatively into succinic acid. In 1937 Krebs and Johnson succeeded in demonstrating this transformation in muscle tissue. In order to isolate the succinic acid it is necessary to carry out the reaction in the presence of malonate which inhibits competitively the further oxidation of succinate. Under these conditions the succinate accumulates and can be identified.

$$\begin{array}{c} CO \cdot COOH \\ | \\ CH_2 \\ | \\ CH_2COOH \end{array} \quad \xrightarrow{+H_2O, -2H} \quad \begin{array}{c} CH_2COOH \\ | \\ CH_2COOH \end{array} + CO_2$$

α-Ketoglutaric   Succinic
acid   acid

Fumarate

1. Fumarate, succinate, and malate have long been known to be interconvertible in biological systems. The ubiquitous succinic dehydrogenase catalyzes the reversible formation of fumarate from succinate; the *fumarase*

$$\begin{array}{c} CH_2COOH \\ | \\ CH_2COOH \end{array} \underset{}{\overset{\pm 2H}{\rightleftharpoons}} \begin{array}{c} CH \cdot COOH \\ \| \\ HOOC \cdot CH \end{array} \underset{}{\overset{\pm H_2O}{\rightleftharpoons}} \begin{array}{c} HOCH \cdot COOH \\ | \\ CH_2COOH \end{array}$$

Succinic   Fumaric   Malic
acid   acid   acid

which brings about the reversible transformation of fumarate to malate is widely distributed in the tissues of animals, plants, and bacteria.

2. Oxidation of fumarate or malate by tissue preparations leads to formation of oxaloacetate. This is probably a dehydrogenation of malate in both cases, the fumarate being first hydrated to form malate.

$$\begin{array}{c} HOCH \cdot COOH \\ | \\ CH_2COOH \end{array} \underset{}{\overset{\pm 2H}{\rightleftharpoons}} \begin{array}{c} CO \cdot COOH \\ | \\ CH_2COOH \end{array}$$

Oxaloacetic acid

Oxaloacetate

1. Decarboxylation of oxaloacetate takes place so readily that there is scarcely need to search for a catalyst. However, such an enzyme has been identified and shown to require magnesium or manganese ion for its activity.

2. Reduction of oxaloacetate can be brought about by enzymes which have been found in muscle and in bacteria. The reaction yields a mixture of malate and fumarate, which is in some tissues further reduced to succinate.

$$
\begin{array}{cccc}
\text{CH}_2\text{COOH} & & \text{CH}_2\text{COOH} & \text{CH}\cdot\text{COOH} \\
| & \underset{\pm 2\text{H}}{\rightleftharpoons} & | & \underset{\pm\text{H}_2\text{O}}{\rightleftharpoons} \quad \| \\
\text{CO}\cdot\text{COOH} & & \text{HCOH}\cdot\text{COOH} & \text{HOOC}\cdot\text{CH} \\
\textbf{Oxaloacetic} & & \textbf{Malic acid} & \textbf{Fumaric acid} \\
\textbf{acid} & & &
\end{array}
$$

3. The amount of oxaloacetate which disappears from muscle suspension is always greater than can be accounted for by decarboxylation and reduction. Search for other products indicated some formation of the five-carbon α-ketoglutarate and the six-carbon citrate.

Pyruvate

Pyruvate is oxidized rapidly by many different varieties of cell. When this oxidation is measured in minced muscle, and in the absence of inhibitors, it is quantitative, $2\frac{1}{2}$ moles of oxygen being used and 3 moles of carbon dioxide formed, per mole of pyruvate disappearing. In the presence of

$$
\text{CH}_3\text{CO}\cdot\text{COOH} + 2\tfrac{1}{2}\text{O}_2 \rightarrow 3\text{CO}_2 + 2\text{H}_2\text{O}
$$

malonate, acting as an inhibitor of succinic dehydrogenase, the pyruvate disappears, but less oxygen is used and succinate accumulates. This suggests that the four-carbon succinate is an intermediate in the oxidation of the three-carbon pyruvate. Furthermore, when a mixture of pyruvate and fumarate is metabolized by muscle suspension, significant amounts of both citrate and α-ketoglutarate form. Here again is the transformation of a short carbon chain into a longer one. These two examples in addition to that of oxalo-acetate in (3) above, point to the conclusion that biological oxidation is not a simple series of catabolic steps, but must include some building up of carbon chains. A number of different schemes have been proposed to account for the facts and these have gradually merged into the modern theory originated in 1937 by Krebs and Johnson.

The Citric Acid Cycle

Understanding of the metabolic importance of the dicarboxylic acids began about 1936. In that year Szent-Györgyi reported that addition of succinate, or of any of the four-carbon acids to which it gives rise on oxidation, acted catalytically upon the oxygen uptake of muscle. That is, the increased oxygen uptake was greater by several fold than would have been found had the added substances acted simply as additional substrates. This suggested that they must be acting in some sort of cyclic mechanism. Szent-Györgyi's theory was that they acted to bridge the gap between the dehydrogenases and the cytochrome system, as indicated in the following scheme. Hydrogen from a reduced coenzyme would follow the lines of the solid arrows, being finally donated to a cytochrome by succinate, activated by succinic dehydrogenase.

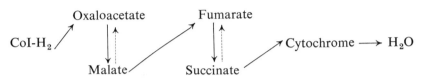

A year later Krebs and Johnson reported new observations which led them to postulate a more inclusive cycle of polycarboxylic acids.

1. Citrate was shown to exert the same catalytic effect on respiration of pigeon breast muscle as did the four-carbon acids.

2. Fumarate or oxaloacetate added to respiring tissue were found to give rise to succinate by *oxidation*, that is, with a simultaneous uptake of oxygen. If the experiment were conducted anaerobically almost no succinate appeared. This is exactly contrary to what might have been expected. Formation of succinate from fumarate by reduction would of course have been familiar enough, yet did not take place. Furthermore, this ordinary reductive formation of succinate from fumarate is completely inhibited by malonate, yet when fumarate was added to respiring tissue poisoned with malonate, succinate still formed, with a concomitant uptake of oxygen. This could only mean that oxidative removal of the four-carbon fumarate led in some undefined way to synthesis of the four-carbon succinate.

The series of cyclic changes which are now believed to be involved in oxidation of pyruvate is shown in Fig. 11.10. The operation of the cycle may be said to begin when acetyl coenzyme A derived from pyruvate condenses with oxaloacetate to form citrate, and to end when oxaloacetate is again reconstituted. Although all the reactions except the decarboxylation of pyruvate are reversible, the cycle has been written with single arrows to make it easier to follow. In the discussion of the individual reactions double arrows are included, and any factors such as metal ions which are essential are written under the arrows. This does not mean that the ion acts only in the reverse reaction.

Reactions of the Citric Acid Cycle

In the reaction sequences of the citric acid cycle three essential cofactors appear to which no previous reference has been made. These substances take part in two similar reaction sequences in which α-keto acids are oxidized and

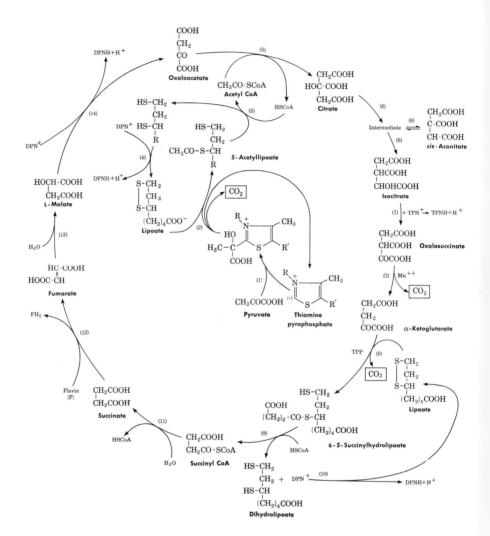

Fig. 11.10. The citric acid cycle.

decarboxylated. The compounds are coenzyme A, thiamine pyrophosphate, and lipoic acid.

Coenzyme A, so called because it was discovered in connection with acetylation reactions, is a substance of primary importance in many metabolic reactions. Like the respiratory coenzymes, it is a complex substance rather like a dinucleotide in general structure, with adenylic acid linked through a second phosphate group to a modified peptide. The complete structure is given on page 444 where it will be seen to include pantothenic acid linked to a mercaptoamine. Pantothenic acid is one of the B vitamins and so it is to be added to the list of those dietary requirements which are known to be used in synthesis of a required coenzyme. For the moment the only thing about the structure of coenzyme A which need be considered is that its functional group is the terminal sulfhydryl group. This group reacts to form

$$R \cdot COOH + HSCoA \rightarrow R \cdot CO \cdot SCoA + H_2O$$
Acyl CoA

acyl derivatives which are very reactive. The most common of these compounds is *acetyl coenzyme A* or acetyl CoA which is the compound which was for many years referred to as "active acetate."

The second new compound is thiamine pyrophosphate which as an essential cofactor in alcoholic fermentation has been known for many years as cocarboxylase. Since it is now known to act as a cofactor in several different reactions this name has become too specific and is giving way to the chemical name above. It is a phosphate derivative of still another of the B vitamins, the one called thiamine or vitamin B_1.

Thiamine pyrophosphate (TPP)

The third new substance is lipoic acid, a disulfide compound which can be reversibly oxidized and reduced and which acts as a hydrogen carrier in several different oxidations.

Lipoic acid   **Dihydrolipoic acid**

Reaction I

The reactions in the center of the circle are preliminary ones which transform pyruvate into acetyl CoA, using the carriers just listed. In the first step pyruvate reacts with phosphorylated thiamine

$$\text{Pyruvate} + \text{Thiamine pyrophosphate} \rightleftharpoons \text{Addition product}$$

in a reaction which has just been elucidated. The activity is believed to lie in that portion of the thiamine molecule which includes a carbon between the charged nitrogen and the sulfur. It will be noted that the structure at this point is roughly that of HCN, with the central carbon holding nitrogen with a double bond and hydrogen with a single one. The thiazolium ring is believed to lose a proton and become a dipolar ion as follows:

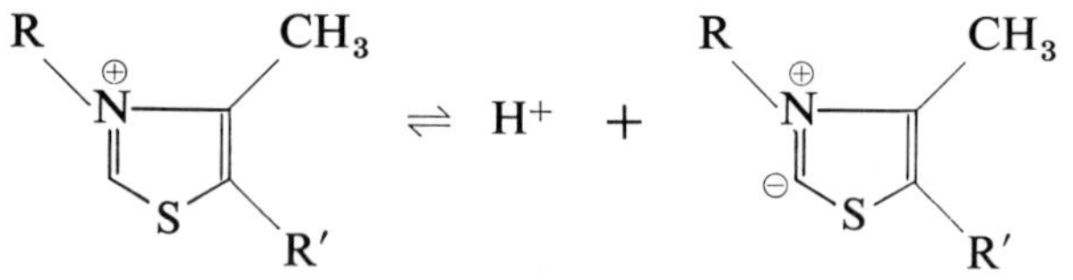

This ion then reacts with a keto acid as hydrogen cyanide acts with carbonyl compounds to form a cyanohydrin type of addition product, as follows, with R and R' standing for all the coenzyme except the thiazolium ring.

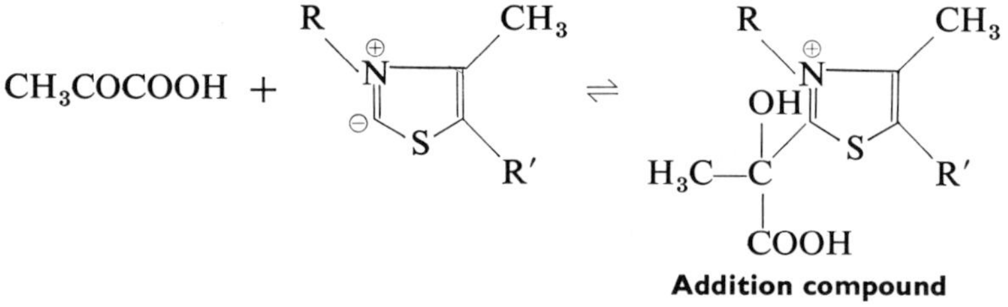

Addition compound

Reaction 2

Thiamine PP addition cpd. + Lipoic acid →

$$CO_2 + \text{Thiamine PP} + 6\text{-}S\text{-Acetylhydrolipoate}$$

The addition product loses carbon dioxide and at the same time transfers the residual acetyl group to lipoic acid to form an acetyl derivative of dihydrolipoate. In this compound the acetyl group is linked to the sulfur on carbon 6. This reaction regenerates the thiamine pyrophosphate (TPP) which can then act to acquire a new molecule of pyruvate.

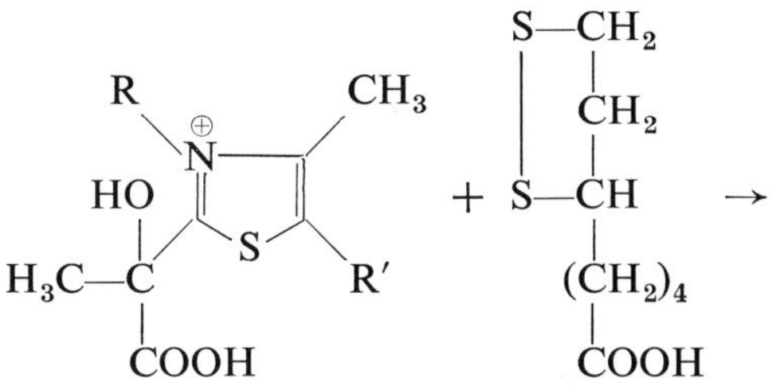

$$\begin{array}{c}
R \quad\quad CH_3 \\
\overset{\oplus}{N} \\
HO \quad\quad\quad S \\
H_3C\!-\!\overset{|}{C} \quad\quad R' \\
\underset{COOH}{|}
\end{array}
\quad+\quad
\begin{array}{c}
S\!-\!CH_2 \\
\underset{|}{CH_2} \\
S\!-\!CH \\
\underset{|}{(CH_2)_4} \\
COOH
\end{array}
\quad\longrightarrow$$

Lipoate

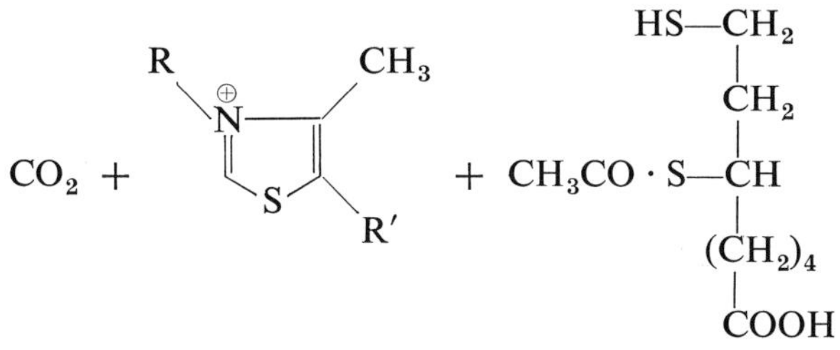

$$CO_2 \;+\;
\begin{array}{c}
R \quad\quad CH_3 \\
\overset{\oplus}{N} \\
S \\
\quad R'
\end{array}
\;+\; CH_3CO\cdot S\!-\!\!
\begin{array}{c}
HS\!-\!CH_2 \\
\underset{|}{CH_2} \\
CH \\
\underset{|}{(CH_2)_4} \\
COOH
\end{array}$$

Acetyldihydrolipoate

Reaction 3

Acetyldihydrolipoate + HSCoA ⇌ Acetyl CoA + Dihydrolipoate

The third acetyl carrier intervenes at this point in the form of coenzyme A which accepts the acetyl group from the lipoate to form another compound in which the acetyl group is linked to the molecule through sulfur. This reaction generates the acetyl coenzyme A with which the cycle proper begins.

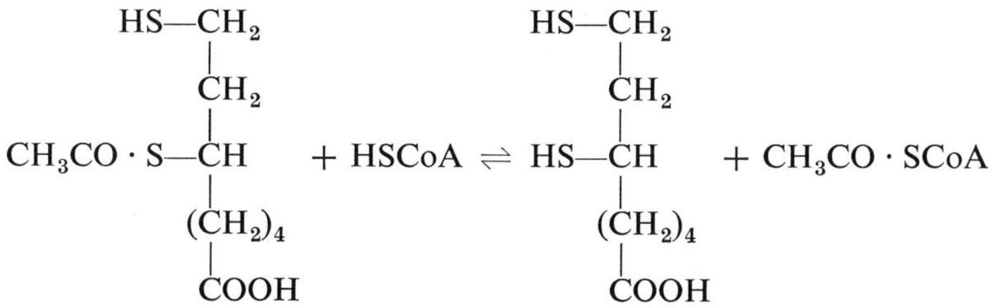

$$
\begin{array}{c}
HS\!-\!CH_2 \\
\underset{|}{CH_2} \\
CH_3CO\cdot S\!-\!CH \\
\underset{|}{(CH_2)_4} \\
COOH
\end{array}
\;+\; HSCoA \;\rightleftharpoons\;
\begin{array}{c}
HS\!-\!CH_2 \\
\underset{|}{CH_2} \\
HS\!-\!CH \\
\underset{|}{(CH_2)_4} \\
COOH
\end{array}
\;+\; CH_3CO\cdot SCoA
$$

CoA   **Acetyl CoA**

Reaction 4

Dihydrolipoate + DPN$^+$ ⇌ DPNH + H$^+$ + Lipoate

Meantime the hydrogens which came to lipoate from pyruvate are transferred to DPN$^+$ and so started on their way to complete oxidation by way of the respiratory carriers. This reaction regenerates the lipoate needed for reaction with more pyruvate. Thus the net result of these first four reactions is a decarboxylation of pyruvate, a reduction of DPN$^+$ and synthesis of acetyl CoA. As acetyl CoA, two carbons of pyruvate enter the citric acid cycle.

The third carbon has already gone off as carbon dioxide. The hydrogens which were transferred to DPN$^+$ will be passed on by way of the cytochromes to molecular oxygen.

Reaction 5

$$\text{Acetyl CoA} + \text{Oxaloacetate} + \text{H}_2\text{O} \underset{\overrightarrow{\quad}}{\overset{\text{citrogenase}}{\rightleftharpoons}} \text{Citrate} + \text{HSCoA}$$

The cycle then begins with condensation of acetyl CoA with oxaloacetate under the influence of an enzyme which was originally called "condensing enzyme," but is now known as *citrogenase*. In this step coenzyme A is freed to act again as an acetyl carrier. The formulas of the compounds involved in reaction 5 are given in the figure.

Reaction 6

The enzyme *aconitase* is widely distributed in nature and has been known for many years to catalyze the reversible isomerization of citrate and iso-

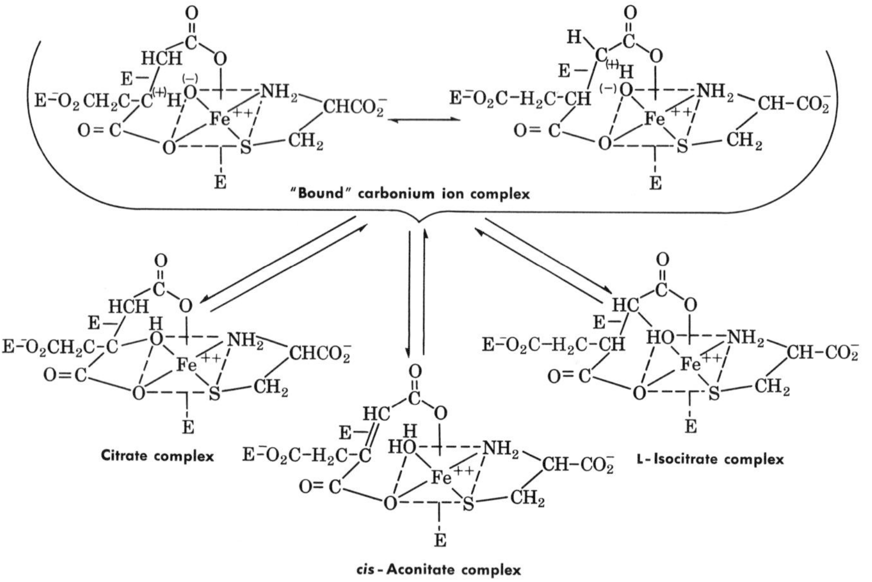

Fig. 11.11. Diagram of the postulated enzyme-bound intermediate which can rearrange to yield either citric acid, isocitric acid, or *cis*aconitic acid. In the complex one primary carboxyl, the tertiary carboxyl and the OH group of citrate are chelated with the Fe^{++}. [From S. R. Dickman and J. F. Speyer, *J. Biol. Chem.*, **220**, 205 (1956).]

citrate. It has been assumed that this takes place through the removal and subsequent addition of water as indicated on page 420. However, recent studies using D$_2$O as solvent have shown that far too little deuterium appears in isocitrate for the *cis*-aconitate to be an obligatory intermediate. Rather the change is believed to involve an intramolecular rearrangement in an enzyme-substrate complex, in which a substance is formed which acts as a common intermediate, and from which any of the three acids can be formed. This intermediate has been postulated as a carbonium ion complex, a suggested structure for which is shown in Fig. 11.11. Since all three acids are in equilibrium with this intermediate, and since the one which reacts further is the isocitrate, the net reaction as far as this cycle is concerned is the formation of equilibrium amounts of isocitrate. Although the amount of isocitrate

$$\text{Citrate} \leftrightharpoons \text{(Intermediate)} \rightleftharpoons \text{Isocitrate}$$
$$\big\updownarrow$$
$$cis\text{-Aconitate}$$

present at equilibrium is small, its continual removal eventually brings about transformation of all the citrate to its isomer.

Reaction 7

$$\text{Isocitrate} + \text{TPN}^+ \underset{\text{Mn}^{++}}{\overset{\text{dehydrogenase}}{\rightleftharpoons}} \alpha\text{-Ketoglutarate} + CO_2 + \text{TPNH} + H^+$$

There are two isocitrate dehydrogenases, both requiring manganese ion and both fairly widely distributed. Both enzymes transfer hydrogen to TPN^+, but the one which acts in the citric acid cycle also acts as a decarboxylase and frees carbon dioxide. This is assumed to take place in the two steps indicated on the chart, though up to the present both steps seem to be catalyzed by a single enzyme and free oxalosuccinate has not been found. This probably results from the fact that it is decarboxylated without ever leaving the enzyme surface, which thus offers an example of a single protein which catalyzes two separate reactions. For clarity the two steps are separated on the chart. In the course of this double-headed reaction a second molecule of carbon dioxide is set free and a second pair of hydrogens is set on the respiratory path.

Reaction 8

$$\alpha\text{-Ketoglutarate} + \text{Lipoate} \underset{\text{(TPP)}}{\overset{\text{dehydrogenase}}{\rightleftharpoons}} \text{6-}S\text{-Succinylhydrolipoate} + CO_2$$

This reaction, which has been telescoped to omit the step in which thiamine pyrophosphate forms an addition product, brings about oxidation and decarboxylation of an α-keto acid exactly as in the preliminary reactions of pyruvate. There is the same requirement for TPP, which first forms an addition product then releases carbon dioxide and transfers the succinyl residue to lipoic acid. At this point then the third and final molecule of carbon dioxide has formed from the original pyruvate.

Reaction 9

$$\text{6-}S\text{-Succinylhydrolipoate} + \text{HSCoA} \overset{\text{thioltransacylase}}{\rightleftharpoons} \text{Hydrolipoate} + \text{Succinyl CoA}$$

This is a transfer of an acyl group to coenzyme A, analogous to the one in reaction 3 in which the acetyl group is transferred.

Reaction 10

$$\text{Hydrolipoate} + \text{DPN}^+ \xrightleftharpoons{\text{dehydrogenase}} \text{Lipoate} + \text{DPNH} + \text{H}^+$$

This reaction, for which coenzyme I is the obligatory cofactor, starts a third pair of hydrogens on their way to oxygen via the cytochromes. The dehydrogenase is the diaphorase referred to on page 415.

Reaction 11

$$\text{Succinyl CoA} + \text{H}_2\text{O} \xrightarrow{\text{deacylase}} \text{Succinate} + \text{HSCoA}$$

This is represented as a simple hydrolysis, which may or may not actually take place. It will be seen later that the freeing of succinate may result from a different reaction in which the energy of the thiol ester bond is conserved. In either reaction succinate is a product.

Reaction 12

$$\text{Succinate} + \text{Flavin} \xrightleftharpoons{\text{dehydrogenase}} \text{Fumarate} + \text{Reduced flavin}$$

The enzyme catalyzing this reaction was discussed on page 411. The flavin referred to is firmly bound to the dehydrogenase protein. It is believed to transfer electrons to cytochrome *b*, forming at the same time a pair of hydrogen ions. These transfers set a fourth pair of hydrogens on the path to oxygen via the cytochromes.

Reaction 13

$$\text{Fumarate} + \text{H}_2\text{O} \xrightleftharpoons{\text{fumarase}} \text{L-Malate}$$

Note that this addition of water is stereospecific so that the product is L-malate.

Reaction 14

$$\text{L-Malate} + \text{DPN}^+ \xrightleftharpoons{\text{dehydrogenase}} \text{Oxaloacetate} + \text{DPNH} + \text{H}^+$$

This step reconstitutes the oxaloacetate with which the cycle began and starts the fifth pair of hydrogens on the respiratory path. Thus in the course of one turn of the cycle five hydrogen pairs react to form, ultimately, five molecules of water using five atoms of oxygen, and three molecules of carbon dioxide are formed. If these figures are compared with the equation on page 422, they will be seen to agree with the stoichiometry of the equation for the complete oxidation of pyruvate. The ten hydrogen atoms will use the two and a half oxygen molecules which appear in the equation. It is true that the equation shows only two molecules of water formed, and the cycle appears to lead to formation of five. This discrepancy disappears when it is noted that in the course of the operation of the cycle three water molecules were used. One was used in formation of citrate, one in the splitting of succinyl CoA, and one was added to fumarate to form malate. Thus there was a net synthesis of two water molecules, as the equation indicates.

Significance of the Citric Acid Cycle

The citric acid cycle is now believed to account for the major part of the respiration of aerobic cells. It will be shown in later chapters that the two main oxidative substrates are glucose and fatty acids. The metabolism of glucose begins with its transformation to yield two molecules of pyruvate from each one of glucose. When fatty acids are oxidized, they give rise almost exclusively to acetyl coenzyme A. Furthermore, the metabolic changes undergone by many amino acids lead either to pyruvate, acetyl coenzyme A, or to one of the intermediates of the citric acid cycle. Any of these intermediates can enter the cycle for complete oxidation. Thus in the last analysis the vast majority of the metabolic paths lead into the citric acid cycle. And of course any of the substances formed in the operation of that cycle can if necessary be withdrawn and used synthetically.

Localization of Oxidation

Any consideration of the number of steps involved in the formation of carbon dioxide and water from a substrate molecule will make it clear that there must be, within the cell, such an organization of enzymes and coenzymes that transfer reactions can take place quickly and smoothly. It has been shown within the last decade that many of the complex multienzyme systems involved in oxidation are localized in mitochondria. When these particles are separated from the cell matrix in such a way as to conserve their structure and contents, they prove to contain all the respiratory coenzymes, the enzymes of the citric acid cycle and those required for the oxidation of fatty acids. These can act effectively only if they are arranged so that the sequence of transfers can be carried out smoothly. This arrangement is associated with the numerous projections or cristae which, like a series of shelves, fill the body of the mitochondrion. Conceivably the membranes revealed by the electron microscope may *be* the enzymes, held in a lipoprotein complex, and arranged in the order in which they are used in the various oxidative sequences. It has indeed been estimated that the enzymes themselves make up 10 to 20 per cent of the total weight of the membranes. At any rate, within these tiny particles so large a part of the energy yielding oxidations takes place that the mitochondria have been called the "power houses" of the cell. This should not be interpreted to mean that it is only in the mitochondria that these oxidative reactions can take place, because here as elsewhere the living cell is arranged to allow of alternative pathways. What it does mean is that the mitochondria account for a large part of the oxidative potential of the cell, and this by virtue of what must be an organization of extraordinary complexity and beauty.

SUGGESTIONS FOR FURTHER READING

The Respiratory Pathway

Green, D. E., Electron transport and oxidative phosphorylation, *Advances in Enzymol.*, *21*, 73 (1959).

James, W. O., Reaction paths in the respiration of higher plants, *Advances in Enzymol.*, *18*, 281 (1957).

Slater, E. C., Respiratory chain in animal tissues, *Advances in Enzymol.*, *20*, 147 (1958).

Stotz, E. H., *et al.*, Components of the cytochrome system, p. 401 in *Enzymes: Units of Biological Structure and Function*, O. H. Gaebler (ed.), Academic, New York, 1956.

Dehydrogenases

Fisher, H. F., Mechanism of the glutamic dehydrogenase reaction, *J. Biol. Chem.*, *235*, 1830 (1960).

Mahler, H. R., and D. G. Elowe, The role of iron in diphosphopyridine nucleotide cytochrome *c* reductase, *J. Biol. Chem.*, *210*, 165 (1954).

Nakamoto, T., and B. Vennesland, Reactions catalyzed by glutamic and isocitric dehydrogenases, *J. Biol. Chem.*, *235*, 202 (1960).

Pullman, M. E., and S. P. Colowick, Preparation of the 2- and 6-pyridones of N^1-methylnicotinamide, *J. Biol. Chem.*, *206*, 121 (1954).

Singer, T. P., and E. B. Kearney, Chemistry, metabolism and scope of action of the pyridine nucleotide coenzymes, *Advances in Enzymol.*, *15*, 79 (1954).

Stern, B. K., and B. Vennesland, Reactions catalyzed by glucose-6-phosphate dehydrogenase and 6-phosphogluconic dehydrogenase, *J. Biol. Chem.*, *235*, 205 (1960).

Wallenfels, K., and H. Sund, Mechanism of hydrogen transfer with pyridine nucleotides, *Biochem. Z.*, *329*, 59 (1957).

Warburg, O., and W. Christian, Pyridine, the hydrogen-transporting part of the fermentation enzymes, *Biochem. Z.*, *287*, 291 (1936).

Westheimer, F. H., *et al.*, Enzymatic transfer of hydrogen from alcohol to DPN, *J. Am. Chem. Soc.*, *73*, 2403 (1951).

Flavin Enzymes

Haas, E., *et al.*, Enzymatic reduction of cytochrome *c*, *J. Biol. Chem.*, *136*, 747 (1940).

Kearney, E. B., Flavin component of mammalian succinic dehydrogenase, *J. Biol. Chem.*, *235*, 865 (1960).

Warburg, O., and W. Christian, Isolation of the prosthetic group of D-amino acid oxidase, *Biochem. Z.*, *298*, 150 (1938).

Iron Pyrrole Enzymes

Clezy, P. S., and J. Barrett, The prosthetic group of cytochrome oxidase. 2. Chemistry of porphyrin *a*, *Biochem. J.*, *78*, 798 (1961).

Keilin, D., On Cytochrome . . . , *Proc. Roy. Soc. (London)*, *B98*, 312 (1925).

Keilin, D., and E. F. Hartree, Cytochrome and cytochrome oxidase, *Proc. Roy. Soc. (London)*, *B127*, 167 (1939).

Morell, D. B., *et al.*, The prosthetic group of cytochrome oxidase. 1. Purification as porphyrin *a* and conversion to haemin *a*, *Biochem. J.*, *78*, 793 (1961).

Theorell, H., On the chemical constitution of cytochrome *c*, *Biochem. Z.*, *298*, 242 (1938).

Theorell, H., Nature and mode of action of oxidizing enzymes, *Science*, *124*, 467 (1956).

Warburg, O., The oxygen transporting respiratory enzyme, *Z. angew. Chem.*, *45*, 1 (1932).

Citric Acid Cycle

Basu, D. K., and D. P. Burma, Dihydrolipoate dehydrogenase from a plant source, *J. Biol. Chem.*, *235*, 509 (1960).

Breslow, R., and E. McNelis, On the mechanism of thiamine action. IV. *J. Am. Chem. Soc.*, *80*, 3719 (1958); V. *ibid.*, *81*, 3080 (1959); VI. *ibid.*, *82*, 2394 (1960).

Koike, M., *et al.*, α-Keto acid dehydrogenation complexes, *J. Biol. Chem.*, *235*, 1924, 1931, 1939 (1960).

Krebs, H. A., The tricarboxylic acid cycle, *The Harvey Lectures*, *44*, 165 (1948–1949).

Massey, V., Role of diaphorase in ketoglutarate oxidation, *Biochim. et Biophys. Acta*, *32*, 286 (1959).

Reed, L. J., Chemistry and function of lipoic acid, *Advances in Enzymol.*, *18*, 319 (1957).

Searls, R. L., *et al.*, On the mechanism of dihydrolipoyl dehydrogenase reaction, *J. Biol. Chem.*, *236*, 2317 (1961).

Searls, R. L., and D. R. Sanadi, α-Ketoglutaric dehydrogenase: Isolation of a flavoprotein component, *J. Biol. Chem.*, *235*, 2485 (1960); A comparative study of dihydrolipoyl dehydrogenase and diaphorase, *ibid.*, *236*, 580 (1961).

Singer, T. P., *et al.*, Succinic dehydrogenase, p. 417 in *Enzymes: Units of Biological Structure and Function*, O. H. Gaebler (ed.), Academic, New York, 1956.

Localization of Oxidation

Chance, B., and B. Thorell, Fluorescence measurements of mitochondrial pyridine nucleotides, *Nature*, *184*, 931 (1959).

Kimura, T., and T. P. Singer, Functional organization of the respiratory chain in liver mitochondria, *Nature*, *184*, 791 (1959).

Perry, R. P., *et al.*, Localization and assay of respiratory enzymes in single living cells, *Nature*, *184*, 929 (1959).

Schneider, W. C., Mitochondrial metabolism, *Advances in Enzymol.*, *21*, 1 (1959).

Biosynthetic mechanisms 12

L IVING CELLS ARE CONTINUOUSLY ENGAGED in two complementary activities. On the one hand they oxidize organic compounds and thus set free all or part of their potential chemical energy. At roughly the same time synthetic reactions are going on which require an energy source. It was noted in the last chapter that the oxidative processes in the cell are so arranged that the energy is released in small increments as protons and electrons are passed along from one respiratory carrier to the next. Since it is highly unlikely that a reaction needing just that amount of energy will be going on at the exact time and place of its release, the cell has evolved an elaborate mechanism for storing these small bundles of energy as they become available. It is the purpose of this chapter to consider these mechanisms and to survey in a general way the uses made of that stored energy.

HIGH ENERGY COMPOUNDS

It is a familiar fact that reactions can be brought about with acetyl chloride or acetic anhydride which take place much less readily with acetic acid itself. The first compounds are said to be more unstable or more reactive than the last. For its synthetic purposes the living cell makes use of a variety of such reactive compounds.

The High Energy "Bond"

The first of the highly reactive metabolites to be recognized were phosphate derivatives such as creatine phosphate, ATP, acetyl phosphate, and the other compounds listed in Table 12.1. These all contain one or more of what Lipmann[1] called "energy rich" bonds, which he indicated in formulas by the

TABLE 12.1. High Energy Phosphate Compounds

Formula	Compound
	Adenosine-5′-triphosphate, ATP
$H_2O_3P \sim NH \cdot C \cdot NH(CH_2)_3CH \cdot COOH$ with $\overset{\|}{NH}$ and $\overset{\|}{NH_2}$	Arginine phosphate
$COOH$ / $CO \sim PO_3H_2$ / CH_2 (with double bond)	Phosphoenolpyruvic acid
$CH_2O \cdot PO_3H_2$ / $CHOH$ / $CO \cdot O \sim PO_3H_2$	1,3-Diphosphoglyceric acid
$NH \sim PO_3H_2$ / $C{=}NH$ / $N \cdot CH_3$ / CH_2COOH	Creatine phosphate
$CH_3CO \cdot O \sim PO_3H_2$	Acetyl phosphate

The ATP formula shown is:

$$NH_2 \text{ purine ring} - C_5H_8O_4 - \overset{O}{\underset{OH}{P}} \cdot O \sim \overset{O}{\underset{OH}{P}} \cdot O \sim \overset{O}{\underset{OH}{P}} \cdot OH$$

---

[1] Fritz Lipmann (1899–) is a Member and Professor of the Rockefeller Institute in New York. He began his career in Berlin and later spent seven years at the Biological Institute of the Carlsberg Foundation in Copenhagen. He has been Professor of Biological Chemistry at Harvard Medical School and Director of Biochemical Research at Massachusetts General Hospital. The concept of the energy-rich bond grew out of his work in enzyme chemistry. In 1953 Lipmann shared the Nobel Prize in Medicine with H. A. Krebs.

wavy lines between phosphorus and oxygen or between phosphorus and nitrogen. The idea of an unstable, or energy-rich, bond arose because of the large differences between the free energy of hydrolysis of such a compound as acetyl phosphate and such an unreactive one as glucose-6-phosphate. This last is an ester, and its free energy of hydrolysis is approximately −3 kcal, whereas hydrolytic removal of a phosphate group from ATP or acetyl phosphate results in a standard free energy change of about −8.4 kcal. Originally this figure was given as −12 kcal per mole, but recent allowance for the heat of ionization of newly formed acid groups reduces the standard free energy change to about the figure given above.[2] Even so there is a substantial difference of 4 or 5 kcal between the free energy of hydrolysis of the two types of compounds. In pointing this out Lipmann wrote as if the difference were entirely localized in the bond which is split in the hydrolysis. It is now recognized that we do not know how the energy is distributed within a compound, and that the distinction is to be made between unstable and reactive *compounds* such as those listed in the table, and less reactive compounds such as the phosphate esters of the sugars.

Oxidative Phosphorylation

It was recognized many years ago that oxidation was usually accompanied in tissue preparations by a loss of inorganic phosphate and an incorporation of phosphate groups into organic compounds. This was called oxidative phosphorylation and proved to be a process which could be "uncoupled" from oxidation itself. This means that cells which normally use the energy of oxidation to synthesize reactive phosphate compounds would continue to use oxygen but would cease to incorporate phosphate in the presence, for example, of 2,4-dinitrophenol or of Dicumarol or of any of a number of so called uncoupling agents.

The importance of this coupled process lies in the fact that it allows the cell to store some of the energy which is released in oxidation, and so prevents its dissipation as heat if there is no immediate use for it. The primary conserver and storehouse of energy in living cells is ATP, which is later called upon to release that energy for many different purposes. These include syntheses, osmotic work such as transfer of ions or molecules against an osmotic gradient, and such specialized processes as muscular contraction or bioluminescence. It is still not known exactly how these energy transfers are effected, but something is now understood about the places in the oxidative cycle at which the transfers take place which make possible the synthesis of

---

[2] It has been pointed out that the figures given above are *standard* free energy changes, that is, they are measured with all reactants at a concentration of $1M$. Under the conditions of acidity and concentration obtaining in a cell the $\Delta F'$ of ATP is close to −12.5 kcal/mole or approximately the value originally suggested.

ATP. The fundamental reaction in this process is the addition of a phosphate group to adenosine diphosphate (ADP).

$$ADP + H_3PO_4 \rightleftharpoons ATP + H_2O$$

The major part of the ATP synthesis in the cell takes place as a result of the energy changes which accompany the transfer of electrons and protons along the respiratory chain. It will be remembered (page 413) that there were three transfers in this sequence which set free relatively large amounts of energy. It has been found, by comparing the moles of oxygen used with the moles of inorganic phosphate esterified, that nearly 3 moles of ATP are formed from ADP for every atom of oxygen reduced to water. Experimentally P/O ratios of approximately 2.8 or even less are usually found, and when succinate is the oxidative substrate the figure is just below 2. These are interpreted to mean that phosphorylation takes place at the places indicated in the diagram, with three bundles of energy conserved in ATP if the oxidation

$$\text{Substrate} \rightarrow \text{DPN}^+ \overset{\overset{\text{ATP}}{\uparrow}}{\rightarrow} \text{FP}_1 \rightarrow \text{cyt. b}_1 \overset{\overset{\text{ATP}}{\uparrow}}{\rightarrow} \text{cyt. } c \rightarrow \text{cyt. } a \overset{\overset{\text{ATP}}{\uparrow}}{\rightarrow} \text{cyt. } a_3 \rightarrow O_2$$

$$\text{Succinate} \rightarrow \text{FP}_2$$

begins with a pyridine nucleotide, but only two if the primary acceptor is the flavin designated as FP_2, as it is when succinate is the substrate.

Localization and mechanism of oxidative phosphorylation

The mechanism of the transfer of phosphate and of energy at the three points noted above is still unknown. As would be expected, the enzymes of oxidative phosphorylation are found to accompany the enzymes of the respiratory chain in the mitochondria. The process has been studied not only in intact mitochondria, but also in fragments obtained by disruption of these small organs. One way in which they can be fragmented is by treatment with digitonin. This reagent causes an apparent solution of the particles, but high speed centrifugation of the cloudy solution yields membrane fragments which can still dehydrogenate β-hydroxybutyrate or succinate and carry on oxidative phosphorylation, though the ability to carry out the reactions of the citric acid cycle has been lost. The results of studies with these mitochondrial fragments suggest that within a mitochondrion there are small unit respiratory assemblies, each complete in itself, distributed more or less evenly in or on the membranes which form the cristae. Lehninger, from whose papers this discussion is derived, pictures the membrane structure diagrammatically as shown in Fig. 12.1. Each square represents one complete unit arranged and held in the lipoprotein matrix of the membrane. Digitonin attacks this lipo-protein fabric along the lines of cleavage between assembly units. When the membrane is thus fragmented, particles result which may be of varying sizes, but so long as a particle includes one complete unit it will be able to carry on certain of the mitochondrial reactions.

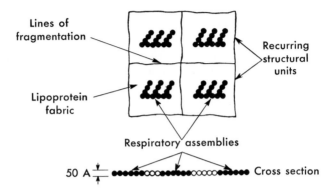

Fig. 12.1. Respiratory enzyme assemblies in recurring units of mitochondrial membrane. The assembly consists of 6 electron-carrier protein molecules, supplemented by three sets of coupling enzymes, each consisting of three proteins as an approximation. [From A. L. Lehninger *et al.*, *Science*, **128**, 450 (1958). Reprinted from *Science* by permission.]

Working with these submitochondrial fragments, Lehninger and his colleagues obtained evidence for the action of some sort of high energy intermediate between the respiratory coenzymes and ATP. Figure 12.2 indicates one way in which such intermediates, formed from the compounds

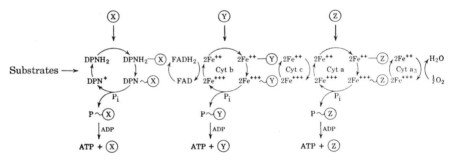

Fig. 12.2. A diagrammatic representation of the phosphorylation-coupled respiratory chain. It is assumed that the coupled carriers are DPN^+, cytochrome *b*, and cytochrome *a*. [From A. L. Lehninger *et al.*, *Science*, **128**, 450 (1958). Reprinted from *Science* by permission.]

X, Y, and Z could mediate phosphate transfer. In the first such synthesis, for example, the reduced pyridine coenzyme is represented as forming an energy-poor compound with X. When this compound is oxidized by a flavin the loss of electrons results in such a redistribution of energy that the oxidized complex, DPN$\sim$X is a high energy compound. As such it can transfer X to inorganic phosphate (P_i), its energy being conserved in P$\sim$X. It is then the reactive P$\sim$X which finally transfers phosphate to ADP to complete the phosphorylation. Similarly oxidation of the cytochrome *b*-Y complex leads to formation of an energy-rich ferric compound, and a similar compound of Z results from oxidation of the reduced cytochrome *a*-Z. At present there is no information available about the chemical nature of X, Y, and Z. It may even be that each of these letters stands for a whole series of transfers rather than a single one, but at least this diagram suggests a possible mechanism for this vitally important synthesis of ATP.

The efficiency of oxidative phosphorylation

It is always interesting to hazard a guess at the efficiency of cellular processes. In the oxidation of 1 mole of glucose in the bomb calorimeter about 690 kcal are released. It is possible to calculate the number of phosphorylations which accompany the complete oxidation of glucose in the cell, and to get from this a rough idea of the amount of the potential energy provided by the glucose which is actually conserved. It was noted in the previous chapter that metabolism of glucose begins with a series of changes in which one molecule of glucose yields two of pyruvate. These reactions are considered in detail in Chapter 15. For the present the important things about this reaction sequence are:

1. In the course of the sequence two pairs of hydrogens are transferred to DPN$^+$ for every glucose molecule metabolized.
2. One molecule of ATP is used to form a phosphate ester.
3. Four molecules of ATP are formed by interaction of ADP with energy-rich phosphate derivatives which are intermediates in the sequence.

In summary, in the transformation of one molecule of glucose to two molecules of pyruvate there is a net synthesis of three molecules of ATP, and two pairs of hydrogens are transferred to the respiratory chain.

The two molecules of pyruvate are then oxidized by way of the citric acid cycle. In the oxidation of a molecule of pyruvate, five pairs of hydrogens are removed from substrate molecules to be passed on to oxygen via the respiratory chain. Since each molecule of glucose yields two of pyruvate, there will be transferred to oxygen in this part of the sequence ten pairs of hydrogens. Eight of these were accepted by pyridine nucleotides, but the two which came from succinate were transferred to a flavoprotein and so furnish less energy for phosphorylation than do the other pairs. Each pair of hydrogens which enters the respiratory chain at the pyridine nucleotide level brings about synthesis of three molecules of ATP as shown in Fig. 12.2. The two pairs contributed by succinate will furnish energy for synthesis of two molecules of ATP per pair. Adding in the two pairs of hydrogens transferred in the course of the glucose-pyruvate transformations gives ten pairs transferred at the pyridine nucleotide level and two at the flavoprotein level. The first group will, in passing down the respiratory chain, synthesize 3 × 10, or 30 molecules of ATP, and the other two pairs will furnish energy for the synthesis of 2 × 2, or 4 more molecules of ATP. There must be added to this the three molecules synthesized during formation of pyruvate, and two more which are formed during the freeing of succinate from coenzyme A in reaction eleven of the citric acid cycle. In the discussion in the previous chapter this was represented as a simple hydrolysis. Since succinyl CoA is a high energy

Guanosine triphosphate (GTP)

compound, the energy released in hydrolysis is large and in the cell is conserved by synthesis of a triphosphate which resembles ATP except that the base is guanine instead of adenine. In some undefined way the breaking of the bond between succinic acid and coenzyme A furnishes energy for formation of a triphosphate from guanosine diphosphate (GDP).

$$GDP + H_3PO_4 + Succinyl\ CoA \rightarrow GTP + Succinate + CoA$$

Since GTP is, like ATP, an energy-rich compound it should be included in those which conserve energy of oxidation in the form of phosphate derivatives. Since each molecule of pyruvate forms one of succinyl CoA, the pyruvate from a molecule of glucose will furnish two molecules of GTP. Thus in total each molecule of glucose furnishes energy for formation of 39 high energy compounds, as shown in Table 12.2.

Taking the rather uncertain, but fairly conservative figure, -8.4 kcal for the $\Delta F'$ of the ATP $\rightarrow$ ADP transformation, we find that about 328 kcal per mole, or over 45 per cent of the total energy of oxidation of glucose is trapped in the form of energy-rich triphosphates, of which ATP is by far the most important.

The donor of the terminal phosphate in oxidative phosphorylation is usually inorganic phosphate, but there were noted in the paragraphs above instances of formation of ATP by transfer of a phosphate group from an energy-rich phosphate derivative. This happens twice in the course of the reactions which transform glucose to pyruvate, there being generated at each step two molecules of an energy-rich phosphate intermediate. The energy of these compounds is conserved when they react with ADP and transfer a phosphate group to form ATP. This type of reaction is sometimes referred to as "substrate level phosphorylation." In such transfers the donor must, of course, be an energy-rich compound, since phosphate transfer to an acceptor is only possible if the rupturing of one bond releases enough energy to form the new one. A high energy compound can then form a new high energy compound, or it can, of course, form compounds which are much

TABLE 12.2. High Energy Compounds Formed from One Molecule of Glucose

Energy Source	Molecules of Nucleoside Triphosphate Formed
Glucose → pyruvate sequence	
2 pairs of hydrogens to DPN$^+$	6
Net synthesis from high energy phosphate intermediates	3
Citric acid cycle	
8 pairs of hydrogens to DPN$^+$	24
2 pairs of hydrogens to flavoprotein	4
Transfer of energy from succinyl CoA	2
Total	39

less reactive such as phosphate esters or inorganic phosphate. But no low energy compound can transfer its phosphate group to form an energy-rich substance unless some external source of energy such as sunlight or oxidation, can be called on.

The Uses of ATP

It may be valuable at this point to indicate some of the ways in which the energy of ATP is used by living cells, though a detailed consideration of the reactions involved must be postponed to later chapters.

The energy of ATP is used for various special biological functions in ways for which as yet there is no explanation. For example it is the splitting of ATP to ADP and inorganic phosphate which furnishes the energy for muscular contraction and for the chemical reactions which result in bioluminescence in the firefly.

ATP is the agent through which the energy of oxidation is transferred to other energy-rich compounds for storage. In the muscles of vertebrates such a storage compound is creatine phosphate, and in the muscles of invertebrates arginine phosphate serves the same purpose. These compounds are both formed by transfer of a phosphate group from ATP. The enzymes involved in transfer of phosphate groups from and to ATP are called *phosphokinases*.

The two reactions indicated in the equations below are therefore catalyzed by creatine phosphokinase and arginine phosphokinase, respectively.

$$\text{Creatine} + \text{ATP} \leftrightharpoons \text{Creatine phosphate} + \text{ADP}$$

$$\text{Arginine} + \text{ATP} \leftrightharpoons \text{Arginine phosphate} + \text{ADP}$$

Since these reactions are reversible, the phosphate can be returned to ADP when ATP is needed, hence the two compounds in which phosphate is linked to nitrogen simply serve to hold a certain amount of energy in reserve.

A more general use for transfer reactions from ATP to some phosphate acceptor is found in the formation of activated compounds which are needed for biosynthesis. As a simple example, galactose reacts with ATP in the presence of galactokinase to form a compound which is analogous to the Cori ester, namely galactose-1-phosphate. It is this phosphorylated derivative which is then used to transfer the galactosyl residue in the synthesis of di- or oligosaccharides. Similarly, when choline is to be used in synthesis of a phosphatide it is first phosphorylated by reaction with ATP. Later chapters will furnish many examples of this type of activation of substrate molecules.

$$(CH_3)_3\overset{+}{N}(CH_2)_2OH + ATP \xrightarrow[\text{phosphokinase}]{\text{choline}} (CH_3)_3\overset{+}{N}(CH_2)_2O \cdot \underset{O}{\overset{OH}{P}} \cdot OH + ADP$$

Phosphoryl choline

Sometimes an activation is achieved, not by transfer of the phosphate group from ATP, but by transfer of the nucleoside part of the molecule, with or without a phosphate group. An example of the latter is the activation of methionine which makes it possible for it to act as a methyl donor and transfer its methyl group to some other compound. Methionine itself cannot bring about such a transfer, but the compound which is formed when methionine reacts with ATP is an active methyl donor.

$$ATP + H_3C \cdot S(CH_2)_2\underset{NH_2}{CH} \cdot COOH \rightarrow$$

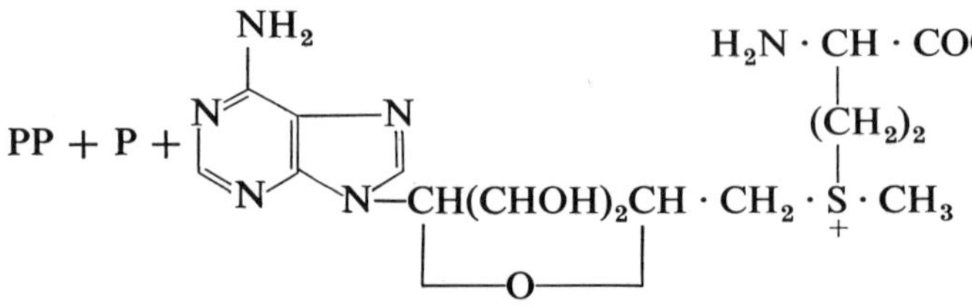

S-Adenosyl-L-methionine

In the activated compound the sulfur has acquired a charge, making it a sulfonium compound, and this change gives it the energy which allows it to carry out methyl group transfer.

Amino acids, before they can take part in protein synthesis, must be activated by reaction with ATP, but the active compound in this reaction is a mixed phosphate-carboxylic anhydride known as an acyl adenylate, the formula for which is indicated below.

$$NH_3^+$$

$$CH(CHOH)_2CH \cdot CH_2 \cdot O \cdot P \cdot O \cdot C \cdot CH \cdot R$$

Aminoacyladenylate

Finally ATP is used in a number of chemical reactions in which we know only that the ATP is hydrolyzed and that simultaneously a synthesis is achieved, but can hazard no explanation of the mechanism by which the energy of the one process is used to bring about the other. For example, reaction of glutamate with ammonia to form glutamine requires the enzyme glutamine synthetase, and also ATP. At present that synthesis is formulated as follows:

$$\text{L-Glutamate} + NH_3 + ATP \rightarrow \text{Glutamine} + ADP + P$$

This is one of many reactions in which the actual role of ATP as a donor of energy awaits elucidation. One suggested mechanism is given in a later section dealing with the synthesis of acetyl coenzyme A.

Acetyl Coenzyme A

Although ATP is the compound in which cells usually store energy, there are several other high energy compounds which are of fundamental importance in many biosyntheses. In view of the fact that heterotrophs must be supplied with organic compounds in the diet, it might have been expected that wherever possible they would use the molecules derived from the foodstuffs with as little alteration as possible. This proved not to be true. Living cells, in carrying out a wide variety of biosyntheses, many of them of great complexity, make use of a relatively small number of quite simple precursor molecules. From these can be built, by diverse metabolic pathways, almost all of the many different types of compounds in living tissue. Among these commonly used synthetic substrates are carbon dioxide, a two-carbon unit related to acetic acid and a one-carbon group related to formic acid or formaldehyde or methyl alcohol. Each of these is used in an activated form.

Acetyl coenzyme A has been referred to in connection with the citric acid cycle. It had long been realized that many metabolic reactions seemed to involve what was referred to as "active acetate." This meant that in the presence of tissue slices or of enzyme extracts, acetate could be used in reactions which did not take place in the absence of catalysts. Such a reaction is the acetylation of choline to form acetyl choline or of sulfanilamide to form the *N*-acetyl excretory product. Both these reactions require the presence of ATP as well as the specific enzymes. In 1945 Lipmann announced the separation from a crude bacterial acetylating preparation of a heat stable compound which was essential to the acetylations and which he named coenzyme A.

Structure of coenzyme A

One of the most interesting developments of recent years has been the recognition of the specific functions in cell metabolism of many of the vitamins, and especially of the group of compounds known collectively as the B vitamins. Beginning in the early years as a supposedly single substance, "water-soluble B," the group now includes at least nine members which are listed in Table 12.3. The use in respiratory coenzymes of nicotinic acid and vitamin B_2 has already been noted, as has the requirement for vitamin B_1 in the decarboxylation of α-keto acids. As noted in the table, pantothenic acid must now be added to the list of vitamins which appear in coenzymes. The formula of coenzyme A shows how the vitamin, pantothenic acid, links

Coenzyme A

mercaptoethylamine to a modified adenine nucleotide. In this large molecule the functional group is the terminal sulfhydryl group which reacts with a carboxyl group to form a highly reactive thiol ester.

Formation of acetyl CoA

The need for ATP in acetylation reactions was referred to above. So far all that is known about many such reactions is that either pyrophosphate

TABLE I2.3. Chief Members of the Group of B Vitamins

Name	Formula	Known Chemical Function
B₁ hydrochloride, thiamine hydrochloride		Thiamine pyrophosphate is cocarboxylase, now known to act in the decarboxylation of other acids than pyruvic.
B₂ or riboflavin		As monophosphate, or as flavin adenine dinucleotide, is part of at least two oxidizing coenzymes
Nicotinic acid		As the amide, furnishes the functional group in DPN⁺(NAD) and TPN⁺ (NADP)
B₆ or pyridoxine	5-Hydroxy-6-methyl-3,4-pyridinedimethanol	As phosphate of the closely related aldehyde, is the coenzyme for transamination and many decarboxylations
Pantothenic acid	HOCH₂ · C(CH₃)₂CHOH · CO · NH(CH₂)₂COOH	In coenzyme A

445

TABLE 12.3 (Continued)

Name	Formula	Known Chemical Function
Biotin		Forms an active complex with carbon dioxide
Inositol	Hexahydroxycyclohexane	
Folic acid	Pteroylglutamic acid	Forms activated one-carbon derivatives

B₁₂ or cyanocobala-mine

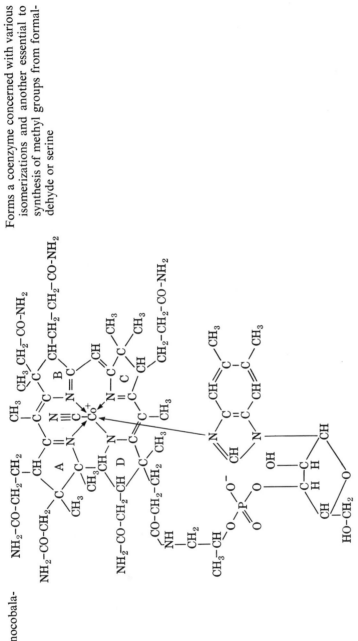

Forms a coenzyme concerned with various isomerizations and another essential to synthesis of methyl groups from formaldehyde or serine or inorganic phosphate is split out and either AMP or ADP remains at the end of the reaction. Many attempts have been made to explain the exact function performed by the triphosphate, which must clearly be related to the formation of acetyl coenzyme A, since when this compound is used instead of acetate, ATP is not required. It has been suggested that acetic acid reacts with ATP to form an active phosphate derivative, or alternatively an active adenylate. Lipmann suggested a mechanism in which ATP reacts first with the enzyme to form an enzyme-adenylate. This would then react with coenzyme A to fix it on the enzyme surface, and the activated enzyme-coenzyme complex would finally react with acetic or other acid. In the following formulation of this suggested sequence Ad—P~PP stands for ATP.

$$E + Ad—P{\sim}PP \leftrightharpoons E{\sim}P—Ad + PP$$

$$E{\sim}P—Ad + HS—CoA \leftrightharpoons E{\sim}S—CoA + Ad—P$$

$$E{\sim}S—CoA + RCOOH \leftrightharpoons E + CoA—S{\sim}COR$$
Acyl CoA

Although this series of reactions accounts adequately for all the products, and assigns a definite function to ATP, there is a more recent explanation which represents another kind of thinking about enzyme reactions. This abandons the attempt to break a complex enzymic catalysis up into a number of steps and suggests that the whole reaction takes place while all the reactants are attached to the enzyme surface, and that no free intermediates ever do form. Figure 12.3 shows how a complex might be formed in which ATP,

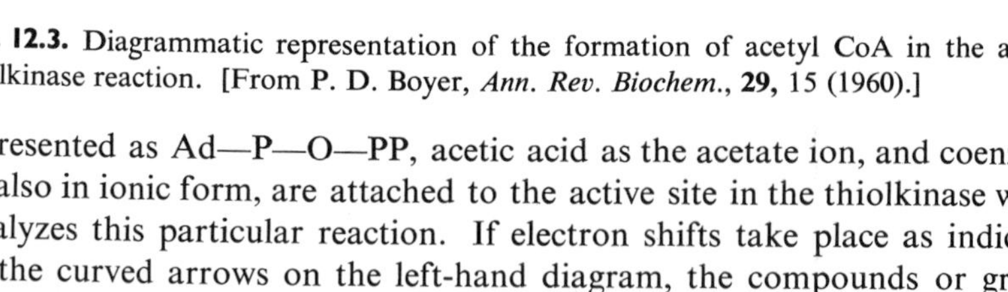

Fig. 12.3. Diagrammatic representation of the formation of acetyl CoA in the acetate thiolkinase reaction. [From P. D. Boyer, *Ann. Rev. Biochem.*, **29**, 15 (1960).]

represented as Ad—P—O—PP, acetic acid as the acetate ion, and coenzyme A, also in ionic form, are attached to the active site in the thiolkinase which catalyzes this particular reaction. If electron shifts take place as indicated by the curved arrows on the left-hand diagram, the compounds or groups represented on the right are formed, still on the enzyme surface. The curved arrows in the right-hand diagram indicate the electron shifts which would reverse the reaction. When reactants are present in sufficient concentration and acetyl coenzyme A is being formed, the products move away from the catalytic sites and new molecules take their places. If the curved arrows in the right-hand diagram are disregarded it can be seen that the products are pyrophosphate (PP—O$^-$), AMP (Ad—P—O), and acetyl coenzyme A (CH$_3$CO—S—CoA). It seems likely that this kind of explanation in terms of a single key transition state will find increasing favor in attempts to explain the mechanism of various enzyme actions.

Whatever the exact mechanism involved, acetic acid is one of several compounds which can in the presence of ATP, and a suitable enzyme or enzymes transfer an acetyl group to coenzyme A. These direct acetyl donors include pyruvate (see page 424) and any of the fatty acids. By a more indirect route many of the amino acids contribute to the synthesis of acetyl CoA. Alanine does so by simple loss of the amino group and formation of the corresponding keto acid, pyruvic acid. Others reach the pyruvate stage by a series of steps. It has already been noted that glucose is metabolized by way of pyruvate, so that its metabolic pathway can either proceed by way of the citric acid cycle to complete oxidation, or it may branch at the pyruvate level to allow two of the carbons to be conserved for synthesis in the form of acetyl coenzyme A. In summary, then, the carbohydrates, the fatty acids, and many of the amino acids are possible sources of acetyl groups for the synthesis of acetyl CoA.

Uses of acetyl CoA

The two carbons which are linked through a thiol ester bond to coenzyme A are part of an energy-rich compound. Rupture of this bond yields energy for transfer of the acetyl group to one of a number of acetyl acceptors. It has already been noted that acetyl CoA acetylates sulfanilamide and choline. A similar reaction gives rise to acetylated amino acids or amino sugars.

$$
\begin{array}{ll}
\begin{array}{l}
\text{CH}_2\text{OH} \\
| \\
\text{CH}_2 \\
| \\
\text{N(CH}_3)_3 \\
| \\
\text{OH} \\
\textbf{Choline}
\end{array}
\quad + \text{CH}_3\text{CO}\sim\text{SCoA} \rightarrow
&
\begin{array}{l}
\text{CH}_2\text{O} \cdot \text{COCH}_3 \\
| \\
\text{CH}_2 \\
| \\
\text{N(CH}_3)_3 \\
| \\
\text{OH} \\
\textbf{Acetyl choline}
\end{array}
\quad + \text{HSCoA}
\end{array}
$$

Sulfanilamide (SO$_2$NH$_2$ ... NH$_2$) + CH$_3$CO$\sim$SCoA → N-Acetyl sulfanilamide (SO$_2$NH$_2$ ... NH · COCH$_3$) + HSCoA

H$_2$N · CH$_2$COOH + CH$_3$CO$\sim$SCoA →

CH$_3$CO · NH · CH$_2$COOH + HSCoA

Acetylglycine

Acids other than acetic acid form acyl coenzyme A complexes which are like the acetyl compound in being highly reactive. Benzoyl CoA, for example, is the form in which benzoic acid reacts with glycine to form hippuric acid, and succinyl CoA is the active succinyl intermediate in the biosynthesis of heme.

$$C_6H_5CO \cdot SCoA + H_2N \cdot CH_2COOH \rightarrow$$
$$C_6H_5CO \cdot NH \cdot CH_2COOH + HSCoA$$

Benzoyl CoA   **Hippuric acid**

Still another reaction of acetyl CoA is the one which begins the citric acid cycle, in which the acetyl group is transferred to oxaloacetate to form citric

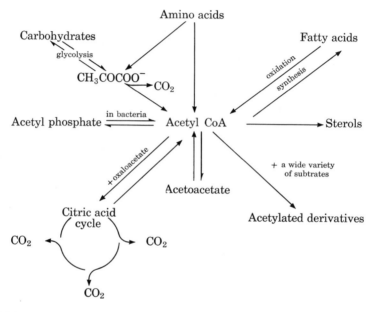

Fig. 12.4. Relationships between the foodstuffs, various metabolites, and acetyl coenzyme A.

acid. These then are a few of the many synthetic reactions in which acetyl CoA is known to take part. The central position occupied by this fundamental building unit is outlined in Fig. 12.4. Some of the transformations indicated there will be considered in detail in later chapters.

Active One Carbon Unit

In many biosyntheses the cells use a single carbon which may come from such a compound as formaldehyde or formic acid, or may be one specific carbon from a more complex carbon compound. The experimental basis for this statement is as follows. When the carbons of glycine are labeled in such a way that both can be identified in the metabolic products, it is found that the α-carbon is incorporated in several different molecules in which the carboxyl carbon is never found. Thus for example the α-carbon of glycine becomes the β-carbon of serine and appears in certain fixed positions in heme and in the methyl group of methionine. This gave rise to the idea that in addition to active acetate there must be in the cell some active one-carbon

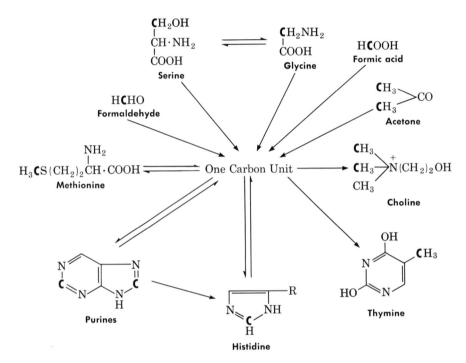

Fig. 12.5. Metabolic interrelationships involving active C_1 units. The carbons which are transferred are indicated in bold-face type.

unit which has been referred to as "active formate." This was perhaps an unfortunate nomenclature since the carbon is not always at the oxidative level of formate, but may be also either active formaldehyde or hydroxymethyl. Some of the interrelationships between the donors and the acceptors of a single carbon are shown in Fig. 12.5, in which the labile carbons are printed in heavy type.

The activating compound for the one-carbon unit is another of the B vitamins, folic acid. The establishment of a given compound as a "vitamin" is not as clear-cut a matter as the list of compounds in Table 12.3 might suggest. For example, it may happen that in one laboratory a certain strain of bacteria will be found to require small amounts-of some factor which is finally separated and identified chemically. Perhaps later in another laboratory a substance which is closely related to the first will prove necessary to the well being of young chicks, while yet a third set of experiments with rats may show that lack of a third related compound causes premature graying of the hair. Something of this sort happened with folic acid. The unit which appears in several different factors required by various microorganisms is pteroylglutamic acid (PGA) which may undergo various minor transformations in order to meet the specific needs of the organism which uses it. One of the metabolically active forms of PGA which has been variously called folinic acid, citrovorum factor, and leucovorin is 5-formyl-5,6,7,8-tetrahydrofolic acid. In this compound the formyl group on nitrogen 5 is activated

5-Formyl-5,6,7,8-tetrahydrofolic acid
Folinic acid

and can be transferred to bring about many different biosyntheses. Another

N¹⁰-Formyltetrahydrofolic acid

active compound is an isomer of folinic acid in which the formyl carbon is attached to the nitrogen at position 10 instead of position 5. For several organisms it has been shown that the transformation of one of these compounds to the other takes place through the intermediate formation of still a third active compound, anhydroleucovorin, in which the methene

N⁵,N¹⁰-Methenyltetrahydrofolic acid
Anhydroleucovorin

group is activated.[3] There is, however, very recent evidence that at least with some organisms there is no separation of the free anhydride so that the isomerization apparently takes place while the reactants are bound to the enzyme surface and may or may not involve a bound form of the anhydro compound. It should be emphasized that the carbon which is activated for transfer may be at various oxidation levels. For example, when the α-carbon of glycine is used to form the β-carbon of serine, it is apparently an hydroxymethyl ($-CH_2OH$) group which is transferred.

While both the N^5- and the N^{10}-substituted compounds and also the anhydro derivative are used in transfer of a single carbon, it may well be that they are not interchangeable. For example, we shall find that in the long course of the synthesis of the purine ring a single carbon is transferred in two places. It has been found that for one of these transfers the anhydro compound is used, while the N^{10}-formyl group is transferred in the other.

Active Carbon Dioxide

Although in animals carbon dioxide is usually considered a catabolic product which is excreted through the lungs, it actually plays an important synthetic role in many cells other than those of green plants. Thus the growth of yeasts, fungi, and bacteria in media which are otherwise adequate is prevented or retarded if all their metabolic carbon dioxide is swept away by a stream of CO_2 free air. Nor is the need for carbon dioxide limited to microorganisms. With various enzyme systems prepared from liver, kidney, or heart it has been shown that oxygen uptake is stimulated by the presence of carbon dioxide. Even more direct evidence has come from experiments with labeled carbon dioxide, which have led to incorporation of the carbon isotope in a number of different cell constituents, including glycogen and cell proteins. Furthermore, injection of labeled bicarbonate in a cow gave rise to labeled lactose, casein, and fat in the milk. All this makes it clear that carbon dioxide finds many uses in the cell as a synthetic substrate. As might have been expected, the primary reactions are all carboxylations, catalyzed by enzymes which are known as carboxylases or decarboxylases depending upon which facet of the reversible reaction is being considered.

Quite recently Lynen[4] and his colleagues have identified an active compound in which carbon dioxide is attached to the B vitamin known as biotin. Like most such activations, this one was discovered as a result of experiments in which the lack of the specific required factor prevented or greatly lessened the amount of some particular biosynthesis. Specifically evidence has been growing for some time that biotin was needed for certain carboxylation

---

[3] The charge may be on N^{10} instead of as shown on N^5.

[4] Feodor Lynen (1911–) has been Professor at Munich University since 1947, and is Director of the Max-Planck Institute for Cell Chemistry.

reactions, and now Lynen has isolated a biotin compound in which carbon dioxide is attached to the vitamin as shown in the formula. This compound

Probable structure of biotin-CO$_2$

then may be considered to be "active CO$_2$," in which the biotin performs the usual coenzyme function when it first accepts the carbon dioxide and then passes it on to some acceptor molecule.

Summary

The primary energy source for all aerobic cells except those which possess chlorophyll, is cellular oxidation. In the course of this oxidation, energy is freed in small units by a series of transfers, some of which free extremely small amounts of energy, but some of which release relatively large amounts. These larger units of energy are conserved in ATP by a process known as oxidative phosphorylation. Later ATP is called upon to furnish energy for a wide variety of cellular purposes.

ATP is the chief among several high energy compounds which occur in living tissue. The others are formed directly or indirectly through transfer of the terminal phosphate group of ATP. When the energy of ATP is thus mobilized for synthesis, any one of several reaction patterns may be followed. There may be a direct reaction between ATP and a substrate to form a reactive phosphate or adenylate or adenosyl derivative, the energy of which can then be used in later stages of the synthesis. Or it may be that ATP and one or two substrate molecules will undergo alterations when all are attached to the enzyme surface, and that free intermediates will never appear, but in either type of reaction the final result will be a splitting of ATP and synthesis of a new, reactive compound.

Some of the reactions referred to above bring about the coupling of the substrate molecule with one of the B vitamins to yield one of three fundamental synthetic substrates. These are acetyl coenzyme A with its thiol ester bond, an active one-carbon unit attached through nitrogen to a reduced folic acid molecule, and an active carbon dioxide in which biotin has been carboxylated with formation of a high energy compound. With these compounds at its disposal, as well as all the many intermediates provided by catabolic reactions, the cell keeps in being that dynamic equilibrium which distinguishes living from nonliving systems. The remaining chapters will consider the reaction sequences by which the absorbed foodstuffs are catabolized and the complex network of reactions by which essential metabolites and enzymes are synthesized.

SUGGESTIONS FOR FURTHER READING

Carleson, G. L., and G. M. Brown, Natural occurrence, enzymatic formation and biochemical significance of a hydroxyethyl derivative of thiamine pyrophosphate, *J. Biol. Chem.*, *236*, 2099 (1961).

Elliot, W. H., Enzymatic activation of cholic acid by guinea pig liver microsomes, *Biochem. J.*, *62*, 427 (1956).

Hartman, S. C., and J. M. Buchanan, Formyl derivatives in purine biosynthesis, *J. Biol. Chem.*, *234*, 1812 (1959).

Huennekens, F. M., and M. J. Osborn, Folic acid coenzymes and one-carbon metabolism, *Advances in Enzymol.*, 21, 369 (1959).

Kay, L. D., *et al.*, Enzymatic conversion of N^5-formyl tetrahydrofolic acid to the N^{10}-compound, *J. Biol. Chem.*, 235, 195 (1960).

Lehninger, A. L., Respiratory energy transformation, in *Biophysical Science*, J. L. Oncley (ed.-in-chief), Wiley, New York, 1959.

Lynen, F., *et al.*, Biochemical function of biotin, *Angew. Chem.*, *71*, 481 (1959).

Lynen, F., *et al.*, Active acetate, its isolation from yeast and its chemical nature, *Ann.*, *574*, 1 (1951).

Strumeyer, D. H., and K. Bloch, Some properties of γ-glutamylcysteine synthetase, *J. Biol. Chem.*, *235*, PC27 (1960).

Stumpf, P. K., Lipid metabolism, *Ann. Rev. Biochem.*, *29*, 261 (1960). This includes a review of recent work on activated CO_2.

Whiteley, H. R., *et al.*, Mechanism of formate activation, *J. Am. Chem. Soc.*, *80*, 757 (1958).

Only the great discoverer has at the same time the gift of selecting

the significant sign, the power to pursue and the patience

to follow to the end the trail which it indicates.

E. N. Da C. ANDRADE (1952)

Metabolism of the compounds of nitrogen

13

A MONG THE MOST FUNDAMENTAL PROCEDURES which all cells must carry out are those in which organic compounds of nitrogen are synthesized. These include the proteins both structural and enzymic, the nitrogenous bases which are found in the nucleoproteins, and many other compounds. Although there are among the many types of living organisms, many individual metabolic differences and certain special needs and abilities, it is astonishing how many of the known cell activities take place in the same way, under the influence of similar enzymes, in all known types of cell. Thus many reactions which were discovered in work with animal tissues have been studied and elaborated using enzymes from bacteria and plants. Many of the sequences considered in this chapter are of this sort and take place in most living cells. Where a reaction belongs only to animal cells, or exclusively to plants or bacteria, this will be noted.

SOURCES OF NITROGEN

In spite of the essential uniformity in cell metabolism, there are wide variations in the sources upon which different organisms can draw for their nitrogen supply. The reason that the metabolism of these various organisms can finally be considered together is that all the preliminary metabolic sequences converge upon ammonia or the closely related amino acids. Once either of these has been formed it is used in very similar ways by all cells.

Plant Sources

Given carbon dioxide, water, a source of nitrogen, and small amounts of other essential elements, green plants can synthesize whatever they need for growth and reproduction. Nitrogen is usually provided in the form of ammonia or nitrates in the soil solution. These compounds are taken into the root hairs and the nitrates are reduced to the level of ammonia. In some plants this reaction takes place almost entirely in the roots. In others part of the nitrate is translocated to other areas before being reduced. The individual steps in the formation of ammonia are not known, though there is some evidence that hydroxyl amine, H_2NOH, is an intermediate. This reduction is an endergonic process and proceeds only when accompanied by an oxidation which furnishes the necessary energy. Once the nitrogen has been reduced, it is used chiefly to form amino acids which then undergo the various transformations which will be considered later in the chapter.

Although inorganic nitrogen compounds furnish the usual and most effectively used form of nitrogen for plants, there are varying amounts of free amino acids in the soil and these can also be absorbed and used. They may arise from hydrolysis of decaying soil proteins, or they may be secreted by soil microorganisms. It has been shown by the use of glutamate labeled with C^{14} as a nutrient for cuttings, that free acids are used by plants, and that the L forms are used preferentially.

Nitrogen Sources of Microorganisms

As might be expected, the wide variety of microbiological types uses a broad spectrum of nitrogen sources, ranging from gaseous nitrogen to polypeptides and proteins.

The simplest of the inorganic nutrients is gaseous nitrogen which can be "fixed," or built into compounds, by both autotrophs and heterotrophs. The autotrophs are the photosynthetic organisms, including the blue green alga, *Nostoc muscorum* and several kinds of bacteria, notably *Rhodospirillum rubrum*. The heterotrophs include the aerobic *Azotobacter* group and the anaerobic *Clostridium pasteurianum*. It is of interest that when other sources of nitrogen are available, nitrogen fixation even with these organisms is inhibited. There is a marked falling off when ammonia is present in the medium, and some inhibition with nitrites, nitrates, and with some amino acids. This undoubtedly reflects the fact that the primary function of any nitrogen source is to make provision for amino acid synthesis and all these compounds either compete with gaseous nitrogen in these syntheses or replace synthetic amino acids. Tracer studies indicate that once the nitrogen has been reduced to the ammonia level it is incorporated into amino acids, with glutamic acid showing the earliest labeling. We shall find that in other types of cell also, glutamic acid seems to be of special metabolic importance.

A special type of nitrogen fixation is that carried out by bacteria of the genus *Rhizobium*. These organisms live in nodules on the roots of leguminous plants (clover, alfalfa, beans, peas, etc.) where they are able to convert atmospheric nitrogen into organic compounds of nitrogen. Since neither the plant alone nor the bacteria alone can carry out this process, it is called symbiotic nitrogen fixation.[1] The reaction takes place only under aerobic conditions, indicating that oxidation of metabolites must provide the energy for the reduction. In this connection it is of interest to recall the presence of a plant hemoglobin in the root nodules of the legumes. It is tempting to speculate that its presence may reflect a need for oxygen for nitrogen fixation beyond that which can be provided by ordinary processes of diffusion into the root. It is this symbiotic formation of compounds of nitrogen from the element which makes leguminous plants useful as fertilizer when they are grown on a field and then turned under.

The other forms of inorganic nitrogen used by microorganisms are nitrites, nitrates, and ammonium salts. These nitrogen-containing ions undergo in different organisms extensive interconversions, in the course of which they may serve either as sources of nitrogen or as sources of energy.

In the soil are two types of bacteria which bring about *oxidation* of nitrogen compounds, a process known as *nitrification*. The *Nitrosomonas* form nitrites from soil ammonia, and the *Nitrobacters* carry the oxidation of nitrites to the nitrate stage. Both steps require molecular oxygen and both are exergonic. The energy derived from these reactions is used as plants use the energy of sunlight, to bring about reduction of carbon dioxide by these organisms. It must, of course, be realized that while part of the available ammonia is thus used as fuel, forming in the process the nitrates which serve as plant food, another part must be conserved and used for synthesis of amino acids.

Another energy-yielding reaction is that known as *denitrification*, since it is the reverse of nitrification. With *Clostridium sporogenes*, for example, nitrate is reduced first to nitrite and then to ammonia. With other denitrifying organisms various intermediates have been identified such as N_2O or N_2, but there is as yet no generally accepted reaction sequence for the reductions. As in nitrification, this redox procedure is carried out to yield energy. The nitrate is simply acting as a substitute for oxygen. In oxidizing such inorganic substances as sulfur, sulfide, thiosulfate, or hydrogen, the denitrifying bacteria obtain energy for synthesis. Obviously those which subsist with nitrate as sole source of nitrogen must reduce part of it to the ammonia level in order to synthesize amino acids and ultimately proteins.

---

[1] Recent work indicates that similar fixation takes place in nodules of some nonleguminous plants, for example the alder. Symbiotic fixation may therefore be a more widely used expedient than has been realized.

Microorganisms which secrete proteases into the medium are able to use protein as a nutrient. Hydrolysis of the protein takes place outside the cell, and the resulting amino acids then diffuse across the membranes and into the cells. This process is thus in method and presumably in purpose analogous to extracellular hydrolysis of food proteins by digestive enzymes.

Some microorganisms also elaborate intracellular enzymes which act to split peptide bonds. In general these are formed relatively late in the growth cycle and act only upon small molecules. How far they exhibit the rigorous specificity of the animal peptidases is not known.

A few microorganisms actually require definite preformed small peptides and in another relatively small group specific amino acids are essential growth factors. For example, *Staphylococcus aureus* can use ammonium salts as sole source of nitrogen only if tryptophan is also provided. It is such need for specific amino acids which has made it possible to use *Leuconostoc mesenteroides*, *Lactobacillus casei*, various *Neurospora crassa* mutants, and a few other forms in the microbiological assay of amino acids (see page 215). Each *Neurospora* mutant requires only a single acid but *Leuconostoc mes.* must have seventeen different amino acids provided. These latter organisms can therefore be used, by omission of any one of the seventeen, to determine the amount of that particular acid in an unknown solution. This need for complex compounds of nitrogen is the exception rather than the rule for microorganisms, but will be referred to again later in connection with the same sort of requirement in animals.

Animal Source of Nitrogen

As has already been noted in Chapter 10 on digestion, animals get their nitrogen largely in the form of proteins. These are hydrolyzed in the digestive tract and the amino acids, absorbed into the blood stream, are carried to the cells. Thus in the nitrogen metabolism of animals as in that of other forms, the amino acids hold a commanding position. The fundamental metabolic difference between animals, on the one hand, and plants and many microorganisms, on the other, arises from the ability of the latter groups to use inorganic sources of nitrogen. Once the nitrogen has been incorporated into amino acids, all cells use them in the network of complex, interlocking organic reactions which constitute the nitrogen metabolism of living cells.

Indispensable Amino Acids

The requirement of some microorganisms for specific amino acids has already been noted. It was recognized early in the century that animals also have such requirements. This was indicated by data such as those plotted in Fig. 13.1. There it is shown that young rats, given zein as their only source of nitrogen, steadily lost weight, and that addition of both tryptophan and lysine was needed to maintain normal growth. Later experiments have shown that man and various laboratory animals require that several different amino

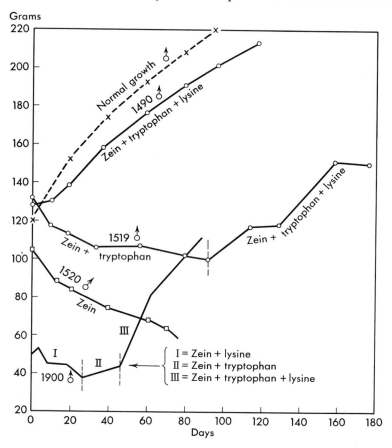

Fig. 13.1. Growth curves for rats on diets in which zein was the only protein. On zein as the sole source of nitrogen there was progressive loss of weight. When the diet was supplemented with lysine alone or with tryptophan alone the loss was smaller, and with some animals body weight was maintained. With additions of both lysine and tryptophan the growth curve was very nearly normal. [Data from T. B. Osborne and L. B. Mendel, *J. Biol. Chem.*, **17**, 325 (1914).]

acids, referred to as "indispensable," be provided in their diets. It was once thought that these requirements indicate that animals cannot synthesize these particular acids at all. More recently Rose[2] has defined an indispensable

----

[2] William S. Rose (1887–   ) is Professor Emeritus of Biochemistry at the University of Illinois. He is responsible for most of the work in which the amino acid requirements of animals are being defined.

TABLE 13.1. **Essential Amino Acids of Different Seeds**

(In grams per 100 g protein)

	Wheat		Rice Grains	Corn		Peas	Soy bean	Recommended Daily Allowance for man
	Flour	Whole		Whole	Zein			
Leucine	7.0	7.0	8.2	15	23.7	7.0	8.0	2.2
Phenylalanine	5.5	5.1	5.0	5.0	6.4	5.0	5.3	2.2
Methionine	2	2.5	3	3.1	2.3	1-3	1.7	2.2
Lysine	1.9	2.7	3.2	2.3	0	6.5	6.8	1.6
Valine	4.1	4.3	6.2	5.3	3.0	5.5	5.3	1.6
Isoleucine	4.2	4.0	5.2	6.4	7.3	5.5	6.0	1.4
Threonine	2.7	3.3	3.8	3.7	3.0	3.9	3.9	1.0
Tryptophan	0.8	1.2	1.3	0.6	0	0.8	1.4	0.5
Arginine	3.9	4.3	7.2	4.8	1.8	7.0	7.3	
Histidine	2.2	2.1	1.7	2.5	1.7	2.2	2.9	

SOURCE: From S. Brohult and E. Sandegren, Seed proteins, *The Proteins*, H. Neurath and K. Bailey (eds.), Vol. 2, p. 487, Academic, New York, 1954.

amino acid as "one which cannot be synthesized by the animal organism out of materials ordinarily available at a speed commensurate with the demands for normal growth." Presumably the acids which are dispensable are either synthesized more rapidly, or are found in ordinary proteins in larger amounts, or are less in demand.

The ultimate source of the indispensable acids for animal diets is plant proteins, since plants synthesize all the acids they need. Table 13.1 indicates the content of the essential acids in various common seeds. For comparison the recommended daily allowance for man is shown. Although not essential for adult males, histidine and arginine are included in the table, since they are essential for several laboratory animals, at least for optimal growth, and arginine is not synthesized fast enough to meet the growth needs of children.

RELATION BETWEEN FOOD AND BODY PROTEINS IN ANIMALS

Inevitably much of the early work on nitrogen metabolism was done with animals, human and otherwise. Many of the results have proved applicable to other types of cells, but some have not. Before going on to consider individual reactions, it will perhaps be helpful to sketch briefly the broad outlines of nitrogen metabolism in animals and the theories which have been evolved to explain it.

Nitrogen Excretion

In the normal animal dietary protein is the source of nitrogen. As this material is metabolized and its nitrogen becomes available to the organism, nitrogen appears in the urine as urea, with smaller quantities of ammonia, creatinine, and uric acid. A further small quantity of nitrogen eliminated in the feces is clearly not of dietary origin, since it is present even when the diet contains no protein. When a fully grown animal is subsisting on a normal and adequate diet, the amount of nitrogen excreted in 24 hours equals the amount ingested. Under these conditions the animal is said to be in nitrogen equilibrium. Obviously growing animals never achieve this state, since they are continually building new protein from ingested nitrogen. Table 13.2 shows approximately the amounts of nitrogen excreted in the urine of a man when he is in nitrogen equilibrium on two different diets, one high in protein, the other low. It will be noted that the fall in urinary nitrogen when he is transferred to the low protein diet is 10 g, 90 per cent of which loss is represented by lowered urea excretion. In contrast, the figure for creatinine is unchanged, and that for uric acid shows a far smaller percentage drop than that for urea.

The figures in both columns of Table 13.2 were obtained after equilibrium on each diet had been achieved. There was, however, a transition period between equilibrium on a high protein diet and the establishment of equilibrium on the low protein diet. The change in diet was made suddenly, from one day to the next, but nitrogen excretion did not drop suddenly to the point

TABLE 13.2. **An Approximate Representation of the Effect of Change from Equilibrium on High to Equilibrium on Low Nitrogen Intake on the Partition of Nitrogen in the Urine of an Adult Human Subject**

Form of Excretion of Nitrogen	Daily Urinary Excretion of Subject in Nitrogen Equilibrium	
	High Nitrogen Diet, g	Low Nitrogen Diet, g
Total nitrogen	15	5
Urea	12	3
Creatinine	0.5	0.5
Ammonia	0.5	0.5
Uric acid	1	0.5
Undetermined	1	0.5

SOURCE: From R. B. Fisher, *Protein Metabolism*, Methuen, London, 1954.

indicated in the second column. For a period of several days excretion exceeded intake in gradually lessening amounts, until equilibrium was again established on the lower level. If the process was reversed, and a high protein diet again provided, a similar lag period resulted, with intake exceeding excretion in gradually diminishing amounts until the new equilibrium was reached.

Early Metabolic Theories

Since the time of Lavoisier various theories have been evolved to explain the food requirements of the living organism. Food was first compared to the fuel of an engine, the living organism thus constituting the working parts of the machine. Not until the early years of the present century was it shown that the character of the "fuel" is important, that protein must be included in a diet and that among proteins only those containing certain specific amino acids are entirely adequate. From these facts, and figures such as those in Table

13.2, Folin[3] deduced that the working parts of the bodily machine, consisting in large part of protein, were subject to continual wear and tear and must therefore require renewal. These working parts were conceived to be essentially stable structures from which bits were worn out and discarded from time to time. When this happened, the organ was believed to replace the lost material from foodstuffs, which must therefore provide a supply of all the amino acids which could not readily be synthesized. According to this theory, nitrogen of the food in excess of each day's need for repair would be excreted. The metabolism of all those molecules derived from the food was referred to as *exogenous* metabolism.

Those reactions by which the structural elements of the organs were degraded to yield excretory products constituted the *endogenous* metabolism. In an adult animal, maintaining a constant body weight, the endogenous metabolism was believed to be small. Thus the bulk of the nitrogen in the urine was supposed to come directly from the food. Obtaining evidence for or against such a theory was, until recently, beset with insuperable difficulties. Amino acids of the food, once absorbed into the blood stream, were indistinguishable from amino acids broken out of body proteins. Not until isotopic N^{15} became available about 1938 was direct attack upon the problem possible.

The Dynamic Nitrogen Equilibrium

The work of Schoenheimer[4] and his colleagues, using isotopic nitrogen (N^{15}) and deuterium (D) to label molecules of individual amino acids, has shown that the theory of separate exogenous and endogenous metabolism is untenable. Far from consisting of stable structures repaired only when parts have "worn out," the living organism is in a continual state of flux. All its proteins are being constantly, and some of them astonishingly rapidly, replaced in whole or in part. The free amino acids present in the fluids and tissues at any given time may have been set free from body proteins or may have come from the foods. Some may have been in and out of body proteins several times. The nitrogen which is excreted may have come almost directly from the foodstuffs or it may come in large part from material set free from the tissues.

---

[3] Otto Folin (1867–1934) was Professor of Biological Chemistry at Harvard from 1909 until his death. He was born in Sweden and came to America at the age of fifteen. He worked in the field of nitrogen metabolism, but is most widely known for the many analytical methods which he and his students perfected.

[4] Rudolf Schoenheimer (1898–1941) was born in Berlin and began his scientific career in Germany. In 1933 political events in Germany forced him to leave his Freiburg laboratory. From that time until his death he worked in the Department of Biochemistry of the College of Physicians and Surgeons, Columbia University, and it is from that laboratory that his fundamental work with isotopic tracers was published.

The early isotope experiments

Schoenheimer obtained the first experimental evidence against the Folin theory when he fed to adult rats L(−)-leucine, labeled with both deuterium and N^{15}, and glycine marked with the nitrogen isotope. The stars in the formula indicate the positions of the isotopic atoms in the leucine.

$$\overset{*}{H_3C} \diagdown$$
$$\underset{\overset{*}{H_3C}}{\diagup}\overset{*}{CH}-\overset{*}{CH_2}-CH-COOH$$
$$\underset{\underset{*}{NH_2}}{|}$$

Leucine

According to the earlier concept, the urine collected during the experimental feeding period should have contained most of the labeled dietary nitrogen. Table 13.3 indicates the actual distribution of N^{15} between excreta and the

TABLE 13.3. Fate of Amino Nitrogen in Normal Adult Rats

(Isotopic amino acids, corresponding to 25 mg N per day for 3 days, were added to normal stock diet)

Material Analyzed	Per Cent of Administered N^{15} Recovered	
	After Feeding L(−)-Leucine	After Feeding Glycine
Excreta		
Feces	2.2	2.6
Urine	27.4	40.8
Animal body		
Nonprotein N	8.2	11.1
Protein N	56.5	44.3
Total	94.3	98.8

SOURCE: Table from R. Schoenheimer, *The Dynamic State of Body Constituents*, Harvard University, Cambridge, Mass., 1949.

body proteins. Although there was no increase in the body weights, more than 50 per cent of the isotopic nitrogen administered in leucine had been incorporated into the body proteins, and less than 30 per cent had been excreted. Similar results have been obtained with a number of other labeled amino acids, indicating that the incorporation of dietary amino acids into the body proteins is far more constant and rapid than had previously seemed likely. Analysis of separate organs and of body fluids showed that the isotopic nitrogen had been built into every organ investigated, as well as into serum proteins, hemoglobin, and skin proteins.

Even more surprising were the results obtained when these same body proteins were hydrolyzed, in order to determine the distribution of N^{15} among the different amino acids. After feeding isotopic leucine, N^{15} was found, not only in the leucine of the organ proteins but also in every other amino acid estimated except lysine. The double labeling of leucine made it possible to say positively that its carbon chain as well as its nitrogen had been incorporated into the tissue proteins. Table 13.4 gives the N^{15} content of the

TABLE 13.4. N^{15} Content of Amino Acids Isolated from Proteins of Rats Given Labeled L-Leucine

(Recoveries are calculated for 100 atom per cent N^{15} in the labeled compound administered)

Amino Acid	Liver	Intestinal Wall	Muscle and Skin
Leucine	7.95	7.35	1.90
Glycine	0.74	0.63	
Tyrosine	0.50	0.94	0.20
Glutamic acid	1.85	2.97	0.89
Aspartic acid	1.16	2.30	0.70
Arginine	0.89	0.43	0.25
Lysine	0.06	0.07	
Amide N	0.78	1.24	

SOURCE: From R. Schoenheimer, *The Dynamic State of Body Constituents*, Harvard University, Cambridge, Mass., 1949.

amino acids isolated from the organ proteins of the rats in this experiment. Of the total N^{15} found in the proteins, only 30 per cent was still attached to the leucine residues, and the remaining 70 per cent was distributed among several other amino acids. Of these, the dicarboxylic acids, aspartic and glutamic acids, had been most active in acquiring new nitrogen. The presence of the nitrogen isotope in leucine itself is not unexpected, but its presence in significant amounts in so many other amino acids indicates an undreamed of lability on the part both of the amino acids and of the structural proteins. Not only has N^{15} been transferred from leucine to at least five other amino acids, but all these acids have replaced other, presumably similar acid residues previously part of the organ proteins. This process involves the opening of at least two peptide links for each acid residue introduced, and their rapid re-formation to hold the new acid. Similar experimental results with other labeled amino acids lead to the belief that the transfer of nitrogen from one amino acid to another (excepting lysine) goes on continuously, and that there is a constant, rapid interchange between the acid residues of body proteins and the pool of free amino acids. It has been estimated that at least 10 per cent of the liver protein of a rat is newly formed in the course of three days, and that one-half of it has been resynthesized in about seven days.

Until Schoenheimer published his results, it was tacitly assumed that synthesis in the animal body takes place only to fill some specific need for a particular compound. This is far from the truth. In one experiment, tyrosine labeled with N^{15} was added to a diet in which enough casein was provided to meet abundantly all amino acid requirements. In spite of this abundance of unlabeled acids, isotopic nitrogen was only partly excreted, and that which was retained was found to have been incorporated in all the amino acids isolated, again excepting lysine. As in previous experiments, a high percentage of the isotope had been used in the synthesis of glutamic acid, although there was already available a generous supply of this acid from the casein. Evidently the body constantly builds dietary nitrogen into nearly all the amino acids, regardless of whether there is a lack or not.

Application of the isotope technique to plant cells is difficult because plants have no protracted period during which their metabolism is analogous to that of a mature animal in nitrogen equilibrium. Nevertheless Vickery[5] and Pucher collaborated with Schoenheimer's group in experiments in which $N^{15}H_4Cl$ was used as a source of nitrogen for a single tobacco plant growing in a culture solution. The results are summarized in Tables 13.5 and 13.6. The first table shows that the isotope found its way in the course of three days into proteins and into various smaller compounds represented by the water- and alcohol-soluble fractions. It is not unexpected to find a high concentration of the isotope in the ammonium ion, but the large amount in the form of amide nitrogen is interesting, indicating the use of ammonia to synthesize two compounds known to be of special importance in plant metabolism. These are the half amides of the two dibasic amino acids, glutamine and asparagine, which may make up 35 to 75 per cent of plant nonprotein nitrogen. In Table 13.6 it is noteworthy that in plants as in animals, a high proportion of the isotope is found in the two dibasic acids, with glutamic acid acquiring the higher proportion.

Out of these experiments has come a new theory of the nature of protein metabolism. Most of the body proteins including those of the blood[6] and of the tissue enzymes are extremely labile. Peptide and other bonds are constantly opening and allowing free amino acids to escape and to merge with

---

[5] Hubert Bradford Vickery was born and educated in Nova Scotia. He has been at the Connecticut Agricultural Experiment Station since 1922, and has been its Director since 1928.

[6] Hemoglobin and collagen are exceptions. Hemoglobin has no appreciable turnover during the life of the erythrocyte, and collagen is almost unchanged during the life span of the rat.

TABLE 13.5. Effect of Administration of Ammonium Chloride with 1.21 Atom Per Cent N^{15} Excess on Certain Nitrogenous Components of Tobacco Plant Tissues

(A single plant 41 days from the seedling stage was treated for 72 hrs. The data are expressed as atom per cent N^{15} excess.)

	Leaf		Stalk		Root	
	Found	Calculated for 100% N^{15} in NH_4Cl Administered	Found	Calculated for 100% N^{15} in NH_4Cl Administered	Found	Calculated for 100% N^{15} in NH_4Cl Administered
Protein N	0.099	8.2	0.184	15.2	0.222	18.4
Ammonia N	0.260	21.5	0.275	22.7	0.779	64.3
Amide N	0.217	17.9	0.286	23.6		
Water-soluble N pptd. by Neuberg reagent	0.184	15.2	0.225	18.6		
Water-soluble N not pptd. by Neuberg reagent	0.123	10.2	0.108	8.9		
Volatile base N	0.030	2.5				
Alcohol-soluble N not soluble in water	0.078	6.4	0.104	8.6	0.200	16.5
Water-soluble N exclusive of ammonia N					0.414	34.2

SOURCE: From H. B. Vickery *et al.*, Assimilation of NH_3-nitrogen by a tobacco plant, *J. Biol. Chem.*, 135, 531 (1940).

those from the foodstuffs. The depleted proteins must simultaneously take up whatever acids they need to replace those just lost, for they themselves remain constant in amount and composition. There is at present no agreement as to whether these changes are brought about by complete breakdown and resynthesis of a protein or by limited removal of individual amino acids and their replacement without any major destruction of the protein fabric.

TABLE 13.6. N^{15} **Concentration (Atom Per Cent Excess) in Amino Acid Fractions from Crude Protein of Leaves of Tobacco Plant to Which Isotopic Nitrogen Had Been Administered**

Amino Acid Fraction	N^{15} Concentration
Total protein	0.099
Arginine	0.086
Histidine	0.090
Glutamic acid	0.128
Aspartic acid	0.113
Copper salts insoluble in water and methanol	0.104
Copper salts insoluble in water but soluble in methanol	0.100
Remaining amino acids	0.096

SOURCE: From H. B. Vickery *et al.*, Assimilation of NH_3-nitrogen by a tobacco plant, *J. Biol. Chem.*, *135*, 531 (1940).

It is presumably with these continual hydrolyses of peptide bonds that the cellular proteases, known collectively as cathepsins are concerned. During life these enzymes bring about controlled hydrolyses which are balanced by syntheses. After death hydrolysis is not followed by synthesis, with the result that the membranes enclosing the cathepsins and other enzymes are digested, thus bringing the proteolytic enzymes in contact with all the cytoplasmic proteins. Autolysis then ensues.

In the living organism the free amino acids, present both inside and outside the cells, constitute a constantly changing metabolic pool in which it is impossible to distinguish the source of any particular acid. From this pool some acids are withdrawn for protein synthesis. Others are degraded, and their nitrogen is excreted by animals. Plants conserve the degradation products by storing them in vacuoles and for the most part use them again in synthesis. It is of interest in this connection to note that some plants do excrete compounds of nitrogen into the soil. This would seem to indicate that they also find themselves at times possessed of more nitrogen compounds than they can use or store, and that any such excess is excreted by way of the roots.

Thus the work of Schoenheimer and his collaborators has revealed in broad outline the elaborate dynamic equilibrium maintained by living cells. For light upon the specific chemical reactions involved in these transformations we must turn to other studies and seek answers to such questions as the following: How is nitrogen removed from an amino acid and where does this removal take place? How is this nitrogen used synthetically and how does it find its way into excretory products? What happens to the rest of the amino acid after its nitrogen has been removed? How is nitrogen transferred from one amino acid to another? How far is the nitrogen metabolism of animals, with their specialized organs, comparable with the metabolism of plants and microorganisms? Such problems as these have been studied in experiments using isotopic labels, with tissue slices, with subcellular particles and with purified enzymes. They have yielded some fairly definitive answers and have left us, as the following pages will show, with many new questions.

METABOLISM OF THE AMINO ACIDS

The first quarter of the twentieth century was marked by a spate of papers concerned primarily with the site of urea formation and to a lesser extent with the whole question of amino acid metabolism. The amino acids of the foodstuffs, absorbed into the capillaries of the villi, pass by way of the portal vein directly to the liver. There many of them are removed from the blood, and at the peak of absorption the amino acid content of the liver may be as high as five times its normal resting value. During the ensuing three or four hours, the amino acid content of the tissue drops, and simultaneously the amount of urea in the blood rises. During this same period there is no such fluctuation in the amino acid content of other tissues. However, all tissues do contain a certain amount of free amino acid, and this raises the question whether the metabolism of amino acids is a function of all tissues, or is restricted to the liver.

Role of the Liver

For many years it was impossible to decide where the amino acids are metabolized, because many of the analytical methods and experimental techniques were too insensitive to detect the differences which must be measured. From the great volume of literature on the subject, the following experimental results indicate how the question was finally answered. Perfusion experiments showed that the surviving mammalian liver could form urea from a wide variety of amino acids added to the perfusion fluid. Urea was also formed when the liver was perfused with a solution which included ammonia, and in this case as well as the former one, the synthesis depended upon effective aeration of the perfusion fluid. Thus it was clear that the transformation either involved an oxidative step or required a source of energy. Clinical studies showed that in patients with extensive liver damage, urea excretion decreased, and simultaneously the excretion of ammonia increased. Finally in 1924 came the now classical paper of Bollman,[7] Mann, and Magath, reporting on the results of complete extirpation of the liver in dogs. This delicate operation was performed in three stages, so that a subsidiary circulation around the liver was developed before the final hepatectomy. The animals recovered from the third operative procedure promptly and were able to survive for four to thirty-four hours if given glucose intravenously. During this time blood and urine analyses were carried out at intervals, and the results were compared with those from carefully chosen control animals. It was found that as long as urine secretion was maintained, the urea content of both blood and urine fell progressively and that there was a simultaneous increase in urinary ammonia. If urinary flow was interrupted, the urea in the blood remained at a constant level and the amino acid concentration rose. These observations, coupled with what was already known, indicated the probable overall course of amino acid metabolism in the intact mammalian animal. Partly because of its strategic position, the liver removes most of the amino acids which enter the circulation from the gut. The amino groups of some of these acids are rapidly split out as ammonia, and from this ammonia urea is synthesized by the liver. The other organ which readily removes ammonia from the amino acids is the kidney, and it is likely that in the intact animal some of the ammonia from which urea is formed by the liver is in the first place set free from amino acids in the kidney.

The importance of the liver in nitrogen metabolism was confirmed in 1943 when it was shown that although animals in which the plasma protein concentration had been greatly reduced replace these compounds surprisingly rapidly, there is no such recovery in hepatectomized dogs. Because of these and many similar results, experiments on individual steps in nitrogen metabolism often begin with enzyme preparations from liver cells.

Deamination

The removal of the amino group from an amino acid is known as deamination. Living cells are able to accomplish this in several different ways, but the reaction which seems to be most fundamental both in plants and animals is the one in which deamination is accompanied by oxidation.

---

[7] Dr. Frank Charles Mann (1887–) is Professor Emeritus of Experimental Medicine at the Mayo Foundation in Rochester, Minnesota, and Dr. Jesse L. Bollman (1896–), Professor of Experimental Pathology. Theirs has been a long and fruitful collaboration concentrated largely in the field of nitrogen metabolism.

Oxidative deamination

The history of our increasing understanding of the oxidative removal of amino groups illustrates admirably the use of many of the different biochemical research techniques. As early as 1928 Neubauer began the study of amino acid metabolism by using acids labeled by phenyl substitution. Feeding of these compounds to animals was followed by excretion of the corresponding aromatic keto acids in the urine. Neubauer suggested then that the first step in amino acid metabolism gives rise to keto acid and ammonia according to the equation

$$R \cdot CH(NH_2)COOH + \tfrac{1}{2}O_2 \rightarrow R \cdot CO \cdot COOH + NH_3$$

A few years later Krebs made an exhaustive study of this reaction. He made use of the tissue slice technique and determined both the Q_{O_2} and the Q_{NH_3}, besides isolating the keto acids in some cases. This study showed that mammalian kidney is the most active deaminating organ in the body, setting free ammonia three times as fast, per gram of dry weight, as the next most active organ, the liver. It should be noted, however, that because of its much greater weight the liver actually deals with the larger proportion of amino acids. Krebs was able to prove that the kidney contains two separate deaminating systems, one of which oxidizes and deaminates the natural or L-amino acids, while the other attacks only the D isomers. Under normal conditions the keto acids which are formed by either system are promptly oxidized or otherwise changed. In order that they may accumulate in sufficient quantity to be isolated, it is necessary to poison the enzymes responsible for their oxidation. Krebs was able to achieve this by the use of arsenic trioxide, in the presence of which the deamination proceeds smoothly, while the further oxidation of the resulting keto acids is blocked. Under these conditions the keto acids accumulated in such quantity that it was possible to isolate them as their 2,4-dinitrophenylhydrazones. In some of the experiments the rate of oxygen uptake was measured at the same time that the rate of synthesis of ammonia and of keto acid was determined. The ratio, oxygen used: ammonia formed: keto acid formed, proved to be close to $1:2:2$, as it should be if the reaction takes place as suggested in Neubauer's equation.

It will be recalled that in the chapter dealing with enzymes, the reaction catalyzed by D-amino acid oxidase was examined as an example of an oxidative enzyme action in which a coenzyme is concerned. It was shown there that the oxidative deamination of a D-amino acid takes place in two steps. There is first an enzymic dehydrogenation of the acid to form an imino acid, followed by a nonenzymic reaction in which the imino acid reacts with water to form ammonia and the corresponding keto acid. Until quite recently the formation of the imino acid was inferred from the transfer of hydrogen to the flavin coenzyme. Spectroscopic evidence has now given direct proof of the formation of such a compound in the oxidative deamination of alanine.

$$R \cdot CH(NH_2) \cdot COOH + FAD \rightarrow R \cdot C(\!=\!\!NH) \cdot COOH + FADH_2$$

| Oxidized coenzyme | Imino acid | Reduced coenzyme |

$$R \cdot C(\!=\!\!NH) \cdot COOH + H_2O \rightarrow R \cdot CO \cdot COOH + NH_3$$

Keto acid

The primary hydrogen acceptor is the flavin adenine dinucleotide which in an isolated system using a purified enzyme passes the hydrogen on to molecular oxygen with formation of hydrogen peroxide. Since this compound in any appreciable quantity is toxic, one must assume that in living tissue much of the hydrogen is passed on to molecular oxygen by way of the cytochromes and leads to formation of water. If any peroxide does form, it may be degraded by catalase, or it may be used as an oxidizing agent fast enough to keep its concentration low.

If the above mechanism holds for the system which catalyzes the metabolism of the natural acids, it would seem that the story of the deamination of amino acids is complete and satisfactory. It presents, however, certain anomalous features. Mammalian kidney oxidizes the unnatural amino acids, with which it normally never has to deal, ten to twenty times as fast as it attacks the natural ones. It is hard to understand why there should be available any enzyme concerned with the metabolism of acids which the organism never meets naturally. It is still more difficult to see why this enzyme should be the more active and stable one. Its greater stability led to its prior separation from the cells, at a time when the enzyme concerned with the natural acids was either completely refractory to extraction or was destroyed in the process. Some years later, Green[8] and his colleagues obtained from rat kidneys an L-amino acid oxidase. This proved to be also a conjugated protein, but the prosthetic group of this L-oxidase is riboflavin monophosphate instead of the flavin adenine dinucleotide which functions with the D-enzyme. Experiments have shown that this L-oxidase can act upon more than half of the naturally occurring amino acids, and that the products are again keto acids, ammonia, and peroxide. However, the original hope that this enzyme would account adequately for the deamination of the natural acids has been disappointed on two counts. In the first place, it is distributed far too narrowly to be quantitatively significant in animal metabolism, being low or absent in cat, dog, guinea pig, rabbit, ox, or sheep tissues. Furthermore, even in purified form its activity is strikingly low. This, of course, agrees with Krebs's original observation that kidney deaminates the unnatural acids far more rapidly than the natural ones. Up to the present no general amino acid oxidases

---

[8] David E. Green (1910–   ) is Professor of Biochemistry at the Institute for Enzyme Research of the University of Wisconsin. He has contributed brilliantly to the development of enzyme biochemistry, and has of late years been particularly interested in the enzymes of the respiratory chain and their relation to mitochondria.

have been found in the tissues of higher plants but they have been obtained from molds and bacteria and an L-amino acid oxidase which is also a flavoprotein is found in snake venom and is referred to as *ophio*-L-amino acid oxidase.

In addition to these general D- and L-amino acid oxidases which attack a number of different acids, there are a few concerned specifically with the metabolism of single acids. There is a *glycine dehydrogenase*[9] which is a flavoprotein, an L-*alanine dehydrogenase*, and an L-*glutamate dehydrogenase* all of which remove two hydrogens from the substrate with subsequent formation of the corresponding keto acid. With glycine the overall reaction is:

$$H_2N \cdot CH_2 \cdot COOH + \tfrac{1}{2}O_2 \rightarrow CHO \cdot COOH + NH_3$$
$$\text{Glycine} \qquad\qquad\qquad \text{Glyoxylic acid}$$

We have already noted the metabolic activity of glutamic acid. The L-glutamate dehydrogenase helps to explain this, for this catalyzes one of the two oxidative deaminations which are readily reversible. This means that this catalyst can be used by the cell to incorporate free ammonia into glutamic acid, and in a subsequent section we shall see that once the nitrogen is built into glutamate it is very readily transferred to other amino acids. As noted in the equations, coenzyme I (DPN$^+$) is the hydrogen acceptor for glutamate

$$
\begin{array}{l}
\text{COOH} \\
|\\
\text{CH} \cdot \text{NH}_2 \\
|\\
\text{CH}_2 \\
|\\
\text{CH}_2 \cdot \text{COOH} \\
\text{Glutamic acid}
\end{array}
\quad
\begin{array}{c}
+ \text{DPN}^+ \rightleftharpoons \\
\textbf{(NAD)}
\end{array}
\quad
\begin{array}{l}
\text{COOH} \\
|\\
\text{C}{=}\text{NH} \\
|\\
\text{CH}_2 \\
|\\
\text{CH}_2 \cdot \text{COOH} \\
\text{α-Iminoglutaric acid}
\end{array}
\quad
\begin{array}{c}
+ \text{DPNH} + \text{H}^+ \\
\textbf{(NADH}_2\textbf{)}
\end{array}
$$

$$
\begin{array}{l}
\text{COOH} \\
|\\
\text{C}{=}\text{NH} \\
|\\
\text{CH}_2 \\
|\\
\text{CH}_2 \cdot \text{COOH} \\
\text{α-Iminoglutaric acid}
\end{array}
\quad
+ \text{H}_2\text{O} \rightleftharpoons
\quad
\begin{array}{l}
\text{COOH} \\
|\\
\text{CO} \\
|\\
\text{CH}_2 \\
|\\
\text{CH}_2\text{COOH} \\
\text{α-Ketoglutaric acid}
\end{array}
\quad
+ \text{NH}_3
$$

dehydrogenase, and the hydrogens are to be thought of as following the usual path through the cytochromes to oxygen. Reversal of the reactions as written would result in synthesis of glutamic acid from α-ketoglutaric acid and ammonia. The enzyme involved in this particular catalysis is widely distributed in plant and animal tissues and in bacteria.

---

[9] The enzymes which catalyze removal of hydrogen are more correctly known as dehydrogenases, though the name oxidase is often used, as it is for the amino acid oxidases.

Quite recently it has been shown (see Goldman reference) that the reaction catalyzed by an alanine dehydrogenase is also reversible. The enzyme was originally found in bacteria but has since been isolated from liver mitochondria. This may mean that this path of amino acid synthesis from ammonia and keto acids is of more general occurrence than has been supposed. It is suggested for the alanine synthesis that the reaction involves a preliminary combination of the enzyme and the ammonium ion and that the subsequent transfer of nitrogen to the keto acid gives an imino acid bound to the enzyme surface. This compound is then reduced, as shown in the equations, where E as usual stands for the enzyme protein:

$$E + NH_4^+ \rightleftharpoons (E\!\!-\!\!NH_4^+)$$

$$(E\!\!-\!\!NH_4^+) + CH_3 \cdot CO \cdot COO^- \rightleftharpoons E\!\!-\!\!CH_3 \cdot \underset{\overset{\|}{NH}}{C} \cdot COO^- + H_2O + H^+$$

$$E\!\!-\!\!CH_3 \cdot \underset{\overset{\|}{NH}}{C} \cdot COO^- + DPNH + H^+ \rightleftharpoons CH_3 \cdot \underset{\overset{|}{NH_2}}{CH} \cdot COO^- + E + DPN^+$$

But even with the addition of enzymes which catalyze reversible reactions or specific deaminations, the roster of those which must be involved in the metabolism of the natural acids is not very satisfying. The present situation has been summed up by Cohen[10] as follows: "The student . . . is presented with the anomalous situation of having comparatively detailed information concerning enzymes whose physiological function is of questionable significance and being virtually ignorant of those enzymes which might be expected to play a more important role." It now seems probable that removal of nitrogen from an amino acid is more often brought about by a different mechanism, known as transamination, which is taken up on page 477 than by oxidative deamination.

Although specific enzymes are largely unidentified, it is still assumed that the reaction mechanism indicated above for the unnatural acids is also characteristic of the natural ones when they do undergo this type of deamination. The ammonia which is set free may then be excreted as urea, or it may be used in synthesis or stored as glutamine, the half amide of glutamic acid, or as asparagine, the half amide of aspartic acid.

Glutamine is known to be formed in liver and in nervous tissue where it may be simply a reserve form of ammonia or may be used in protein synthesis, since the two amide residues occur as such in proteins. Both amides occur in relatively high concentration is some plant tissues, where they have long been

---

[10] Philip P. Cohen (1908–   ) is Professor of Physiological Chemistry at the University of Wisconsin Medical School, and has been since 1948 Head of the Department. His work is chiefly in the field of nitrogen metabolism, and has of late been concerned with urea synthesis.

$$
\begin{array}{cc}
\text{CONH}_2 & \text{CONH}_2 \\
| & | \\
\text{CH}_2 & \text{CH}_2 \\
| & | \\
\text{CH} \cdot \text{NH}_2 & \text{CH}_2 \\
| & | \\
\text{COOH} & \text{CH} \cdot \text{NH}_2 \\
& | \\
& \text{COOH}
\end{array}
$$

Asparagine	**Glutamine**

considered important in the storage of ammonia. The enzymes glutaminase and asparaginase which catalyze the reversible hydrolysis of the amides are widely distributed and would free ammonia when needed. Experiments with plants have shown a progressive loss of glutamine from tissue which is synthesizing protein. While this may reflect some synthetic use of the amide itself, it is considered to depend more upon the use of the amide nitrogen in synthesis of other amino acids.

Other deamination mechanisms

Although the enzymes of oxidative deamination are widely distributed in plants and animals, other pathways for removal of nitrogen from an amino acid are known. One of these involves a simultaneous deamination and desaturation. The enzyme, known as *aspartase*, is found in bacteria and some plants and catalyzes the reversible transformation of aspartic acid to fumaric acid and ammonia. This reaction is important for the same reason

$$
\begin{array}{cc}
\text{COOH} & \\
| & \\
\text{CH} \cdot \text{NH}_2 & \quad\quad \text{CH} \cdot \text{COOH} \\
| \quad \xrightleftharpoons[\text{aspartase}]{} & \quad\quad\quad \| \quad\quad\quad + \text{NH}_3 \\
\text{CH}_2 & \quad\quad \text{HOOC} \cdot \text{CH} \\
| & \\
\text{COOH} & \\
\textbf{Aspartic acid} & \quad\quad\quad \textbf{Fumaric acid}
\end{array}
$$

that the dehydrogenations of glutamate and of alanine are important. The reverse reaction results in incorporation of ammonia into an amino acid. Serine and threonine also undergo anomalous deaminations which are described on page 494.

Still another deamination mechanism has been found in anaerobic bacteria. They remove amino groups reductively, forming ammonia and the corresponding fatty acid. The hydrogens used in the reduction are furnished by DPNH which thus would act to link some previous oxidation of a metabolite with the reductive deamination of an amino acid.

$$
\text{R} \cdot \text{CH(NH}_2) \cdot \text{COOH} + \text{DPNH} + \text{H}^+ \rightarrow
$$
$$
\text{R} \cdot \text{CH}_2 \cdot \text{COOH} + \text{NH}_3 + \text{DPN}^+
$$

Transamination

In most plant and animal tissues the main organic products of deamination are the keto acids, which then undergo further transformation. They may be oxidized completely to carbon dioxide and water. They may be used for synthesis of carbohydrate or of fatty metabolites. Or they may acquire new amino groups and so again become members of the metabolic pool of amino acids. This last reaction is known as transamination.

In 1937 Braunstein and Kritzmann reported from the Institute for Experimental Medicine in Moscow their discovery of an enzymic reaction by which certain keto acids may be transformed into amino acids. They showed that many different plant and animal tissues contain an enzyme which catalyzes a reaction between a keto acid and an amino acid, in the course of which the amino acid donates its basic group to the keto acid. In the original experiments glutamic acid reacted with pyruvic acid to form alanine, itself becoming α-ketoglutaric acid. Because of this interchange the authors referred to the reaction as "umaminierung," which has been translated transamination.

$$
\begin{array}{lllll}
CH_2 \cdot COOH & CH_3 & & CH_2 \cdot COOH & CH_3 \\
| & | & \text{transaminase} & | & | \\
CH_2 & + CO & \rightleftharpoons & CH_2 & + CH \cdot NH_2 \\
| & | & & | & | \\
CH(NH_2) \cdot COOH & COOH & & CO \cdot COOH & COOH \\
\textbf{Glutamic} & \textbf{Pyruvic} & & \textbf{α-Ketoglutaric} & \textbf{Alanine} \\
\textbf{acid} & \textbf{acid} & & \textbf{acid} &
\end{array}
$$

The discoverers assumed that the transamination reaction had a very broad application and that any amino acid could thus transfer its amino group to any one of a wide variety of keto acids. For some years this was questioned, as the first transaminases to be isolated proved to be very specific and to catalyze transfer of amino groups from glutamate to just two keto acids. Later work, however, has fully established the general scope of the reaction. Transaminases have been found in bacteria, in higher plants, and in various animal tissues. They catalyze the transfer of amino groups from a wide variety of amino acids to a list of different keto acids which continues to grow.

Deamination transforms the amino acids into keto acids. Many of these keto acids then accept new amino groups from other amino acids in the vicinity, and in this way any isotopic nitrogen administered in an amino acid is soon distributed at random among most of the members of the entire pool. It will be remembered that lysine was the one amino acid which did not acquire labeled nitrogen in the Schoenheimer experiments. Threonine is the only other acid which has since proved to share this inertness. This is now taken to mean that for some unknown reason these two acids do not take part in the transamination reactions which otherwise are so characteristic of this group of compounds.

Quite recently it has been found that it is not only the free acids which undergo transamination. Liver enzymes bring about the transfer of the α-amino group of glutamine to a number of different keto acids, with simultaneous hydrolysis of the amide itself to a free keto acid. The properties of the enzyme (or enzymes) involved show that it is quite distinct from the transaminases which act on the free amino acids. Here then is a definite function for glutamine in animal metabolism. It is likely that both glutamine and asparagine perform a like function in plants.

The significance of the transamination reaction lies in the fact that keto acids arise not only in deamination of amino acids but also in the course of carbohydrate breakdown in plants, animals, and microorganisms. Furthermore, it is very likely that several of these compounds are formed also in the course of photosynthesis. Under these circumstances the synthesis of amino acids from keto acids by transamination is not merely a kind of Grand March, with amino acids changing partners all down the line, but neither increasing nor decreasing in total amount. The process is, on the other hand, a true synthesis in the sense that entirely new amino acids with new carbon chains will arise. Such a synthesis is indicated below with the nitrogen coming from ammonia by way of the reversed L-glutamate dehydrogenase reaction and the carbon skeleton from synthetic reactions in the course of which microorganisms use pyruvic acid to build up the branched chain keto acid. It will be remembered that leucine is an indispensable amino acid, hence this reaction is not characteristic of animal cells.

$$
\begin{array}{ccc}
& \text{COOH} & \text{COOH} \\
& | & | \\
& \text{CO} & \text{CH} \cdot \text{NH}_2 \\
& | & | \\
\text{NH}_3 + & \text{CH}_2 \quad + \text{DPNH} + \text{H}^+ \rightleftharpoons & \text{CH}_2 \quad + \text{DPN}^+ + \text{H}_2\text{O} \\
& | & | \\
& \text{CH}_2 & \text{CH}_2 \\
& | & | \\
& \text{COOH} & \text{COOH} \\
& \alpha\text{-Ketoglutaric acid} & \text{Glutamic acid}
\end{array}
$$

$$
\begin{array}{cccc}
\text{COOH} & \text{COOH} & \text{COOH} & \text{COOH} \\
| & | & | & | \\
\text{CH} \cdot \text{NH}_2 & \text{CO} & \text{CO} & \text{CH} \cdot \text{NH}_2 \\
| & | & | & | \\
\text{CH}_2 \quad + & \text{CH}_2 \quad \rightarrow & \text{CH}_2 \quad + & \text{CH}_2 \\
| & | & | & | \\
\text{CH}_2 & \text{CH} & \text{CH}_2 & \text{CH} \\
| & \diagup \diagdown & | & \diagup \diagdown \\
\text{COOH} & \text{CH}_3 \quad \text{CH}_3 & \text{COOH} & \text{CH}_3 \quad \text{CH}_3 \\
\textbf{Glutamic} & \alpha\textbf{-Ketoisocaproic} & & \textbf{Leucine} \\
\textbf{acid} & \textbf{acid from the} & & \\
& \textbf{metabolic pool} & &
\end{array}
$$

Mechanism of transamination

Reactions similar to enzymic transaminations may be brought about at elevated temperatures without the use of a biocatalyst. In such reactions there is evidence that the transfer takes place through the intermediate formation of a compound of the type known as a *Schiff's base*. Braunstein and Kritzmann suggested a similar mechanism for the enzymic reaction.

$$
\begin{array}{c}
R \\ | \\ CO \\ | \\ COOH
\end{array}
\; + \;
\begin{array}{c}
R_1 \\ | \\ H_2N \cdot CH \\ | \\ COOH
\end{array}
\;\xrightleftharpoons[]{-H_2O}\;
\begin{array}{cc}
R & R_1 \\ | & | \\ C{=}N \cdot CH & \\ | & | \\ COOH & COOH
\end{array}
\;\rightleftharpoons\;
\begin{array}{cc}
R & R_1 \\ | & | \\ C{=}N \cdot C^- & + H^+ \\ | & | \\ COOH & COOH
\end{array}
\;\rightleftharpoons
$$

Schiff's base

$$
\begin{array}{cc}
R & R_1 \\ | & | \\ {}^-C{-}N{=}C & \\ | & | \\ COOH & COOH
\end{array}
\;\xrightleftharpoons[]{+H^+}\;
\begin{array}{cc}
R & R_1 \\ | & | \\ CH{-}N{=}C & \\ | & | \\ COOH & COOH
\end{array}
\;\xrightleftharpoons[]{\pm H_2O}\;
\begin{array}{cc}
R & R_1 \\ | & | \\ CH(NH_2) & + CO \\ | & | \\ COOH & COOH
\end{array}
$$

According to this scheme there is first formed an addition compound, which by the two-stage shift of a proton undergoes an intramolecular rearrangement which moves the double bond from one side of the nitrogen to the other. Hydrolysis of the rearranged addition product yields the new keto and amino acids.

This mechanism, with the understanding that it took place with the reactants bound to the enzyme surface, was accepted until it was shown that most of the transaminases occur as conjugated proteins. The obligatory coenzyme proves to be a phosphorylated derivative of vitamin B_6. The substance which is called vitamin B_6 is the pyridine derivative, pyridoxine. The formulas show the relationship to pyridoxine of the two compounds, pyridoxal and pyridoxamine, which in phosphorylated form act as coenzymes of transamination.

Pyridoxine   **Pyridoxal**   **Pyridoxamine**

It has now been shown that the transamination reaction takes place in two steps, in the course of which the coenzyme transfers an amino group by being alternately aminated and deaminated. The first step is the transfer of an amino group to the enzyme-pyridoxal phosphate complex from an α-amino acid, probably through intermediate formation of an addition compound of the Schiff's base type, with linkage of the amino acid to the pyridoxal phosphate at the aldehyde group. This yields a keto acid and pyridoxamine phosphate-enzyme. The curves shown in Fig. 2.13 on page 39 give the absorbancy of the two forms of the enzyme in (*a*) and the changing absorbancy as the pyridoxal form changes to the pyridoxamine in (*b*).

Amino acid   **Pyridoxal phosphate**   **Keto acid**   **Pyridoxamine phosphate**

The newly formed pyridoxamine phosphate then takes part in a similar reaction with a keto acid, regenerating the pyridoxal phosphate and forming a new amino acid.

The net result may then be summed up in the typical transamination equation.

Transmethylation

The indispensable amino acid methionine is one of several compounds which take part in a reaction known as transmethylation. Compounds containing methyl groups are of fundamental importance to the animal economy. These include *methionine* itself, *choline*, which forms part of more than one phospholipid and which as acetylcholine plays a part in transmission of nerve impulses, and *creatine*, which as creatine phosphate is part of the elaborate chemical system which accompanies muscular contraction. The nicotinamide which is the functional part of the pyridine coenzymes is methylated before excretion to form N^1-methylnicotinamide. These compounds, except methionine, have methyl groups attached to nitrogen.

$$-CONH_2$$

N^1-Methylnicotinamide

In plants also many compounds are formed which contain methyl groups attached either through nitrogen or through oxygen. For example caffeine, found in tea and maté leaves as well as in the coffee bean, has three methyl groups attached through nitrogen. Lignin, the plant polymer which with cellulose makes up the supporting structure of plant stems and which constitutes 25 to 30 per cent of wood is an important plant constituent in which methyl groups are attached through oxygen to a phenolic ring. Table 13.7

TABLE 13.7. Some Important Methylated Compounds

Compound	Formula
Acetylcholine	$(CH_3)_3\overset{+}{N} \cdot CH_2 \cdot CH_2O \cdot OCCH_3$
Caffeine 1,3,7-trimethyl-2,6-dioxopurine	
Creatine phosphate	$H_2O_3P \cdot HN \cdot C \cdot N \cdot CH_2COOH$ with HN and CH_3
Methionine	$CH_3S \cdot CH_2 \cdot CH_2 \cdot CH \cdot COOH$ with NH_2
Nicotine	
Ricinine	

lists, with formulas, a few compounds of biological importance which contain methyl groups.

Until perhaps a decade ago it was assumed that animals required preformed methyl groups in their diet. This conclusion was based originally upon the observation that the "fatty livers" and faulty growth which developed in animals which lacked choline in the diet could be prevented not only by choline but also by methionine. Later du Vigneaud's[11] work with methyl groups isotopically labeled with C^{14} and deuterium made it clear that in living cells these groups are transferred reversibly between methionine and choline. The importance of this transmethylation reaction is not diminished by our present knowledge that animal cells can also synthesize methyl groups from glycine or serine or other one-carbon donors. Transmethylation is still a valuable and much used metabolic device, since it now appears that the methyl groups synthesized from the various precursors may be first incorporated into methionine and then transferred in formation of some at least of the methylated compounds.

Detailed studies using purified enzyme systems showed that neither choline nor methionine acted directly as methyl donors until they had been activated in some way. Choline must first be oxidized in the tissues to betaine, which can then transfer one of its three methyl groups to such an acceptor as homocysteine.[12]

$$(CH_3)_3\overset{+}{N} \cdot CH_2 \cdot CH_2OH \xrightarrow{\text{FAD}} \xrightarrow{\text{DPN}^+} (CH_3)_3\overset{+}{N} \cdot CH_2 \cdot COO^-$$

$$\text{Choline} \qquad \text{Oxidation} \qquad \text{Betaine}$$

$$(CH_3)_3\overset{+}{N} \cdot CH_2 \cdot COO^- + HS \cdot CH_2 \cdot CH_2 \cdot \underset{\underset{NH_2}{|}}{CH} \cdot COOH \rightarrow$$

$$\text{Homocysteine}$$

$$H_3C \cdot S \cdot CH_2 \cdot CH_2 \cdot \underset{\underset{NH_2}{|}}{CH} \cdot COOH + (CH_3)_2 \cdot N \cdot CH_2 \cdot COO^-$$

$$\text{Methionine} \qquad\qquad\qquad \text{Dimethylglycine}$$

The two arrows in the first equation indicate that the oxidation is a two-step reaction involving two dehydrogenases with different coenzymes.

---

[11] Vincent du Vigneaud (1901–) is Professor of Biochemistry at the Cornell University Medical College in New York. His biochemical research has reflected his interest in classical organic chemistry, and he and his students have made fundamental contributions to our knowledge of amino acid chemistry and metabolism, sulfur metabolism, and the chemistry of biotin, penicillin, and oxytocin. In 1955 he was awarded the Nobel Prize in Chemistry.

[12] The prefix homo- is used to indicate that a compound is the next higher homologue of the more common substance. Thus homocysteine has one more carbon than cysteine and homoserine is $HOCH_2CH_2CH(NH_2)COOH$.

The need to activate methionine itself to allow it to function as a methyl donor was indicated by experiments with purified enzymes in which methionine proved incapable of transmethylating unless either ATP or an ATP-generating system were present. This led to the recognition of *S*-adenosylmethionine as the substance previously referred to as "active methionine." This compound can transfer its sulfur-linked methyl group in the absence of

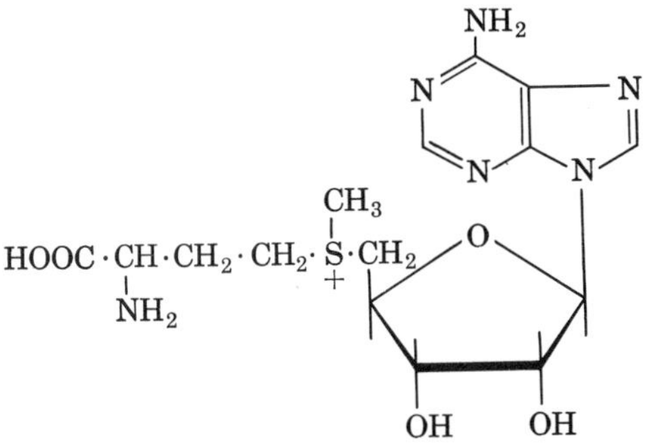

S - Adenosyl - L - methionine

ATP. Other methyl donors have been found such as dimethylthetin, dimethylpropiothetin, and *S*-methylmethionine. The formulas of these compounds are given in Table 13.8. Of the compounds listed, dimethylthetin is the only

TABLE 13.8. Methyl Donors

Donor	Formula
S-Adenosyl-L-methionine	Adenine-CH · (CHOH)$_2$ · CH · CH$_2$ · $\overset{+}{S}$ · (CH$_2$)$_2$ · CH · COOH $\quad$ with CH · O · CH bridge, $\overset{\mid}{CH_3}$, $\overset{\mid}{NH_2}$
Betaine	(CH$_3$)$_3\overset{+}{N}$ · CH$_2$COO$^-$
Dimethylpropiothetin	(CH$_3$)$_2\overset{+}{S}$ · CH$_2$ · CH$_2$COO$^-$
Dimethylthetin	(CH$_3$)$_2\overset{+}{S}$ · CH$_2$COO$^-$
S-Methylmethionine	(CH$_3$)$_2\overset{+}{S}$ · CH$_2$ · CH$_2$ · CHCOOH $\overset{\mid}{NH_2}$

one which is not known to occur in nature. The others may all be considered natural methyl donors in the cells in which they are found.

It will be noted that in all the compounds which have labile methyl groups this group is attached to a charged sulfur or nitrogen atom. Such compounds are called *onium* compounds, and are assumed to be of the high energy type.

In the synthesis of methionine from choline (betaine) and vice versa, the methyl group moves between attachment to sulfur and attachment to nitrogen. In the formation of the complex woody polymer, lignin, it has recently been shown for the first time that plant cells can transfer the labeled methyl group of *S*-adenosylmethionine to form a methoxyl group. The structure of lignin is still unknown, but one of its degradation products is vanillin, and it is assumed that this compound preserves an arrangement of methoxyl and phenolic hydroxyl which was present in the polymer.

OH

—OCH$_3$

CHO
Vanillin

The methyl transfer was indicated in experiments in which barley or tobacco plants growing in nutrient solutions containing methionine doubly labeled in its methyl group formed lignin which decomposed to yield vanillin doubly labeled in its methoxyl group. Plants, like animals, can also synthesize methyl groups from various one-carbon precursors, but when both formaldehyde and methionine were present, the rate of transmethylation far exceeded the rate of synthesis *de novo*. Other examples of the transfer of methyl groups in plants include the formation of nicotine for which methionine furnishes the *N*-methyl group, and the formation of the methoxyl group of ricinine, found in castor beans. It therefore appears that in plants as well as in animals and microorganisms, transfer of intact methyl groups is a commonly used synthetic expedient.

Creatine synthesis

One of the first reaction sequences to be worked out in detail through the use of isotopic markers was the one which leads to the synthesis of creatine. Since one step in this synthesis is a transmethylation, the experiments will be considered at this point.

It has long been clear that the body is capable of synthesizing whatever creatine it needs, since its excretory product, creatinine, appears in constant

NH$_2$
|
C=NH
|
H$_3$C · N
|
CH$_2$ · COOH
Creatine

$$
\begin{array}{c}
\text{H} \\
\text{N} \\
\text{NH=C} \quad \text{CO} \\
\text{N——CH}_2 \\
\text{CH}_3
\end{array}
$$
Creatinine

amount in the urine even when the diet contains no creatine. The search for the precursors of creatine was a long one, but yielded only equivocal results until the advent of isotopic tracers. Following the administration of N^{15} in the α position in several different amino acids, as well as in urea and ammonia, the composition of the tissue creatine was investigated. Of the amino acids investigated only glycine gave rise to muscle creatine containing enough of the isotope to indicate a true precursor. To determine the position taken by the N^{15} in the creatine molecule, it was degraded by boiling with alkali, which brings about the following hydrolysis:

$$
\begin{array}{ccc}
\begin{array}{c}
NH_2 \\
| \\
C\!=\!NH \\
| \\
*N \cdot CH_3 \\
| \\
CH_2 \cdot COOH \\
\textbf{Creatine}
\end{array}
& + 2H_2O \xrightarrow{\text{Ba(OH)}_2} &
\begin{array}{c}
CH_3 \\
| \\
*NH \\
| \\
CH_2 \\
| \\
COOH \\
\textbf{Sarcosine}
\end{array}
& + 2NH_3 + CO_2
\end{array}
$$

As indicated by the starred atoms in the formulas, the tracer was found almost entirely in the sarcosine. This showed that glycine contributed to creatine its own α-nitrogen, but not nitrogen for the synthesis of the amidine group

$(NH_2 \cdot \overset{|}{C}\!=\!NH)$.

Various possible precursors of the amidine group were then investigated, and of these only guanidoacetic acid $(NH_2 \cdot C(\!=\!NH) \cdot NH \cdot CH_2COOH)$ or glycocyamine proved to contribute to the synthesis of creatine. It therefore seemed likely that glycine is first transformed into guanidoacetic acid, and that transfer of a methyl group then completes the synthesis. This reaction sequence was proved by experiments in which arginine, labeled in its amidine group, was fed to rats. Again the creatine was isolated and hydrolyzed, but this time the isotope was nearly all found in the ammonia set free. It had therefore been almost exclusively in the amidine group of the creatine. In the following equations the marked nitrogens in the two compounds are differently labeled to indicate the source of each nitrogen in the creatine precursor.

$$
\begin{array}{c}
\overset{\bullet}{N}H_2 \\
| \\
CH_2 \\
| \\
COOH \\
\textbf{Glycine}
\end{array}
+
\begin{array}{c}
\overset{*}{N}H_2 \\
| \\
C\!=\!\overset{*}{N}H \\
| \\
NH \\
| \\
(CH_2)_3 \\
| \\
CH(NH_2) \cdot COOH \\
\textbf{Arginine}
\end{array}
\rightarrow
\begin{array}{c}
\overset{*}{N}H_2 \\
| \\
C\!=\!\overset{*}{N}H \\
| \\
\bullet NH \\
| \\
CH_2 \\
| \\
COOH \\
\textbf{Guanidoacetic acid} \\
\textbf{or glycocyamine}
\end{array}
+
\begin{array}{c}
NH_2 \\
| \\
(CH_2)_3 \\
| \\
CH \cdot NH_2 \\
| \\
COOH \\
\textbf{Ornithine}
\end{array}
$$

Thus two carbons and one nitrogen of creatine come from glycine and the amidine group from arginine.

It remained for du Vigneaud and his colleagues to show that a third amino acid, methionine, is the source of the methyl group. Methionine marked with deuterium in its methyl group (trideuteromethionine) was fed to rats and subsequently creatine was isolated from their muscles. It proved to contain a methyl group clearly marked with deuterium, thus proving that transmethylation had provided the methyl group.

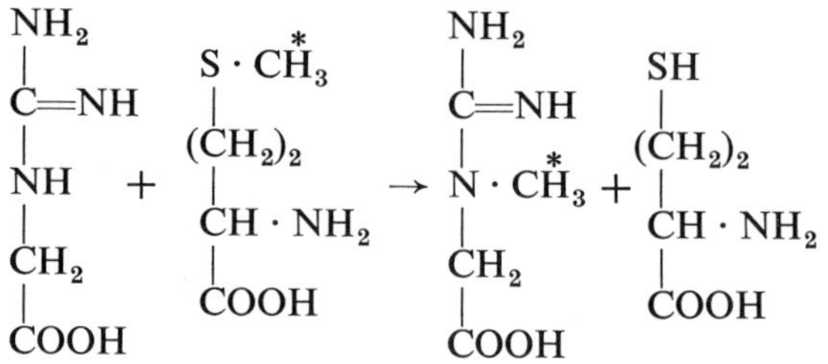

$$
\begin{array}{c}
\begin{array}{c}
\text{NH}_2 \\
| \\
\text{C=\!NH} \\
| \\
\text{NH} \\
| \\
\text{CH}_2 \\
| \\
\text{COOH}
\end{array}
\quad + \quad
\begin{array}{c}
\overset{*}{\text{S}\cdot\text{CH}_3} \\
| \\
(\text{CH}_2)_2 \\
| \\
\text{CH}\cdot\text{NH}_2 \\
| \\
\text{COOH}
\end{array}
\quad \rightarrow \quad
\begin{array}{c}
\text{NH}_2 \\
| \\
\text{C=\!NH} \\
| \\
\text{N}\cdot\overset{*}{\text{CH}_3} \\
| \\
\text{CH}_2 \\
| \\
\text{COOH}
\end{array}
\quad + \quad
\begin{array}{c}
\text{SH} \\
| \\
(\text{CH}_2)_2 \\
| \\
\text{CH}\cdot\text{NH}_2 \\
| \\
\text{COOH}
\end{array}
\end{array}
$$

Guanidoacetic acid   **Methionine**   **Creatine**   **Homocysteine**

It seems that the indispensability of methionine resides largely in its ability to furnish labile methyl groups. The following chart, adapted from Schoenheimer's book, indicates the way in which creatine is derived from three different amino acids.

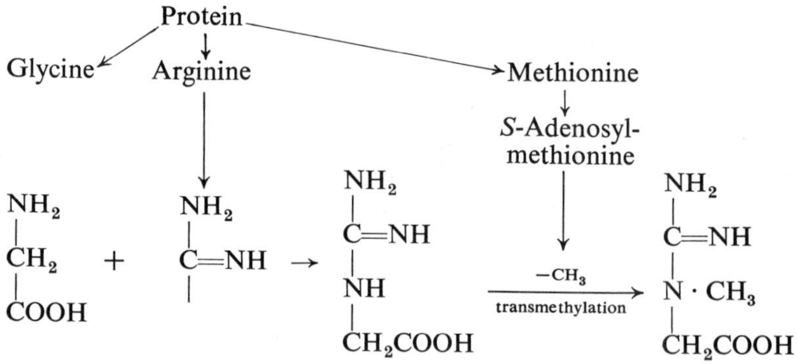

Glycine ← Protein → Arginine → Methionine → S-Adenosylmethionine

$$
\begin{array}{c}
\text{NH}_2 \\
| \\
\text{CH}_2 \\
| \\
\text{COOH}
\end{array}
\quad + \quad
\begin{array}{c}
\text{NH}_2 \\
| \\
\text{C=\!NH} \\
| \\
\end{array}
\quad \rightarrow \quad
\begin{array}{c}
\text{NH}_2 \\
| \\
\text{C=\!NH} \\
| \\
\text{NH} \\
| \\
\text{CH}_2\text{COOH}
\end{array}
\quad \xrightarrow[\text{transmethylation}]{-\text{CH}_3} \quad
\begin{array}{c}
\text{NH}_2 \\
| \\
\text{C=\!NH} \\
| \\
\text{N}\cdot\text{CH}_3 \\
| \\
\text{CH}_2\text{COOH}
\end{array}
$$

Guanidoacetic acid   **Creatine**

Decarboxylation

It was noted in Chapter 5 that enzymes known as *decarboxylases* act upon certain of the amino acids as indicated in the following general equation:

$$\text{R}\cdot\text{CH}\cdot(\text{NH}_2)\cdot\text{COOH} \rightarrow \text{R}\cdot\text{CH}_2\cdot\text{NH}_2 + \text{CO}_2$$

Many of the enzymes are of bacterial origin and each is specific for a particular amino acid. The removal of carbon dioxide gives rise to amines many of which have pronounced physiological effects and some of which are more or less toxic. When these are formed in the intestines as a result of bacterial action, they may be absorbed and give rise to "autointoxication." The body meets this emergency by detoxicating and excreting the offending molecules, and so long as excretion keeps pace with absorption there are no ill effects. Some important decarboxylases are listed in Table 13.9 with their sources, substrates, and the products which form. All require pyridoxal phosphate as coenzyme, and it is probable that formation of a Schiff's base of the type shown on page 479 precedes the decarboxylation, with the pyridoxal phosphate furnishing the —C=O group.

Detoxication

The toxic amines constitute one of a varied group of substances which must undergo some transformation before they can be safely excreted by the kidney. Some of the reactions by which this detoxication takes place have been mentioned in other connections, but they will be summarized here since proteins not only furnish some of the toxic molecules as in the instance just referred to but also provide several of the compounds used for detoxication. In general a substance is detoxicated either by oxidation or by conjugation with another molecule.

Oxidation

There are present in animal and plant tissues a number of monoamine oxidases with rather broad specificities. They act upon amines according to the following general equation:

$$\text{Amine} + O_2 \rightarrow \text{Aldehyde} + NH_3 + H_2O_2$$

In this reaction the toxic amines are transformed into nontoxic compounds of carbon, which can be further oxidized, and ammonia, a normal metabolite for which there are both synthetic and excretory pathways. For the detoxication of the diamines, diamine oxidases which catalyze the oxidation of a long list of diamines have been found in plants, bacteria, and animal tissues. The oxidations of some diamines are complete and lead to formation of carbon dioxide, water and ammonia. With other substrates the oxidation stops with formation of an aminoaldehyde.

Conjugation with acids

1. SULFURIC ACID. An enzyme known as tryptophanase acts upon tryptophan or tryptamine to form two malodorous compounds, skatole and

TABLE 13.9. Some Amino Acid Decarboxylations[a]

Substrate	Product	Enzyme Source
$H_2N \cdot C \cdot NH(CH_2)_3 \cdot CH \cdot COOH$ ‖ — NH NH_2 **L-Arginine**	$H_2N \cdot C \cdot NH(CH_2)_3 \cdot CH_2 \cdot NH_2$ ‖ NH **Agmatine**	Bacteria
$HOOC \cdot CH_2 \cdot CH \cdot COOH$ — NH_2 **L-Aspartic acid**	$\xrightarrow{\text{(α-carboxylase)}}$ $HOOC \cdot CH_2 \cdot CH_2 \cdot NH_2$ **β-Alanine**	Bacteria
	$\xrightarrow{\text{(β-carboxylase)}}$ $H_3C \cdot CH \cdot COOH$ — NH_2 **L-Alanine**	Bacteria
$HO_3S \cdot CH_2 \cdot CH \cdot COOH$ — NH_2 **L-Cysteic acid**	$HO_3S \cdot CH_2 \cdot CH_2 \cdot NH_2$ **Taurine**	Animal tissues
$HO_2S \cdot CH_2 \cdot CH \cdot COOH$ — NH_2 **L-Cysteine sulfinic acid**	$HO_2S \cdot CH_2 \cdot CH_2 \cdot NH_2$ **Hypotaurine**	Liver and kidney
$HOOC(CH_2)_2 \cdot CH \cdot COOH$ — NH_2 **L-Glutamic acid**	$HOOC(CH_2)_3 \cdot NH_2$ **γ-Aminobutyrate**	Yeast, brain, plants and bacteria

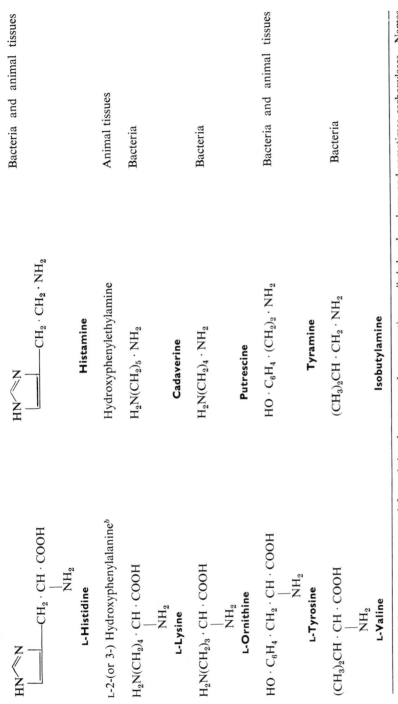

HN⟩N —CH$_2$·CH·COOH
        │
        NH$_2$
L-Histidine
	HN⟩N —CH$_2$·CH$_2$·NH$_2$
	Histamine
		Bacteria and animal tissues

L-2-(or 3-) Hydroxyphenylalanine[b]	Hydroxyphenylethylamine	Animal tissues

H$_2$N(CH$_2$)$_4$·CH·COOH
         │
         NH$_2$
L-Lysine
	H$_2$N(CH$_2$)$_5$·NH$_2$
	Cadaverine
		Bacteria

H$_2$N(CH$_2$)$_3$·CH·COOH
         │
         NH$_2$
L-Ornithine
	H$_2$N(CH$_2$)$_4$·NH$_2$
	Putrescine
		Bacteria

HO·C$_6$H$_4$·CH$_2$·CH·COOH
           │
           NH$_2$
L-Tyrosine
	HO·C$_6$H$_4$·(CH$_2$)$_2$·NH$_2$
	Tyramine
		Bacteria and animal tissues

(CH$_3$)$_2$CH·CH·COOH
        │
        NH$_2$
L-Valine
	(CH$_3$)$_2$CH·CH$_2$·NH$_2$
	Isobutylamine
		Bacteria

[a] In general the enzymes are named from their substrates, and are sometimes called decarboxylases and sometimes carboxylases. Names have been included only when two act upon one substrate.

[b] The enzyme which acts upon hydroxyphenylalanine is sometimes called DOPA decarboxylase. This came about because it also acts upon hydroxytyrosine (dioxyphenylalanine), and this reaction was extensively studied in the early days.

indole, said to be largely responsible for the odor of feces. When these substances are absorbed they undergo a series of changes and are ultimately

Indole   **Skatole or β-methylindole**

conjugated with inorganic sulfate before excretion. The broad outlines of the process are indicated.

Indole   **Indoxyl**

Indoxyl sulfuric acid   **Indican**

Phenolic hydroxyl groups are also often linked to sulfate in the course of detoxication.

The formation of such sulfate derivatives is one of the many synthetic procedures which it is now known must be preceded by activation of one of the reactants. In this case sulfate is activated by formation of a high energy intermediate, the need for which was indicated as usual by the observation that incorporation of sulfate required either an oxidizing system which could form ATP, or preformed ATP. The "active sulfate" has now been characterized as 3′-phosphoadenosine-5′-phosphosulfate, usually abbreviated to

PAPS

PAPS. The enzyme system needed for synthesis of PAPS has been found in plant, animal, and microbial cells. The reaction takes place in two steps.

The first is catalyzed by an enzyme, ATP-sulfurylase which mediates the displacement of the pyrophosphate from ATP and its replacement by the sulfate group to form adenosine-5′-phosphosulfate (APS). This step gives rise to an anhydride link between sulfate and phosphate groups as shown in the formula for PAPS.

$$ATP + SO_4^{--} \rightarrow APS + PP$$

In the second step carbon 3′ of the ribose in the phosphosulfate compound is phosphorylated to form the activated compound. The enzyme for this reaction is called APS-kinase since it mediates the transfer of a phosphate group from ATP to the substrate, APS.

$$APS + ATP \rightarrow PAPS + ADP$$

The activated compound PAPS is not only important in detoxications but is actually a focal substance in the biological use of sulfate groups. These can be transferred from PAPS under the influence of specific sulfokinases to a wide variety of acceptors. Indoxyl and phenols form the so called "ethereal sulfates" which occur in urine, through transfer of the sulfate group to the ring-linked hydroxyl groups. Quite recently it has been shown that similar aliphatic sulfates are formed from a series of alcohols ranging from methyl to amyl alcohol and that the sulfate group can also be transferred to the nitrogen of aryl amines to form sulfamates with the grouping —NHSO₃H.

Sulfate has long been known to be part of the complex mucopolysaccharides, heparin, and the chondroitin sulfates. It has recently been shown that synthesis of these compounds also requires PAPS as sulfate donor, with the sulfate being transferred not to the separate monose units before polymerization, but to the preformed polymer itself. Other compounds which have been shown to arise from sulfate transfer from PAPS are the sulfolipids of brain and the steroid sulfates which are found in the urine.

2. GLUCURONIC ACID. In Chapter 4 it was mentioned that aromatic acids and phenols are sometimes excreted after conjugation with glucuronic acid (page 139). This reaction, like the one just discussed, has been shown to take place through an activated intermediate. The activation is brought about not by ATP but by a similar triphosphate in which the base is the pyrimidine uracil. We shall find that this particular nucleotide derivative seems to be particularly suitable for transfer of carbohydrate residues.

The synthesis of the activated glucuronide incidentally clears up a long standing mystery, namely the mechanism by which the living cell manages to oxidize a primary alcohol group in glucose without affecting the very reactive aldehyde group. It has now been shown that formation of a glycoside with uridine diphosphate precedes the oxidation, which thus takes place after the specially reactive group has been blocked. The following equations in which

U stands for the uridyl group (uracil-ribose) indicate the reactions by which active uridine diphosphate glucuronide is formed from uridine diphosphate.

$$\text{UDP} + \text{ATP} \xrightarrow[\text{phate kinase}]{\text{nucleosidediphos-}} \text{UTP} + \text{ADP}$$

$$\text{Glucose-1-P} + \text{UTP} \xrightarrow[\text{phorylase}]{\text{UDPG pyrophos-}} \text{UDPglucoside} + \text{PP}$$

UDP glucoside   UDP glucuronide

The activated glucuronide group can then be transferred under the influence of a transferring enzyme, UDP-transglucuronylase, to various acceptors such as menthol or phenols. With resacetophenone the detoxication product has the formula:

Resacetophenone glucuronide

3. ACETIC ACID. Toxic amino groups are frequently acetylated before being excreted. For example unnatural amino acids as well as various drugs such as sulfanilamide are excreted in the acetylated form. All these reactions are brought about by the high energy compound acetyl coenzyme A which is formed in abundance in many metabolic sequences.

4. CYSTEINE. Certain aromatic compounds are excreted in conjugated molecules which include acetylated cysteine and are known as mercapturic acids. It is now suggested that the conjugation takes place between the toxic compound and the cysteine while the latter is part of a polypeptide, probably GSH. Later, hydrolysis frees the cysteine derivative which is then acetylated in the usual way by acetyl coenzyme A. The compound excreted after administration of bromobenzene to dogs has the formula below.

$$\text{Br} - \bigcirc - \text{S} \cdot \text{CH}_2 \cdot \text{CH} \cdot \text{COOH}$$
$$\underset{\text{NH} \cdot \text{COCH}_3}{|}$$

p-Bromophenylmercapturic acid

5. GLYCINE. Reference has already been made to the detoxication of benzoic acid by conjugation with glycine (see page 450). Other aromatic acids form similar detoxication products, phenylacetic acid being excreted as phenaceturic acid.

$$C_6H_5CH_2COOH \rightarrow C_6H_5CH_2CONHCH_2COOH$$
Phenylacetic acid   **Phenaceturic acid**

Formation of these compounds requires preliminary activation of the aromatic acids by coenzyme A, forming an acyl coenzyme A. This is believed to take place through a transfer reaction involving acetyl coenzyme A. This compound in the presence of ATP and a suitable enzyme transfers the coenzyme to an acceptor acid forming a high energy thiol ester in accordance with the following equation:

$$CH_3CO \cdot SCoA + RCOO^- + ATP \rightarrow$$
$$RCO \cdot SCoA + CH_3COO^- + ADP + P$$
Acyl CoA

Interaction of the acyl coenzyme A with the amino group of glycine then gives the conjugate which is excreted.

$$RCO \cdot SCoA + H_2NCH_2COOH \rightarrow RCO \cdot HNCH_2COOH + HSCoA$$
Acyl CoA   **CoA**

The body is apparently capable of synthesizing glycine rapidly enough if necessary to detoxicate even very large doses of aromatic acids which appear in the urine within the following 24 hours.

As far as we know all these various detoxication procedures are the work of the liver. Proteins furnish not only glycine and cysteine as detoxicating agents but probably the sulfate also. Oxidation of cysteine by living cells yields as one product inorganic sulfate, part of which is excreted but part of which is available for detoxication purposes as well as other syntheses. It is a striking thing that the animal body is equipped to deal so effectively with toxic substances which are entirely foreign to its economy.

Metabolism of Individual Amino Acids

There is now a voluminous literature dealing with the biosynthesis, interrelationships and degradation products of the individual amino acids in animals, plants, and microorganisms. A detailed consideration of all these reactions is beyond the scope of this book. Furthermore, many of them cannot be taken up profitably except on the basis of a prior understanding of carbohydrate and lipid metabolism, both of which are closely linked to that of the proteins. In the following paragraphs therefore only a few outstanding relationships and reactions will be considered.

Glycine-serine-threonine

One such relationship is the ready interconversion of glycine and serine. Serine, by rupture of the bond between the α- and the β-carbons forms glycine and a 1-carbon unit which is probably a $-CH_2OH$ group attached to tetrahydropteroylglutamic acid ($PGAH_4$). Most of the glycine synthesized by animal cells is the result of this cleavage, which with its reversal to form serine from glycine is believed to operate continuously. Decarboxylation of serine yields ethanolamine from which choline is synthesized.

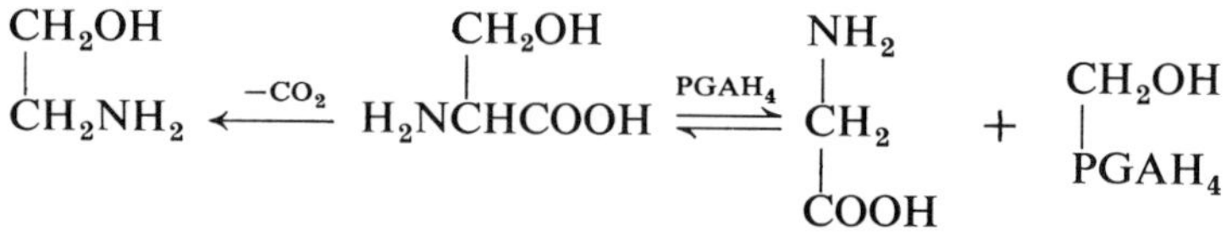

$$
\underset{\substack{\text{Ethanol-} \\ \text{amine}}}{\overset{\substack{CH_2OH \\ | \\ CH_2NH_2}}{}} \xleftarrow{\ -CO_2\ } \underset{\text{Serine}}{\overset{\substack{CH_2OH \\ | \\ H_2NCHCOOH}}{}} \underset{PGAH_4}{\overset{}{\rightleftharpoons}} \underset{\text{Glycine}}{\overset{\substack{NH_2 \\ | \\ CH_2 \\ | \\ COOH}}{}} + \underset{\substack{\text{Active} \\ \text{hydroxymethyl}}}{\overset{\substack{CH_2OH \\ | \\ PGAH_4}}{}}
$$

The other hydroxyamino acid, threonine, undergoes a similar cleavage to yield glycine and acetaldehyde. The latter compound is readily oxidized to acetic acid which in turn acts as a source of acetyl coenzyme A. In this way

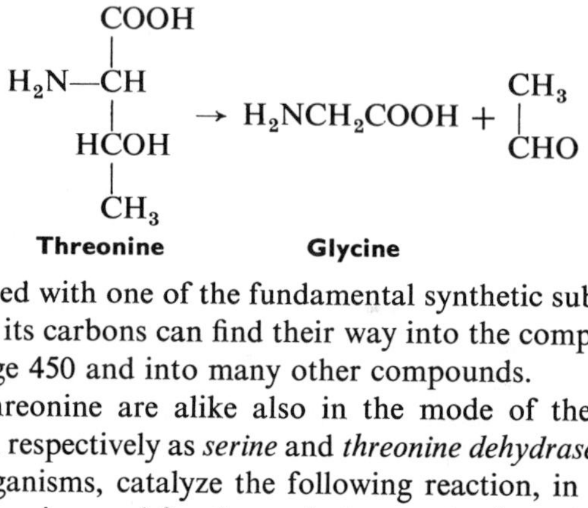

$$
\underset{\text{Threonine}}{\overset{\substack{COOH \\ | \\ H_2N-CH \\ | \\ HCOH \\ | \\ CH_3}}{}} \rightarrow \underset{\text{Glycine}}{H_2NCH_2COOH} + \overset{\substack{CH_3 \\ | \\ CHO}}{}
$$

threonine is linked with one of the fundamental synthetic substrates of living cells and two of its carbons can find their way into the compounds shown in the chart on page 450 and into many other compounds.

Serine and threonine are alike also in the mode of their deamination. Enzymes known respectively as *serine* and *threonine dehydrases*, found in liver and in microorganisms, catalyze the following reaction, in which R stands for hydrogen in serine, and for the methyl group in threonine.

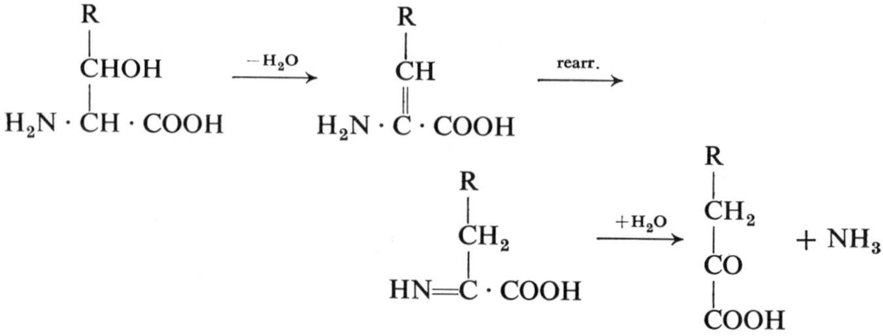

$$
\overset{\substack{R \\ | \\ CHOH \\ | \\ H_2N \cdot CH \cdot COOH}}{} \xrightarrow{-H_2O} \overset{\substack{R \\ | \\ CH \\ \| \\ H_2N \cdot C \cdot COOH}}{} \xrightarrow{\text{rearr.}}
$$

$$
\overset{\substack{R \\ | \\ CH_2 \\ | \\ HN=C \cdot COOH}}{} \xrightarrow{+H_2O} \overset{\substack{R \\ | \\ CH_2 \\ | \\ CO \\ | \\ COOH}}{} + NH_3
$$

The final products are pyruvate and ammonia from serine and α-ketobutyrate and ammonia from threonine.

Glutamic acid-proline-arginine

A second group of acids which are interconvertible consists of glutamic acid, proline, and arginine. The conversion of proline to glutamic acid has long been known, but the individual steps in the conversion are still being examined. The crucial intermediate in animal metabolism seems to be

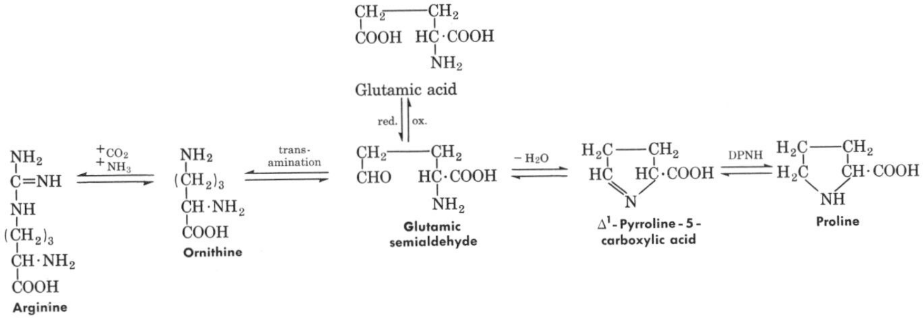

Fig. 13.2. Relationships of glutamic acid, proline, ornithine, and arginine.

glutamic semialdehyde from which by one path arginine can be synthesized, and by another proline. Figure 13.2 summarizes these interrelationships. The transformation of ornithine to arginine is part of the sequence by which urea is formed, and is taken up in detail on page 509.

Closely related to proline is hydroxyproline which occurs uniquely in the structural protein collagen, which includes also a high percentage of proline. As might have been foreseen, proline is a precursor of hydroxyproline, though it appears that free hydroxyproline is not an intermediate in collagen synthesis. It has been suggested that this is because it is synthesized in an "activated" form, perhaps bound to the enzyme, and that it is this bound form of the acid which transfers the hydroxyproline residue to collagen. These suggested relationships are summarized below:

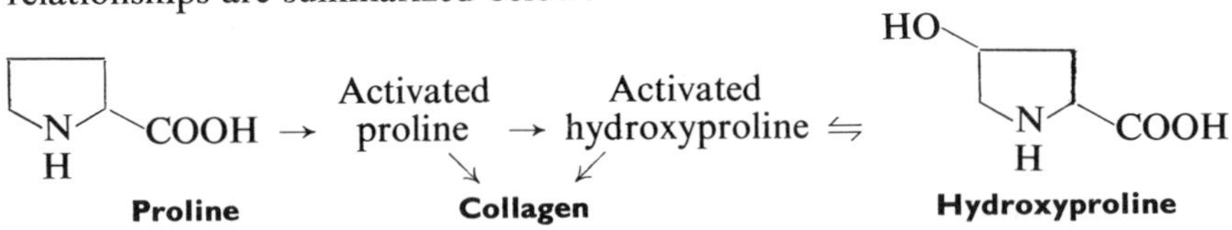

It is probable that the oxidation of the carbon chains of the prolines and arginine as well as of glutamic acid takes place by way of the citric acid cycle. This would involve the conversion of the other acids to glutamic acid, the deamination of this acid, and the entrance of the resulting α-ketoglutarate into the cycle.

Branched chain acids

The amino acids with branched chains, valine, leucine, and isoleucine are among the indispensable acids and so it has been of interest to discover how these chains are formed in organisms which are capable of synthesizing them. For each acid the branched chain α-keto acid is built up and then the amino group is introduced by transamination from glutamic acid. The branching of the chain is achieved by condensation at a keto group. In Fig. 13.3 the

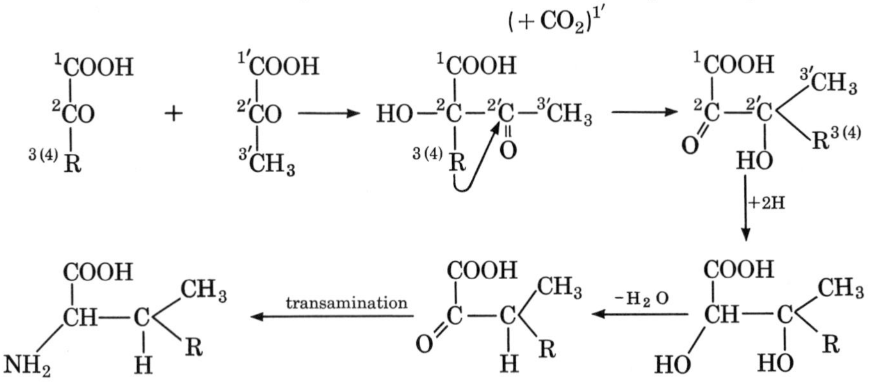

Fig. 13.3. Biosynthesis of valine or isoleucine. (When R is CH_3-, the acid formed is valine, when it is C_2H_5-, the product is isoleucine.) [From W. E. Knox and E. J. Behrman, *Ann. Rev. Biochem.*, **28**, 245 (1959).]

syntheses of α-ketoisovalerate and valine are indicated if the initial substrate is pyruvate, in which case R stands for CH_3-. When R stands for C_2H_5- and therefore includes carbons 3 and 4 of α-ketobutyrate, the products are α-keto-β-methylvalerate and isoleucine. The biosynthesis of the keto analogue of leucine goes on from α-ketoisovalerate, and the chain is again lengthened by condensation at the keto group. This last sequence has been established in work with isotopically labeled compounds but the individual steps have not been entirely clarified.

The catabolism of these acids is interesting because of the intervention of coenzyme A at an early stage. Figure 13.4 gives the stages in the metabolism of leucine, and similar reactions are believed to account for the breakdown of isoleucine and valine.

An important function of leucine is indicated by its relationship to mevalonic acid.

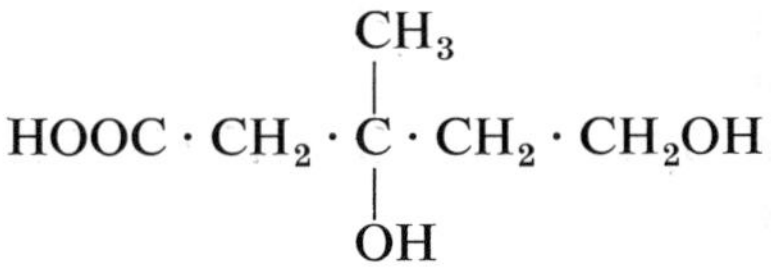

$$\overset{CH_3}{\underset{OH}{HOOC \cdot CH_2 \cdot \overset{|}{\underset{|}{C}} \cdot CH_2 \cdot CH_2OH}}$$

Mevalonic acid

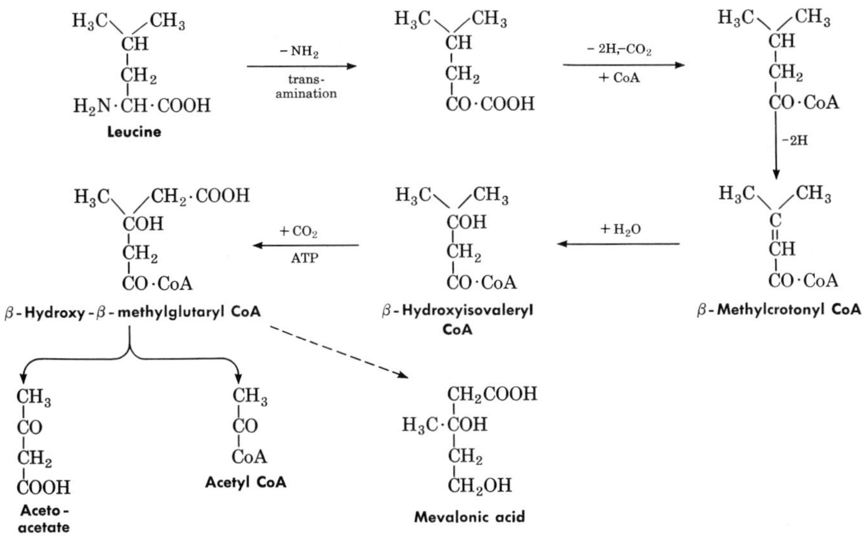

Fig. 13.4. Catabolism of leucine.

This compound, which is an intermediate in the synthesis of cholesterol, has as a precursor the β-hydroxy-β-methylglutaric acid which appears, conjugated with coenzyme A, among the breakdown products of leucine. Reduction of the free carboxyl group and removal of the coenzyme gives mevalonic acid. It seems likely that the utilization of leucine in the biosynthesis of carotene involves the same intermediates. These uses of mevalonic acid are considered on page 572.

Ring formation

The genesis of the rings in phenylalanine, tyrosine, histidine, and tryptophan has of course been extensively studied. It is interesting that these parts of four amino acids all arise from carbohydrate sources. The precursor of the benzene rings, including that which is part of the indole group of tryptophan is shikimic acid, the relationship of which to glucose is obvious, although the series of reactions by which it is formed from glucose is far from simple.

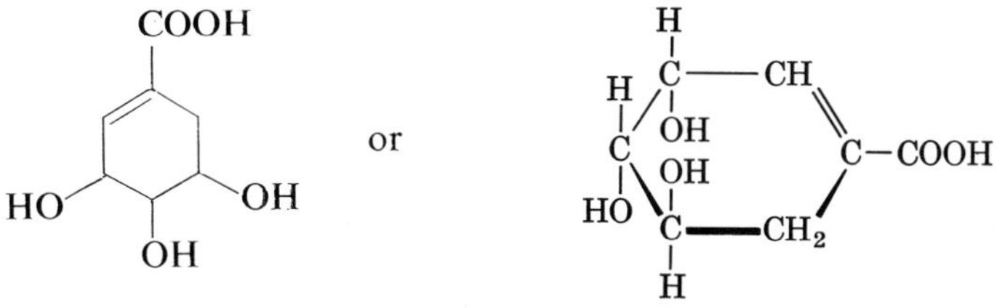

Shikimic acid

It will be shown in Chapter 15 that in the course of its metabolism, glucose is transformed into a number of phosphorylated derivatives, among them erythrose-4 phosphate, and phosphoenolpyruvic acid. The formulation below shows how these two substances are used by *Escherichia coli* in the synthesis of shikimic acid.

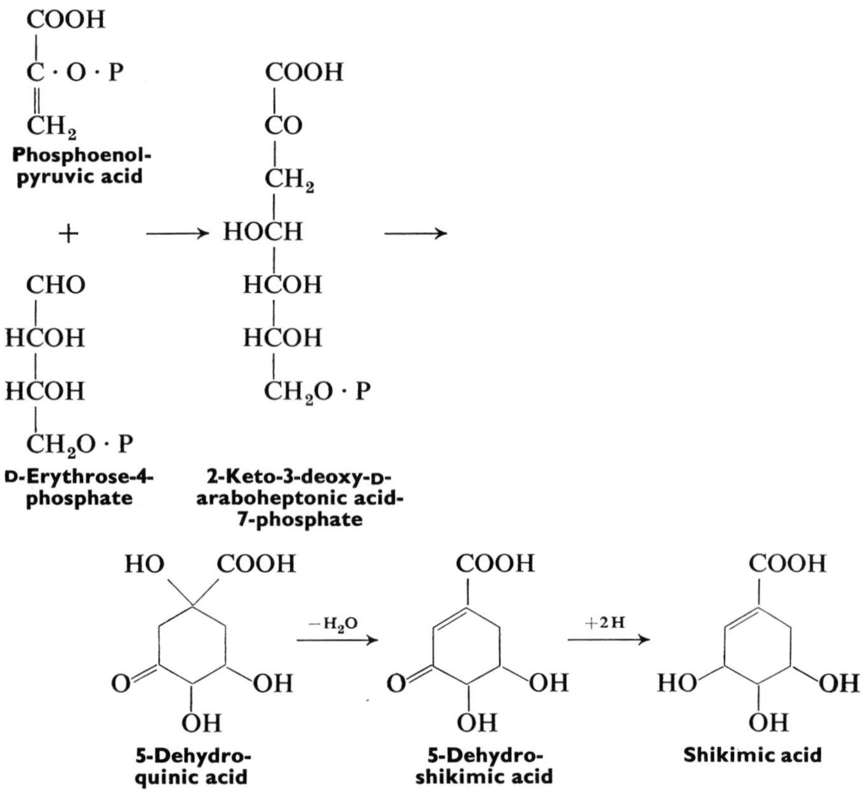

COOH
|
$\overset{\|}{C} \cdot O \cdot P$
‖
CH₂

**Phosphoenol-
pyruvic acid**

+

CHO
|
HCOH
|
HCOH
|
CH₂O · P

**D-Erythrose-4-
phosphate**

⟶

COOH
|
CO
|
CH₂
|
HOCH
|
HCOH
|
HCOH
|
CH₂O · P

**2-Keto-3-deoxy-D-
araboheptonic acid-
7-phosphate**

⟶

**5-Dehydro-
quinic acid** **5-Dehydro-
shikimic acid** **Shikimic acid**

The formation of tyrosine and phenylalanine from shikimic acid involves as intermediate prephenic acid, formed by conjugation of phosphorylated shikimic acid with pyruvate.

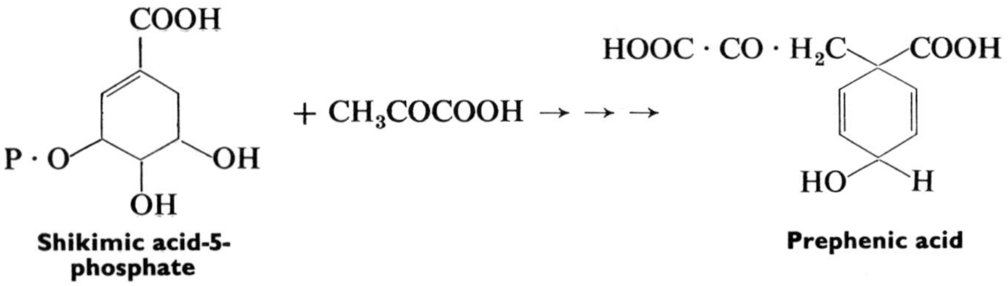

**Shikimic acid-5-
phosphate**

+ CH₃COCOOH → → →

Prephenic acid

Removal of carbon dioxide and water, followed by amination, yields phenylalanine, while removal of carbon dioxide and hydrogen, again followed by amination, leads to synthesis of tyrosine.

Phenylpyruvic acid   **Phenylalanine**

p-Hydroxyphenylpyruvic acid   **Tyrosine**

The evidence indicates that both transformation sequences take place, and that the reactions are irreversible in *E. coli*. Tyrosine can also be formed by hydroxylation of phenylalanine under the influence of an enzyme system found in liver. The complete system includes two enzymes, reduced TPN$^+$, a cofactor related to the pteroyl group in folic acid and molecular oxygen. Several pteridines serve as cofactor, but the most active compound is 2-amino-4-hydroxy-6-methyltetrahydropteridine which is oxidized at the same time that an oxygen enters the amino acid. The TPNH is needed for reduction of the cofactor, so that it can act again.

2-Amino-4-hydroxy-6-methyltetrahydropteridine

The scheme proposed for the formation of tyrosine from phenylalanine follows:

Phenylalanine + O_2 + Tetrahydropteridine →
$\qquad\qquad$ Tyrosine + ox. Pteridine + H_2O

ox. Pteridine + TPNH → Tetrahydropteridine + TPN$^+$

The imidazole ring of histidine is built up to include carbons from ribose, a carbon and a nitrogen from adenine, and a nitrogen from glutamine. The synthesis takes place in at least three stages, as follows:

1. Ribose-5-phosphate is activated by reaction with ATP, yielding AMP and introducing a pyrophosphate group on carbon 1 of the ribose. (See page 501 for the formula of this compound.)

2. This compound then transfers a phosphoribosyl group to N-1 of the adenine moiety in the AMP with a splitting out of pyrophosphate. This intermediate has the structure below.

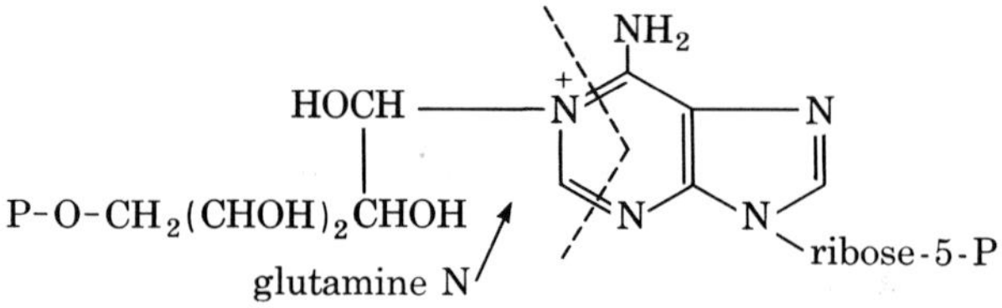

$$HOCH \underline{\quad\quad} N^{+}$$

$$P-O-CH_2(CHOH)_2CHOH$$

glutamine N

NH$_2$

N

N   N

ribose-5-P

Phosphoribosyl adenylic acid

3. The third stage, which may include more than one step, requires participation of glutamine. Cleavage of the phosphoribosyl adenylic acid as indicated by the dotted lines, and introduction of a second nitrogen from glutamine results in formation of imidazoleglycerol phosphate from the

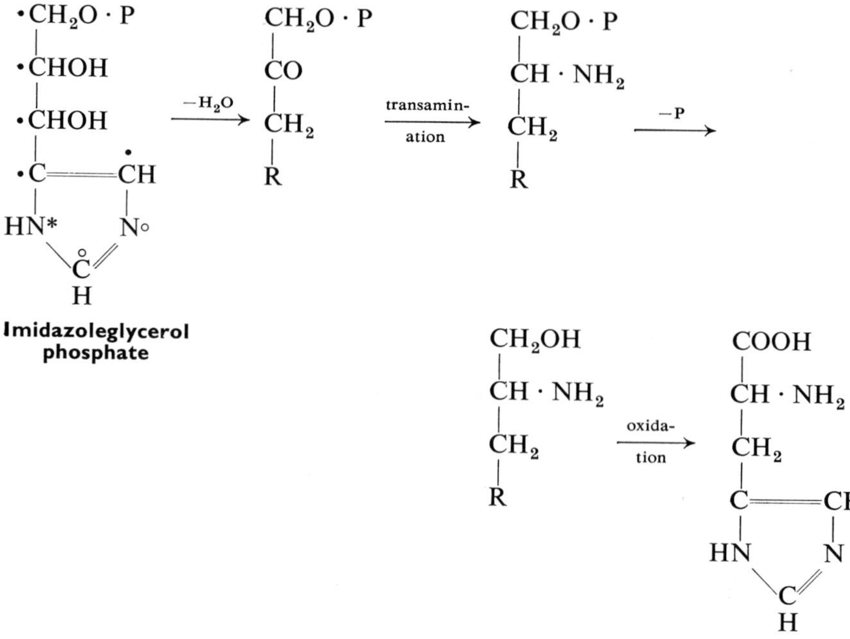

$$\cdot CH_2O \cdot P$$
$$\cdot CHOH$$
$$\cdot CHOH$$
$$\cdot C \underline{\quad} CH$$
$$HN^{*} \quad N^{\circ}$$
$$\diagdown C \diagup$$
$$H$$

Imidazoleglycerol phosphate

$\xrightarrow{-H_2O}$

$$CH_2O \cdot P$$
$$CO$$
$$CH_2$$
$$R$$

$\xrightarrow[\text{ation}]{\text{transamin-}}$

$$CH_2O \cdot P$$
$$CH \cdot NH_2$$
$$CH_2$$
$$R$$

$\xrightarrow{-P}$

$$CH_2OH$$
$$CH \cdot NH_2$$
$$CH_2$$
$$R$$

$\xrightarrow[\text{tion}]{\text{oxida-}}$

$$COOH$$
$$CH \cdot NH_2$$
$$CH_2$$
$$C \underline{\quad} CH$$
$$HN \quad N$$
$$\diagdown C \diagup$$
$$H$$

L-Histidinol   **L-Histidine**

• = atoms from ribose;   ∘ = atoms from adenine;   * = atom from glutamine group on the left, and a complex ribotide made up of the ribose phosphate previously attached to N-9 of adenine, now attached to a substituted imidazole ring. Further transformations of the imidazoleglycerol phosphate conserves in histidine the side chain derived from ribose as indicated in the formulation above. It will be shown on page 527 that the complex ribotide referred to above is known as 5-amino-4-imidazole carboxamide ribotide (AICAR) and that it is a precursor of the purines.

The indole group of tryptophan is built up from the six-membered ring of shikimic acid, beginning as in the synthesis of prephenic acid with a phosphorylation. In the following scheme in which some of the intermediates are indicated, note that in this synthesis as in the synthesis of histidine, glutamine provides one of the nitrogens. In the first stages indolyl-3-glycerol phosphate is synthesized using the same activated 5-phosphoribosyl-1-pyrophosphate that began the histidine synthesis.

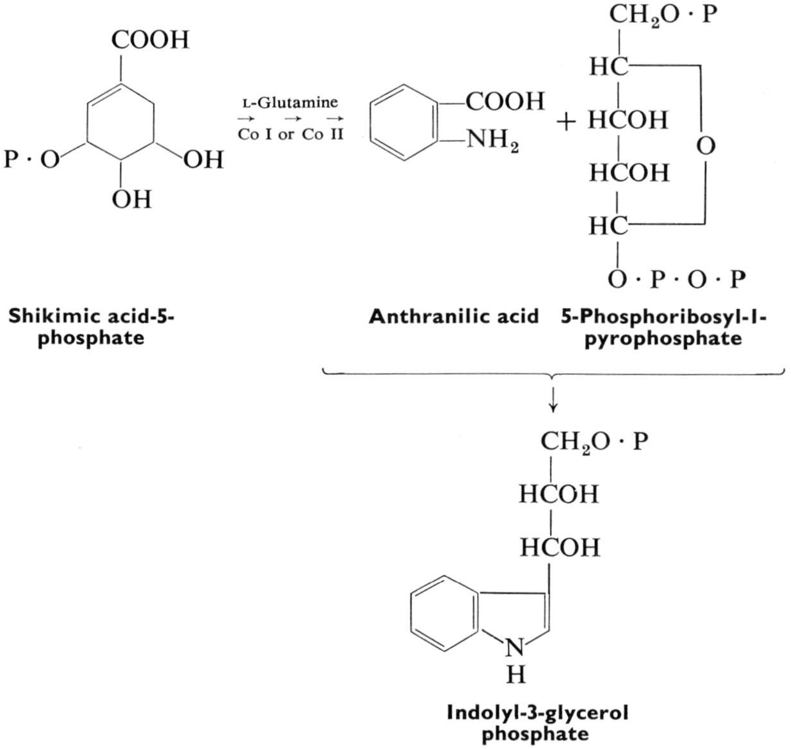

Shikimic acid-5-phosphate   **Anthranilic acid   5-Phosphoribosyl-1-pyrophosphate**

Indolyl-3-glycerol phosphate

The subsequent formation of tryptophan involves a condensation with serine in which the other reactant seems to be a bound form of indole rather than the free compound. This linkage between indole and the enzyme, tryptophan synthetase, is formed with a splitting out of triose phosphate from the indolyl-3-glycerol phosphate. This removal of the three carbons and the conjugation with serine means that in this synthesis three of the ribose carbons are finally discarded and the side chain of tryptophan comes from another amino acid, serine. In this the tryptophan synthesis is not analogous to that of histidine. The reaction sequence may be outlined as follows:

$$\text{Indolylglyceryl phosphate} + \text{Enzyme} \rightarrow \text{Enzyme-indole} + \text{Triose phosphate}$$

$$\text{Enzyme-indole} + \text{L-serine} \rightarrow \text{L-tryptophan} + \text{Enzyme}$$

Tryptophan is the source of nicotinic acid (the vitamin niacin) and therefore the precursor of the pyridine coenzymes in animals, birds and at least some microorganisms. Interestingly it appears not to be a precursor of the same compound in corn or tobacco plants. Another compound which is derived from tryptophan and which is of importance in plants is indoleacetic acid. This substance is a normal urinary constituent and is the plant growth hormone known as auxin. The conversion of tryptophan to auxin involves loss of the α-amino group and the carboxyl group, and these two steps seem to take place in either order, as indicated in the following scheme.

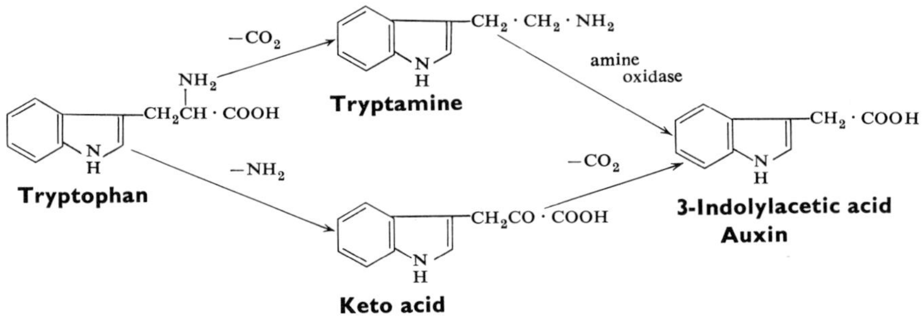

Amino acids containing sulfur

The sulfur-containing acids, cystine, cysteine, and methionine, are metabolically closely interrelated. The readily reversible oxidation-reduction of the cystine-cysteine pair makes them in effect a single acid, and methionine can furnish sulfur for cysteine synthesis as indicated below, through condensation with serine and subsequent cleavage of the condensation product. The net result is transfer of sulfur from a four-carbon compound to the three-carbon cysteine, the carbons of which thus come from serine.

Methionine

$\Big\downarrow$ trans-
methylation

$$\underset{\substack{\text{Homo-}\\ \text{cysteine}}}{\begin{array}{l} CH_2 \cdot SH \\ | \\ CH_2 \\ | \\ CH \cdot NH_2 \\ | \\ COOH \end{array}} \quad + \quad \underset{\text{Serine}}{\begin{array}{l} CH_2OH \\ | \\ CH \cdot NH_2 \\ | \\ COOH \end{array}} \quad \xrightarrow{\;-H_2O\;}$$

$$\underset{\text{Cystathionine}}{\begin{array}{l} CH_2\!-\!\!-S\!-\!\!-CH_2 \\ | \qquad\qquad | \\ CH_2 \qquad\; CH \cdot NH_2 \\ | \qquad\qquad | \\ CH \cdot NH_2 \quad COOH \\ | \\ COOH \end{array}} \quad \xrightarrow[\text{ase}]{\text{cystathion-}} \quad \underset{\text{Vinylglycine}}{\begin{array}{l} CH_2 \\ \| \\ CH \\ | \\ CH \cdot NH_2 \\ | \\ COOH \end{array}} \quad + \quad \underset{\text{Cysteine}}{\begin{array}{l} CH_2 \cdot SH \\ | \\ CH \cdot NH_2 \\ | \\ COOH \end{array}}$$

The vinylglycine undergoes several transformations, yielding eventually α-ketobutyrate and ammonia.

As noted above (page 493), cysteine is the source of inorganic sulfate groups which may be used in synthesis or excreted as such. Cysteine has also been shown by the use of isotopic labels to be the source of taurine which appears in the bile salts (page 376). Some of the intermediates in this transformation are shown. The path through hypotaurine has until recently been

$$\underset{\text{Cysteine}}{\begin{array}{l} CH_2 \cdot SH \\ | \\ NH_2 \cdot CH \cdot COOH \end{array}} \xrightarrow{\text{ox.}} \underset{\text{Cysteine sulfinic acid}}{\begin{array}{l} CH_2 \cdot SO_2H \\ | \\ H_2N \cdot CH \cdot COOH \end{array}} \xrightarrow{\text{ox.}} \underset{\text{Cysteic acid}}{\begin{array}{l} CH_2 \cdot SO_3H \\ | \\ H_2N \cdot CH \cdot COOH \end{array}}$$

$$\underset{\text{Pyruvate}\,+\,SO_3^{--}}{} \qquad\qquad \Big\downarrow{-CO_2} \qquad\qquad \Big\downarrow{-CO_2}$$

$$\underset{\text{Hypotaurine}}{H_2N \cdot CH_2 \cdot CH_2 \cdot SO_2H} \xrightarrow{\text{ox.}} \underset{\text{Taurine}}{H_2N \cdot CH_2 \cdot CH_2 \cdot SO_3H}$$

$$SO_4^{--}$$

considered the important one in the formation of taurine, but quite recently a specific cysteic acid decarboxylase has been found in chick embryo that may indicate that the cysteic acid route is also important.

Lysine

A special interest attaches to lysine because in the early Schoenheimer experiments it was the only acid tested which did not acquire isotopic nitrogen. This is now known to depend upon the fact that lysine is one of two acids, threonine being the other, which does not take part in transaminations. Its degradation in animal tissues takes place through formation of a ring compound, pipecolic acid, and leads ultimately to formation of glutamic acid.

$$
\begin{array}{c}
CH_2 \cdot NH_2 \\
| \\
(CH_2)_3 \\
| \\
CH \cdot NH_2 \\
| \\
COOH
\end{array}
\rightarrow \rightarrow \rightarrow
\quad\text{[Pipecolic acid ring structure]}\quad
\rightarrow \rightarrow \rightarrow
\begin{array}{c}
NH_2 \cdot CH \cdot COOH \\
| \\
(CH_2)_3 \\
| \\
COOH
\end{array}
$$

$$
\begin{array}{c}
H \\
N \\
H_2C \qquad CH—COOH \\
| \qquad\qquad | \\
H_2C \qquad CH_2 \\
C \\
H_2
\end{array}
$$

L-Lysine   **Pipecolic acid**   **L-α-Aminoadipic acid**

$$\Big\downarrow {-CO_2, -NH_3}$$

$$
\text{Glutamic acid} \leftarrow \text{α-Ketoglutaric acid} \leftarrow
\begin{array}{c}
COOH \\
| \\
(CH_2)_3 \\
| \\
COOH
\end{array}
$$

Glutaric acid

Uses of the Amino Acids

Obviously the primary function of the amino acids is to serve as substrates for protein synthesis. This will be considered later in the chapter. Another use was exemplified in the synthesis of creatine, for which glycine, arginine, and methionine are all essential. There are a number of other metabolic sequences for which specific amino acids are required, and these also will be taken up in connection with the reactions themselves. But beyond these uses of intact amino acids there are a number of biosyntheses which make use of compounds derived by more or less complete degradation of the amino acids.

Ketogenesis and glycogenesis

In the early years, biochemists were much concerned to discover whether or not proteins were "transformed" in the body into either of the other primary foodstuffs. The first experimental investigations of this question made use of diabetic animals. In severe diabetes glucose is not oxidized but excreted in the urine, hence the glucose excretion of a diabetic on a sugar-free diet is a measure of glucose synthesis. It was found that administration of certain amino acids to the experimental animals led to a concomitant increase in glucose excretion. Furthermore, when these same acids were fed to animals whose glycogen stores had been depleted by starvation, the deposition of glycogen in the liver again indicated carbohydrate synthesis from the acids. Later results with labeled acids have confirmed the early ones by showing incorporation of the labels into liver glycogen. Those acids which lead to carbohydrate synthesis are said to be *glycogenic*.

In cases of severe diabetes it is not only the carbohydrate metabolism which is deranged. Failure of the organism to metabolize normally the fat of the

TABLE 13.10.   Metabolic Uses of Amino Acids

Glycogenic Amino Acids	Ketogenic Amino Acids
Glycine	Leucine
Alanine	Tyrosine
Serine	Phenylalanine
Cysteine	
Aspartic acid	
Glutamic acid	
Proline	
Oxyproline	
Ornithine	
Arginine	
Threonine	

diet gives rise in blood and urine to a group of compounds known as "ketone bodies," of which the most fundamental is acetoacetate, $CH_3CO \cdot CH_2COOH$. Administration of a few of the amino acids to diabetic animals was followed by an increased excretion of ketone bodies, thus linking the metabolism of the amino acids to that of the fats. Amino acids in this category are said to be *ketogenic*. The acids in the two groups are listed in Table 13.10. It should be noted that some acids do not appear in either list.

The metabolic pool

It is now recognized that the experimental results just outlined do not indicate the kind of transformations which the earlier workers envisaged. The equilibrium maintained by the metabolic pool of amino acids is a dynamic one not only in the extent to which amino acids are interconvertible and in the way in which they are used for protein synthesis, but also in the way in which their degradation products are caught up into the metabolic machinery. A study of the catabolism of the individual acids has shown that the metabolic paths of a majority of them converge either upon pyruvate or upon acetyl coenzyme A. Some acids, for example serine and alanine, form pyruvate directly or nearly so. Others yield it because they can be transformed into serine. Another pathway to pyruvate is taken by those acids which are degraded to form compounds which are members of the citric acid cycle. Any such compound entering the cycle will ultimately become incorporated into oxaloacetate. This substance may then reenter the cycle and go on to complete oxidation, or it may, on the other hand, yield pyruvate (or a phosphate ester of pyruvate) by decarboxylation. This reaction is catalyzed by *oxaloacetokinase*, and the source of the phosphate group is not ATP, but guanosine triphosphate (GTP) or inosine triphosphate (ITP). In the latter the base is hypoxanthine. Thus any compound which can enter the citric

$$
\begin{array}{ccc}
\begin{array}{l} \text{COOH} \\ | \\ \text{CO} \\ | \\ \text{CH}_2 \cdot \text{COOH} \end{array}
&
+ \ \begin{array}{c} \text{GTP} \\ \text{or} \\ \text{ITP} \end{array} \ \rightarrow
&
\begin{array}{l} \text{COOH} \\ | \\ \text{CO} \cdot \text{PO}_3\text{H}_2 + \text{CO}_2 + \\ \| \\ \text{CH}_2 \end{array}
\ \begin{array}{c} \text{GDP} \\ \text{or} \\ \text{IDP} \end{array}
\end{array}
$$

Oxaloacetic acid   **Phosphoenol-pyruvic acid**

acid cycle may eventually yield phosphopyruvate. Members of the cycle are formed by deamination of glutamate, which yields α-ketobutyrate, and of aspartate, which forms oxaloacetate. Furthermore, all those acids which are interconvertible with glutamate, or which yield it by degradation, form α-ketobutyrate and ultimately pyruvate by a longer series of reactions. These acids are the prolines, arginine, lysine, and histidine.

The other compound which may be derived from a number of the amino acids is acetyl coenzyme A. The oxidative breakdown of phenylalanine begins with its oxidation to tyrosine, which is then transformed ultimately into fumarate which enters the citric acid cycle, and acetoacetate. This substance is a good acetyl donor and yields acetyl coenzyme A in the tissues. It has already been noted that the branched chain acids are metabolized after conjugation with coenzyme A. Leucine is degraded to acetoacetate and acetyl coenzyme A. With isoleucine, acetyl coenzyme A is also one of the products, and propionyl coenzyme A is the other. Degradation of valine leads to formation of propionyl coenzyme A. Since the metabolism of propionic acid involves addition of carbon dioxide to form succinic acid, which is again a member of the citric acid cycle, it is clear that metabolism of the branched chain acids also leads finally either to pyruvate or to acetyl coenzyme A. Some of these relationships are shown in Fig. 13.5.

The information now available on the degradation products of the individual amino acids makes it clear how they could be used in synthesis of fats and carbohydrates. Pyruvate holds a central position in carbohydrate metabolism since it is both a breakdown product and a synthetic substrate. Acetyl coenzyme A holds a similar commanding position in fat metabolism and is indeed the unique substrate from which fatty acids are synthesized *de novo*. These particular syntheses can and do take place, but represent only part of the metabolic transformations by which the cell makes use of small molecules derived from the amino acids. When they are needed for synthesis, they are caught up into a variety of synthetic sequences and used. On the other hand, many of them are oxidized completely, the citric acid intermediates entering the cycle and going on to final formation of carbon dioxide and

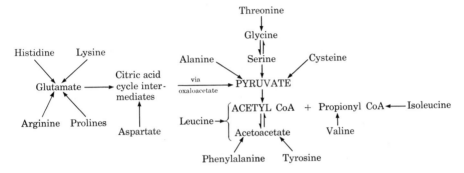

Fig. 13.5. Some catabolic relationships of the amino acids.

water, and the pyruvate or acetyl coenzyme A condensing with oxaloacetate to enter the cycle for complete oxidation.

Still another use which is made of amino acids of the pool was indicated on page 451 in Chapter 12. That chart shows that serine, glycine, methionine, and histidine can all contribute single carbons to form one of the folic acid derivatives which carries an activated one-carbon unit. In this way a carbon from each of these acids may find its way into a purine or imidazole ring or into the labile methyl groups which appear in a number of different compounds.

EXCRETION OF NITROGEN

The chief problem of nitrogen excretion arises from the necessity to dispose of the ammonia formed when the amino acids undergo breakdown in the body. One of the human excretory products listed in Table 13.2, creatinine, is formed by dehydration of body creatine in preparation for its excretion. Although this reaction is reversible in the laboratory, it is one of the few irreversible metabolic reactions. The amount of creatinine excreted is remarkably independent of the diet and varies within very narrow limits. A normal man excretes 1.5–2.0 g per day. Presumably the body synthesizes creatine at this rate.

The amounts of the other nitrogenous constituents of the urine depend largely upon the diet. Since in man uric acid is the end product of purine metabolism, its excretion varies with the amount of nucleoprotein ingested. On a diet which includes a high percentage of liver or sweetbreads, both rich in nuclear material, the daily output of uric acid may be as high as 2 g, while on a purine-free diet this may fall to 0.1 g. In health and on an average diet, an adult male excretes about 0.7 g of uric acid per day.

Ammonia and urea both arise from the amino acids, and consequently the amounts of these substances excreted vary with the protein intake. "Ammonia" appears in the urine as ammonium salts of various organic and inorganic acids, hydrochloric, sulfuric, and phosphoric predominating. It was noted earlier that the kidney is the most active deaminating organ in the body. This ability rapidly to set free ammonia from amino acids is very necessary for an organ which must from time to time neutralize undetermined amounts of acid for excretion. On an acid-forming diet the amount of ammonia excreted is high, whereas base-forming foods tend to lower the ammonia excretion. Ordinarily about 2.5–6 per cent of the total urinary nitrogen is in the form of ammonium ions. The remainder of the ammonia derived from the amino acids is converted in man to urea.

In birds and reptiles, on the other hand, the excreta contain little or no urea, since these animals form uric acid from their excess ammonia. This has been explained as an adaptation of these forms to a relative water shortage. Thus it is assumed that excretion of ammonia is the simplest and most primitive arrangement for getting rid of waste nitrogen. This is perfectly feasible so long as an animal living in water can wash away ammonia with a copious stream of urine. But ammonia is a toxic substance, and life on dry land was hardly possible until some mechanism had been developed for transforming it into something less noxious. One group of organisms, including the primates, the amphibia, and the elasmobranch fish, solved the problem by converting the ammonia into urea which is comparatively innocuous and is excreted in the urine at such a rate that its concentration in the body fluids never becomes dangerous. But the birds and some of the reptiles had a double problem. Not only must their own bodies adapt to a certain scarcity of water, but their eggs are enclosed in shells or tough membranes which exclude water entirely. During the development of the embryo nitrogenous wastes form from the stored reserves of protein foods, and if these were allowed to accumulate as ammonia or as urea, their concentration inside the shell would soon become lethal. This unhappy result is avoided because these organisms transform metabolic ammonia into the harmless and insoluble uric acid which precipitates and is thus effectively removed from the fluids of the embryo. The assumption is that this mechanism, essential to survival inside the egg, is carried into adult life. Animals which excrete the major part of their waste nitrogen as uric acid are said to be *uricotelic*, while those which excrete predominantly urea are *ureotelic*. The synthetic formation of uric acid as opposed to the degradative one which is responsible for the presence of uric acid in mammalian excreta, is considered in the last section of this chapter.

Urea Synthesis

The work of Bollman and his colleagues, to which reference has already been made (page 471), proved that urea formation takes place only in the liver and that it is preceded by the freeing of ammonia from the amino acids. In 1932 Krebs and Henseleit concluded that urea formation from ammonia is one of those cyclical procedures so often used by living cells. Working with tissue slices, they found that urea is formed by liver either from ammonia or from amino acids. The rate of formation varied somewhat with variation in the amino acid precursor, but when arginine was furnished in the nutrient solution the amount of urea formed greatly exceeded that which could have arisen by deamination of the acid itself. This suggested that arginine was functioning in a cyclical process, and being used repeatedly.

It was already known that the liver contains an enzyme, arginase, which catalyzes the splitting of arginine to yield urea and the simpler diamino acid, ornithine. In the equation below the starred atoms have been isotopically

$$
\begin{array}{ccc}
\overset{*}{N}H_2 & & \\
| & & NH_2 & \overset{*}{N}H_2 \\
C=\overset{*}{N}H & & | & \diagup \\
| & \xrightarrow[\text{arginase}]{+H_2O} & (CH_2)_3 & + CO \\
NH & & | & \diagdown \\
| & & CH \cdot NH_2 & \overset{*}{N}H_2 \\
(CH_2)_3 & & | & \\
| & & COOH & \\
CH(NH_2)COOH & & & \\
\textbf{Arginine} & & \textbf{Ornithine} & \textbf{Urea}
\end{array}
$$

labeled in the biosynthesis of arginine in experimental animals fed labeled ammonia or amino acids. The arginine isolated from the body proteins proved to have the label in the positions indicated, and hydrolysis of this arginine with arginase yielded urea labeled in both nitrogens, and unlabeled ornithine. On the basis of their experiments Krebs and Henseleit suggested that ammonia is transformed into urea in the series of reactions outlined in Fig. 13.6. Ammonia and carbon dioxide react with ornithine to form citrulline which then condenses with a second molecule of ammonia to form arginine. The action of arginase upon the arginine then frees urea and reconstitutes the starting substance, ornithine.

Since Krebs made his original suggestion, work with isotopically labeled molecules has abundantly confirmed the general outline of his mechanism of urea formation. But when it became possible to isolate the individual enzymes it was shown that both of the synthetic steps were more complicated than was originally supposed. Citrulline synthesis is being studied intensively by P. P. Cohen and his colleagues, while much of the work which has clarified the synthesis of arginine comes from Ratner[13] and her associates. The reaction

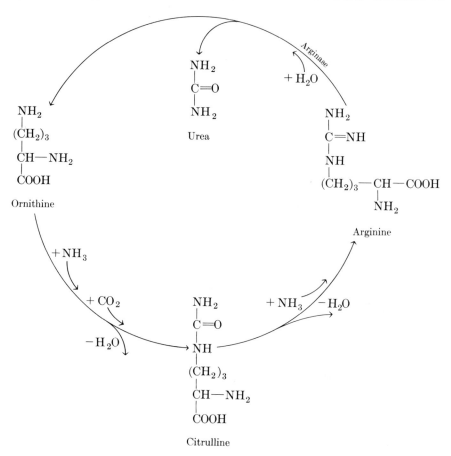

Fig. 13.6. Krebs urea cycle.

sequence as it is now understood is summarized below. The atoms shown in heavy type are those which will appear in the urea molecule. The nitrogen which enters the cycle in aspartic acid may have come from ammonia, in which case it will have come there through a transamination reaction with

---

[13] Dr. Sarah Ratner (1903–) is Associate Professor of Biochemistry at the New York University Medical College. Her chief research interest has been in the field of amino acid metabolism, and of late especially in the reactions of the urea cycle.

glutamic acid. Glutamic acid in turn may have acquired it from ammonia through catalysis by L-glutamate dehydrogenase, or may have acquired it by transamination from any of the amino acids. This means, of course, that although aspartate is an essential reactant the nitrogen which reaches urea by way of this compound may have come from any of the amino acids.

Synthesis of citrulline

This reaction takes place in two steps, one of which requires the presence of both ATP and a cofactor, *N*-acetylglutamate. The part played by the cofactor is not understood, but it has been clearly shown to be essential with enzymes from liver.

$$NH_3 + CO_2 + ATP \leftrightarrows H_2N \cdot CO \cdot O \cdot PO_3H_2 + ADP \qquad (1)$$
Carbamyl phosphate

N-acetylglutamate is an obligatory cofactor in this step. The enzyme is known as *carbamate phosphokinase*. There is clearly still much to be done on this part of the cycle, since recent results indicate that biotin is also required. This suggests an activation of carbon dioxide such as that referred to on page 454.

$$
\begin{array}{c}
NH_2 \\
| \\
(CH_2)_3 \\
| \\
CH \cdot NH_2 \\
| \\
COOH \\
\textbf{Ornithine}
\end{array}
+
\begin{array}{c}
CO \cdot NH_2 \\
| \\
O \cdot PO_3H_2
\end{array}
\leftrightarrows
\begin{array}{c}
NH \cdot CO \cdot NH_2 \\
| \\
(CH_2)_3 \\
| \\
CH \cdot NH_2 \\
| \\
COOH \\
\textbf{Citrulline}
\end{array}
+ H_3PO_4 \qquad (2)
$$

The enzyme for this step is *ornithine transcarbamylase*

Synthesis of arginine

This is also a two-step reaction and uses the aspartic acid referred to above, which serves to bring into the cycle the second nitrogen for urea formation.

$$
\begin{array}{c}
NH \\
\| \\
C \cdot OH \\
| \\
NH \\
| \\
(CH_2)_3 \\
| \\
CH \cdot NH_2 \\
| \\
COOH \\
\textbf{Citrulline} \\
\textbf{(Enol form)}
\end{array}
+
\begin{array}{c}
COOH \\
| \\
H_2N \cdot CH \\
| \\
CH_2 \\
| \\
COOH \\
\textbf{Aspartic acid}
\end{array}
+ ATP \leftrightarrows
\begin{array}{c}
NH \quad\quad COOH \\
\| \quad\quad\quad | \\
C{-}NH{-}CH \\
| \quad\quad\quad | \\
NH \quad\quad CH_2 \\
| \quad\quad\quad | \\
(CH_2)_3 \quad COOH \\
| \\
CH \cdot NH_2 \\
| \\
COOH \\
\textbf{Arginosuccinic acid}
\end{array}
+ AMP + PP \quad (3)
$$

The enzyme for this step is *arginosuccinate synthetase*.

$$
\underset{\text{Arginosuccinic acid}}{
\begin{array}{l}
\overset{\displaystyle NH}{\underset{\displaystyle \|}{}} \\
\mathbf{C}\!\!-\!\!\mathbf{NH}\!\!-\!\!\overset{\displaystyle COOH}{\underset{\displaystyle |}{CH}} \\
\underset{\displaystyle |}{NH} \qquad \underset{\displaystyle |}{CH_2} \\
(CH_2)_3 \qquad COOH \\
\underset{\displaystyle |}{CH\cdot NH_2} \\
COOH
\end{array}}
\leftrightharpoons
\underset{\text{Arginine}}{
\begin{array}{l}
\overset{\displaystyle NH}{\underset{\displaystyle \|}{}} \\
\mathbf{C}\!\!-\!\!NH_2 \\
\underset{\displaystyle |}{NH} \\
(CH_2)_3 \\
\underset{\displaystyle |}{CH\cdot NH_2} \\
COOH
\end{array}}
\; + \;
\underset{\text{Fumaric acid}}{
\begin{array}{l}
HC\cdot COOH \\
\|\quad\quad \\
HOOC\cdot CH
\end{array}}
\qquad (4)
$$

This step is catalyzed by arginosuccinase.

The arginine is then hydrolyzed by arginase, and the cycle ends with the reconstituted ornithine and with a molecule of fumarate. Fumarase catalyzes the addition of water to fumarate to form malate, oxidation of which yields oxaloacetate. This keto acid can then form aspartate by transamination, thus putting a new nitrogen in position for urea synthesis.

$$
\underset{\text{Fumaric acid}}{
\begin{array}{l}
HC\cdot COOH \\
\|\quad\quad \\
HOOC\cdot CH
\end{array}}
\underset{\xrightleftharpoons{\pm H_2O}}{}
\underset{\text{Malic acid}}{
\begin{array}{l}
CH_2COOH \\
| \\
CHOH\cdot COOH
\end{array}}
\underset{\text{red.}}{\overset{\text{ox.}}{\rightleftharpoons}}
$$

$$
\underset{\substack{\text{Oxaloacetic}\\\text{acid}}}{
\begin{array}{l}
CH_2COOH \\
| \\
CO\cdot COOH
\end{array}}
\underset{\xrightleftharpoons{\text{transamination}}}{}
\underset{\substack{\text{Aspartic}\\\text{acid}}}{
\begin{array}{l}
CH_2COOH \\
| \\
CH\cdot NH_2 \\
| \\
COOH
\end{array}}
$$

Excretion of the Bases in Mammals

It will be recalled that the nucleic acids are polynucleotides in which one base-sugar unit is linked to the next by a phosphoric ester link from carbon 3 of one ribose to carbon 5 of the adjacent one. These acids are degraded by hydrolyses catalyzed by various *nucleases*. The action of pancreatic ribonuclease was referred to on page 242 where it was shown to act upon RNA to set free pyrimidine nucleoside-3′-phosphates. This would leave many oligonucleotides rich in purine bases. A similar enzyme, but one with a rather broader specificity in that it frees both purine and pyrimidine nucleotides has been isolated from tobacco leaves. In recent years work is progressing in the purification and characterization of a number of intracellular ribonucleases as well as of other deoxyribonucleases which act specifically upon DNA. It may then be assumed that early steps in the degradation of the nucleic acids lead to formation of various 3′- and 5′-nucleoside phosphates, by way of the intermediate formation of oligo- and dinucleotides.

The mononucleotides are further disrupted either by hydrolysis or by phosphorolysis. A number of *phosphatases* are known which bring about hydrolytic removal of phosphoric acid from mononucleotides and other esters. In animal tissues, at least, the separation of the base from the sugar in the resulting nucleoside seems to be a phosphorolysis which yields the free base and the sugar phosphate. Enzymes which bring about this type of reaction are known as *phosphorylases*.

| Uridine | Ribose - 1 - phosphate | Uracil |

Of the three types of small molecules which are the ultimate products of nucleic acid breakdown only the bases need be considered here. Phosphoric acid is ubiquitous, and the sugars or sugar phosphates will follow well-known paths of carbohydrate metabolism.

The pyrimidine bases are degraded with opening of the ring and formation of various small molecules including ammonia and carbon dioxide and amino acids which may then be further degraded or which may be used in synthesis. For example, breakdown of uracil yields β-alanine ($H_2N \cdot CH_2 \cdot CH_2 \cdot COOH$) which may be incorporated into coenzyme A.

The purine bases are much less completely broken down before excretion. In man the end product of purine metabolism is uric acid which with its intact purine rings is formed from the commonly occurring bases as indicated in Fig. 13.7.

Although in man and the higher apes uric acid is excreted as such, in most other mammals uric acid is degraded oxidatively to form the more soluble substance, allantoin. This reaction probably involves one or more intermediates, but its course has not been finally clarified. In fish and amphibia

| Uric acid | Allantoin | Allantoic acid |

and more primitive organisms, allantoin may be degraded to allantoic acid, and this may be further broken down to urea and glyoxylate.

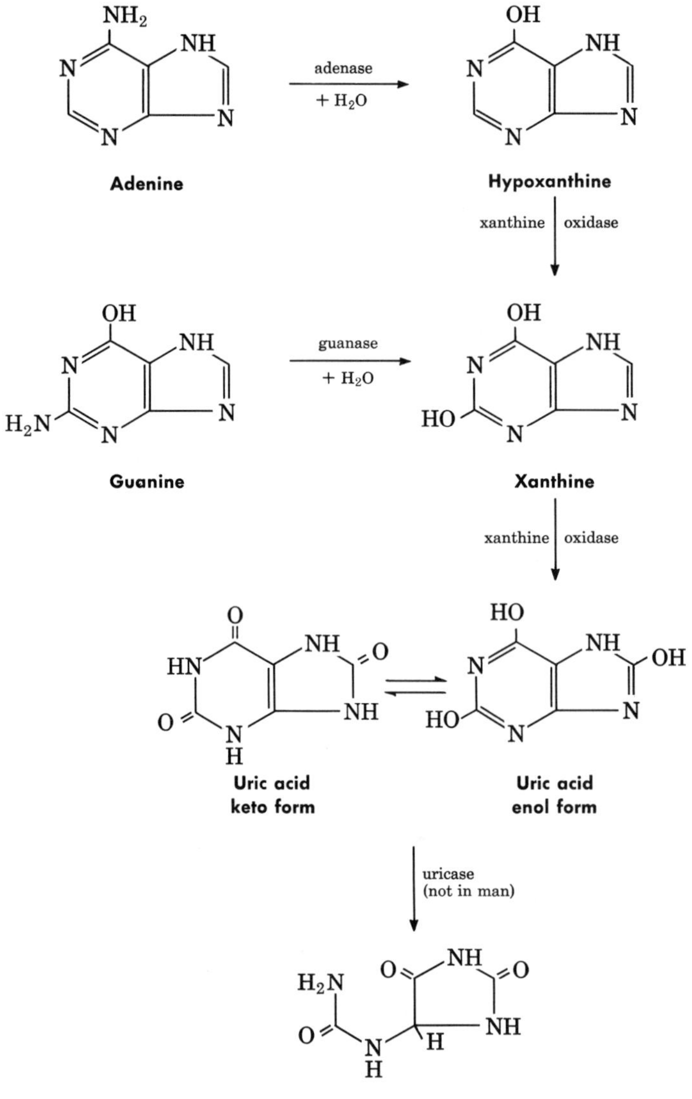

Fig. 13.7. Degradation of the purines.

To the statement that most mammals except man degrade uric acid to allantoin there is one strange exception. About 1915 Stanley Benedict discovered that the Dalmatian coach hound alone among dogs excretes uric acid. Why the primates and this one breed of dog should thus share the misfortune of being subject to gout is a mystery. Being incapable of oxidizing uric acid certain people, when its excretion does not keep pace with its formation, deposit the excess in the joints. The tendency to form such deposits seems to be a familial matter associated with a hereditary tendency to high blood uric acid values.

The uric acid excreted by birds and reptiles represents a true synthesis from small molecules. This process is considered in the following section.

BIOSYNTHESIS OF NITROGEN COMPOUNDS

For many years, in default of any better explanation, biochemists emphasized the reversibility of most metabolic reactions and tried to explain the syntheses which take place in living tissue as simply the reversal of the catabolic reactions. A truer picture could not be drawn until it had become possible to isolate and purify large numbers of enzymes, to fractionate the cell contents in the ultracentrifuge, and to study the reactions carried on by each separate part with labeled substrates. As a result of work in many laboratories and with many different techniques, information has become available within the last few years which makes it possible now to trace some at least of the events connected with various biosyntheses. It should be remembered in reading the following discussion that it is an interim report on work in progress, and so is subject to correction and quite certainly to elaboration whenever a "reaction" proves to consist of several steps, each with specific enzymes and cofactors.

Synthesis of Heme

It was noted in Chapter 9 that isotopic labeling experiments had shown that heme is synthesized from glycine and acetate. This synthesis proved to involve as intermediate an activated form of succinic acid. For some years this was spoken of as "succinyl-X" since it was believed to differ from succinyl coenzyme A. It has now been shown that succinic acid is in fact activated by conjugation with coenzyme A. It will be remembered that there is a complicated stage in the citric acid cycle at which α-ketoglutarate is decarboxylated and the succinyl residue is passed along in turn to thiamine pyrophosphate, to lipoic acid, and finally to coenzyme A. The succinyl coenzyme A may then lose the coenzyme and go on to oxidation in the cycle. But it may be withdrawn to be used in the synthesis of heme. In this connection it is interesting to note that the ability to synthesize hemoproteins seems to be quite widespread in aerobic cells, as indeed might have been expected in view of the presence in all of them of several different cytochromes.

The next intermediate in heme synthesis to be identified was δ-amino-levulinic acid, which is formed from succinyl coenzyme A and glycine. It can readily be seen that this will involve a decarboxylation, and for several years the reaction was formulated as a preliminary condensation of the two reacting molecules to form α-amino-β-ketoadipic acid, followed by decarboxylation

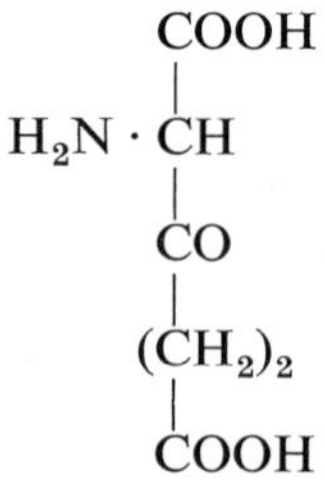

$$
\begin{array}{cc}
\text{COOH} & \text{NH}_2 \\
| & | \\
\text{H}_2\text{N}\cdot\text{CH} & \text{CH}_2 \\
| & | \\
\text{CO} & \text{CO} \\
| & | \\
(\text{CH}_2)_2 & (\text{CH}_2)_2 \\
| & | \\
\text{COOH} & \text{COOH}
\end{array}
$$

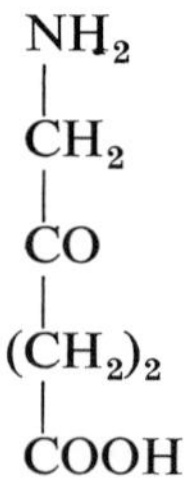

α-Amino-β-keto-   δ-Aminolevulinic
adipic acid   acid

to give the δ-aminolevulinic acid. In 1959 Shemin and his colleagues showed that this reaction, like many decarboxylations, requires the presence of pyridoxal phosphate as coenzyme. They worked with bacterial enzymes, but the reaction has the same coenzyme requirement when catalyzed by other tissue enzymes. From an analysis of the kinetics of the reaction Shemin and his group propose the following reaction sequence.

Enzyme (E) + Pyridoxal-5-phosphate (PyP) $\leftrightarrows$ E-PyP
E-PyP + Glycine (G) $\leftrightarrows$ E-PyP-G
E-PyP-G + Succinyl CoA $\rightarrow$ CoA + E-PyP-G-succinate
E-PyP-G-succinate $\rightarrow$ E-PyP-δ-aminolevulinate (δ-ALA) + CO$_2$
E-PyP-δ-ALA $\rightarrow$ E-PyP + δ-aminolevulinate

In the reaction between glycine and the coenzyme a compound of the Schiff's base type is formed, as indicated in the discussion of transaminations. In a simple decarboxylation this compound then loses carbon dioxide. In this reaction it is believed that this decarboxylation step is preceded by an interaction between the glycine and the succinyl coenzyme A while both are attached to the enzyme surface. Then, after loss of carbon dioxide, the cleavage of the enzyme-coenzyme-product complex is probably a hydrolysis.

When δ-aminolevulinic acid has formed, it is then acted upon by the enzyme *aminolevulinate dehydrase* which has been isolated from both animal

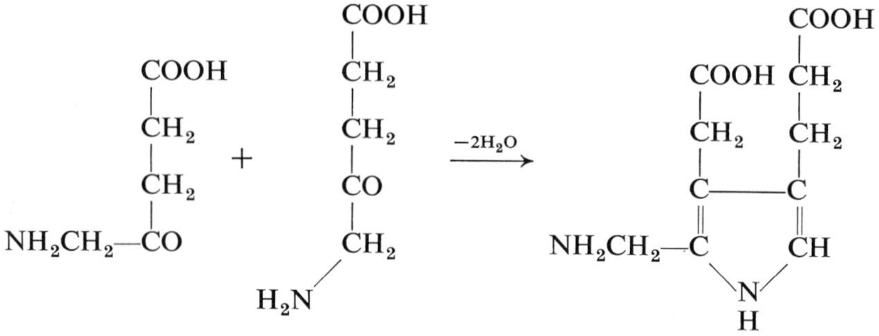

$$
\begin{array}{ccc}
 & \text{COOH} & \\
\text{COOH} & | & \\
| & \text{CH}_2 & \\
\text{CH}_2 & | & \\
| & \text{CH}_2 & \\
\text{CH}_2 \quad + & | & \xrightarrow{-2\text{H}_2\text{O}} \\
| & \text{CO} & \\
\text{NH}_2\text{CH}_2{-}\text{CO} & | & \\
 & \text{CH}_2 & \\
 & \diagup & \\
 & \text{H}_2\text{N} &
\end{array}
$$

$$
\begin{array}{cc}
 & \text{COOH} \\
 & | \\
\text{COOH} & \text{CH}_2 \\
| & | \\
\text{CH}_2 & \text{CH}_2 \\
| & | \\
\text{C}{-}\!\!-\!\!-\text{C} \\
\| \quad \| \\
\text{NH}_2\text{CH}_2{-}\text{C} \quad \text{CH} \\
\diagdown \quad \diagup \\
\text{N} \\
| \\
\text{H}
\end{array}
$$

Porphobilinogen

and bacterial tissues. It catalyzes a condensation of two molecules of the acid with elimination of two molecules of water. This yields a substituted pyrrole known as porphobilinogen. This substance had previously been identified as an excretory product in patients with acute porphyria and has since been shown with isotopic labeling to be an effective precursor of heme.

Formation of heme from porphobilinogen requires condensation of four molecules and alteration of all except two of the side chains. The exact mechanism of the condensations has not yet been established, but it has been shown that two intermediates are uroporphyrinogen I and III. It will be

$P = -CH_2 \cdot CH_2 \cdot COOH$
$A = -CH_2COOH$

Uroporphyrinogen I

noted in the formula given for uroporphyrinogen I that no two propionic acid side chains are in neighboring positions. In the III isomer a shift has occurred and one pair of pyrrole rings has the side chain arrangement at positions 6 and 7 which is characteristic of heme. This rearrangement is thought to take place in a circuitous series of reactions which has not yet been completely worked out, nor have the reactions by which the other side chains are transformed and the unsaturation introduced into the molecule. The broad outlines of the synthesis are known, but there are certainly many intermediate steps to be discovered.

Protein Synthesis

Chemically the formation of protein from amino acids is simple, requiring only formation of a series of peptide bonds. The questions which arise in this connection are two: what is the immediate source of the energy which must be expended in the endergonic reaction of peptide bond formation, and how are the order of the acids and final structure of the protein determined? There is imposing evidence that the codes in accordance with which the amino acids are assembled are implicit in the base order in the DNA of the nucleus, but only recently has there been any indication how that code is brought to bear upon the acids.

Since the middle 1950's it has become apparent that the influence of nuclear DNA is exerted indirectly. It was first shown that liver slices incubated with labeled amino acids incorporated these acids into liver proteins. Later when fragmented cells were separated into fractions by differential centrifugation, it was discovered that there was more and earlier labeling in the microsomes than in nuclei or mitochondria. Study of the catalyses brought about by the microsomal fraction and by the enzymes present in the cell sap has made possible the following general outline of the course of protein synthesis.

Hoagland[14] found that in the presence of enzymes which are precipitated from the cell sap at pH 5, amino acids react with ATP to form mixed anhydrides, known as aminoacyl adenylates, which are bound to the enzyme.

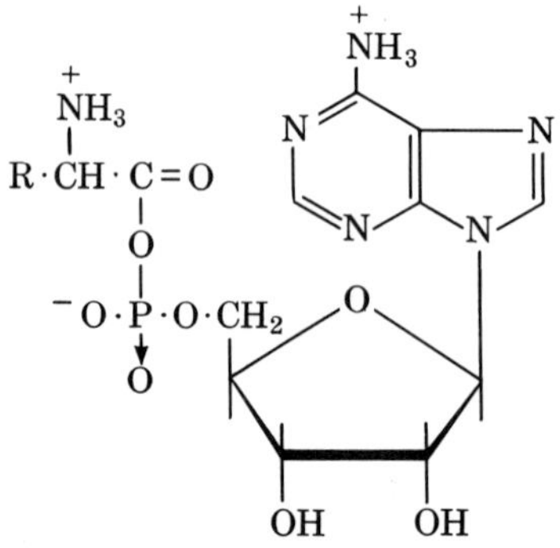

Aminoacyl adenylate

The general reaction may be represented as follows, with E standing for the enzyme:

$$R \cdot CH(NH_2) \cdot COOH + ATP + E \xrightleftharpoons{Mg^{++}} \text{E-aminoacyl adenylate} + PP$$

So many enzymes, each specific for a single amino acid, have now been isolated that it is believed that the cell provides a different enzyme for each amino acid, and even for glutamine, for example, as distinct from glutamic acid.

It will be remembered that there is a special small RNA found in cell sap and known as soluble RNA or SRNA (see page 249). It has now been shown that the second step in protein synthesis is the transfer of the aminoacyl group, from its attachment to adenylic acid and to the enzyme, to form some sort of

---

[14] Mahlon B. Hoagland (1921–) is Associate Professor of Bacteriology at Harvard Medical School. He is known particularly for his contributions to our knowledge of protein biosynthesis.

covalent link with SRNA. This transfer seems to be catalyzed by the same enzyme which originally brought about activation of the amino acid. The exact nature of the binding is not known, but some specific requirements for its formation have been uncovered. The three terminal nucleotides of SRNA must be two cytidylic acid residues and one adenylic acid attached in that order so that the end of the molecule may be represented:

$$SRNA—CMP—CMP—AMP$$

One link between the transferred aminoacyl group and the soluble RNA is probably an ester link between the free 2'- or 3'-hydroxyl on the ribose of the terminal nucleotide and the carboxyl group of the aminoacyl moiety. Although such a link is believed to be formed by every amino acid, there must clearly be other binding sites on the SRNA or on the enzyme surface to account for the amino acid specificity.

It will be remembered that the microsomal fraction consists of a membrane, largely lipid in nature, to which are attached small nucleoprotein particles or ribosomes. When radioactive amino acids were used for protein synthesis *in vivo*, it was found as outlined above that they were incorporated into SRNA prior to their incorporation into proteins. Experiments *in vitro* have now shown that the amino acids bound to SRNA are next transferred to the ribosomes carrying with them the adenine to which they were bound in SRNA. This is indicated by the fact that when a mixture of aminoacyl-SRNA complexes labeled with C^{14} in their terminal adenosines transfer the amino acids to microsomal RNA, twelve times as many molecules of radioactive adenine are transferred as of any single amino acid. This suggests a simultaneous transfer of all the bound amino acids to microsomal RNA. As was noted in Chapter 5, the RNA of the microsomal particles is believed to have been synthesized in the nucleus in accordance with the DNA codes of the various genes, and therefore to carry the code itself. This is what makes it possible for it to assemble the amino acids in the correct order for combination into whatever polypeptide is in process of synthesis. For the transfer from SRNA to microsomal RNA, using enzymes from mammalian liver, both ATP and the triphosphate of guanosine, GTP, are obligatory cofactors, but their function is not known. With some bacterial systems the guanosine triphosphate is not required.

The final step in protein synthesis, that is, the transfer of the aminoacyl residues from their attachment to microsomal RNA to form free proteins, still awaits elucidation. This may involve formation of the actual polypeptide in the microsomal particle and its subsequent extrusion, or it may be that the bound residues undergo one or more transformations before being finally removed from the RNA and linked into a protein or polypeptide molecule.

In connection with the type of activation just discussed, it is of interest that in formation of the two peptide bonds in GSH, RNA is required for one but not for the other. Glutathione is synthesized in two steps, as follows:

$$
\begin{array}{l}
COOH \\
| \\
CH_2 \\
| \\
CH_2 \quad + H_2N \cdot CH \quad + ATP \rightarrow \\
| \\
CH \cdot NH_2 \\
| \\
COOH
\end{array}
\quad
\begin{array}{l}
CH_2SH \\
| \\
CH \\
| \\
COOH
\end{array}
$$

$$
\begin{array}{l}
CH_2SH \\
| \\
CO \cdot NH \cdot CH \\
| \qquad\quad | \\
CH_2 \qquad COOH \\
| \\
CH_2 \\
| \\
CH \cdot NH_2 \\
| \\
COOH \quad (+ ADP + P)
\end{array}
\quad + ATP +
\begin{array}{l}
NH_2 \\
| \\
CH_2 \quad \rightarrow \\
| \\
COOH
\end{array}
$$

Glutamic acid   Cysteine   γ-Glutamyl-cysteine

$$
\begin{array}{l}
CH_2SH \\
| \\
CO\!-\!NH\!-\!CH \\
| \qquad\qquad | \\
CH_2 \qquad CO \\
| \qquad\qquad | \\
CH_2 \qquad NH \qquad + ADP + P \\
| \qquad\qquad | \\
CH \cdot NH_2 \quad CH_2 \\
| \qquad\qquad | \\
COOH \qquad COOH
\end{array}
$$

GSH
γ-Glutamylcysteinyl-glycine

SRNA is not needed for formation of the dipeptide, but final synthesis of the tripeptide involves a prior linking of the intermediate dipeptide, γ-glutamyl-cysteine, to SRNA with splitting of ATP to ADP and inorganic phosphate. It is then this activated dipeptide which reacts with glycine.

Biosynthesis of Nucleic Acids

As a result of recent work, information is now available on two different phases of the biosynthesis of nucleic acids. It has long been known from work with labeled precursors that the purine and pyrimidine bases are synthesized in the living cell from small molecules. The chemistry of the series of reactions by which the two types of ring compound are evolved has now been completely worked out, and most if not all the individual enzymes isolated. At the other end of the process, enzymes have been obtained which bring about polymerization of mononucleotides to yield molecules which are indistinguishable from natural nucleic acids.

Pyrimidine biosynthesis

Ammonia, carbon dioxide, and aspartic acid furnish the atoms for the synthesis of the pyrimidine ring, but in this reaction sequence, as in the one which leads to purine synthesis, the base is not obtained free, but as part of a mononucleotide.

Pyrimidine synthesis begins with the same carbamyl phosphate which takes part in the synthesis of urea. It will be remembered that with enzymes from animal tissues, *N*-acetylglutamate is an obligatory cofactor, but bacterial enzymes show no such requirement. Catalyzed by *carbamate phosphokinase*, ammonia and carbon dioxide react in the presence of ATP (and *N*-acetylglutamate) to form carbamyl phosphate.

$$CO_2 + NH_3 + ATP \leftrightharpoons H_2N \cdot CO \cdot O \cdot P + ADP$$

Carbamyl phosphate

In the second step *aspartate transcarbamylase* catalyzes the transfer of the carbamyl group from phosphate to aspartic acid, forming carbamyl aspartate, also known as ureidosuccinic acid. This compound loses water with formation of the ring compound dihydroorotic acid. The enzyme for the dehydration is *dihydroorotase*.

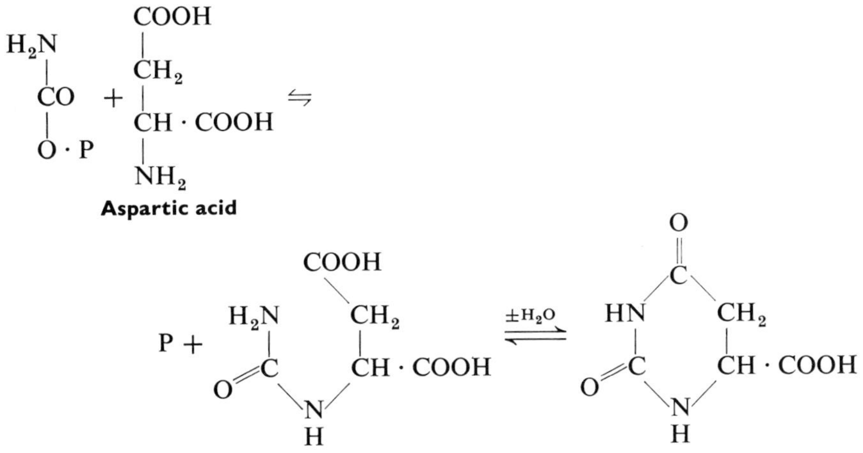

Aspartic acid

Carbamylaspartate   **Dihydroorotic acid**

Removal of two hydrogens from carbons 4 and 5 of dihydroorotic acid is catalyzed by a specific reductase for which DPN$^+$ is the coenzyme. This introduces the double bond between carbons 4 and 5, and completes formation of the typical pyrimidine ring, though the presence of the carboxyl group attached to carbon 4 keeps it from being a true pyrimidine base.

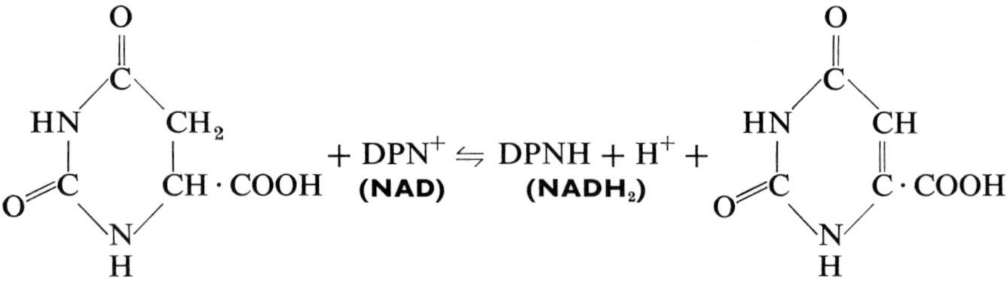

Dihydroorotic acid $+ DPN^+ \rightleftharpoons DPNH + H^+ +$ (NAD)   (NADH$_2$)   Orotic acid

At this point ribose phosphate is introduced into the molecule by use of the phosphate derivative known as 5-phosphoribosyl-1-pyrophosphate (PRPP) and previously referred to in connection with the biosynthesis of histidine (page 500). This substance is formed by interaction of ribose-5-phosphate with ATP, and reacts with orotic acid as shown in the equation:

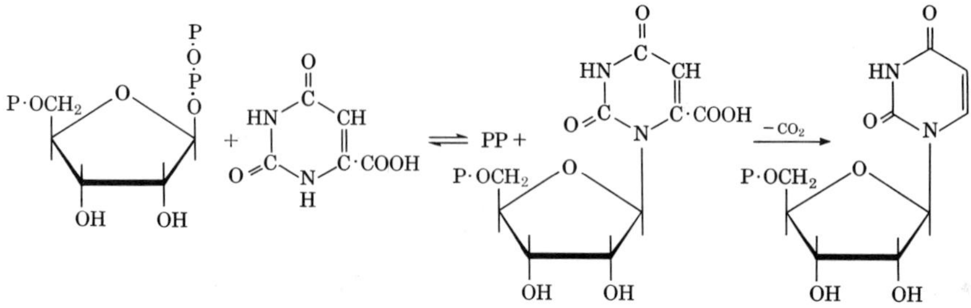

PRPP   Orotic acid   Orotidine - 5′- phosphate   Uridylic acid

Decarboxylation of this nucleotide by a specific decarboxylase yields uridine-5-phosphate or uridylic acid. This substance is then modified to form the other pyrimidine nucleotides. For example, after reaction with ATP which transforms it into the triphosphate, ammonia is introduced into the base to form cytidine triphosphate. In the formulations below RTP stands for ribose with a triphosphate group at carbon 5 as in ATP.

$$UMP + ATP \rightleftharpoons UTP + AMP$$
(Uridylic acid)

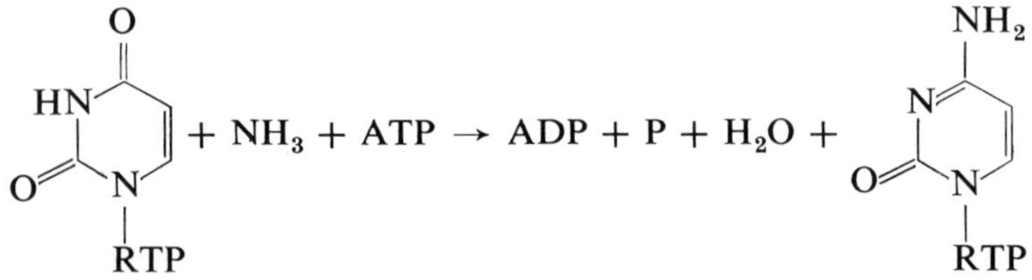

$+ NH_3 + ATP \rightarrow ADP + P + H_2O +$

Uridine triphosphate
UTP

Cytidine triphosphate
CTP

There is evidence too that uridylic acid is also the precursor of the deoxy-ribosides. Thus it seems that synthesis of all the pyrimidine mononucleotides found in nucleic acids follows a common path up to the formation of uridylic acid and that the other pyrimidine nucleotides are derived by modification of this compound.

Purine biosynthesis

Most of the experimental material used in the study of purine biosynthesis has come from pigeons because the avian excretion of nitrogen as uric acid ensures a high concentration of the enzymes in their cells and particularly in the livers. In the early experiments various labeled molecules were fed to

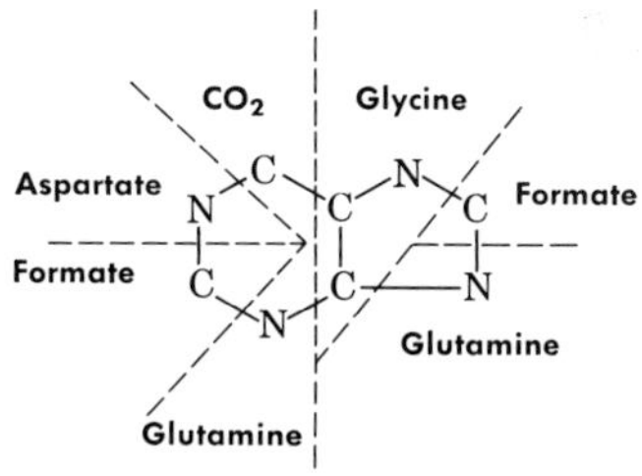

Fig. 13.8. Precursors of the purine rings.

pigeons after which the distribution of the isotopes was determined both in excreted uric acid and in tissue nucleic acids. These experiments showed that the various atoms in the purine rings originated as indicated in Fig. 13.8. Later work, chiefly with purified enzymes from pigeon liver, has now elucidated step by step the rather complex reaction sequence in which the various precursors are used to build up the purine molecule. In this synthesis, as in that of the pyrimidine bases, it is a mononucleotide which is first formed, namely, inosinic acid. The two people chiefly responsible for this work are

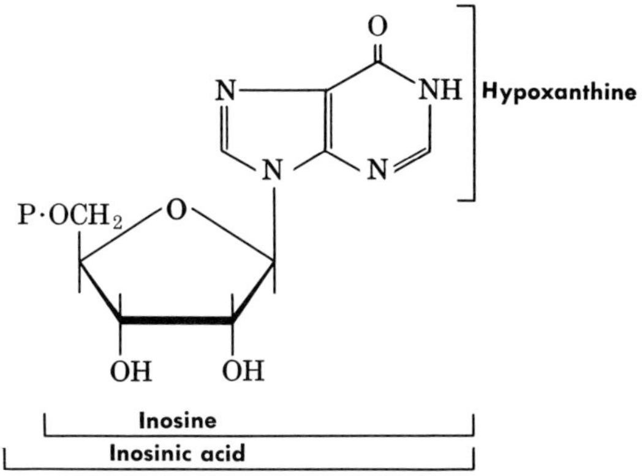

J. M. Buchanan[15] and G. R. Greenberg[16]. It was shown that the earliest labeling of a purine appears in hypoxanthine and its derivatives, inosinic acid and inosine. The relative specific activities when radioactive precursors had been provided, suggested that inosinic acid was actually the first labeled compound, and that the others came from this.

The purine story begins with the isolation of the compound 5-amino-4-imidazolecarboxamide (AICA) from bacterial cultures in which growth had been inhibited by sulfathiazole.

5-Amino-4-imidazolecarboxamide (AICA)

When this compound, labeled with C^{14}, was fed to rats and pigeons it proved to be a purine precursor, the label appearing in rat nucleic acids and in the uric acid excreted by pigeons. The steps in the synthesis of purine, which proved to include not AICA itself but a derivative, are outlined below. Whether mentioned or not, each step is catalyzed by a specific enzyme.

1. The synthesis begins with the formation from ribose-5-phosphate and ATP of the same 5-phosphoribosylpyrophosphate (PRPP) which also takes part in pyrimidine and histidine biosynthesis.

2. A nitrogen is introduced from glutamine when PRPP interacts with glutamine to form 5-phosphoribosylamine (PRA). In the equation $G\text{-}CONH_2$ stands for γ-glutamine.

---

[15] John M. Buchanan (1917–) is now Professor and Head of Division of Biochemistry at the Massachusetts Institute of Technology. His earlier work was published from the University of Pennsylvania.

[16] G. Robert Greenberg (1918–) is Professor of Biochemistry at the University of Michigan, but between 1946 and 1957 he was at Western Reserve.

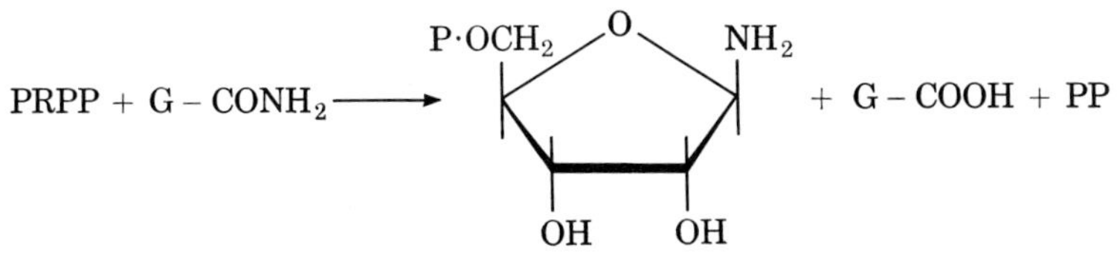

$$PRPP + G-CONH_2 \longrightarrow \text{[ring structure]} + G-COOH + PP$$

5 - Phosphoribosylamine
PRA

3. Interaction of PRA with glycine, in the presence of ATP, yields glycinamide ribotide (GAR).

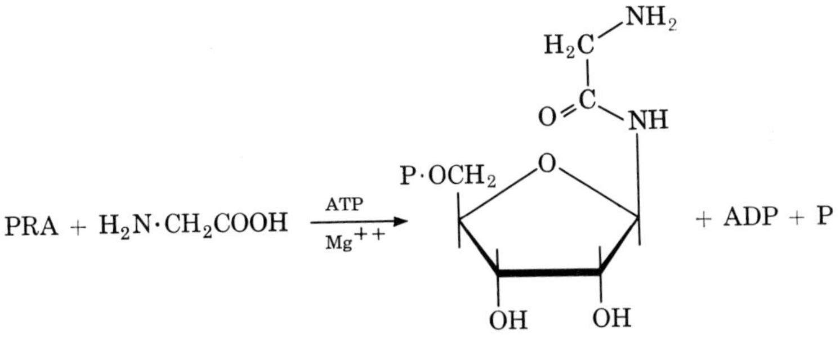

$$PRA + H_2N \cdot CH_2COOH \xrightarrow[Mg^{++}]{ATP} \text{[ring structure]} + ADP + P$$

Glycinamide ribotide
GAR

4. At this point the first one-carbon unit is introduced, attached to tetrahydrofolic acid, as is usual in the activation of such units. For this particular synthetic step 5,10-anhydroformyltetrahydrofolic acid is the actual formylating agent. The new product is formylglycinamide ribotide (FGAR). FH_4 stands for tetrahydrofolic acid.

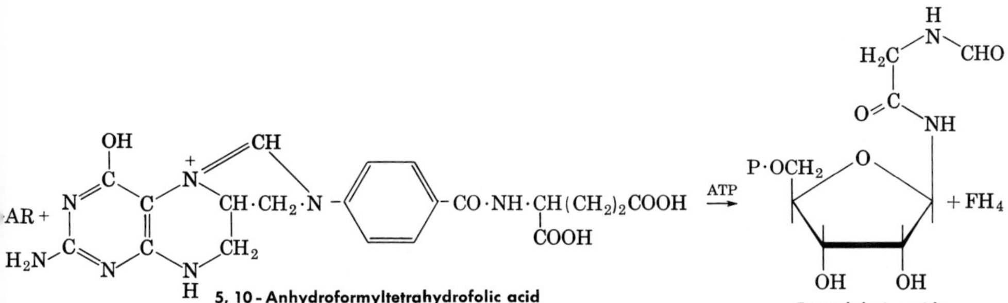

$$AR + \text{[structure]} -CO \cdot NH \cdot CH(CH_2)_2COOH \xrightarrow{ATP} \text{[ring structure]} + FH_4$$

5, 10 - Anhydroformyltetrahydrofolic acid
$(FH_4 \equiv CH)$

Formylglycinamide
ribotide (FGAR)

5. Incubation of FGAR with the specific enzyme, plus Mg^{++} ions, ATP, and glutamine introduces a second nitrogen in the form of an imino

group ($=NH$) in a compound named formylglycinamidine ribotide (FGAM).

$$FGAR + G-CONH_2 \xrightarrow[Mg^{++}]{ATP} \quad [\text{Formylglycinamidine ribotide (FGAM)}] \quad + G-COOH + ADP + P$$

Formylglycinamidine ribotide (FGAM)

6. FGAM loses water and rearranges in the presence of another specific enzyme, ATP, K^+ and Mg^{++} ions to complete the imidazole ring in the substance 5-aminoimidazole ribotide (AIR).

$$FGAM + ATP \cdot \xrightarrow[+ Mg^{++}, K^+]{-H_2O} \quad [\text{AIR structure}] \quad + ADP + P$$

5-Aminoimidazole ribotide (AIR)

7. AIR reacts with aspartate and bicarbonate (or CO_2) in the presence of

$$AIR + \underset{\substack{\text{Aspartic} \\ \text{acid}}}{\overset{\displaystyle CH_2COOH}{\underset{\displaystyle COOH}{CH \cdot NH_2}}} + CO_2 + ATP \xrightarrow{Mg^{++}} \quad [\text{SAICAR structure}] \quad + ADP + P$$

Succino-5-amino-4-imidazolecarboxamide ribotide (SAICAR)

ATP to form the next intermediate in purine synthesis, through which the nitrogen of aspartate is introduced. The product is succino-5-amino-4-imidazolecarboxamide ribotide (SAICAR). This is one of the reactions which actually takes place in steps, with carboxylation preceding interaction with aspartate. The product, with its two carboxyl groups and its ionizable phosphate, is formed as a multiply charged anion.

8. When SAICAR is treated with the required enzyme, it splits out fumarate and leaves 5-amino-4-imidazolecarboxamide ribotide (AICAR), which is the ribose phosphate derivative of the compound which was first identified as a purine precursor.

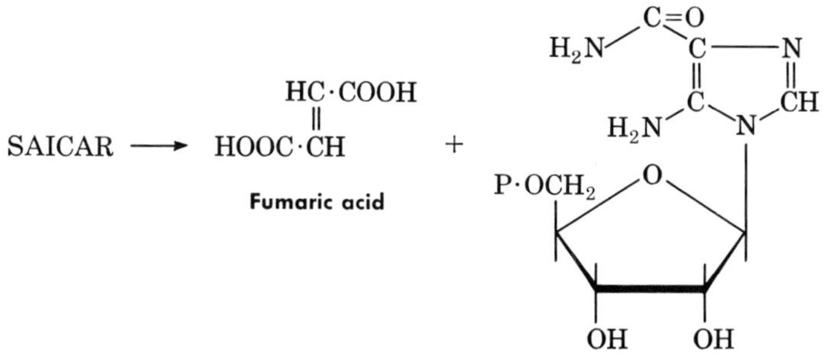

SAICAR $\longrightarrow$ HOOC·CH   +

$$\begin{array}{c} \text{HC·COOH} \\ \| \\ \text{HOOC·CH} \end{array}$$

Fumaric acid

5 - Amino - 4 - imidazolecarbox -
amide ribotide
AICAR

9. Before closure of the second ring another formyl group must be introduced. The reagent is tetrahydrofolic acid with a formyl (—CHO) group attached at the N^{10} position. It thus differs from the compound used in

AICAR + FH_4—N^{10}—CHO $\xrightarrow{K^+}$ + FH_4

Formyl AICAR
FAICAR

the previous step in which a one-carbon unit was introduced. The new product is formyl AICAR (FAICAR).

10. In the final step water is split out and the ring is closed, yielding inosinic acid, which is hypoxanthine mononucleotide. As with the pyrimidine mononucleotide, this substance is then transformed into other nucleotides by reactions in which adenine and guanine residues are formed from the hypoxanthine of this primary synthetic product. These interconversions are summarized in Fig. 13.9. There it is shown how the splitting of the compound, phosphoribosyl adenylic acid, gives rise on the one hand to the histidine precursor, imidazoleglycerol phosphate, and on the other to the purine precursor, AICAR.

FAICAR $\xrightarrow{\pm H_2O}$

Inosinic acid
IMP

As has just been indicated, the AICAR forms inosine monophosphate by addition of a single carbon, indicated on Fig. 13.9 as "C" in reaction 2. By reactions 8 and 9 the inosinic acid is transformed into guanosine monophosphate, while reactions 3 and 4 yield adenosine monophosphate. These two sequences thus provide both purine bases which occur in nucleic acids.

Biosynthesis of nucleic acids

Biosynthesis of a nucleic acid involves a copolymerization of a mixture of four different ribonucleotides or deoxyribonucleotides. Recent knowledge of the catalysis of this reaction comes from two laboratories. Ochoa[17] and his colleagues at New York University Medical College have purified enzymes from bacteria and from some plant and animal sources which bring about the synthesis of RNA from suitable ribonucleotide mixtures, while Kornberg[18] and his associates have purified a similar enzyme from *E. coli* which causes

---

[17] Severo Ochoa (1905–   ) was born in Spain and took his medical degree in Madrid, where he began his research. Between 1936 and 1941 he worked in Heidelberg and at Oxford, coming to the United States in 1941. He is now Professor and Chairman of the Biochemistry Department at New York University Medical School. In 1959 he shared with Arthur Kornberg the Nobel Prize in Medicine and Physiology.

[18] Arthur Kornberg (1918–   ) began his medical career with the National Institutes of

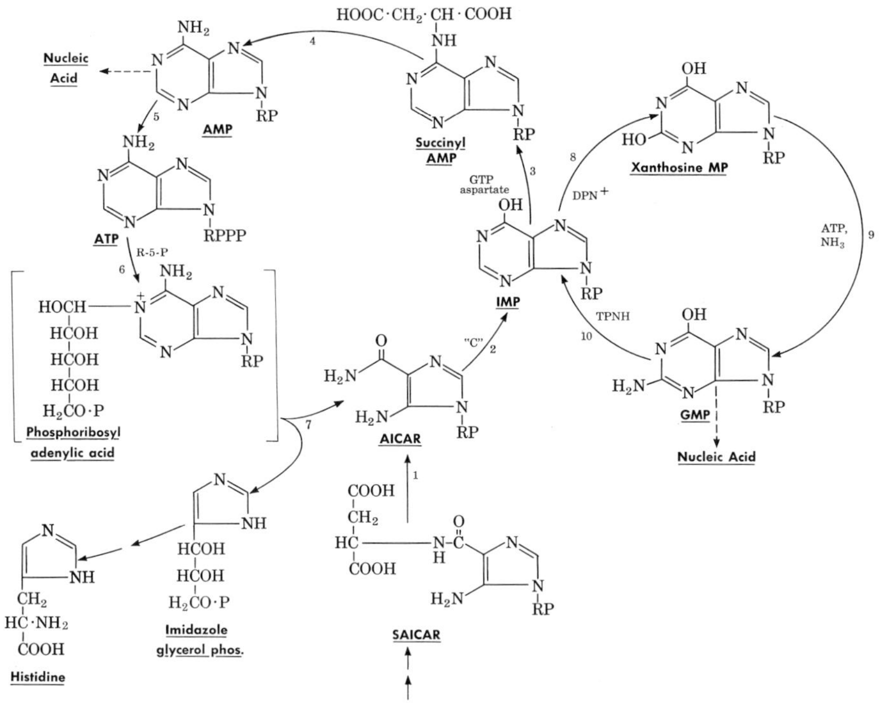

Fig. 13.9. Interconversions of purine nucleotides, showing also the relation of the purine cycle to histidine synthesis. [Adapted from B. Magasanik and D. Karibian, *J. Biol. Chem.*, **235**, 2679 (1960).]

polymerization of deoxyribonucleotides to form DNA. The Ochoa reaction uses a mixture of nucleoside diphosphates, requires a small amount of polynucleotide as a primer, and yields polymers with molecular weights up to 350,000. Hydrolysis of the synthetic product by enzymes which attack specific links made it clear that the phosphate links are like those in the natural nucleic acids in that they bind carbon 3 of one ribose to carbon 5 of its neighbor. It appears likely that *in vivo* this polymerization takes place in the nucleus, since when tissue slices are used with radioactive nucleotides, the nuclear material is labeled earliest.

The Kornberg polymerization is similar in that it also requires a primer. But it begins not with di- but with triphosphates of the deoxynucleosides.

Health where between 1947 and 1953 he was Chief of the Enzyme and Metabolism Section. His work on nucleic acid synthesis was begun while he was Professor of Microbiology and Head of Department at Washington University Medical School in St. Louis, but he is now Professor of Biochemistry in the Medical School at Stanford University. In 1959 he shared with Ochoa the Nobel Prize in Medicine and Physiology.

When these substances polymerize, pyrophosphate is split out and a substance is formed with a molecular weight of 5×10^6 which is said to be "indistinguishable from DNA" both as to base content and nucleotide sequence. It is of special interest that the primer is apparently a single strand DNA, since native double helix DNA is inactive until after it has been denatured. Therefore it appears that the action of the polymerizing enzyme is consistent with the genetic requirements, i.e., separation of the double helix into two complementary single strands and synthesis of new double helices like the original, using the single strands as templates.

The substrates for both the nucleic acid polymerizations are phosphates containing at least one of the phosphate bonds which hydrolyze with a large drop in free energy. It is this energy which is used in forming the links in the polymer. Whether this polymerization, like the rather similar protein synthesis, will prove to consist of a number of separate steps remains to be discovered.

SUGGESTIONS FOR FURTHER READING

General

The *Annual Review of Biochemistry* and the *Annual Review of Plant Physiology* carry one or two articles each year which cover some part of the subject of this chapter.

Lamanna, C., and M. F. Mallette, *Basic Bacteriology*, Williams and Wilkins, Baltimore, Md., 1959.

Oginsky, E. L., and W. W. Umbreit, *Introduction to Bacterial Physiology*, Freeman, San Francisco, Calif., 1959.

Schoenheimer, R., *The Dynamic State of Body Constituents*, Harvard University, Cambridge, Mass., 1949.

> Schoenheimer and his colleagues have an interesting series of papers in *J. Biol. Chem.*, *127*, *130*, and *131* (1939) which give the results of the early experiments with N^{15} and also discuss some of the precautions which must be taken in working with isotopes.

Vickery, H. B., *et al.*, Assimilation of ammonia nitrogen by the tobacco plant, *J. Biol. Chem.*, *135*, 531 (1940).

Amino Acid Metabolism

Ames, B. N., *et al.*, First step in histidine biosynthesis, *J. Biol. Chem.*, *236*, 2019 (1961).

Armstrong, B. F., and R. P. Wagner, Biosynthesis of valine and isoleucine, *J. Biol. Chem.*, *236*, 2027 (1961).

Balinsky, D., and D. D. Davies, Aromatic biosynthesis in higher plants, I, *Biochem. J.*, *80*, 292 (1961) ; II, *ibid.*, *80*, 296 (1961); III, *ibid.*, *80*, 300 (1961).

Booth, J., *et al.*, An enzyme from rat liver catalyzing conjugations with glutathione, *Biochem. J.*, *79*, 516 (1961).

Byerrum, R. U., *et al.*, Incorporation of glycine into nicotine in tobacco plant metabolism, *J. Biol. Chem.*, *210*, 645 (1954).

Hatch, F. T., *et al.*, Enzymatic synthesis of the methyl group of methionine, I, *J. Biol. Chem.*, *236*, 1095 (1961).

Matsuo, Y., and D. M. Greenberg, A crystalline enzyme that cleaves ... cystathionine, *J. Biol. Chem.*, *234*, 516 (1959).

McElroy, W. D., and M. Glass (eds.), *A Symposium on Amino Acid Metabolism*, Johns Hopkins Press, Baltimore, Md., 1955.

Moyed, H. S., and B. Magasanik, Biosynthesis of imidazole ring of histidine, *J. Biol. Chem.*, *235*, 149 (1960).

Nadkarni, G. B., *et al.*, Gluconeogenesis from glycine and serine in the rat, *J. Biol. Chem.*, *235*, 420 (1960).

Neidle, A., and H. Waelsch, Origin of the imidazole ring of histidine, *J. Biol. Chem.*, *234*, 586 (1959).

Strassman, M., *et al.*, Biosynthesis of valine, *J. Am. Chem. Soc.*, *77*, 1261 (1955).

Strassman, M., *et al.*, Biosynthesis of isoleucine, *J. Am. Chem. Soc.*, *78*, 228 (1956).

Strecker, H. J., Interconversion of glutamic acid and proline, *J. Biol. Chem.*, *235*, 3218 (1960).

Takeyama, S., *et al.*, Enzymatic synthesis of the methyl group of methionine, II, *J. Biol. Chem.*, *236*, 1102 (1961).

Umbarger, H. E., *et al.*, Acetolactate ... intermediate in valine biosynthesis, *J. Am. Chem. Soc.*, *79*, 2980 (1957).

Wixom, R. L., *et al.*, Valine biosynthesis in yeast, *J. Biol. Chem.*, *235*, 128 (1960).

Deamination

Blanchard, M., *et al.*, Isolation of L-amino acid oxidase, *J. Biol. Chem.*, *161*, 583 (1945).

Braunstein, A. E., and R. M. Asarkh, The mode of deamination of L-amino acids in surviving tissue, *J. Biol. Chem.*, *157*, 421 (1945).

Fisher, H. F., Mechanism of glutamic dehydrogenase reaction, *J. Biol. Chem.*, *235*, 1830 (1960).

Goldman, D. S., Purification, properties and mechanism of action of alanine dehydrogenase, *Biochim. et Biophys. Acta*, *34*, 527 (1959).

Pitt, B. M., Formation of α-imino acids in the enzymatic oxidation of amino acids, *J. Am. Chem. Soc.*, *80*, 3799 (1958).

Transamination

Braunstein, A. E., Transamination and the integrative functions of the dicarboxylic acids in nitrogen metabolism, *Advances in Protein Chem.*, *3*, 1 (1947).

Heyl, D., *et al.*, Phosphates of the vitamin B_6 group: Structure of codecarboxylase, *J. Am. Chem. Soc.*, *73*, 3430 (1951).

Jenkins, W. T., *et al.*, Glutamic aspartic transaminase. I. *J. Biol. Chem.*, *234*, 51 (1959).

Jenkins, W. T., and I. W. Sizer, Glutamic aspartic transaminase. II. *J. Biol. Chem.*, *234*, 1179 (1959).

Jenkins, W. T., and I. W. Sizer, Glutamic aspartic transaminase. IV. Mechanism of transamination, *J. Biol. Chem.*, *235*, 620 (1960).

Meister, A., *et al.*, Coenzyme activation of glutamic-aspartic apotransaminase, *J. Biol. Chem.*, *206*, 89 (1954).

Transmethylation

Byerrum, R. U., *et al.*, Incorporation of formate and the methyl group of methionine into methoxyl groups of lignin, *J. Biol. Chem.*, *210*, 633 (1954).
Cantoni, G. L., Methylation of nicotinamide with a soluble enzyme system from rat liver, *J. Biol. Chem.*, *189*, 203 (1951).
Cantoni, G. L., *S*-Adenosylmethionine, *J. Biol. Chem.*, *204*, 403 (1953).
Challenger, F., Biological methylation, *Advances in Enzymol.*, *12*, 429 (1951).
du Vigneaud, V., *et al.*, Effect of choline on the ability of homocystine to replace methionine in the diet, *J. Biol. Chem.*, *131*, 57 (1939).
du Vigneaud, V., *et al.*, Transfer of the methyl group from methionine to choline and creatine, *J. Biol. Chem.*, *134*, 787 (1940).
Wilson, J. D., *et al.*, Precursors of the methyl groups of choline in rat liver, *J. Biol. Chem.*, *235*, 3213 (1960).

Urea Synthesis

Brown, G. W., Jr., and P. P. Cohen, Quantitative assay of urea cycle enzymes in liver, *J. Biol. Chem.*, *234*, 1769 (1959). This carries a good set of back references to urea synthesis.
Caravaca, J., and S. Grisolia, Synthesis of citrulline with animal and bacterial enzymes, *J. Biol. Chem.*, *235*, 684 (1960).
Cohen, P. P., and S. Grisolia, Role of carbamyl-L-glutamic acid in the enzymatic synthesis of citrulline from ornithine, *J. Biol. Chem.*, *182*, 747 (1950).
Grisolia, S., *et al.*, Carbon dioxide and ammonia fixation in the biosynthesis of citrulline, *J. Biol. Chem.*, *191*, 203 (1951).
Krebs, H. A., and K. Henseleit, Urea formation in the animal body, *Z. physiol. Chem.*, *210*, 33 (1932).
Marshall, M., *et al.*, Physical and kinetic properties of carbamyl phosphate synthetase from frog liver, *J. Biol. Chem.*, *236*, 2229 (1961).
Petrack, B., and S. Ratner, Biosynthesis of urea. VII. *J. Biol. Chem.*, *233*, 1494 (1958).
Rochovansky, O., and S. Ratner, Studies on the mechanism of the arginosuccinate synthetase reaction, *J. Biol. Chem.*, *236*, 2256 (1961).

Hemoglobin

Gerald, P. S., and V. M. Ingram, . . . Nomenclature of hemoglobins, *Science*, *134*, 2037 (1961).
Granick, S., and D. Mauzerall, Porphyrin biosynthesis in erythrocytes, *J. Biol. Chem.*, *232*, 1119 (1958).
Kikuchi, G., *et al.*, Enzymatic synthesis of δ-aminolevulinic acid, *J. Biol. Chem.*, *233*, 1214 (1958).
Kikuchi, G., *et al.*, Mechanism of enzymatic synthesis of δ-aminolevulinic acid, *Federation Proc.*, *18*, 259 (1959).
Lockwood, W. H., and A. Benson, Enzymic condensation of porphobilinogen to porphyrins, *Biochem. J.*, *75*, 372 (1960).

Mauzerall, D., Condensation of porphobilinogen to uroporphyrinogen, *J. Am. Chem. Soc.*, *82*, 2605 (1960).

Perutz, M. F., *et al.*, Structure of Haemoglobin, *Nature*, *185*, 416 (1960).

Sano, S., and S. Granick, Mitochondrial coproporphyrinogen oxidase and proto-porphyrin formation, *J. Biol. Chem.*, *236*, 1173 (1961).

Protein Biosynthesis

In *Chemical and Engineering News*, *39* (nos. 19, 20, and 21) (1961), three articles on "The Chemistry of Life" summarize recent results in the field of protein bio-synthesis.

In the *Journal of Biological Chemistry* for June, 1961, beginning on page 1726, are four articles concerned with enzymic synthesis of aminoacyl derivatives of RNA.

Craddock, V. M., and M. V. Simpson, Amino acid activating enzymes in rat liver mitochondria, *Biochem. J.*, *80*, 348 (1961).

Dintzis, H. M., Assembly of the peptide chains of hemoglobin, *Proc. Natl. Acad. Sci. U. S.*, *47*, 247 (1961).

Grossi, L. G., and K. Moldave, Effect of soluble factors on the transfer of amino acids from soluble RNA to microsomal proteins, *J. Biol. Chem.*, *235*, 2370 (1960).

Hoagland, M. B., An enzymic mechanism for amino acid activation in animal tissues, *Biochim. et Biophys. Acta*, *16*, 288 (1955).

Hoagland, M. B., *et al.*, A soluble RNA intermediate in protein synthesis, *J. Biol. Chem.*, *231*, 241 (1958).

Hunter, G. D., *et al.*, Protein synthesis by membrane of *B. Megaterium*, *Biochem. J.*, *73*, 369 (1959).

Krishnaswamy, P. R., and A. Meister, Enzymatic synthesis and reactions of amino acyl adenylates, *J. Biol. Chem.*, *235*, 408 (1960).

Moldave, K., Labeling *in vitro* of intermediates in amino acid incorporation, *J. Biol. Chem.*, *235*, 2365 (1960).

Roodyn, D. B., *et al.*, Protein synthesis in mitochondria, *Biochem. J.*, *80*, 9 (1961).

Wong, K. K., and K. Moldave, Enzymatic participation of enzyme-bound amino acyl adenylates in amino acid incorporation into protein, *J. Biol. Chem.*, *235*, 694 (1960).

GSH Biosynthesis

Bates, H. M., and F. Lipmann, γ-Glutamylcysteinyl RNA as intermediary in GSH synthesis, *J. Biol. Chem.*, *235*, PC22 (1960).

Strumeyer, D. H., and K. Bloch, Properties of γ-glutamylcysteine synthetase, *J. Biol. Chem.*, *235*, PC27 (1960).

Purine and Pyrimidine Biosynthesis

Blair, D. G. R., *et al.*, Formation of orotidine 5′-phosphate by enzymes from rat liver, *J. Biol. Chem.*, *235*, 2379 (1960).

Buchanan, J. M., and S. C. Hartman, Enzymatic reactions in the synthesis of the purines, *Advances in Enzymol.*, *21*, 199 (1959).

Hartman, S. C., and J. M. Buchanan, *J. Biol. Chem.*, *234*, 1812 (1959). This is the last in a long series of papers, and it gives references to the earlier ones which trace step by step the story of purine biosynthesis.

Magasanik, B., and D. Karibian, Purine nucleotide cycles and their metabolic role, *J. Biol. Chem.*, *235*, 2672 (1960).

Reichard, P., Enzymatic synthesis of pyrimidines, *Advances in Enzymol.*, *21*, 263 (1959).

Shepherdson, M., and A. B. Pardee, Aspartate transcarbamylase, *J. Biol. Chem.*, *235*, 3233 (1960).

Nucleic Acid Biosynthesis

Bollum, F. J., Calf thymus polymerase, *J. Biol. Chem.*, *235*, 2399 (1960).

Davidson, J. N., *Biochemistry of the Nucleic Acids*, 4th ed., Methuen, London (1960).

Kornberg, A., Biologic synthesis of DNA, *Science*, 131, 1503 (1960).

Kornberg, A., Biosynthesis of nucleic acids, in *Biophysical Science*, J. L. Oncley, (ed.-in chief), Wiley, New York, 1959.

Ochoa, S., Enzymatic synthesis of ribonucleic acid-like polynucleotides, *Federation Proc.*, *15*, 832 (1956).

Schachman, H. K., *et al.*, Enzymatic synthesis of DNA, *J. Biol. Chem.*, *235*, 3242 (1960).

Singer, M. F., *et al.*, Oligonucleotides as primers for polynucleotide phosphorylase, *J. Biol. Chem.*, *235*, 738 (1960).

I think it worth your while to consider whether a new line of advance in

biology. . . may not come from researches motivated by a full conviction

that each observed event in the complex behaviour of a living system is

associated with equally complex and, surely, equally biological, events

at the molecular level of its constitution.

F. G. HOPKINS: *Linacre Lecture* (1938)

Metabolism of the lipids 14

L IPIDS ARE AN ESSENTIAL PART OF THE DIET of all heterotrophic organisms, in which they not only serve as easily oxidizable substrates, but form an integral part of essential cell structures. It is found, therefore, that even with a diet that makes other adequate provision for energy needs at least 16 per cent of the caloric intake must be in the form of fat if growth is to be normal.

Investigation of the metabolic changes undergone by the lipids has been beset with difficulties. The fats themselves are too insoluble in water to be used readily as experimental substrates with tissue slices or purified enzymes. Yet the soluble soaps which they yield on hydrolysis are so toxic to living tissue that they can be used in only very low concentrations, and the calcium and magnesium soaps are so insoluble that the ionic ratios in a nutrient solution are upset by precipitation if fatty acids are added. Furthermore, for a long time the enzymes involved in lipid metabolism resisted efforts to extract them from the tissues. As a result much of the early experimental work had to be done with whole animals. Even tissue slices yielded equivocal results since it was difficult to know whether failure of a given reaction meant that the enzymes were absent or merely that the substrate provided was unable to penetrate the cell membrane. In recent years many of the enzymes which catalyze the metabolic changes of the lipids have been isolated and purified. Their use has been facilitated by the discovery that fatty substances can be brought into contact with them by the use of detergents or other emulsifying agents. Among the natural emulsifying agents which have been used in this way are heparin, taurocholic acid and microsomal membranes which are themselves lipoprotein in nature. These last preparations probably act by adsorbing both enzyme and substrate on their surface, thus bringing them into effective contact.

OCCURRENCE OF THE LIPIDS

The lipids of living organisms may be divided roughly into those which serve primarily as a store of oxidizable substrate and those which are part of the structural elements of the cell. In animals there are in addition those which are found circulating in the blood plasma.

The storage lipids, called *depot fats* in animals, consist largely of tri-glycerides[1] deposited in subcutaneous and intramuscular connective tissue and in the mesentery. This fat, found inside the walls of the so-called fat cells, constitutes the chief reserve fuel of the body. The fats which are stored in some plant seeds are also reserve fuel, called upon to furnish energy for the developing plant.

As contrasted with the carbohydrates and proteins the fats are particularly well adapted to serve as a source of energy. In the first place they contain a smaller proportion of oxygen than is present in the other two types of food-stuff and therefore provide, per gram, more combustible carbon and hydrogen. As a result, the energy set free in oxidation of 1 g of fat is over twice that obtained from the same weight of either carbohydrate or protein. As a fuel the fats have another advantage. Because of their high percentage of hydro-gen, they produce when oxidized a larger amount of water than do equal weights of the other foodstuffs. This is important to such an animal as the camel, living under conditions of water shortage, since it is apparently able to satisfy its minimum requirements for moisture by relying for long periods upon oxidation of body fats.

A subsidiary use for the depot fats in animals depends upon the fact that they are in part laid down around the vital organs. In such locations they probably serve as an insulating material, protecting these organs from mechanical injury and against heat loss.

It is a matter of common observation that the fat content of an animal can vary within wide limits, rising on a generous diet and falling rapidly during starvation when the depot fats become the chief source of oxidizable material. But even when the starvation is prolonged to the point of death, the body lipids do not entirely disappear. Obviously some of these substances are so essential that they cannot be mobilized to serve as fuel even when the organism is in desperate need of oxidizable substrates. These are the lipids which form

---

[1] As noted on page 260, there are a few organisms in which waxes are stored instead of triglycerides.

part of the actual structural fabric of the tissues, and they are, of course, found in plant and bacterial as well as in animal cells.

The lipids carried in the blood stream are of two sorts. There are those which begin to appear about two hours after ingestion of a meal, rendering the plasma more or less opaque, and which disappear into the tissues in the course of a few hours. The emulsified particles which give to the plasma this temporary milky appearance are known as *chylomicrons*, and this temporary excess of plasma lipid is said to be an *alimentary lipemia*. In addition to this lipid material, the concentration of which varies with the diet and the time of day, the blood carries a relatively constant amount of lipid which is not

TABLE 14.1. Average Lipid Values in Blood Plasma of Normal Fasting Animals[a]

Lipid	Guinea Pig	Albino Rat	Rabbit	Cat	Man
Total lipid[b]	169	230	243	376	530
Neutral fat	73	85	105	108	142
Total fatty acids	116	152	169	228	316
Total cholesterol	32	52	45	93	152
Ester cholesterol	21	31	23	63	106
Phospholipid	51	83	78	132	165

SOURCE: Data from E. M. Boyd, Species variation in normal plasma lipids estimated by oxidative micromethods, *J. Biol. Chem.*, *143*, 131 (1942).

[a] Values are given in mg/100 ml of plasma.

[b] It is now believed that none of the lipids is free in the plasma, but that all are part of complex lipoprotein aggregates in which varying proportions of the various lipid species are bound to protein.

removed in starvation. It is this lipid which is referred to as *plasma lipids*. Table 14.1 gives for several species the average values for the lipids of fasting plasma, that is, plasma from blood drawn in the morning before any food is eaten.

Most lipids other than those of the adipose tissues but including those of the plasma occur in living organisms in the form of lipoprotein complexes of varying degrees of stability. It has already been noted on page 274 that with most tissues lipids have to be set free from such combinations before anything approaching complete extraction can be achieved. Reference has also frequently been made to the structural lipid-protein complexes which are believed to make up the cell membranes. Evidence for this belief has been obtained from plant, microbial, and animal cells, and for internal membranes of the small subcellular particles such as nuclei, mitochondria, and chloroplasts as well as for the limiting cell membranes. These structures are believed to consist of alternating layers of protein and lipid associated in some way, but probably not covalently bonded to each other.

Much of the recent work on lipoproteins has been done on the macro-molecules isolated from serum by a series of flotation procedures. This involves long spinning in the ultracentrifuge of either serum alone or serum rendered denser by addition of strong salt solutions, such as sodium bromide or chloride. When native serum is subjected to centrifugation at 40,000 rpm for 24 hours, there collects in the top of the tube a lipoprotein sample which is less dense than the rest of the serum. This is removed, the density of the serum, originally 1.006 g per ml, is raised to 1.070 g per ml, and the centrifuga-tion is repeated. This brings to the top a lipoprotein sample with a density slightly lower than 1.070 g per ml. Repetition of the procedure after bringing the density of the residual fluid to 1.218 g per ml isolates a third lipoprotein sample with a density of 1.203 g per ml and effectively clears the fluid of lipoprotein. The three products obtained in the experiment just outlined are not homogeneous although references in the literature to α-lipoprotein and β-lipoprotein sound as if a single substance were involved. The fraction originally called α-lipoprotein is also known as the high density lipoprotein (HDL), and it has been shown to consist of particles of at least three different densities. Lipoprotein classes are probably better distinguished by their standardized flotation rates, S_f°, which is the rate at which they come to the top in a solution having a density of 1.063 g per ml when centrifuged at 52,640 rpm at 26°. At this density the HDL complexes would, of course, sediment. The lightest of the three fractions referred to above had standard-ized flotation rates greater than S_f° 20, and the rates for the next heavier fraction were in the range S_f° 20–0. These experimental details have been given partly to make clear the meaning of flotation rates, and partly to emphasize the heterogeneous nature of the lipoprotein preparations.

Lipoprotein macromolecules consist of proteins, which may be albumins or globulins, bound to various mixtures of all lipid classes. For example, one partially purified serum lipoprotein had the following composition:

	Per Cent
Cholesterol	
Free	8
Esterified	29
Phospholipid	21
Protein	17
Triglycerides	25

Heavier fractions from the same serum had higher proportions of phospho-lipid and relatively less cholesterol and triglycerides. Nothing is certainly known of the way in which the various molecules are bound to each other, though the ease with which most of the lipids are set free indicates that it is probably not through covalent bonds. One suggestion is that the paraffin chains of the lipids are oriented toward lipophilic groups of the proteins, with hydrophilic groupings of both proteins and lipids directed outwards. This would result in a binding of water on the surface of the particle and would account for the failure of such a solvent as ether to penetrate.

The chylomicrons which circulate in the blood for a few hours after a meal were at first believed to consist of emulsified triglycerides. While they do consist predominantly of triglycerides, it has now been shown that they are lipoprotein in nature and include small amounts of phospholipids and of cholesterol. One of the proteins associated with chylomicrons appears to be identical with that in α-lipoprotein of serum. This suggests that the chylomicrons may be formed from plasma lipoproteins by temporary accretions of triglycerides when they are pouring in from the gut.

In summary, adipose tissue is the only one in which free triglycerides occur in appreciable amounts. Elsewhere in cells or plasma the lipids are found in macromolecules which include protein, or sometimes polysaccharides, as well as varying proportions of the different lipid classes. No single pure sample of a lipoprotein has yet been isolated, though data are appearing about the lipid composition of various fractions isolated by centrifugation and having consequently a roughly uniform density.

THE LIPID EQUILIBRIUM

Although in recent years lipid metabolism has been studied with enzymes from plants, animals and microorganisms, the broad outlines were discovered long ago in work with whole animals. Many of these discoveries and the vocabulary to which they gave rise have been built into modern biochemical thought. For this reason it is necessary to consider briefly some of the early experiments, though few of them led to very precise chemical results.

The most important experimental animal in the early years was the diabetic, whether as a human patient or as a laboratory animal rendered experimentally "diabetic." There were a number of procedures which caused animals subjected to them to excrete large amounts of glucose in the urine, though not all of them caused the other manifestations of a true diabetes. The earliest experimental condition resembling diabetes was induced by puncturing a specific spot in the medulla oblongata. This led to a rise in blood sugar, or *hyperglycemia*, and to increased excretion of glucose (*glucosuria*). Similar results are obtained by injection of the glucoside, phlorizin, or by removal of the pancreas (pancreatectomy). As noted on page 505, a diabetic animal not only fails to metabolize glucose normally as indicated by high glucose excretion, but also forms abnormal amounts of the ketone bodies which arise largely from the metabolism of the fatty acids.

Fatty Liver and Lipotropic Factors

About 5 per cent of the total dry weight of the normal liver consists of lipid material, chiefly glycerides and phospholipids. But in various clinical disorders, including diabetes and acute yellow atrophy of the liver, the amount of fat may reach 50 per cent of the total weight, changing completely the appearance and texture of the organ. Such fatty livers can be induced experimentally by starvation, by administration of liver poisons such as carbon tetrachloride or phosphorus, by removal of the pancreas, or by excessive feeding of fat or cholesterol. Apparently all these diverse conditions share the property of disrupting normal fat metabolism. In the course of the search for the cause and for means of preventing fatty livers much was learned of the ways in which lipids are normally metabolized.

The fatty infiltration of the liver which accompanies diabetes in depancreatized animals is much reduced if the animal is fed raw pancreas. This was at first attributed to the replacement of the pancreatic digestive enzymes and the resulting improvement in fat digestion. But Best[2] and his colleagues showed that the same curative effect was exerted by the mixed phospholipid fraction of pancreatic tissue, and later that either lecithin or choline or the closely related betaine could replace the tissue extract. A substance which like choline cures or prevents fatty liver under conditions in which it tends to appear is said to exert a *lipotropic* action.

Certain proteins also exert a lipotropic effect which proved to be proportional to their methionine content. It will be recalled that methionine is a source of labile methyl groups and as such contributes to the biosynthesis of choline. Thus its action as well as that of betaine in prevention of fatty liver probably depends on their activity in promoting synthesis of choline which in turn is needed for formation of lecithin and other compound lipids.

Still another lipotropic agent is inositol. Since the phospholipid fraction is now known to include more than one phosphoinositide, the efficacy of this substance can also be explained in terms of promotion of phospholipid synthesis. It has long been a theory that a certain amount of phospholipid synthesis is an essential part of the process of oxidation of fatty acids, but while some of the evidence is suggestive, it is certainly not conclusive.

Several of the B vitamins have been shown to exert effects, adverse or favorable, on fat deposition in the liver, and several different hormones have also been connected with fat metabolism. But there is no general agreement

---

[2] The major contribution of Charles Herbert Best (1899–   ) to biochemistry was made when he collaborated with Banting in the isolation of insulin. He has since become Professor of Physiology at the University of Toronto and Director of the Banting and Best Department of Medical Research. When in 1923 the Nobel Prize in Medicine was awarded for the discovery of insulin, it went officially to Banting and MacLeod, but it was then shared with their colleagues, Best and J. B. Collip.

either on which hormones are involved, or on their specific functions. It seems clear that a normally functioning fat metabolism is the result of a complex balance of forces, many of which are still undefined. It is probable that the abnormality known as fatty liver may then arise as a result of any one or more of several possible imbalances, some of which are rectified by administration of substances which are essential to phospholipid synthesis.

It is generally agreed that the liver is the focal point of fat metabolism and that the first step in the mobilization of depot fat for use is its transfer to the liver. When this transfer takes place under such conditions that the fat cannot be metabolized as fast as it arrives, the excess is deposited in the liver cells.

Ketogenesis

Another abnormal condition which is associated with the liver and with a deranged fat metabolism is the one known as *ketosis*, in which the three so-called ketone bodies appear in excessive amounts in blood and urine. These substances are acetoacetate, β-hydroxybutyrate, and acetone. Of these

$$CH_3 \cdot CHOH \cdot CH_2 \cdot COO^- \underset{}{\overset{\pm 2H}{\rightleftharpoons}}$$

$$CH_3 \cdot CO \cdot CH_2 \cdot COO^- \xrightarrow{-CO_2} CH_3 \cdot CO \cdot CH_3$$

three, acetoacetate is the direct metabolite derived from fatty acids, and it in turn gives rise to the other two as indicated on the arrows.

Early experiments indicated that the liver is the site of formation of ketone bodies and that they arise chiefly from fatty acids. For example, various organs were perfused with fatty acids, but only the liver produced significant amounts of ketone bodies. Various possible precursors were tested, not only in perfusion experiments but in experiments with tissue slices and with whole animals, and it was only in the presence of fats or of fatty acids that detectable amounts of ketone bodies formed. This was hard to understand, since clinical ketosis generally occurs in conjunction with a disturbance of carbohydrate metabolism and can usually be alleviated by treatment which promotes the utilization of carbohydrate. Thus ketosis is a common accompaniment of severe diabetes and is alleviated by insulin therapy. These observations led at one time to the theory that fatty acids can be oxidized only if carbohydrates are being metabolized at the same time. Fats were said to "burn in the flame of carbohydrates." Medical textbooks listed certain foods as "ketogenic" or "antiketogenic," and prescribed definite ratios of the two. Fats were considered ketogenic and carbohydrates antiketogenic, but the position of a protein depended, as noted in the previous chapter, upon its constituent amino acids.

It is now recognized that acetoacetate is a normal product of fatty acid metabolism and that it can be oxidized by all tissues except the liver. Acetoacetate formed in the liver must be carried to other tissues for complete oxidation. When for any reason the rate of formation of acetoacetate in the liver exceeds the rate of removal, as it may do when the liver is oxidizing an excessive proportion of fat, its heightened concentration leads to formation of the other two ketone bodies.

In summary: Metabolism of the depot fats begins with their transport to the liver.

Some of the fatty acids are there degraded in such a way that acetoacetate is one product. This substance is normally distributed to all the peripheral organs where it may be oxidized or may be used in biosynthesis.

When for any reason the ability of the liver to metabolize carbohydrates is lost or lessened, the resulting rapid mobilization of the depot fat results in its being deposited in the liver faster than it can be used, and the liver tissue becomes infiltrated with excess fat.

When the liver is degrading fatty acids to the acetoacetate stage faster than the peripheral tissues can use the acetoacetate, this substance is transformed in part into the other two ketone bodies, and all three of these compounds appear in blood and urine.

Sources of the Body Lipids

In animals the constituents of the various lipids, such as fatty acids, glycerol, choline, and sterols, may be derived directly from the foods or they may be synthesized from small molecules.

The use of dietary lipids

In general each species of animal on a normal mixed diet lays down a characteristic type of fat. Thus mutton fat is grossly distinguishable from pig fat and proves to contain certain definite fatty acids in an approximately constant ratio. On the other hand, it is possible, by feeding large amounts of a given fat, to modify very materially the characteristic pattern of a particular species. In the data in Table 14.2 both tendencies are illustrated. The animals are clearly changing somewhat the pattern set by the food fats, since the iodine numbers of the body fats are neither as high nor as low as those of the foods which have extreme values. On the other hand, the unsaturation of the body fats does reflect the degree of unsaturation of the foods, showing that some at least of the fatty acids of the diet have been incorporated unchanged into the body fat. Later work with isotopic tracers has shown that dietary acids containing ten carbons or less are normally oxidized completely, but that some of the longer acids are used directly in synthesis.

Although a high fat diet may thus lead to an extensive use of preformed

TABLE 14.2. Influence of Food Fat upon Body Fat of Rats

Food Fat (60% of total calories = fat; 40% of total calories = skimmed milk)	Iodine No. of Food Fat	Iodine No. of Body Fat (Average value for 6 animals)
Soybean oil	132.3	122.5
Corn oil	124.3	114.2
Cottonseed oil	108.1	107.4
Crisco	78.8	81.8
Butter fat	35.8	55.5
Cocoanut oil	7.7	35.3

SOURCE: Data from W. E. Anderson and L. B. Mendel, The relation of diet to the quality of fat produced in the animal body, *J. Biol. Chem.*, *76*, 729 (1928).

acids in fat synthesis, on a mixed diet only part of the body fats arise directly from fats of the food. Normally both carbohydrates and proteins contribute to the synthesis of lipid constituents by furnishing in the course of their catabolism either acetyl coenzyme A or some other small molecule which is a lipid precursor.

Interconversions of the foodstuffs

As was noted in the previous chapter, many early experiments were concerned with possible "conversions" of one foodstuff into another. With whole animals such changes were studied in various sorts of balance experiments. One of the earliest, carried out in 1860, compared the amounts of fat, protein, and carbohydrate in the diet of pigs with the amounts of each which were either oxidized, excreted, or stored in the carcasses.

Another experimental approach depended upon measurements of the *respiratory quotient* or R.Q. of organisms or, later, of tissue slices. The respiratory quotient is defined as the ratio of the volume of carbon dioxide evolved by an animal or tissue to the volume of oxygen consumed. In order to obtain a theoretical figure for carbohydrates, proteins, and fats it is necessary to assume an average formula for the last two. In the following equations this has been done by using glucose as a typical carbohydrate and triolein as a typical fat.

$$C_6H_{12}O_6 + 6O_2 \rightarrow 6CO_2 + 6H_2O$$

$$\text{R.Q.} = \frac{6CO_2}{6O_2} = 1$$

$$C_{57}H_{104}O_6 + 80O_2 \rightarrow 57CO_2 + 52H_2O$$

$$\text{R.Q.} = \frac{57}{80} = 0.71$$

In order to obtain a comparable figure for proteins, allowance must be made for the fact that some of the molecule is eliminated as urea, leaving only part of the carbon to be oxidized. Figures for an average protein indicate that 1 g of urinary nitrogen corresponds to the metabolism of 6.25 g of protein, the absorption of 5.91 liters of oxygen and the evolution of 4.76 liters of carbon dioxide.

$$\text{R.Q. for protein} = \frac{4.76}{5.91} = 0.801$$

Thus an R.Q. of 1 indicates the exclusive combustion of carbohydrate, and one as low as 0.7 shows that the oxidative substrate is fat. From intermediate values it is possible, if the nitrogen excretion is known, to calculate the amounts of each of the primary foodstuffs being oxidized.

If there is an extensive conversion of carbohydrate to fat, the respiratory quotient also reflects this. Formation of fatty acids from sugars is a reductive process, leading to an R.Q. higher than 1. Thus rats on a diet composed exclusively of dextrin gave R.Q. values of 1.5 to 2.0 and yeasts using sugars as substrates for fat synthesis have given R.Q. values of 1.15 to 1.50.

Many of the "interconversion" problems have now only an academic interest. It is recognized that all types of foodstuff in the course of their catabolism furnish small molecules which can be caught up in the synthetic machinery and so find their way into fats, carbohydrates, or proteins. It is now the biosynthetic pathways by which these molecules are formed or used that are of interest, and these are being explored with isotopic tracers. Hence in the latest journals papers appear concerned with the same old problem, but attacking it now in terms of the chemical mechanisms involved and of following the path of specific, labeled atoms from one foodstuff to their incorporation in another.

Lability of Body Lipids

To a generation plagued by the curse of overweight, few things have seemed more permanent and stable than animal depot fats. It therefore came as a great surprise when the first of the isotope experiments carried out by Schoenheimer and his associates showed that body fats are part of a very mobile equilibrium in which they are continually being reconstituted from fats of the diet. For example, in their very first experiment a fat was labeled by partially saturating the double bonds in olive oil with deuterium. This oil was then fed to mice in such limited amounts that they actually lost weight. According to all the older theories of fat metabolism they should have oxidized all of the dietary fat as well as part of their lipid reserves. Yet when the animals were sacrificed after several days the greater part of the deuterium was still present either in the depot or the organ fats. Later work has abundantly confirmed what was foreshadowed in this experiment: that the body fats are in a state of rapid flux, being continually broken down and then reconstituted from the metabolic pool. The time required for complete renewal of any lipid fraction varies widely from one species to another and from one organ to another. Rittenberg and Schoenheimer estimated that in mice half of the depot fats were reconstituted in the course of seven days, while more than half of the fatty acids present in the liver had been newly incorporated within one day. The rapidity of this process in the liver is another indication of the importance of this organ in lipid metabolism.

Some indications of the way in which this mobile equilibrium functions were obtained in experiments which showed (*a*) the readiness with which fatty acids undergo minor transformations and (*b*) the speed with which the hydrogen of body water is incorporated into fatty acids.

Palmitic acid labeled with deuterium stably bound to carbon was mixed with butter and fed to rats as part of an adequate mixed diet. After eight days it was found that 44 per cent of the deuterium administered was still present in the body lipids. Of this more than half was found in palmitic acid, as might have been expected if food fatty acids are used directly in synthesis of body lipids. But the label was also found in stearic acid, and in myristic, lauric, and palmitoleic acids. Its presence in stearic acid meant that the carbon chain of palmitic acid had been lengthened by two carbons to form the eighteen-carbon stearic acid. Myristic and lauric acids resulted from removal of two and of four carbons respectively, while the presence of the label in the unsaturated palmitoleic acid indicated removal of a pair of hydrogens from palmitic acid. It should be noted that none of these reactions took place because the animals had need of those particular acids. The butter of the diet included adequate amounts of all of them. Evidently the transformation mechanism acts continuously and automatically, providing a supply of mixed fatty acids from which the body lipids are regenerated.

Side by side with the utilization of dietary fatty acids, other dietary constituents contribute to the body lipids through synthesis. It was noted above that formation of fatty acids from carbohydrate is a reductive process, and Schoenheimer carried out experiments to see whether hydrogens for the fatty acid chains could be derived from body water. He fed or injected heavy water which would then distribute itself through all the body fluids. In the course of a few days the fats of the body were marked with the heavy isotope, and analysis showed that it was present in palmitic, stearic, and some unsaturated acids. The labeled unsaturated acids did not include linoleic acid, and this was not surprising, for earlier work had shown that this acid with its double bonds at positions 9 and 12 is an "essential" fatty acid, and must be provided in the diet.

To summarize: The cells are continually degrading their stores of lipids and simultaneously replacing these stores by synthesis, using both the fatty acids of the diet and other acids which have been newly formed. These latter may result from comparatively minor changes in preexisting fatty acids by which the chain is lengthened or shortened, dehydrogenated or saturated at a double bond. New acids are also synthesized from nonlipid precursors, with part of the hydrogen coming from body water.

TABLE 14.3. The Lability of Tissue Lipids as Measured by Turnover Number and Half-Life Time[a]

Turnover Number

Animal	Liver		Intestinal Mucosa
	Phospholipids, days	Cholesterol, hrs	Phospholipids, hrs
Rat	1	40	0.5
Cat	5+		8
Cat			8

Half Life

Animal	Triglycerides, days		Total Fatty Acids, days				Cholesterol, days		
	Depot	Liver	Liver Sat.	Unsat.	Carcase Sat.	Unsat.	Liver	Intes- itnal	Car- case
Mouse	5–9								
	5–6	2.6–3.3							
Rat			Less than 1	2	16–17	19–20			
			0.8	2.2					
Mouse									15–25
Rat							6		31–32
Rabbit							3	1.5	12

[a] These figures have been obtained by various experimental techniques and over the course of nearly 20 years.

Later work with various types of labels has attempted to assess somewhat more specifically the rates of lipid renewal. Rates are expressed as *turnover time*, or time required for the complete renewal of a given lipid, or as *half life*, which is the time taken to attain half the maximum level of a label when the labeled precursor is administered frequently over a long period of time. Sometimes a labeled precursor is fed, and the rate of its incorporation into some lipid is determined. In other experiments the label is fed until the lipid under examination is heavily labeled. Then the labeled precursor is replaced by an unlabeled form, and the rate of disappearance of the label is measured.

There are many technical reasons why the two methods do not yield concordant results. The rate of formation of labeled lipid from a labeled precursor depends, among other factors, upon the rate at which the precursor moves into the cell, the rate at which intermediates are formed, and the availability in the cell of unlabeled precursors. In spite of these and many other factors which sometimes make the data hard to interpret, a few conclusions do seem to have general validity.

The fatty acids of both triglycerides and phospholipids undergo continuous and fairly rapid turnover. The actual rates vary from species to species and from organ to organ. Table 14.3 brings together figures from a number of different workers and gives a rough indication of the rates at which different lipid fractions are replaced in different species and organs. None of the figures is beyond reproach, but in view of the lack of experimental uniformity the degree of agreement is striking. The outstanding exception is in the figures for liver cholesterol which vary from a half life of 6 days in one experiment with rats to a total turnover time of only 40 hours in another.

DEGRADATION OF THE LIPIDS

The first step in the catabolism of the lipids is assumed to be hydrolysis, since living cells are supplied with a variety of lipolytic enzymes. Simple lipases bring about hydrolysis of free triglycerides, and lipoprotein lipase frees the fatty acids from triglycerides which are part of a lipoprotein complex. Various phospholipases, sometimes called lecithinases, hydrolyze the fatty acid ester bonds in the compound lipids, phosphatases act upon phosphoester bonds, and peptide linkages are presumably attacked by peptidases. Of all the small molecules thus set free, the fatty acids are the most characteristic and perhaps the most important, since it is oxidation of these long chain molecules which accounts for the high caloric value of the fats.

Metabolism of the Fatty Acids

Most of the early work on fatty acid oxidation was done with animals, but the results have proved to be widely applicable to plants and bacteria. All the enzymes concerned in the typical fatty acid oxidation are localized in the mitochondria where, as we shall see, the breakdown products feed into the citric acid cycle. There is recent evidence that plants have, in addition to this fundamental sequence, an alternative oxidative process the enzymes of which are found in the cytoplasm.

β-Oxidation

The first comprehensive theory of fatty acid oxidation was elaborated by Knoop about 1905 and was based upon the following experimental evidence.

Long before the days of isotopic labels Knoop conceived the idea of marking a fatty acid with a phenyl ring, which is not oxidized in the body but is excreted after conjugation with glycine. He synthesized a series of ω-phenyl fatty acids having two, three, four, or five carbons in the side chain, and fed these compounds to dogs. The aromatic compounds which he later isolated from the urine proved to be one of two substances, depending on the length of the side chain in the acid administered. When the side chain had contained an odd number of carbons, the nonoxidizable residue was excreted as hippuric acid, $C_6H_5 \cdot CO \cdot NH \cdot CH_2 \cdot COOH$. From acids with an even number of carbons, phenylaceturic acid was formed and excreted. From these results Knoop reasoned that the fatty acids were degraded by loss of two carbon atoms at a time and that when two more could not be removed without rupture of the phenyl ring, the residue was conjugated with glycine and excreted. This process is known as β-oxidation since the β-carbon becomes the terminal, carboxyl carbon after each oxidative step. The degradation is illustrated for an acid of each type in the following sequences:

$$C_6H_5 \cdot CH_2 \cdot CH_2 \cdot CH_2 \cdot CH_2 \cdot COOH \rightarrow C_6H_5 \cdot CH_2 \cdot CH_2 \cdot COOH \rightarrow$$
δ-Phenylvaleric acid

$$C_6H_5COOH \rightarrow C_6H_5CO \cdot NH \cdot CH_2 \cdot COOH$$
Hippuric acid

$$C_6H_5 \cdot CH_2 \cdot CH_2 \cdot CH_2 \cdot COOH \rightarrow C_6H_5 \cdot CH_2 \cdot COOH \rightarrow$$
γ-Phenylbutyric acid

$$C_6H_5 \cdot CH_2 \cdot CO \cdot NH \cdot CH_2 \cdot COOH$$
Phenylaceturic acid

Because of the known relation between fatty acids and ketone bodies, Knoop suggested that the intermediate steps in the removal of a pair of carbons involved formation of a keto acid. Knoop's suggested reaction mechanism involved the reactions shown in the following sequences:

$$R \cdot CH_2 \cdot CH_2 \cdot COOH \xrightarrow{+\frac{1}{2}O_2} R \cdot CHOH \cdot CH_2 \cdot COOH$$

$$R \cdot CHOH \cdot CH_2 \cdot COOH \xrightarrow{-2H} R \cdot CO \cdot CH_2 \cdot COOH$$

$$R \cdot CO \cdot CH_2 \cdot COOH \xrightarrow{+H_2O} R \cdot COOH + CH_3COOH$$

Repetition of this sequence would lead ultimately to complete transformation of any even numbered acid into two-carbon fragments, here shown as acetic acid.

This formulation accounted adequately for many of the facts then known and indeed for some that were to be discovered much later. Since nearly all of the naturally occurring fatty acids have even numbers of carbons, each would eventually yield the four-carbon butyric acid in the course of its degradation. Further passage of this substance through the suggested sequence of changes would lead, in the penultimate step, to formation of acetoacetate, and it was assumed that in ketosis for some unknown reason the sequence was interrupted at this point with formation of the other two ketone bodies from acetoacetate. This all seemed the more reasonable in that perfusion experiments had shown that it is only acids with even numbers of carbon atoms which give rise to appreciable amounts of acetoacetate in the liver.

Knoop's sequence was also compatible with some of the early isotope experiments. It will be recalled that when palmitic acid labeled with deuterium is metabolized by rats, changes in chain length were always in units of two carbons at a time, added to or removed from the original acid.

Knoop's original theory made no attempt to follow the "acetate" molecules to their final oxidation to carbon dioxide and water. It is now known that the two-carbon fragment formed in stepwise degradation of fatty acids is the ubiquitous acetyl coenzyme A, which normally condenses with oxaloacetate and enters the citric acid cycle. It will be recalled that the enzymes of this cycle, as well as those of fatty acid oxidation, are localized in the mitochondria.

Enzymes of the fatty acid spiral

Nearly fifty years after Knoop's experiments, D. E. Green and his group at Wisconsin isolated the enzymes which catalyze the reactions of β-oxidation. The process begins with formation of an acyl coenzyme A compound. This is catalyzed by one of two *fatty acyl CoA synthetases*, one of which acts upon fatty acids from C_4 to C_{11}, while the other acts upon higher fatty acids. The thiol ester which forms is a high energy compound, and as usual the energy is provided by ATP.

$$RCH_2 \cdot CH_2 \cdot COOH + ATP + HSCoA^3 \rightarrow$$
$$RCH_2 \cdot CH_2 \cdot CO \cdot SCoA + AMP + PP + H_2O \quad (1)$$

The second step is catalyzed by one of several *fatty acyl CoA dehydrogenases*. Three of these enzymes were originally isolated from pig heart, each being specific for acyl derivatives of different chain lengths. All three contain FAD as hydrogen acceptor. The one which acts upon thiol esters of chain length C_4 to C_8 was originally isolated as a green copper flavoprotein, but it has recently been shown that removal of the copper does not affect its catalytic activity. These enzymes in the presence of their specific substrates bring about dehydrogenation to form the trans isomers of derivatives of crotonic

---

[3] The coenzyme is often abbreviated simply CoA, but sometimes it appears as HCoA or as HSCoA.

acid ($CH_3 \cdot CH{=}CH \cdot COOH$), and transfer of the hydrogens to FAD. It

$$RCH_2 \cdot CH_2 \cdot CO \cdot SCoA + FAD \leftrightharpoons$$
$$RCH{=}CH \cdot CO \cdot SCoA + FADH_2 \quad (2)$$

is assumed that these hydrogens, like others which have been taken up by a coenzyme, are ultimately passed on to oxygen by way of the cytochromes. There is some evidence that this requires the intervention of another flavin which is known as the "electron transferring flavoprotein," ETF.

The third step in this oxidative sequence is hydration of the double bond, catalyzed by an enzyme known as *crotonase*. This enzyme is one of those which seem to unite in one molecule the ability to catalyze several different reactions. It not only brings about hydration of both *cis-* and *trans-*crotonic acid derivatives, but acts as a racemase upon the hydroxy acid which is formed at the four-carbon stage, bringing the D and the L forms of β-hydroxybutyryl CoA into equilibrium. What part, if any, these catalytic powers play in the β-oxidation sequence is not known. As shown in the equation, its best known catalytic action leads to formation of L-β-hydroxyacyl CoA.

$$RCH{=}CH \cdot CO \cdot SCoA + H_2O \rightleftharpoons RCHOH \cdot CH_2 \cdot CO \cdot SCoA \quad (3)$$

The fourth stage is again a dehydrogenation, catalyzed by an L-*β-hydroxyacyl CoA dehydrogenase* for which DPN^+ is the required coenzyme.

$$RCHOH \cdot CH_2 \cdot CO \cdot SCoA + DPN^+ \rightleftharpoons$$
$$RCO \cdot CH_2 \cdot CO \cdot SCoA + DPNH + H^+ \quad (4)$$

Finally, by interaction with a second molecule of coenzyme A, this β-ketoacyl CoA loses two carbons in the form of acetyl CoA. The shortened acyl CoA which remains is thus ready to enter upon another turn of the spiral, beginning with reaction (2). The enzyme which catalyzes reaction (5) is a *transacylase*

$$RCO \cdot CH_2 \cdot CO \cdot SCoA + HSCoA \rightleftharpoons$$
$$RCO \cdot SCoA + CH_3CO \cdot SCoA \quad (5)$$

which transfers the RCO— group to the new molecule of coenzyme A and frees one molecule of acetyl CoA. Normally the spiral is repeated as often as is necessary to split all the even numbered fatty acids into these active two-carbon fragments. These may then condense with oxaloacetate and enter the citric acid cycle for complete oxidation, but they may also be used in a number of other ways, one of which is considered in the following section.

Formation of acetoacetate

According to the reaction sequence just outlined, every even-numbered fatty acid will yield, near the end of its degradation, the thiol ester of the four-carbon β-keto acid, acetoacetic acid. If ketone body formation depended only upon some inhibition at this point, which would prevent the normal metabolism of this compound, then each fatty acid molecule could form only one molecule of acetoacetate. That this is not the explanation became clear when it was shown in experiments with isotopic labels that octanoic acid gives rise to more ketone bodies than an equimolar amount of butyric acid. Furthermore, with liver slices the amount of acetoacetate formed from added fatty acids was definitely more than could be accounted for on the basis of one mole of acetoacetate from each mole of acid metabolized, and odd-numbered acids did prove to give rise to small but significant amounts of ketone bodies. This has led to the theory that part at least of the acetoacetate is formed synthetically from acetyl CoA. This "β-oxidation-condensation" theory assumes that in the oxidation of a fatty acid the chain is degraded completely to acetyl CoA and that much of the acetoacetate results from recombination of some of these fragments to form acetoacetyl CoA.

$$2CH_3 \cdot CO \cdot SCoA \rightarrow HSCoA + CH_3 \cdot CO \cdot CH_2 \cdot CO \cdot SCoA$$

The enzyme which catalyzes this reaction is sometimes called a *transacetylase* and sometimes a *β-ketothiolase*. By this mechanism varying amounts of acetoacetate can arise from a single fatty acid molecule, depending upon the extent to which acetyl CoA is withdrawn for other metabolic purposes.

Removal of the coenzyme to free the acetoacetate seems to be achieved in several different ways. In skeletal and heart muscle and in some other tissues coenzyme A is not freed directly by hydrolysis, but is transferred to succinate, yielding activated succinate. This compound may then use its thiol ester bond to furnish energy for a synthesis or it may undergo hydrolysis with consequent sacrifice of the energy of that bond. Both of these possibilities are illustrated in the equations.

$$CH_3CO \cdot CH_2 \cdot CO \cdot SCoA + HOOC \cdot CH_2 \cdot CH_2 \cdot COOH \rightleftharpoons$$
$$HOOC \cdot CH_2 \cdot CH_2 \cdot CO \cdot SCoA + CH_3CO \cdot CH_2 \cdot COOH$$

$$HOOC \cdot CH_2 \cdot CH_2 \cdot CO \cdot SCoA + H_2O \rightleftharpoons$$
$$HOOC \cdot CH_2 \cdot CH_2 \cdot COOH + SHCoA$$

$$HOOC \cdot CH_2 \cdot CH_2 \cdot CO \cdot SCoA + ADP + P \rightleftharpoons$$
$$HOOC \cdot CH_2 \cdot CH_2 \cdot COOH + ATP + SHCoA$$

In the third equation the use of the energy of the thiol ester in synthesis is illustrated. The enzyme which catalyzes the first reaction is a *transferase* (specifically acetoacetyl CoA succinate CoA transferase), the enzyme which brings about hydrolysis is a *deacylase*, while the third reaction requires an enzyme known as *succinyl CoA synthetase*, or *P-enzyme*. This reaction is an example of what was referred to earlier (page 441) as phosphorylation at the substrate level as opposed to oxidative phosphorylation. The energy of the thiol ester has been conserved in the newly formed phosphate link of ATP.

Although there is some evidence that freeing of acetoacetate can take place in the liver through a simple hydrolysis catalyzed by a specific deacylase, Lynen has shown that it also takes place in a strangely complicated cycle. The two enzymes which take part in the reaction have been separated and purified and have been shown to catalyze the two reactions indicated below.

$$
\begin{array}{c}
CO \cdot CoA \\
| \\
CH_2 \\
| \\
CO \\
| \\
CH_3
\end{array}
+ CH_3CO \cdot CoA + H_2O
\underset{\text{enzyme}}{\overset{\text{condensing}}{\rightleftharpoons}}
\begin{array}{c}
CO \cdot CoA \\
| \\
CH_2 \\
| \\
HOC \cdot CH_2 \cdot COOH \\
| \\
CH_3
\end{array}
+ HCoA
$$

β-Hydroxy-β-methylglutaryl CoA

$$+ H_2O \Big|\ \overset{\text{cleavage}}{\underset{\text{enzyme}}{\downarrow}}$$

$$CH_3CO \cdot CH_2 \cdot COOH + CH_3CO \cdot CoA$$

Net: Acetoacetyl CoA + H_2O → Acetoacetate + CoA

It will be recalled that β-hydroxy-β-methylglutaryl CoA is an intermediate in the catabolism of leucine and in the synthesis of mevalonic acid (page 497). This reaction sequence is therefore of special interest in its linking of protein metabolism with that of the fats. The synthetic use of mevalonic acid is taken up later in this chapter.

All of this still leaves unanswered the question why, in some circumstances which seem often to involve diminished carbohydrate metabolism, acetoacetyl CoA is shunted out of its normal path and gives rise to free acid. Since much of this free acid is a result of recombination of acetyl CoA, perhaps the question is, why does the metabolism of this compound sometimes lead to formation of excessive amounts of acetoacetate? It must be said at the outset that there is as yet no definite answer to these questions. It has been suggested that ketone body formation results when acetyl CoA piles up for lack of the oxaloacetate that would be needed to throw it into the citric acid cycle. This seems to be disproved by the fact that liver slices from starved rats formed acetoacetate at ten times the normal rate, although their concentration of oxaloacetate was normal. This could mean that while the amount of oxalo-acetate was normal, the amounts of acetyl CoA, as a result of increased dependence upon fatty acid oxidation, were far above normal and so had to be removed by some nonoxidative mechanism.

One major use of acetyl CoA other than for oxidation is in the synthesis *de novo* of fatty acids. It has already been noted that this is a reductive process which will be shown to involve reduction of carbonyl groups to

CH$_2$— groups. For this a supply of reduced pyridine coenzymes is essential. Here again, carbohydrates as important oxidative substrates, transferring hydrogens to the pyridine coenzymes, are the source of a reactant needed for an important synthetic use of acetyl CoA. It may be that lack of these reducing agents when carbohydrate oxidation is curtailed limits the synthetic use of acetyl CoA and so allows it to reach such concentrations that it is removed by recombination to form acetoacetate. Clearly new experimental data are needed before this old, old question of the reason for ketosis can be finally answered.

α-Oxidation

Although plant mitochondria are supplied with the enzymes which bring about complete oxidation of fatty acids via β-oxidation and the citric acid cycle, there is evidence that in plants an alternative pathway is available. This reaction, first reported in 1956 by Stumpf, is catalyzed by a peroxidase which brings about, in the presence of H$_2$O$_2$, the decarboxylation of fatty acids of chain length C$_{14}$ to C$_{18}$.

$$R \cdot CH_2 \cdot CH_2 \cdot COOH + 2H_2O_2 \rightarrow CO_2 + R \cdot CH_2 \cdot CHO + 3H_2O$$

In a second step the aldehyde is oxidized by a DPN$^+$-specific dehydrogenase to yield an acid, shorter by one carbon than the original.

$$R \cdot CH_2 \cdot CHO + H_2O + DPN^+ \leftrightharpoons R \cdot CH_2 \cdot COOH + DPNH + H^+$$

The enzymes which bring about this oxidative removal of a single carbon were obtained from cytoplasmic material of peanut cotyledons after removal of mitochondria and microsomes by high speed centrifugation. The relative importance of this metabolic path will have to be established by further work.

Metabolism of propionic acid

Removal of two carbons at a time from the odd-numbered fatty acids leads eventually to propionyl CoA. It will be recalled that this compound is also an end product in the catabolism of valine and isoleucine. It has further been shown that free propionic acid is oxidized by liver slices and that this process begins with activation of the acid through formation of the coenzyme A derivative.

$$CH_3 \cdot CH_2 \cdot COOH + ATP + SHCoA \rightarrow$$
$$CH_3 \cdot CH_2 \cdot CO \cdot SCoA + AMP + PP$$

The further utilization of propionyl CoA in animal tissues has been shown to involve its conversion to succinic acid. This reaction sequence has a special interest in that vitamin B$_{12}$ appears to be involved at one stage, probably as a coenzyme essential to the isomerization outlined below.

The first step in the utilization of propionyl CoA is its carboxylation in the presence of ATP and bicarbonate. It will be noted that in this reaction the

$$CH_3 \cdot CH_2 \cdot CO \cdot CoA + CO_2 + ATP \rightarrow$$
$$HOOC \cdot CH(CH_3) \cdot CO \cdot CoA + ADP + P$$

Methylmalonyl CoA

new carboxyl group goes, not to the terminal carbon, but to the central one. The methylmalonyl CoA which forms is an isomer of succinyl CoA and rearranges to form the succinyl derivative. This had been shown to occur through a transcarboxylation. The reaction was clarified when the isomerization of unlabeled methylmalonyl CoA was carried out in the presence of C^{14}-labeled propionyl CoA. The succinyl CoA which formed proved to carry the label, showing that the isomerization was not a matter of migration within the methylmalonyl CoA molecule, but involved a transfer of a carboxyl group to propionyl CoA. As the equation shows, this leaves a new molecule of

$$
\begin{array}{cccc}
\text{COOH} & \text{CH}_3 & \text{CH}_3 & \text{COOH} \\
| & | & | & | \\
\text{CH}_3 \cdot \text{CH} \quad + \text{CH}_2 & \leftrightharpoons & \text{CH}_2 \quad + \text{CH}_2 \\
| & | & | & | \\
\text{CO} \cdot \text{CoA} & *\text{CO} \cdot \text{CoA} & \text{CO} \cdot \text{CoA} & \text{CH}_2 \\
& & & | \\
& & & *\text{CO} \cdot \text{CoA}
\end{array}
$$

Succinyl CoA

propionyl CoA which can again acquire a carboxyl group from methylmalonyl CoA, and so the sequence can go on until all the propionyl CoA has been transformed into succinyl CoA. Clearly this is but a beginning in the clarification of this unusual reaction, since it is hard to imagine a mechanism for the postulated direct transfer of a carboxyl group, and little is known of the part played in these reactions by the vitamin B_{12}, which has been shown to be essential.

Succinyl CoA as a member of the citric acid cycle is probably oxidized by way of that cycle, though it may, of course, be diverted to synthetic ends, such as heme synthesis.

Desaturation of fatty acids

The formation of unsaturated palmitoleic acid from palmitic acid in Schoenheimer's isotope experiments indicates that animal tissues are able to remove hydrogens from a fatty acid chain. This result was unexpected for it had long been known that certain polyunsaturated acids are essential dietary factors. Young animals which lack the essential fatty acids in the diet fail to grow and later fail to reproduce normally, and develop characteristic skin lesions. The presence of either linoleic, linolenic, or arachidonic acid satisfies the requirement, but many other unsaturated acids do not. This indicates that these compounds, which are required in very small amounts, must have an arrangement of double bonds which the body cannot duplicate, at any rate not fast enough to meet the demand. Since desaturation is possible, as shown by the Schoenheimer experiment and by the reactions of the β-oxidation sequence, the trouble must arise from an inability to place those double bonds in specific positions.

It has been established that linoleic (9,12-octadecadienoic acid), arachidonic (5,8,11,14-eicosatetraenoic acid) and γ-linolenic (6,9,12-octadecatrienoic acid) are highly potent in stimulating growth and curing dermal lesions. Many other highly unsaturated acids, including α-linolenic (9,12,15-octadecatrienoic acid), which do stimulate growth fail to cure the skin lesions. This indicates that the essential configuration involves at least two double bonds at the sixth and the ninth carbon *counting from the methyl end* of the chain. Thus the essential structure may be represented:

$$CH_3 \cdot (CH_2)_4 \cdot (CH=CH \cdot CH_2)_2 \cdot R$$

This is sometimes referred to as a 6,9-diene, and the pattern as a 1,4 double bond pattern which in the polyunsaturated essential fatty acids may be repeated more than once. Arachidonic acid, for example, which has three to five times the essential fatty acid (EFA) potency of linoleic acid, includes two such diene patterns. It now seems clear that increasing the unsaturation toward the methyl end of the chain results in loss of potency, while continuation of the pattern toward the carboxyl end enhances potency.

It has been believed for several years that the essential eighteen-carbon linoleic acid is in part transformed in the body to the more potent twenty-carbon arachidonic acid. Isotope experiments indicated that in this reaction the carbon chain of linoleic acid was incorporated as a unit, to which two additional carbons were transferred from acetyl CoA. The probable pathway for this transformation has now been established and is shown in the chart.

$$CH_3(CH_2)_4CH=CHCH_2CH=CH(CH_2)_7COOH$$
Linoleic acid

$$\downarrow -2H$$

$$CH_3(CH_2)_4CH=CHCH_2CH=CHCH_2CH=CH(CH_2)_4COOH$$
γ-Linolenic acid

$$\downarrow +C_2$$

$$CH_3(CH_2)_4(CH=CHCH_2)_3(CH_2)_5COOH$$
Homo-γ-linolenic acid

$$\downarrow -2H$$

$$CH_3(CH_2)_4(CH=CHCH_2)_4(CH_2)_2COOH$$
Arachidonic acid

This is clearly an incomplete formulation since the experiments were done with whole animals and hence there is no information upon requirements for coenzyme A or other cofactors.

The mechanism of desaturation has been very much clarified by recent work from Bloch's[5] laboratory using enzymes from yeast. The yeast strain used in these experiments requires unsaturated fatty acids in the nutrient solution if it is grown anaerobically, but under aerobic conditions is capable of carrying out the necessary desaturation. Two enzyme fractions have been identified, one soluble and the other bound to particles. Together they bring about formation of palmitoleic acid from palmitic and of oleic acid from stearic.

The reaction begins, as might have been foreseen, with formation of the coenzyme A derivative. The activated acid is then transformed in the presence of TPNH, molecular oxygen and the particulate enzyme fraction, with formation of the Δ^9-monounsaturated acid. This transformation takes place in two steps, the first of which is catalyzed by a typical *oxygenase* of the group sometimes called "mixed function oxidases." These enzymes bring about the transfer of one oxygen atom to the substrate while the other oxygen atom is reduced to water by a hydrogen donor other than the substrate. In the desaturation reaction this results in formation of an hydroxy acid and oxidation of TPNH by the second oxygen atom. In the light of the latest results the desaturation of stearic acid to form oleic acid may be formulated as follows:

$$\text{Stearic acid} \xrightarrow{\text{CoA, ATP}} \text{Stearyl CoA}$$

Stearyl CoA   **Oleyl CoA**

Degradation of the Phospholipids

Although enzymes are known which attack specifically many of the links of the compound lipids, very little is known of the actual course of degradation

[4] Konrad Bloch (1912–) was born in Germany but has spent most of his professional life in the United States. He did research at Columbia and at Chicago before becoming Higgins Professor of Chemistry at Harvard in 1954.

of these compounds in the digestive tract or in the tissues. Many of the known enzymes attack the intact lipid molecule, but it is not possible to show how they, or similar enzymes, act in sequence to bring about complete hydrolysis to simple units. Nevertheless it must be assumed that such hydrolysis does take place in the tissues and that this is followed either by oxidative destruction of the fragments or by their use in synthesis.

Among the well-known enzymes which act upon compound lipids are three which were originally named lecithinases but are now referred to as phospholipases A, B, and C (or D) since they act not only upon lecithins but also upon phosphatidyl ethanolamine and phosphatidyl serine, but not upon the corresponding inositol compounds.

Phospholipase A was originally isolated from snake venom and is found also in venoms of scorpions and wasps. It attacks specifically the β-ester link in the lipid, setting free one fatty acid. As already noted, this is usually an unsaturated acid. The remaining lipid is known as a lysolecithin, for example, if the original substrate was lecithin. Lysophosphatides exert a

$$
\begin{array}{l}
CH_2O \cdot OCR \\
| \\
HOCH \qquad O \\
| \qquad\qquad \uparrow \\
CH_2O \cdot P \cdot O \left\{\begin{array}{l} \text{choline or} \\ \text{ethanolamine} \\ \text{or serine} \end{array}\right. \\
\qquad\quad | \\
\qquad\quad O^-
\end{array}
$$

Lysophosphatide

strong hemolytic effect, causing destruction of both red and white blood cells. It is this action which is believed to account for the toxicity of snake and other venoms. With this property it might have been expected that such compounds would not be encountered in animal tissues. Strangely enough they have been shown to be minor components of the phosphatides of egg yolk and of serum. Presumably their hemolytic properties are suppressed in the presence of high concentrations of other phospholipids.

Phospholipase B acts upon the lyso derivatives of the three phosphatidyl compounds to remove the second fatty acid residue while leaving both phosphoester links intact. A somewhat similar enzyme from *Penicillium notatum* appears to liberate both fatty acids, not only from the three phosphatidyl compounds listed above but also from a monophosphoinositide, which is structurally like the others. Phospholipase B occurs in some animal and plant tissues as well as in snake and insect venoms.

Phospholipase C is again a product of snake venoms and bacterial toxins, but has also been found in brain tissue. Its substrate is intact phospholipids in which it splits the ester bond between phosphoric acid and glycerol yielding the phosphorylated base and a diglyceride. It acts to split the corresponding phosphoester bond in sphingomyelin. There is some confusion about the naming of these enzymes, and in some recent papers this phospholipase is called phospholipase D.

There is, however, a fourth enzyme which comes from plant tissue and acts upon intact phosphatidyl choline, ethanolamine, or serine to split the bond between the phosphoric acid and the nitrogenous compound, freeing the latter and leaving a phosphatidic acid. This is also known as phospholipase D.

This about exhausts our information on fairly well-characterized enzymes which act specifically upon phospholipids. In addition, a diesterase found in rat liver acts upon L-α-glycerophosphoryl choline or ethanolamine to free the base from glycerophosphate. There are also relatively unspecific lipases and phosphatases some of which may split fatty acid ester or phosphoester bonds from partially degraded molecules.

Of the small units set free if and wherever these hydrolyses do take place in tissues, the fatty acids of course become part of the general metabolic pool of these compounds. Glycerol and any carbohydrates from the cerebrosides will follow the paths of carbohydrate metabolism which is to be considered in the next chapter. This is true also of inositol which is acted upon by an enzyme found in rat kidney and transformed into glucuronic acid. The relationship of this compound to glucose is obvious, and indeed in one reaction sequence by which glucose is metabolized, glucuronic acid is an intermediate. This leaves the nitrogenous compounds. Serine and ethanolamine have already been considered in connection with amino acid metabolism. The degradation of choline to glycine involves its oxidation to betaine, loss of one methyl group from betaine by transmethylation (page 482) and of the other two by oxidation. Thus the degradation of the nitrogen compounds which form part of the compound lipids funnels into the stream of amino acid metabolism.

Steroid Metabolism

In animal metabolism the key compound among the steroids is cholesterol, important not only as a constituent of the lipoproteins but as the precursor of the steroid hormones.

These hormones are usually classified according to their place of origin or to their physiological effects. The *corticosteroids* comprise a large number of steroid hormones which are elaborated in the adrenal cortex and are concerned with regulation of carbohydrate metabolism and of electrolyte balance. Two other groups of steroids are known respectively as the *androgens*, which stimulate the development of the secondary male sex characteristics, and the *estrogens*, which control the cyclical changes in the uterus and the development of secondary sex characteristics in the female.

Of the large number of steroids which have been isolated from adrenal tissue, corticosterone and cortisol are secreted in highest concentrations. Cortisone has a special interest because of its dramatic curative effect on some types of arthritis, and aldosterone is the one which is most active in prolonging life in adrenalectomized animals. Specifically, cortisol, cortisone, and corticosterone are concerned with carbohydrate metabolism. This is shown whether their stimulatory effect is measured in terms of increased glycogen deposition in the liver or of stimulation of muscle-work performance. The latter measures carbohydrate metabolism because it depends entirely upon oxidation of glucose for its needed energy. Aldosterone promotes retention of sodium ion and excretion of potassium ion. It is of interest that these highly potent compounds seem to be metabolized with great rapidity. The half life of aldosterone has been estimated to be less than half an hour and that of corticosterone about 1 hour. The formulas of these four cortical hormones, shown below, make clear the close structural relationship between

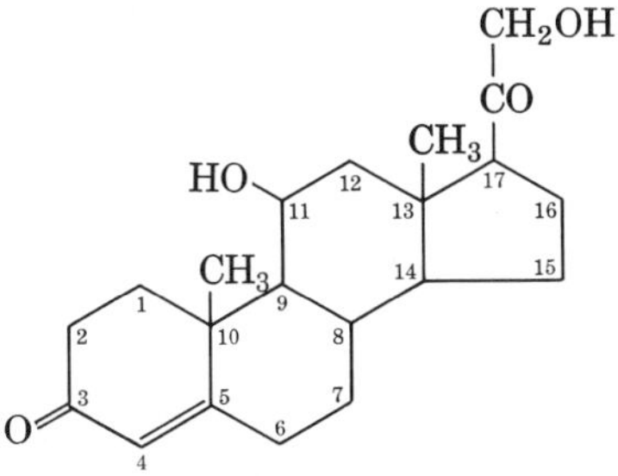

Corticosterone

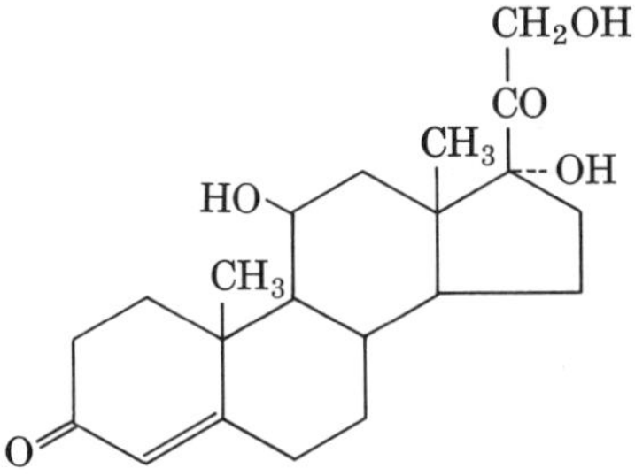

Cortisol

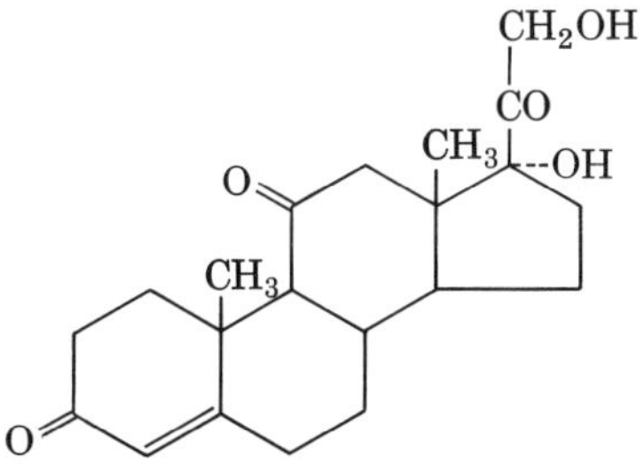

Cortisone

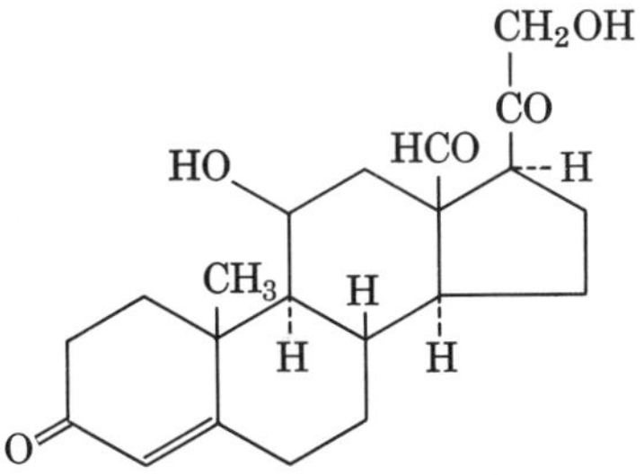

Aldosterone

them. In the formula for aldosterone and in those for pregnane and estrane, the hydrogens at the asymmetric carbons are shown. In other formulas these hydrogens are omitted. Recent evidence indicates that for high potency the corticosteroids must carry an oxygen at carbon 11.

All the compounds above, as well as the many other corticosteroids, may be considered to be derivatives of one of two stereoisomeric parent hydrocarbons known as pregnane and allopregnane. In the rational nomenclature of these compounds they are named as derivatives of one or the other of these parent compounds. The formula of pregnane is given below. Allopregnane differs from it in having a trans instead of a cis relationship between the A and B rings, and in having the hydrogen at carbon 5 in the α orientation instead of the β.

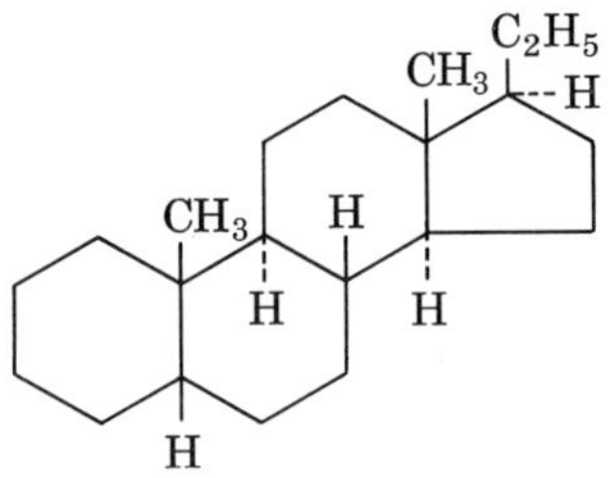

Pregnane

The estrogenic hormones arise chiefly in the ovaries and are structurally distinguished by the absence of the familiar methyl group on carbon 10, by the aromatic character of ring A and by the lack of any side chain at carbon 17. Of the three very similar compounds, estrone, estriol, and estradiol, estradiol is the most potent in several experimental animals though this seems not to be true in humans. The structures of estrone and estradiol are indicated below. Estriol differs from the diol only in having a third hydroxyl at carbon 16.

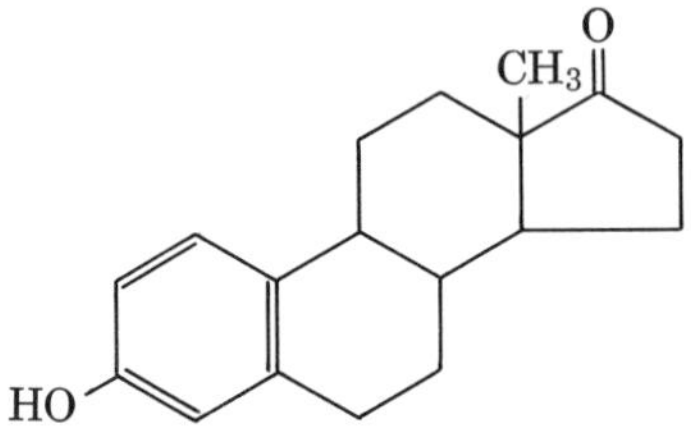

Estrone

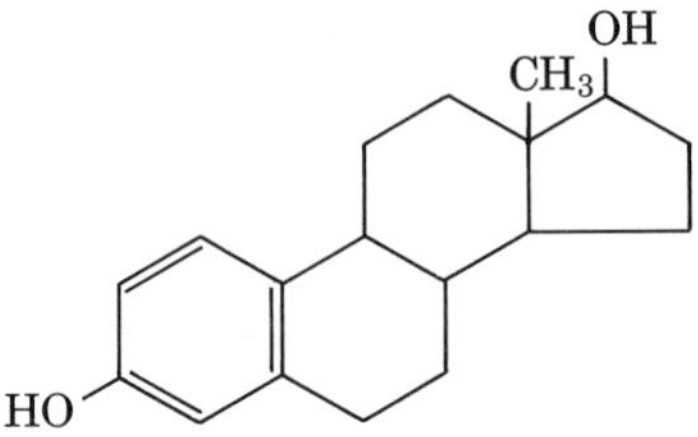

Estradiol

The parent hydrocarbon of this group of compounds is the eighteen-carbon, fully saturated compound known as estrane, the formula for which is shown below. A fourth hormone secreted by the ovary is progesterone. This compound stimulates proliferation of the uterine mucosa in preparation for the receipt of the fertilized ovum, and is important throughout pregnancy. Parturition takes place when the progesterone concentration falls, or its ratio

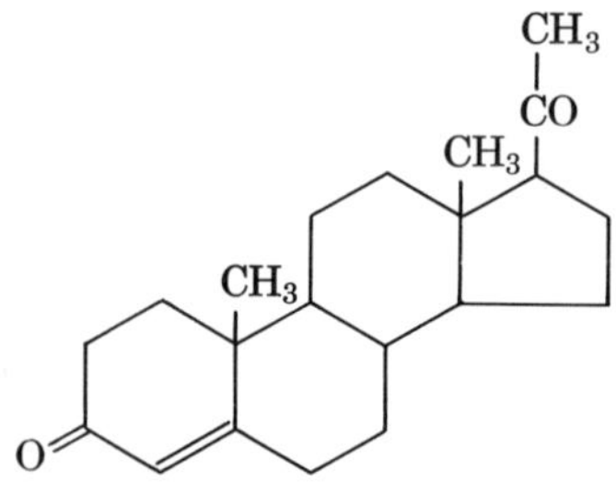

Progesterone

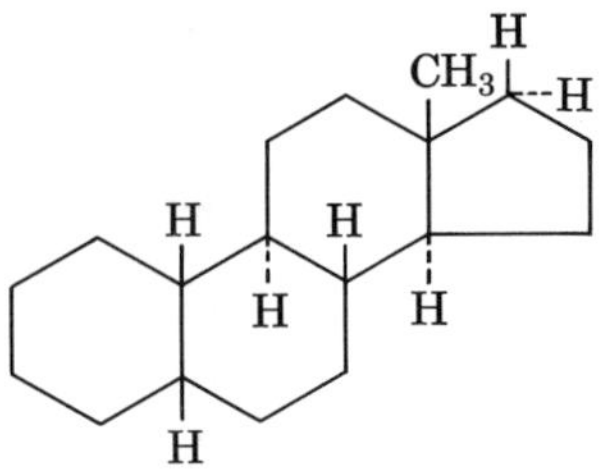

Estrane

to the estrogenic hormones is lowered. As its formula indicates, progesterone is more closely related structurally to the adrenal hormones than to the estrogens.

The major androgen is testosterone which arises chiefly in the testes. The hydrocarbon to which this and other androgenic steroids are related is known as androstane. It differs from estrane only in having a methyl group instead of a hydrogen on carbon 10.

Testosterone

All these compounds are closely related not only structurally but metabolically. This is indicated by the fact that the various hormones are not secreted exclusively by a single organ as the above discussion might seem to imply. It has been found that androgens arise in small amounts in the ovaries and estrogens in the testes. The adrenals elaborate not only progesterone in addition to the typical corticosteroids, but also estrogens and androgens. Furthermore, estrogens or androgens administered to animals or used with tissue slices are each transformed into the other type of hormone. This seeming lack of a clear distinction between compounds which have such definite and very different physiological activities is explained by their biosynthetic pathways as outlined in Fig. 14.1. There it is shown not only that cholesterol is a common precursor but also that well beyond the cholesterol stage the steroid hormones follow a common synthetic pathway. Not all the intermediates are known, and of those that are known some have been omitted from the chart. But what is there should make clear the reasons why any given organ may synthesize small amounts of atypical hormones, and why the androgens and estrogens are so readily interconvertible by living cells. There must be operative under normal conditions a very pretty balance of enzymic forces to assure the formation of the necessary amounts of the proper hormones.

Excretion of the steroid hormones

The study of the metabolism of the steroid hormones was given an enormous impetus when it was discovered many years ago that various closely related compounds exerted a carcinogenic effect. The hope aroused at that time that identification of some abnormal steroid metabolite would furnish a clue to the cause of cancer has not been fulfilled. But over the years, from the urine of normal people and of people with tumors and from animals with

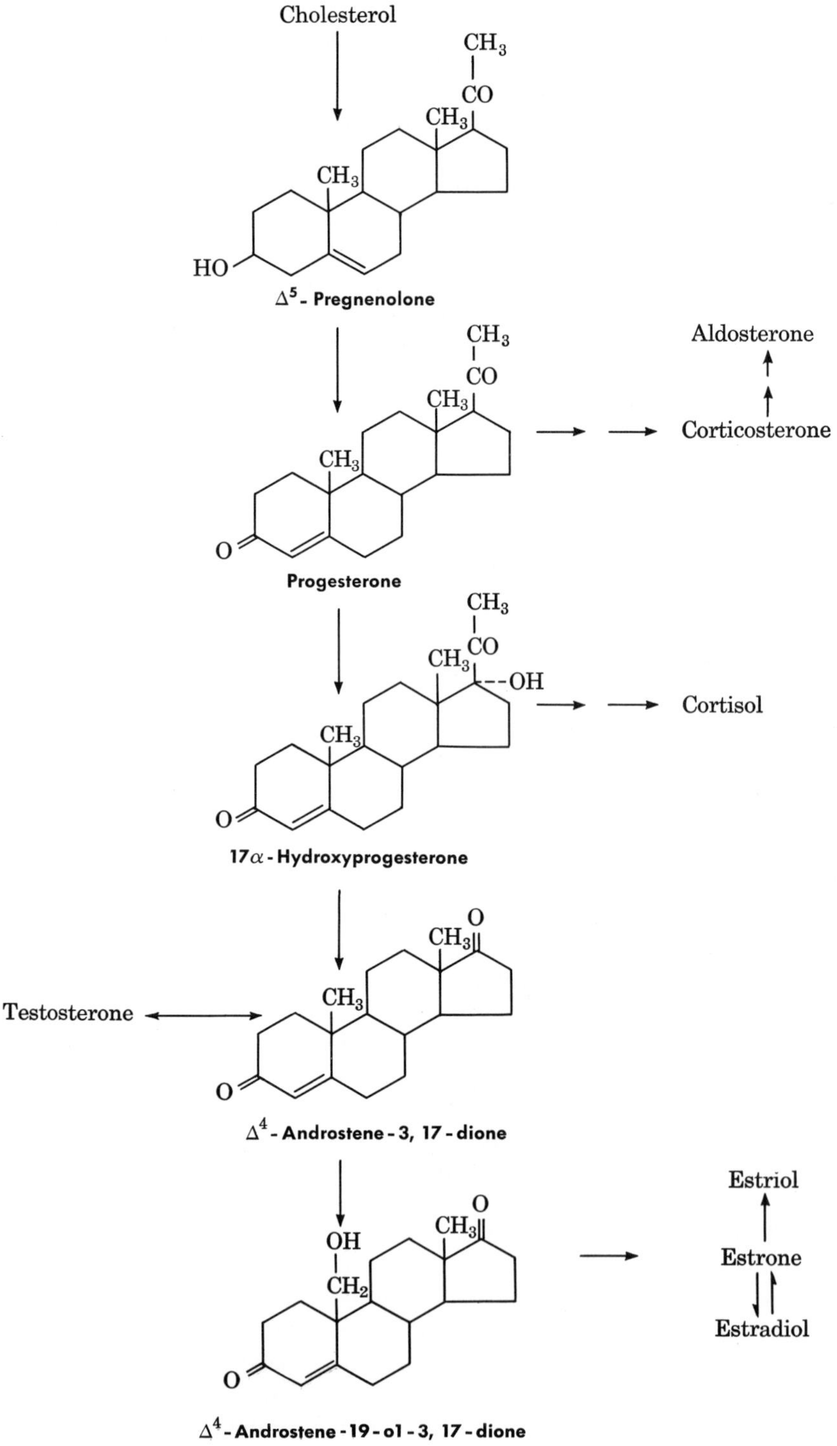

Fig. 14.1. Biosynthetic pathways of the steroid hormones.

various types of experimental tumors, a great number of steroid compounds have been isolated and identified. The changes which take place before excretion of the steroids include reduction of double bonds and of keto groups, oxidative removal of side chains and of the hydrogens of hydroxyl groups. The compounds which are formed by various combinations of these fundamental reactions comprise a long list to which additions are still being made. These compounds are inactive physiologically, or only weakly active, and are usually excreted after conjugation with glucuronic acid or with sulfate. As is usual in formation of such derivatives, the glucuronic acid is transferred to the steroid from uridinediphosphoglucuronic acid, and the sulfate reacts in the form of 3'-phosphoadenosine-5'-phosphosulfate (PAPS). After isolation of these compounds from urine the steroids can be freed enzymically from their conjugated derivatives, a β-glucuronidase hydrolyzing the glycosidic bond and a specific steroid sulfatase removing the sulfate group.

While the main vehicle for excretion of the hormones is the urine, the degradation products of cholesterol are excreted largely in the feces. The major end products of cholesterol metabolism are the bile acids which were described on page 374. These are compounds in which cholic acid or closely related derivatives of cholic acid have been conjugated with glycine or with taurine in preparation for their secretion into the bile. It will be remembered that of these compounds which thus find their way into the intestine, a major portion is reabsorbed and carried back to the liver. Those which remain in the intestines are acted upon by microorganisms, so that in order to identify the "primary" bile acids, that is, those which are synthesized in the liver from cholesterol, it was necessary to investigate, not the fecal excretion of steroids, but freshly secreted bile obtained from a bile fistula.

Of the various bile acids which have been found in human and other biles it now appears that the primary product is cholic acid which is formed in the liver from cholesterol. The other steroid compounds are then derived from cholic acid either through the agency of liver enzymes or through the action of enzymes elaborated by intestinal microorganisms. It appears that this general pattern is followed by all species so far investigated. It is still not possible to write a complete reaction sequence, but certain facts have emerged which make it possible to suggest a probable sequence.

All the primary products so far identified have an hydroxyl group in the 7α position. This makes it clear that deoxycholic acid which lacks this group and which was previously believed to lie between cholesterol and cholic acid is actually not formed in liver at all, but is a product of bacterial action on cholic acid. Another product of bacterial action is the substance which used to be called coprosterol and is now known as coprostanol. This substance is derived from cholesterol itself which is reduced by intestinal bacteria with elimination of the double bond. This reaction is clearly not a simple one step reduction, since it involves a shift in the spatial relation of rings

A and B from trans to cis, but the exact course of the reduction is not known.

The suggested relationships between cholesterol and some of its excretory products are outlined in Fig. 14.2. The solid arrows indicate reactions

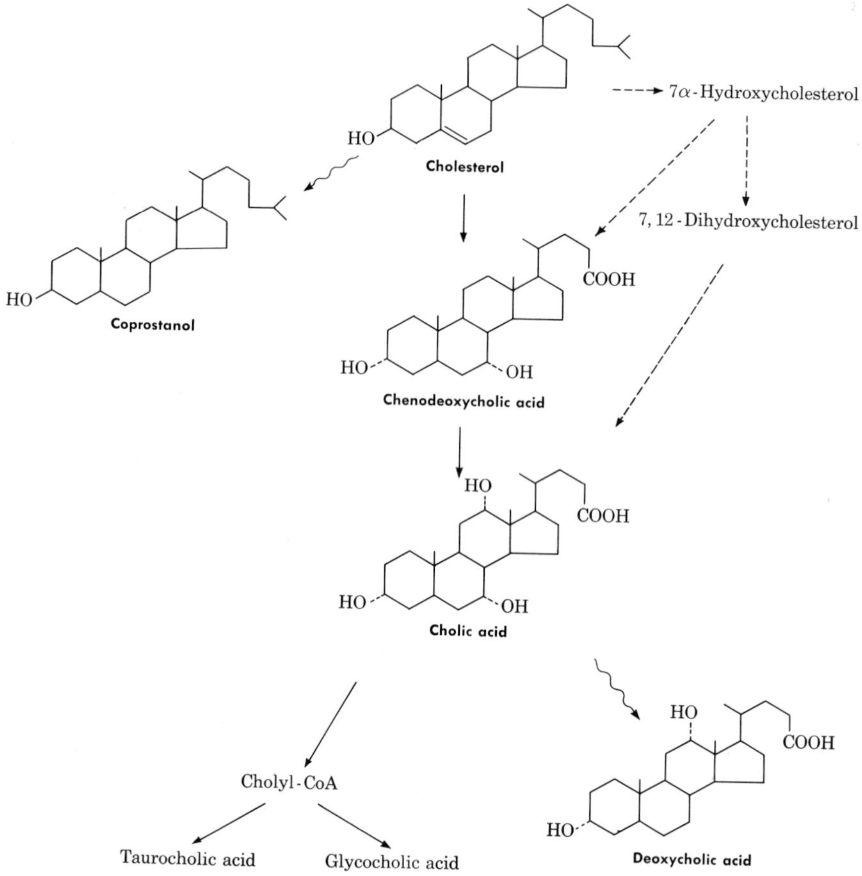

Fig. 14.2. Postulated stages in the biosynthesis of bile acids. → = reactions catalyzed by liver enzymes; ⟶ = reactions which seem probable; ⤳= reactions caused by intestinal bacteria.

which are known to take place in liver, the dotted arrows reactions which seem to be highly probable, and the wavy arrows reactions which are due to intestinal microorganisms. Although the only conjugations which are shown on the chart are those with cholic acid itself, obviously the other acids shown could form coenzyme A derivatives which would react with glycine or taurine.

BIOSYNTHESIS OF THE LIPIDS

It has long been known that fatty acids and sterols are synthesized from small molecules, but it is only in recent years that the enzyme systems have begun to be recognized and the chemical sequences clarified.

Fatty Acid Synthesis

Much was made in the early years of the fact that the reactions of the β-oxidation sequence were reversible and until about 1953 it was assumed that synthesis was a reversal of oxidative degradation. In that year it was shown that highly purified enzymes of β-oxidation brought about no synthesis of long chain acids, though previously such synthesis had been found with cruder preparations.

A new approach to the problem was sought by Wakil and his group when they began an elaborate fractionation and purification of the enzymes in pigeon liver which catalyze fatty acid synthesis. They isolated four fractions, precipitated in sequence by increasing concentrations of ammonium sulfate, and then further purified each fraction. While each alone was inactive, a mixture of three of the four with essential cofactors did catalyze synthesis of long chain acids from acetate. The essential cofactors were ATP, CoA, DPNH, TPN^+, Mn^{++}, and isocitrate. A similar system was obtained from chicken liver, with roughly the same requirements. Under optimum conditions these enzyme fractions brought about synthesis of fatty acids of which approximately 80 per cent were palmitic acid, 17 per cent myristic (C_{14}), and the remainder lauric (C_{12}) and decanoic acids.

In some of these experiments bicarbonate buffer had been used, and then in 1957 it was shown that (*a*) carbon dioxide greatly stimulated fatty acid synthesis and (*b*) labeled carbon dioxide did not appear in the products. A later discovery that biotin was an essential cofactor again directed attention to the role of carbon dioxide, since it is now believed that carbon dioxide is activated by attachment to biotin.

After further purification of the enzyme fractions by gel adsorption (G) and column chromatography (C) it became possible to demonstrate a stepwise synthesis of fatty acids. The purified enzyme first designated R_{1GC} (meaning precipitated first by the lowest concentration of $(NH_4)_2SO_4$, and purified by the two techniques above), and later named *acetyl CoA carboxylase*, brought about reaction between acetyl CoA and CO_2 in the presence of ATP to form malonyl CoA. The specific function of ATP is not known, though it certainly furnishes energy for activation of the CO_2. Malonyl CoA in

$$ATP + CO_2 + CH_3 \cdot CO \cdot CoA \xrightarrow[\text{biotin}]{Mn^{++}} ADP + P + \text{Malonyl CoA}$$

turn became a substrate for the R_{2GC} enzyme fraction which in the presence of TPNH and acetyl CoA catalyzed the formation of long chain fatty acids. Present evidence points to the following reaction sequence, although the substances in brackets have not yet been proved to participate.

$$CH_3 \cdot CO \cdot CoA + CO_2 + ATP \xrightarrow[R_{1GC}]{\text{biotin}} HOOC \cdot CH_2 \cdot CO \cdot CoA$$
Malonyl CoA

$$CH_3 \cdot CO \cdot CoA + HOOC \cdot CH_2 \cdot CO \cdot CoA \xrightarrow{R_{2GC}}$$

$$[CH_3 \cdot CO \cdot CH(COOH) \cdot CO \cdot CoA \xrightarrow{\text{TPNH}}$$

$$CH_3 \cdot CHOH \cdot CH(COOH) \cdot CO \cdot CoA \xrightarrow{-H_2O}$$

$$CH_3 \cdot CH{=}C(COOH) \cdot CO \cdot CoA \xrightarrow{\text{TPNH}}$$

$$CH_3 \cdot CH_2 \cdot CH(COOH)CO \cdot CoA] \xrightarrow{-CO_2} CH_3 \cdot CH_2 \cdot CH_2 \cdot CO \cdot CoA$$
Butyryl CoA

This new four-carbon acyl CoA will then react with a second molecule of malonyl CoA to begin again the sequence catalyzed by R_{2GC}, thus adding

$$CH_3 \cdot CH_2 \cdot CH_2 \cdot CO \cdot CoA + HOOC \cdot CH_2 \cdot CO \cdot CoA \rightarrow$$
$$CH_3 \cdot CH_2 \cdot CH_2 \cdot CO \cdot CH(COOH) \cdot CO \cdot CoA$$

four carbons in a block. Experiment has shown that this in fact takes place and that butyryl CoA is indeed incorporated as a unit into palmitate.

Here the story of fatty acid synthesis stood in the summer of 1960 when a note from Wakil indicated that the enzyme system just described may not be the only one which brings about synthesis of fatty acids. That first system was precipitated from the supernatant after removal of mitochondria and microsomes. Wakil now finds that there is a different fatty acid synthesizing system in the mitochondria. Unlike the nonmitochondrial system it shows no requirement for carbon dioxide, though it does require ATP and the pyridine coenzymes. When acetyl CoA was incubated anaerobically with ATP, reduced pyridine coenzymes, and mitochondrial protein, fatty acids were synthesized. The major component was stearic acid (40 per cent), with 20 per cent each of palmitic, myristic, and lauric acids. Here clearly is a new fatty acid synthesizing system the details of which are still to be worked out.

Biosynthesis of Triglycerides and Phospholipids

These two biosyntheses are considered together because it has been found that up to the final steps they follow a common pathway. These syntheses like so many others were once thought to be reversals of the catabolic hydrolyses, but when it was shown that ATP was required for incorporation of fatty acids into neutral fat, this hypothesis became untenable. It was then shown that phosphatidic acids and D-α,β-diglycerides were essential intermediates in the biosynthesis of such phospholipids as lecithin, and later that these compounds are also precursors of triglycerides. The sequence of reactions which leads to both types of product is indicated in Fig. 14.3. Here

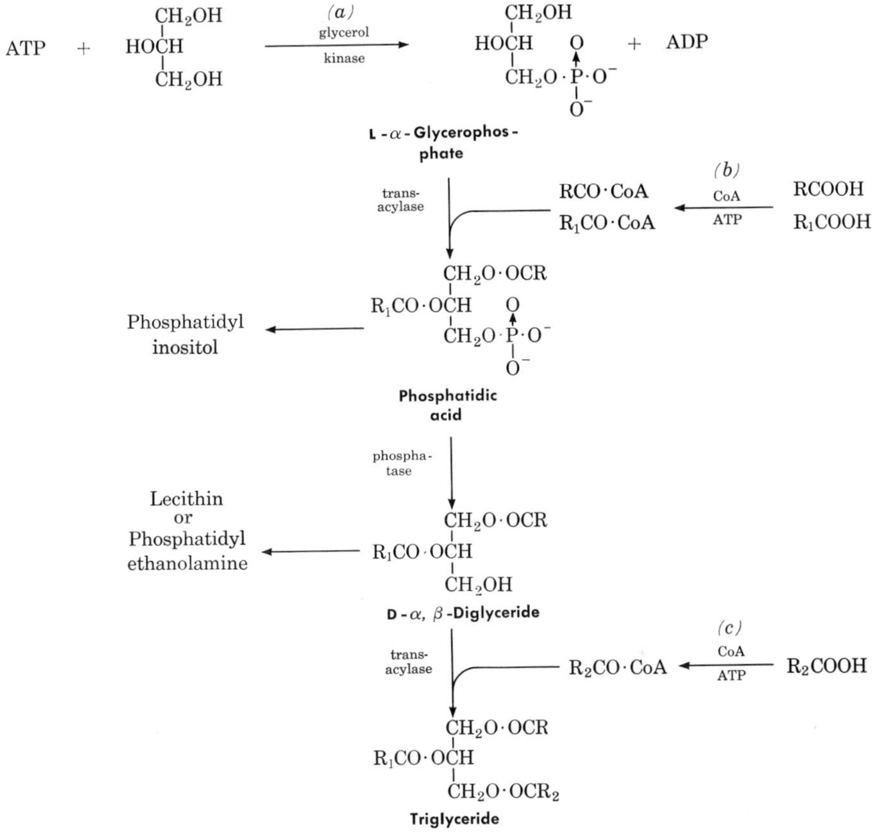

Fig. 14.3. Biosynthesis of triglycerides and phospholipids.

as elsewhere the breakdown of ATP provides the free energy which makes the syntheses possible. One mole of ATP is used in phosphorylation of glycerol, and three in the coupling of 3 moles of fatty acid with coenzyme A. This latter reaction, (b) and (c) on the chart, is catalyzed by one of the fatty acyl CoA synthetases and is accompanied by a splitting of ATP to AMP.

It should be noted that the recently discovered correspondence between preferential placing of unsaturated acids on the β-carbon of glycerol in both phospholipids and triglycerides lends support to this formulation. This does not mean that identical α,β-diglycerides will be withdrawn for each type of final synthesis. In a pool of such diglycerides some will contain the acyl groups which are required for synthesis of phospholipids and others will be adapted to the broader specificity of triglyceride synthesis. What the scheme intends to show is that from a mixture of saturated and unsaturated fatty acids the essential diglycerides are formed by a series of identical stages.

Biosynthesis of the three types of phospholipids indicated on the chart proved to require the presence of cytidine triphosphate (CTP). Thus the energy of another nucleoside triphosphate is found to serve synthetic ends. ATP is, of course, not only the most generally and widely useful of these compounds but also the ultimate source of the energy for all of them, since each of the others acquires its second and third phosphate group by transfer from ATP. Nevertheless it has been noted, and will be emphasized in the next chapter, that for transfer of carbohydrate residues a uridine phosphate derivative seems to be especially suitable, and now it is found that in biosynthesis of the compound lipids it is cytidine triphosphate which is used.

Formation of inositol monophosphatide begins, as shown in Fig. 14.3, with a phosphatidic acid. This compound reacts with CTP to form a CDP-diglyceride which has the formula shown below. The reaction sequence is

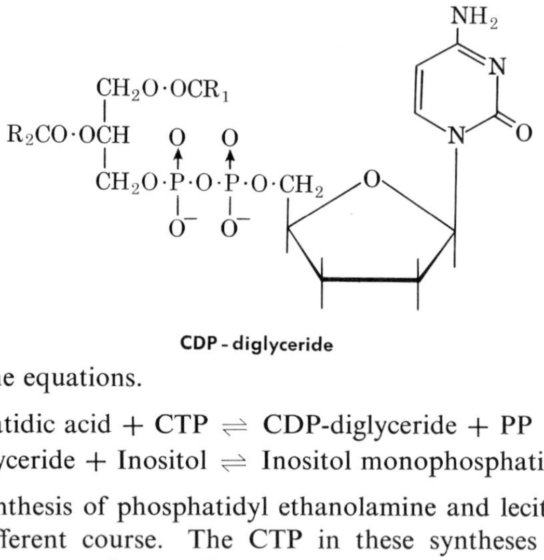

$$
\begin{array}{l}
\mathrm{CH_2O \cdot OCR_1} \\
\mathrm{R_2CO \cdot OCH} \\
\mathrm{CH_2O \cdot P \cdot O \cdot P \cdot O \cdot CH_2 \cdots}
\end{array}
$$

CDP - diglyceride

outlined in the equations.

$$\text{Phosphatidic acid} + \text{CTP} \rightleftharpoons \text{CDP-diglyceride} + \text{PP}$$

$$\text{CDP-diglyceride} + \text{Inositol} \rightleftharpoons \text{Inositol monophosphatide} + \text{CMP}$$

For the synthesis of phosphatidyl ethanolamine and lecithin the reaction follows a different course. The CTP in these syntheses reacts with the nitrogenous compounds to activate them rather than the glyceryl moiety. The steps in this reaction sequence are shown in Fig. 14.4 where it is shown that the cytidine monophosphate which entered the reaction sequence in reaction 2 is reconstituted in reaction 4.

The nitrogen compounds in the phospholipids arise in the normal course of nitrogen metabolism. Serine, of course, is derived directly from protein hydrolysis. Decarboxylation of serine yields ethanolamine which means that either serine or glycine can act as precursor of this compound. Ethanolamine in turn is transformed into choline by the introduction of three methyl groups. Isotopic evidence indicates that these groups are introduced in a stepwise manner so that the sequence is from ethanolamine to the mono-, the di-, and finally the trimethyl derivative. Of these three groups the first

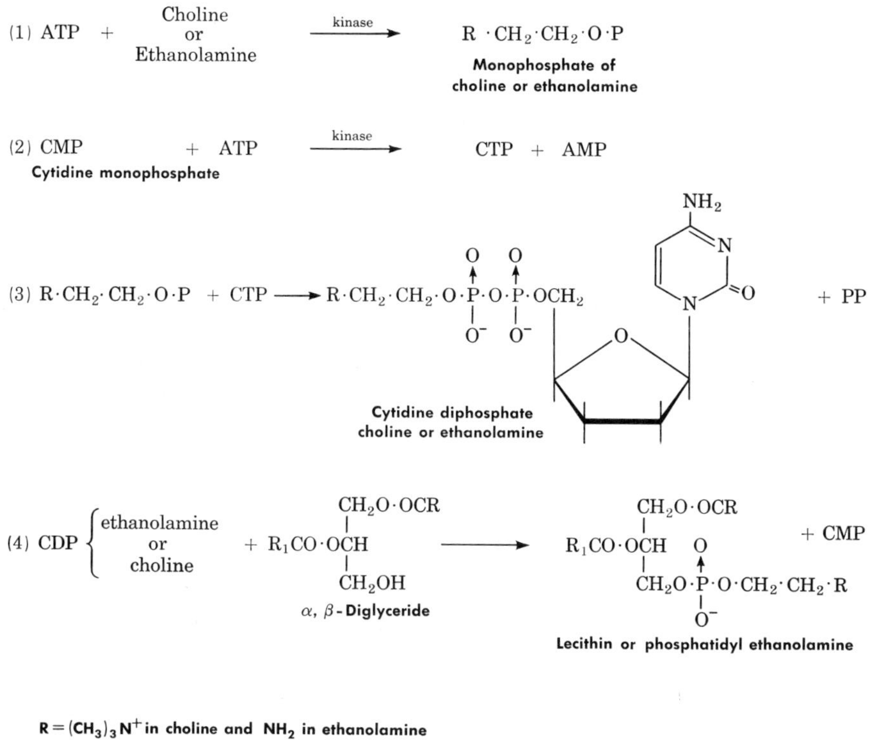

(1) $ATP +$ Choline or Ethanolamine $\xrightarrow{\text{kinase}}$ $R \cdot CH_2 \cdot CH_2 \cdot O \cdot P$

Monophosphate of choline or ethanolamine

(2) CMP + ATP $\xrightarrow{\text{kinase}}$ CTP + AMP

Cytidine monophosphate

(3) $R \cdot CH_2 \cdot CH_2 \cdot O \cdot P + CTP \longrightarrow R \cdot CH_2 \cdot CH_2 \cdot O \cdot \overset{O}{\underset{O^-}{\overset{\uparrow}{P}}} \cdot O \cdot \overset{O}{\underset{O^-}{\overset{\uparrow}{P}}} \cdot OCH_2 \cdots + PP$

Cytidine diphosphate choline or ethanolamine

(4) CDP $\begin{cases} \text{ethanolamine} \\ \text{or} \\ \text{choline} \end{cases}$ $+ R_1CO \cdot O\overset{\displaystyle CH_2O \cdot OCR}{\underset{\displaystyle CH_2OH}{CH}}$ $\longrightarrow$ $R_1CO \cdot O\overset{\displaystyle CH_2O \cdot OCR}{\underset{\displaystyle CH_2O \cdot \underset{O^-}{\overset{O}{P}} \cdot O \cdot CH_2 \cdot CH_2 \cdot R}{CH}}$ $+ CMP$

α, β-Diglyceride

Lecithin or phosphatidyl ethanolamine

$R = (CH_3)_3 N^+$ in choline and NH_2 in ethanolamine

Fig. 14.4. Synthesis of lecithin and phosphatidyl ethanolamine.

two are synthesized from one-carbon units, and only the third is furnished in a transmethylation from methionine.

Biosynthesis of the Steroids

One of the great triumphs of modern biochemistry is the elucidation of the reactions by which cholesterol is synthesized from acetate in living cells. It has already been noted that this synthesis is a preliminary to the synthesis of a great many other compounds of fundamental biological importance.

Once it had been established that all the carbons of cholesterol were derived from acetate, the use of acetate-1-C^{14} or acetate-2-C^{14} made it possible to determine the source of each carbon in cholesterol. The labeled acetate was used with rat liver slices, and the cholesterol which formed was then systematically degraded in order to determine which carbons were labeled by each of the two types of labeled acetate. Much of this work was carried out by Cornforth, Popják, and their colleagues in London, and by Bloch and his colleagues in this country. It established the distribution of the methyl (m) and carboxyl (c) carbons in cholesterol as shown below.

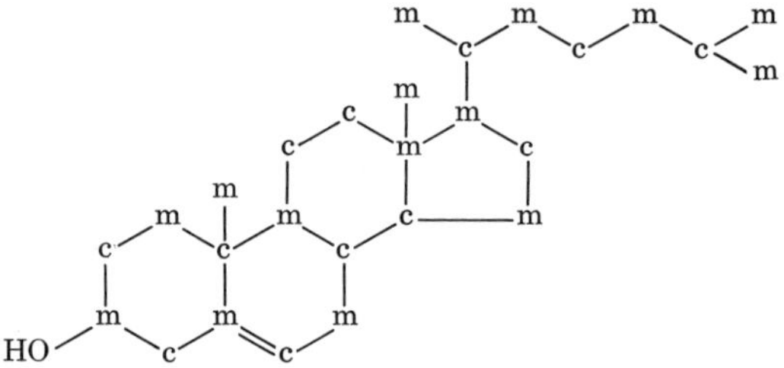

The first intermediate between acetate and cholesterol to be identified was the triterpene, squalene. This compound was first isolated from rat liver and then was shown to be an effective precursor of cholesterol. Since squalene contains thirty carbon atoms and cholesterol only twenty-seven,

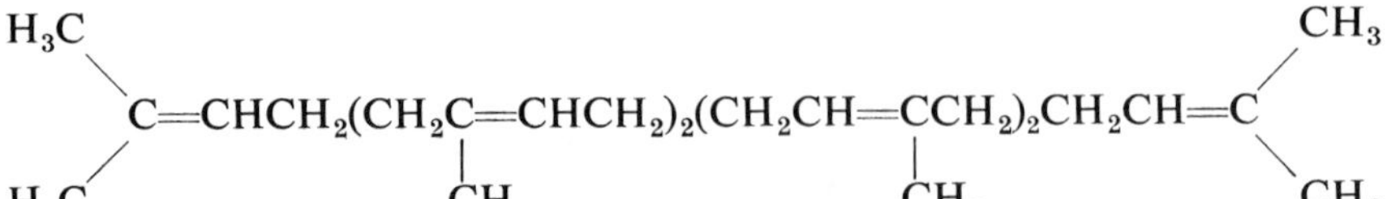

Squalene

formation of cholesterol involves a cyclization, with formation of the rings and removal of three carbons.

Squalene is one of many naturally occurring substances of which rubber is an outstanding example, which are made up of isoprene $(CH_2\!=\!C \cdot CH\!=\!CH_2)$

$$\underset{\displaystyle CH_3}{|}$$

units. Compounds which contain two such units are known as monoterpenes, and so squalene with six is a triterpene. When the units polymerize, each unit loses one double bond, and the remaining one shifts its position. In squalene the three left-hand or the three right-hand units are said to be united "head to tail" but in the center of the molecule two units form a head-to-head bond so that the molecule is symmetrical, with four carbons instead of three between the tertiary carbons in the center.

When squalene synthesized in liver slices from labeled acetate was degraded, the distribution of acetate carbons in each isoprene unit was found to be the following:

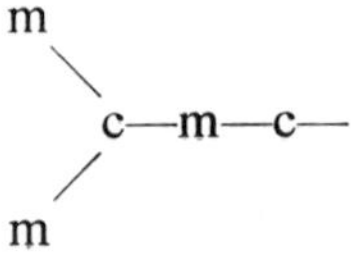

This known arrangement in squalene made it possible to check the various mechanisms suggested for cyclization of squalene against the known distribution of methyl and carboxyl carbons in cholesterol. This established the folding pattern of squalene as shown. According to this, one methyl group shifts from position 8 (numbering as in the steroids) to position 13. Three other methyl groups have ultimately to be eliminated, and it will be noted

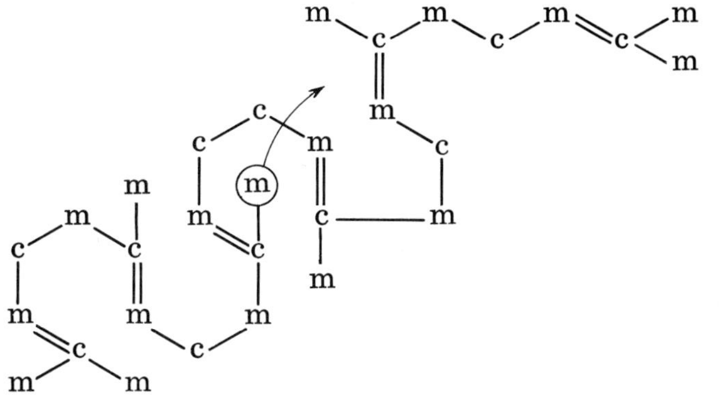

that each goes from a point at which a bond must form to complete the rings. According to present theories the cyclization, once initiated, takes place in a concerted manner, with no formation of stable intermediates. It takes place only under aerobic conditions, and this may mean that it is initiated by activated oxygen.

It has now been shown that the trimethyl sterol, lanosterol, is a precursor of cholesterol and several closely related sterols have been partially identified

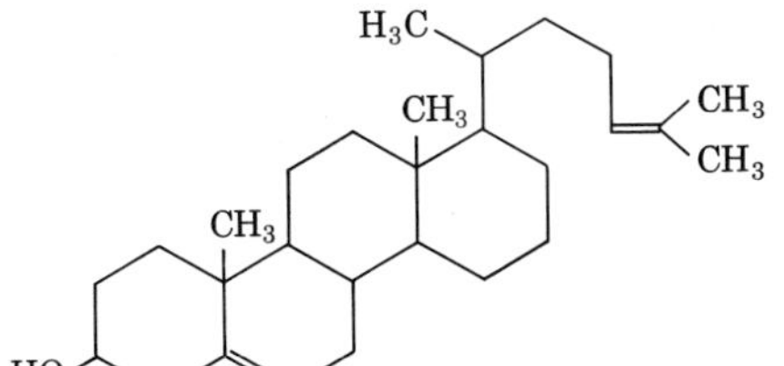

Desmosterol

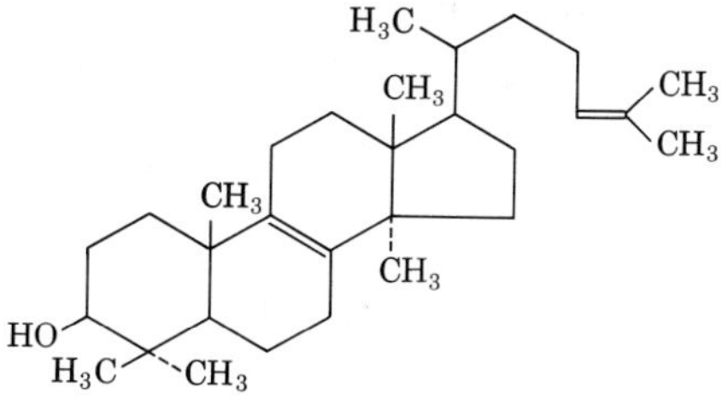

Lanosterol

as intermediates between lanosterol and cholesterol. There is evidence that the methyl groups which are eliminated are oxidized progressively to alcohol and carboxyl groups with decarboxylation the final step. The desmosterol, for which the formula is given, is one probable intermediate between lanosterol and cholesterol.

At this point then it was possible to outline in a general way the synthesis of cholesterol from acetate, with the understanding that there were many unknown intermediates at both ends of the sequence.

Acetate → → → Squalene → Lanosterol → → Desmosterol → Cholesterol

During 1959 and 1960 the early stages, between acetate and squalene, were clarified. It has been mentioned before (pages 497 and 552) that mevalonic acid is a key intermediate in the synthesis of cholesterol, and that this substance is readily formed in tissues from β-hydroxy-β-methylglutaric acid (HMG). The transformation requires preliminary esterification of HMG with coenzyme A, after which a TPN^+-specific reduction yields mevalonic acid. This reductive step is one of the very small number of biological reactions which are known to be irreversible. The steps between acetate, or acetyl CoA and mevalonic acid may be shown as follows:

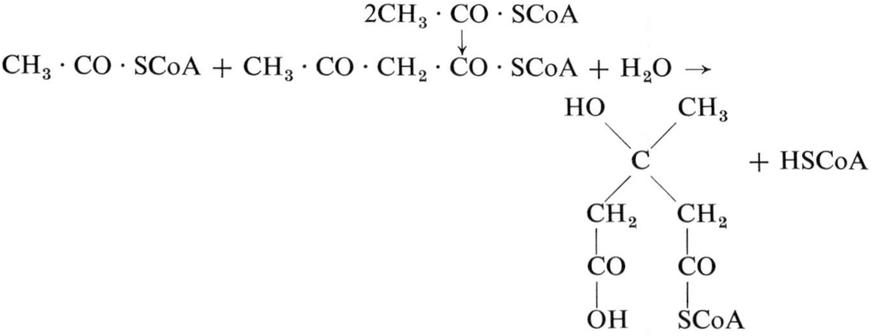

$$2CH_3 \cdot CO \cdot SCoA$$
$$\downarrow$$

$$CH_3 \cdot CO \cdot SCoA + CH_3 \cdot CO \cdot CH_2 \cdot CO \cdot SCoA + H_2O \rightarrow$$

$$
\begin{array}{ccc}
HO & & CH_3 \\
& \diagdown \diagup & \\
& C & + HSCoA \\
& \diagup \diagdown & \\
CH_2 & & CH_2 \\
| & & | \\
CO & & CO \\
| & & | \\
OH & & SCoA
\end{array}
$$

HMG-CoA

It will be remembered that HMG-CoA can be cleaved by liver cells to free acetoacetate. It can likewise be called upon for synthesis of mevalonic acid through reduction of the free carboxyl group.

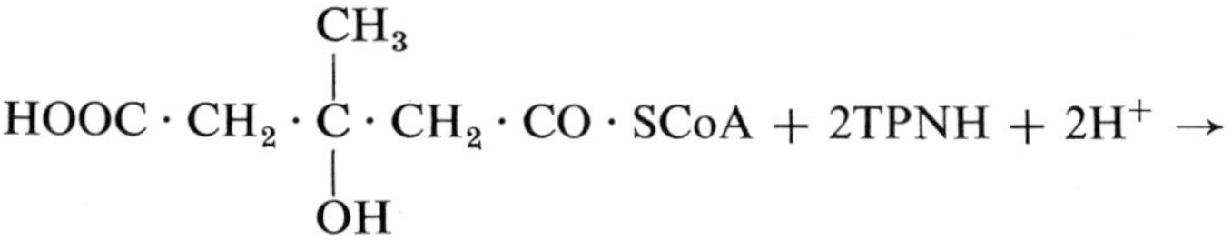

$$
\begin{array}{c}
CH_3 \\
| \\
HOOC \cdot CH_2 \cdot C \cdot CH_2 \cdot CO \cdot SCoA + 2TPNH + 2H^+ \rightarrow \\
| \\
OH
\end{array}
$$

HMG-CoA

$$
\begin{array}{c}
CH_3 \\
| \\
HOCH_2 \cdot CH_2 \cdot C—CH_2COOH + 2TPN^+ + HSCoA \\
| \\
OH
\end{array}
$$

Mevalonic acid

In 1958 and 1959 Lynen elucidated the steps which lie between mevalonic acid and squalene. They involve preliminary formation of phosphate derivatives, and a rather complicated metabolic expedient which is used in other cellular reactions. This begins with two isomeric forms being brought into equilibrium by means of an isomerase, in order that two differently structured molecules may condense to form a larger molecule. Mevalonic acid is first transformed into a pyrophosphate derivative by stepwise transfers of phosphate from ATP. The pyrophosphate then loses water and carbon dioxide

$$
\begin{array}{ccc}
\text{COOH} & & \text{COOH} \\
| & & | \\
\text{CH}_2 & & \text{CH}_2 \\
| & \xrightarrow{\text{2ATP}} & | & \xrightarrow[-\text{H}_2\text{O}]{-\text{CO}_2} \\
\text{H}_3\text{C} \cdot \text{C} \cdot \text{OH} & & \text{CH}_3 \cdot \text{C} \cdot \text{OH} \\
| & & | \\
\text{CH}_2 & & \text{CH}_2 \\
| & & | \\
\text{CH}_2\text{OH} & & \text{CH}_2\text{O} \cdot \text{P} \cdot \text{O} \cdot \text{P}
\end{array}
$$

**Mevalonic acid-
5-pyrophosphate**

$$
\begin{array}{ccc}
\text{CH}_2 & & \text{CH}_3 \\
\| & & | \\
\text{H}_3\text{C} \cdot \text{C} & \underset{\text{isomerase}}{\rightleftharpoons} & \text{H}_3\text{C} \cdot \text{C} \\
| & & \| \\
\text{CH}_2 & & \text{CH} \\
| & & | \\
\text{CH}_2\text{O} \cdot \text{P} \cdot \text{O} \cdot \text{P} & & \text{CH}_2\text{O} \cdot \text{P} \cdot \text{O} \cdot \text{P}
\end{array}
$$

**Δ^3-Isopentenyl
pyrophosphate**   **γ,γ-Dimethylallyl
pyrophosphate**

to form the first substance with an isoprene structure, Δ^3-isopentenyl pyrophosphate. Part of this isomerizes to shift the double bond to the Δ^2 position, thus providing two molecules each with high energy pyrophosphate bonds. These interact to form geranyl pyrophosphate, with elimination of one pyrophosphate group.

$$
\begin{array}{cc}
\text{CH}_3 \cdot \text{C}{=}\text{CH} \cdot \text{CH}_2 \cdot \text{O} \cdot \text{PP} + \text{CH}_2{=}\text{C} \cdot \text{CH}_2 \cdot \text{CH}_2\text{O} \cdot \text{PP} \rightarrow \\
\quad | \qquad\qquad\qquad\qquad\qquad | \\
\quad \text{CH}_3 \qquad\qquad\qquad\qquad\quad \text{CH}_3
\end{array}
$$

$$
\begin{array}{c}
\text{CH}_3 \cdot \text{C}{=}\text{CH} \cdot \text{CH}_2 \cdot \text{CH}_2 \cdot \text{C}{=}\text{CH} \cdot \text{CH}_2\text{O} \cdot \text{PP} + \text{PP} \\
\quad | \qquad\qquad\qquad\qquad\quad | \\
\quad \text{CH}_3 \qquad\qquad\qquad\quad \text{CH}_3
\end{array}
$$

Geranyl pyrophosphate

Interaction of geranyl pyrophosphate with a second molecule of isopentenyl pyrophosphate adds another isoprene unit to form farnesyl pyrophosphate, which had previously been shown to be an intermediate in squalene synthesis.

$$
\begin{array}{ccc}
\text{CH}_3 & \text{CH}_3 & \text{CH}_3 \\
| & | & | \\
\text{CH}_3\text{C}{=}\text{CH} \cdot \text{CH}_2 \cdot \text{CH}_2 \cdot \text{C}{=}\text{CH} \cdot \text{CH}_2 \cdot \text{CH}_2 \cdot \text{C}{=}\text{CH} \cdot \text{CH}_2\text{O} \cdot \text{PP}
\end{array}
$$

Farnesyl pyrophosphate

This compound with its fifteen carbons is just half a squalene molecule, which would result if two molecules united through the carbons which hold the pyrophosphate groups. This is a complicated reaction which involves removal of both pyrophosphates and its mechanism has not yet been clarified, except that it requires the presence of TPNH.

$$2 \text{ Farnesyl pyrophosphate} \xrightarrow{\text{TPNH}} \text{Squalene} + 2\text{PP}$$

It was noted above that the isoprene structure exhibited by squalene is characteristic of a number of important plant products. Of these rubber is the best known. This compound is estimated to contain many thousand isoprene units and is known to use acetate as a precursor. Thus it seems likely that the synthetic pathway for rubber begins with the transformations just outlined. The same might be said of the large group of plant derivatives known as terpenes, two members of which are the geraniol and farnesol referred to above. The terpenes are essentially hydrocarbons, straight chain or cyclic, for which Ruzicka[5] formulated the "isoprene rule" several years ago. This called attention to the fact that the carbon skeletons of these compounds, diverse as they appear at first sight, can all be considered polyisoprenes in which the units are either united "head to tail" as in geraniol, or "head to head" as in the center of the squalene molecule. This rule is now sometimes called the "biogenetic isoprene rule" and Popják writing about it in 1958 made the following comment: "It is a remarkable feature of this hypothesis that after certain well-defined assumptions are made, all the known C_{30} cyclic triterpenes and lanosterol may be derived with their full structural and configurational details from an all *trans*-squalene." The formulas of two of the cyclic terpenes are given below.

Camphor   **Menthol**

---

[5] Leopold Ruzicka (1887–) is Professor of Chemistry at the Federal Institute of Technology in Zurich. In 1939 he was awarded the Nobel Prize in Chemistry. His field has been pure organic chemistry.

A second group of compounds which are structurally related to isoprene is the carotenoid group. These include many colored plant products of which the three compounds known as α-, β- and γ-carotene ($C_{40}H_{56}$) and the A vitamins have a special importance in nutrition. The formula of β-carotene is given below. The other two carotenes are like this except for slight changes in the region marked ring II.

β-Carotene

The fat-soluble A vitamins seem to serve diverse functions, most of which cannot be described in chemical terms, though these and other fat-soluble vitamins are believed to be integral parts of the tissue lipoproteins. As a precursor of the photosensitive pigment rhodopsin, β-carotene is concerned with prevention of night blindness and perhaps with other visual events. The visual pigments are conjugated proteins in which a carotenoid known as retinine acts as prosthetic group. The immediate precursor of retinine is vitamin A_1 which, as its formula indicates, is just half a carotene molecule.

Vitamin A₁

The possibilities for geometrical isomerism in this unsaturated compound mean that there are several forms of vitamin A, of which the one known as A_1 is an all trans isomer. Before its transformation to retinine the arrangement at carbons 4 and 5 is isomerized to a cis form. Oxidation of this isomer yields the corresponding aldehyde which is the retinine known as neoretinine-*b*.

In green plants carotenoids occur in close association with chlorophyll, and are believed to play a part in the photosynthetic process. It has been shown that β-carotene is synthesized from labeled acetate, that the distribution of the label is similar to that found in squalene from the same precursor and that mevalonic acid is an intermediate. All the evidence therefore points to mevalonic acid as the source of the isoprene units in β-carotene and presumptively in other carotenoids. That this acid can be derived from proteins as well as from acetate is emphasized by recent work showing that labeled leucine is incorporated into carotene by the mold *Phycomyces*

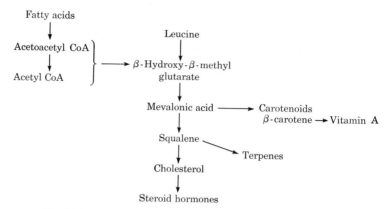

Fig. 14.5. Biosynthetic pathways to the isoprenoid compounds.

blakesleeanus. The fundamental importance of this biosynthetic pathway is summarized in Fig. 14.5.

SUGGESTIONS FOR FURTHER READING

General

Deuel, H. J., Jr., *The Lipids*, 3 vols., Interscience, New York, 1951–1957.

Lovern, J. A., *Chemistry of Lipids of Biochemical Significance*, 2nd ed., Methuen, London, 1957.

Stumpf, P. K., and C. Bradbeer, Fat metabolism in higher plants, *Ann. Rev. Plant Physiol.*, *10*, 197 (1959).

Lipoproteins

The book by Lovern, *op. cit.*, has a good discussion of these complexes and the experimental problems they pose.

Green, C., *et al.*, Lipid composition of lipoproteins of normal human plasma, *J. Biol. Chem.*, *235*, 2884 (1960).

Nelson, G. J., and N. K. Freeman, . . . Composition of human serum lipoprotein fractions, *J. Biol. Chem.*, *235*, 578 (1960).

Rodbell, M., Removal and metabolism of chylomicrons by adipose tissue *in vitro*, *J. Biol. Chem.*, *235*, 1613 (1960).

Oxidation of Fatty Acids

Green, D. E., and S. Mii, Fatty acid oxidation with soluble enzymes from animal tissues, *Federation Proc.*, *12*, 211 (1953).

Green, D. E., *et al.*, Butyryl coenzyme A dehydrogenase, *J. Biol. Chem.*, *206*, 1 (1954).

Kaziro, Y., *et al.*, Metabolism of propionic acid in animal tissues, *J. Biol. Chem.*, *236*, 1917 (1961).

Kennedy, E. P., Metabolism of lipides, *Ann. Rev. Biochem.*, *26*, 119 (1957).

Knoop, F., Catabolism of aromatic fatty acids in the animal body, *Beitr. chem. Physiol. u. Pathol.*, *6*, 150 (1905).

Krebs, H. A., Physiological role of the ketone bodies, *Biochem. J.*, *80*, 225 (1961).

Lynen, F., Lipide metabolism, *Ann. Rev. Biochem.*, *24*, 653 (1955).

Williamson, J. R., and H. A. Krebs, Acetoacetate as fuel of respiration in the perfused rat heart, *Biochem. J.*, *80*, 540 (1961).

Triglyceride Synthesis

Hanahan, D. J., *et al.*, *J. Biol. Chem.*, *235*, 1917 (1960), discusses this synthesis.

Kennedy, E. P., *Ann. Rev. Biochem.*, *26*, 119 (1957).

Weiss, S. B., *et al.*, Enzymatic synthesis of triglycerides, *J. Biol. Chem.*, *235*, 40 (1960).

Phospholipids

Agranoff, B. W., *et al.*, Enzymatic synthesis of inositol phosphatide, *J. Biol. Chem.*, *233*, 1077 (1958).

Brady, R. O., *et al.*, Enzymatic synthesis of sphingosine, *J. Biol. Chem.*, *233*, 1072 (1958).

Hanahan, D. J., *et al.*, Site of attack of phospholipase A on lecithin, *J. Biol. Chem.*, *235*, 1917 (1960).

Kiyasu, J. Y., and E. P. Kennedy, Enzymatic synthesis of plasmalogens, *J. Biol. Chem.*, *235*, 2590 (1960).

Paulus, H., and E. P. Kennedy, Enzymatic synthesis of inositol monophosphatide, *J. Biol. Chem.*, *235*, 1303 (1960).

Fatty Acid Synthesis

Brady, R. O., *et al.*, Biosynthesis of fatty acids, *J. Biol. Chem.*, *235*, 3093, 3099 (1960).

Bressler, R., and S. J. Wakil, Conversion of malonyl coenzyme A to long chain fatty acids, *J. Biol. Chem*, *236*, 1643 (1961).

Formica, J. V., and R. O. Brady, Enzymatic carboxylation of acetyl coenzyme A, *J. Am. Chem. Soc.*, *81*, 752 (1959).

Hornung, M. G., *et al.*, Enzymatic synthesis of branched chain and odd-numbered fatty acids (in adipose tissue), *J. Biol. Chem.*, *236*, 669 (1961).

Martin, D. B., *et al.*, Purification and properties of a long chain fatty acid-synthesizing system (from adipose tissue), *J. Biol. Chem.*, *236*, 663 (1961).

Popják, G., *et al.*, Mode of formation of milk fatty acids from acetate in the goat, *Biochem. J.*, *48*, 612 (1951).

Stumpf, P. K., Lipid metabolism, *Ann. Rev. Biochem.*, *29*, 261 (1960).

Wakil, S. J., A malonic acid derivative as an intermediate in fatty acid synthesis, *J. Am. Chem. Soc.*, *80*, 6465 (1958).

Wakil, S. J., *et al.*, Synthesis of fatty acids by mitochondria, *J. Biol. Chem.*, *235*, PC31 (1960).

Desaturation of Fatty Acids

Bloomfield, D. K., and K. Bloch, Formation of Δ^9-unsaturated fatty acids, *J. Biol. Chem.*, *235*, 337 (1960).

Fulco, A. J., and J. F. Mead, Biosynthesis of octadecadienoic acids of the rat, *J. Biol. Chem.*, *235*, 3379 (1960).

Howton, D. R., and J. F. Mead, Conversion of 8,11,14-eicosatrienoic acid to arachidonic acid in the rat, *J. Biol. Chem.*, *235*, 3385 (1960).

Lennarz, W. J., and K. Bloch, Hydroxystearic acids and the biosynthesis of un-saturated fatty acids, *J. Biol. Chem.*, *235*, PC26 (1960).

Biosynthesis of Steroids and Related Compounds

Agranoff, B. W., *et al.*, Isopentenyl pyrophosphate isomerase, *J. Biol. Chem.*, *235*, 326 (1960). Contains a good discussion of the reactions from acetate to squalene.

Bergström, S., *et al.*, Metabolism of bile acids in python and constrictor snakes, *J. Biol. Chem.*, *235*, 983 (1960). Has a good discussion of bile acid formation.

Braithwaite, G. D., and T. W. Goodwin, Incorporation of [^{14}C] acetate, [^{14}C] mevalonate and $^{14}CO_2$ into β-carotene by a fungus . . . , *Biochem. J.*, *76*, 5 (1960).

Durr, I. F., and H. Rudney, Reduction of β-hydroxy-β-methylglutaryl coenzyme A to mevalonic acid, *J. Biol. Chem.*, *235*, 2572 (1960).

Kandutsch, A. A., and A. E. Russell, A metabolic pathway from lanosterol to cholesterol, *J. Biol. Chem.*, *235*, 2256 (1960).

Lynen, F., *et al.*, Biosynthesis of terpenes. III. *Angew. Chem.*, *70*, 738 (1958); VI. *ibid.*, *71*, 657 (1959).

Popják, G., *et al.*, Mechanism of squalene biosynthesis from farnesyl pyrophosphate and from mevalonate, *J. Biol. Chem.*, *236*, 1934 (1961).

Popják, G., and J. W. Cornforth, Biosynthesis of cholesterol, *Advances in Enzymol.*, *22*, 281 (1960).

Pudles, J., and K. Bloch, Conversion of 4-hydroxymethylene-Δ^7-cholesten-3-one to cholesterol, *J. Biol. Chem.*, *235*, 3417 (1960).

Rudney, H., and J. J. Ferguson, Biosynthesis of β-hydroxy-β-methylglutaryl coenzyme A, *J. Am. Chem. Soc.*, *79*, 5580 (1957).

Samuelsson, B., Mechanism of the biological formation of deoxycholic acid from cholic acid, *J. Biol. Chem.*, *235*, 361 (1960).

Steinberg, D., and J. Avigan, Role of desmosterol in biosynthesis of cholesterol, *J. Biol. Chem.*, *235*, 3127 (1960).

Stokes, W. M., and W. A. Fish, Occurrence of desmosterol (24-dehydrocholesterol) in rat liver, *J. Biol. Chem.*, *235*, 2604 (1960).

Wells, W. W., and C. L. Lorah, Conversion of synthetic methostenol-4-C^{14} to cholesterol, *J. Biol. Chem.*, *235*, 978 (1960).

There is no good evidence that in any of its manifestations life evades the second law of thermodynamics, but in the downward course of the energy-flow it interposes a barrier and dams up a reservoir which provides potential for its own remarkable activities.

F. G. HOPKINS (1933)

Carbohydrate metabolism 15

G LUCOSE WAS ONE OF THE FIRST SUBSTANCES for which it was proved that its metabolism follows nearly identical paths in a wide variety of plant, animal, and microbial cells. The degradation of glucose to carbon dioxide and water involves a series of individual reactions which may be classified for convenience in two groups. As a result of the reactions which constitute the first stage, each molecule of glucose yields two of pyruvate if the cell is metabolizing under normal aerobic conditions. In the second stage the pyruvate is oxidized to carbon dioxide and water by way of the citric acid cycle. However, if the cell is metabolizing anaerobically the pyruvate is not oxidized but, depending upon the catalysts available, may yield one of several possible derivatives, among them lactic acid or ethyl alcohol. It is with the reactions which take place under anaerobic conditions that the first part of the present chapter is concerned. The experimental evidence cited was obtained largely in work with muscle, but the chemical events which this work elucidated are of very nearly universal significance.

ANAEROBIC CARBOHYDRATE METABOLISM

Beginning in the early years of the twentieth century there were prosecuted two distinct lines of inquiry into anaerobic carbohydrate metabolism. That these two would ultimately prove to be two phases of a single problem could not possibly have been foreseen. The commercial importance of brewing led to a study of the chemistry of alcohólic fermentation by yeast, the process in which glucose or other monose is degraded almost quantitatively to alcohol and carbon dioxide.

$$C_6H_{12}O_6 \rightarrow 2CO_2 + 2C_2H_5OH$$
Glucose

At the same time the physiologists were concerned with the similar reaction which was believed to yield the energy for muscular contraction, namely the "fermentation" or anaerobic transformation of muscle glycogen to lactic acid.

$$(C_6H_{10}O_5)_n + (n - 1)H_2O \rightarrow 2nCH_3CHOHCOOH$$
Glycogen   **Lactic acid**

It was Pasteur who introduced the use of the term "fermentation" for the anaerobic reactions of living cells, and defined fermentation as "life without oxygen."

From the beginning it was recognized that alcoholic and lactic acid fermentations had one thing in common. Both, from the point of view of utilization of glucose, are wasteful. Pasteur had discovered that, although yeasts could grow and multiply in complete absence of oxygen, they degraded much less glucose when oxygen was available. This glucose-sparing action of oxygen is known as the "Pasteur effect" and is characteristic in greater or less degree of most aerobic cells. It means, of course, that combustion of carbohydrate to carbon dioxide and water makes available to the cells more energy than can be derived from its transformation to such an intermediate product as lactic acid or alcohol.

When glucose is burned in the calorimeter, the loss of free energy amounts to about 686,000 cal per mole ($\Delta F = -686,000$ cal per mole). When a cell oxidizes glucose completely, this energy is made available. We have already seen, in Chapter 11, how it is stored in the form of ATP, which later releases it for a variety of purposes.

When glucose is transformed into alcohol, a large part of the chemical energy of the glucose molecule remains locked up in the alcohol. The change in free energy associated with complete combustion of ethyl alcohol is approximately 317,000 cal per mole, or 634,000 cal for the two moles formed from each mole of glucose. This means that the energy which becomes available to the cell when 1 mole of glucose is fermented to alcohol and carbon dioxide is only 686,000 minus 634,000, or approximately 52,000 cal per mole of glucose. It is therefore evident that in order to obtain a given amount of energy, fermenting cells will have to degrade far more glucose than would be needed under aerobic conditions. But although it seems obvious that less glucose would be needed under aerobic conditions, the mechanism by which the presence of oxygen limits the use of glucose is still not understood.

Muscle as Experimental Material

Muscle has much to recommend it as an experimental material. Certain muscles, such as the sartorius or the gastrocnemius muscles, can be removed from the body uninjured and will, when stimulated, perform amounts of work which are easily measurable, and which can be correlated with the attendant chemical changes.

Muscular tissue consists essentially of bundles of fibers made up of elongated cells highly specialized for contractility. Muscle cells contain about 25 per cent of solid matter, of which roughly four-fifths is protein. Employing different preliminary treatments, two proteins, *actin* and *myosin*, have been extracted from muscle. In the living tissue these two constitute the major part of the protein content, and there is a good deal of evidence that they are there united in a complex known as *actomyosin*. This substance is believed to be the actual contractile unit in the living muscle cell.

Myosin is a typical elongated fibrous protein and might therefore be expected to have the ability to contract as wool does, through a folding or coiling of its carbon chain. Actually it has never been possible to bring about contraction of purified myosin.

Actin makes up 15 to 20 per cent of the total muscle protein and as ordinarily isolated consists of globular molecules known as G-actin. When small amounts of salts are added to its solution, profound and highly anomalous changes take place in its physical properties. These are believed to result from its transformation into a fibrous form. Hence in this state it is known as F-actin. If myosin is added to the solution of F-actin a highly viscous artificial actomyosin results, and this complex does undergo contraction under certain conditions. The ultimate objective in the study of muscle metabolism is the elucidation of the linking of this physical change with the chemical events which accompany or induce it.

Early Work on Muscular Contraction

It had long been known that lactic acid is formed in muscles, but at the turn of the century there was much conflicting evidence both as to the amount of the acid in resting muscle, and as to its relation to contraction. In 1907 Fletcher and Hopkins at Cambridge published the now classical paper which put the study of muscle chemistry on a firm basis. They used frog muscles in pairs, stimulating one and keeping the other under otherwise identical conditions as a control. At the end of an experiment the muscles were suddenly chilled by immersion in ice-cold alcohol. This killed the tissue enzymes so that the subsequent grinding with sand did not give rise to enzymatic changes unrelated to the experiment in hand. Analysis of the alcohol extracts from the paired muscles then showed what chemical changes had taken place as a result of the stimulation. The results were clear-cut and may be summarized as follows:

1. Resting muscle contains only traces of lactic acid.
2. Muscle can contract in an atmosphere of nitrogen, i.e., in complete absence of oxygen.
3. During these anaerobic contractions, lactic acid forms in increasing amounts, reaching a maximum when the fatigued muscle is no longer responsive to stimulation.
4. When a fatigued muscle is allowed to rest in an atmosphere of oxygen, it recovers its irritability, and the lactic acid simultaneously disappears.
5. Stimulation of a muscle in oxygen gives rise to less lactic acid than is formed anaerobically.

In 1920 came the first of Meyerhof's[1] long series of contributions to muscle chemistry. He showed that during stimulation glycogen disappears in amounts equivalent to the lactic acid which forms. At this time the chemical events in muscle might have been outlined in some such scheme as the following:

$$\text{I.} \quad \underset{\textbf{Glycogen}}{(C_6H_{10}O_5)_n} \xrightarrow[\text{contraction}]{\text{anaerobic}} \underset{\textbf{Lactic acid}}{2n\,CH_3CHOH \cdot COOH} \xrightarrow[\text{recovery}]{\text{aerobic}} CO_2 + H_2O$$

It was believed that the first step was the crucial one in which degradation of glycogen to lactic acid furnished the energy for contraction.

In later quantitative experiments with frog muscles Meyerhof measured the oxygen uptake during recovery. He found, to everyone's surprise, that the amount of oxygen used was only about one-quarter to one-fifth of that which would have been needed to oxidize all the lactic acid which disappeared. Furthermore, during recovery the glycogen stores which had been depleted by contraction were reconstituted. From these results Meyerhof concluded that most or all of the lactic acid formed in the muscle during contraction is resynthesized to glycogen during recovery, the necessary energy for this synthesis being obtained by oxidation of something. Since the R.Q. of the reaction was about 1, the "something" might equally well have been glucose or part of the lactic acid, and there was no way to choose between them. At

---

[1] Otto Meyerhof (1884–1951) had had a brilliant career in biochemistry at Berlin and Heidelberg before political events in Germany forced him to seek what proved to be only a temporary refuge as Director of Biochemical Research at the University of Paris. The coming of the Germans in 1940 again drove him into exile, by which biochemistry in the United States has been greatly enriched. As Research Professor of Physiological Chemistry in the School of Medicine of the University of Pennsylvania he directed an active research program until shortly before his death. In 1923 Meyerhof and A. V. Hill of London shared the Nobel Prize in Medicine, awarded for their contributions to muscle chemistry and physiology.

this time the chemical changes in frog muscle were formulated according to the following scheme. The energy for contraction was still believed to come

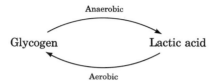

from the anaerobic formation of lactic acid, while the oxidation was explained as a "rewinding of the clock" in which as much of the lactic acid as possible was again raised to the energy level of glycogen. Muscles were said to go into "oxygen debt" when they formed during prolonged contraction amounts of lactic acid which had later to be removed by oxidation.

This simple scheme did not prove to be an accurate description of events in the muscles of higher vertebrates. But it was adapted to their needs by the discovery that in these animals most of the lactic acid formed during contraction diffused into the blood and so was carried back to the liver and there synthesized into glycogen. Thus ultimately the lactic acid might be considered a source of fresh stores of muscle glycogen, since the liver glycogen would furnish glucose to the blood and this in turn might go into the muscle cells as muscle glycogen.

Muscle Extracts

An enormous impetus was given to progress in muscle chemistry by Meyerhof's discovery about 1926 that extraction of ice-cold minced muscle with saline yields an opalescent cell-free solution which contains no oxidizing enzymes, but does include all the enzymes required for the transformation of glycogen to lactic acid. Thus the way was opened for a direct chemical attack upon the problem of the intermediate steps involved in the anaerobic degradation of glycogen.

Dialysis of muscle extract led to its separation into a thermolabile inactive protein part, and what proved ultimately to be a mixture of thermostable coenzymes. Addition of fresh, boiled muscle juice to the inactive protein part restored the activity. By about 1930 Lohmann had shown that the dialyzate contained two essential ions, Mg^{++} and $H_2PO_4^{-}$, and a third substance the importance of which could not have been guessed at that time. This was adenosine triphosphate which has proved to have an importance far beyond its use in carbohydrate metabolism.

The discovery of ATP was not the first hint of the involvement of phosphate in carbohydrate metabolism. As early as 1914 Gustav Embden at the University of Frankfurt had isolated a hexose phosphate mixture from muscle and named it "lactacidogen" to indicate that it was a precursor of lactic acid. It was also known that when muscle extract acts upon glycogen, the concentration of inorganic phosphate falls, and it was believed that this indicated its conversion to a hexose phosphate. Accordingly the dialyzed extract, inactive toward glycogen, was next tested with hexose phosphate as substrate. Under these conditions the extract was able to catalyze formation of lactic acid. This could only mean that the hexose phosphate was an intermediate product between glycogen and lactic acid, and that dialysis had removed from the extract the factors essential to formation of the hexose phosphate from glycogen. Thus the series of events as understood about 1931 might have been formulated as follows:

III. $\text{Glycogen} \xrightarrow[\text{Mg}^{++},\ \text{H}_2\text{PO}_4^-]{\text{ATP}} \text{Hexose phosphate} \rightarrow \text{Lactic acid}$

Iodoacetate Inhibition

And then, just when it seemed that the metabolic path from glycogen to lactic acid might be elucidated, came reports of an experiment which made it seem for a time that lactic acid formation had no vital connection with muscular contraction. Einar Lundsgaard of the University of Copenhagen, working with muscles poisoned with the enzyme inhibitor, iodoacetic acid (CH_2ICOOH), found that although they formed no lactic acid they were still able to contract for a short time. Further investigation showed that the length of time during which isolated muscle remained irritable depended upon the concentration in the muscle of a very labile phosphate compound, *creatine phosphate* or phosphagen.

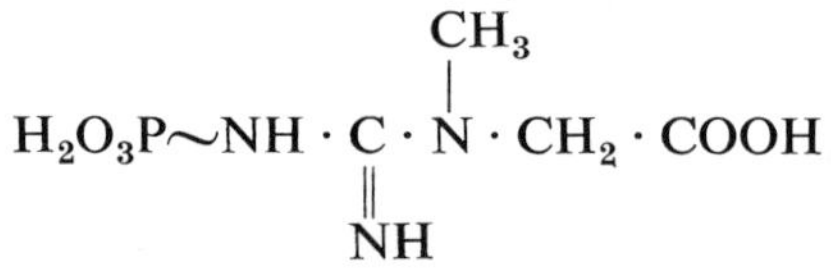

$$H_2O_3P\sim NH \cdot \overset{\displaystyle CH_3}{\underset{\displaystyle \underset{NH}{\|}}{C}} \cdot N \cdot CH_2 \cdot COOH$$

Creatine phosphate

As the formula indicates, this compound is of the energy-rich type, and it might well therefore furnish the energy for contraction as Lundsgaard suggested. But muscles contain also ATP with its high energy content, and this compound was already known to play a part in the carbohydrate metabolism of muscle. For several years there was therefore some disagreement about the roles of these two compounds in muscular contraction. It was the proof of a unique relationship between the muscle protein, myosin, and ATP which led to the present belief that the energy reserves which are called upon at the moment of contraction are probably those of the phosphorylated nucleotide. It was found that the phosphate groups are freely and reversibly transferable between ATP and phosphocreatine, though in this reaction only the terminal phosphate residue of the triphosphate is transferred, leaving adenosine diphosphate.

$$ATP + Creatine \rightleftharpoons ADP + Phosphocreatine$$

It is now believed that when the need arises for energy for contraction it is furnished by a rupture of the terminal phosphate bond of ATP. At this point the presence of a mobile reserve of high energy phosphate in phosphocreatine makes possible the immediate reconstitution of ATP as indicated in the equation. These two compounds will thus keep the contractile machinery in action until the processes of carbohydrate breakdown in the muscle can begin to generate fresh stores of energy.

The fact, referred to above, which relates ATP in a very special way to contraction is as follows: When highly purified myosin is added to ATP it brings about the hydrolytic removal of the terminal phosphate residue. That is to say, it acts as if myosin were the enzyme adenosine triphosphatase, or ATPase. This fact was first noted in 1939 by Engelhardt and Ljubimowa of the Institute of Biochemistry in Moscow, and has since been abundantly confirmed. At the same time there is evidence that ATP exerts a reciprocal influence upon myosin, an influence which brings about an increased coiling of the protein chain. This situation was described by Engelhardt in 1946 as follows: "Myosin can be compared with the piston, and ATP with the explosive mixture of a combustion engine. The ingenuity of nature consists in providing the piston with the properties of the ignition plug as well."

The claim of myosin to be both contracting protein and enzyme protein has not gone unchallenged. Meyerhof, for example, believed that the enzyme is a separate entity adsorbed on the myosin and carried along through the various steps in its purification. But whether they prove to be one substance or two in close association, there is now fairly general agreement that in the living muscle ATP is the substance which initiates the changes in myosin which give rise to contraction. Among the vertebrates the energy needed for the immediate rephosphorylation of ADP is stored as phosphocreatine, but among the invertebrates a similar compound of arginine serves this same purpose. In arginine phosphate there is an energy-rich linkage between phosphorus and nitrogen, as there is in creatine phosphate, and this makes possible

$$H_2O_3P{\sim}NH \cdot C \cdot NH(CH_2)_3CH \cdot COOH$$
$$\underset{\displaystyle NH}{\overset{\displaystyle \|}{}} \qquad \underset{\displaystyle NH_2}{\overset{\displaystyle |}{}}$$

Arginine phosphate

a similar transfer of a phosphate group to ADP, with formation of ATP.

The Glycolytic Sequence

It would be far too time-consuming to continue to follow historically the slow and sometimes faltering steps by which the complex series of reactions

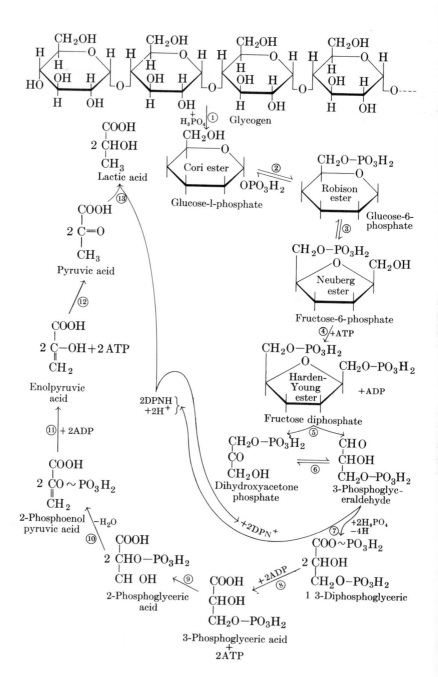

Fig. 15.1. The reactions of the glycolytic sequence.

now known as "glycolysis" or the Embden-Meyerhof sequence was finally brought to light. The methods used were standard ones. Enzyme inhibitors were used to cause one intermediate compound or another to accumulate, as phosphoglyceric acid accumulates in the presence of fluoride, or succinate in the presence of the competitive inhibitor, malonate. In other experiments enzymic reactions were carried out in the presence of a compound which would combine with some intermediate and trap it in a form that could be isolated. This was first done by Carl Neuberg in a study of alcoholic fermentation, when he showed that acetaldehyde was an intermediate by carrying out the fermentation in the presence of sodium bisulfite. The crude muscle extract itself was fractioned again and again by the classical methods of enzyme chemistry until one by one the various specific enzymes had been isolated and concentrated, and many of them crystallized. This all finally led to the realization that at least twelve separate enzymic reactions are involved in the fermentation of glycogen to lactic acid, with as many separate enzymes and a number of coenzymes. The scheme in Fig. 15.1 indicates the sequence of the reactions and the points in the series at which ATP is either used or synthesized. When it is being used, it appears on the arrow. The net result is synthesis of three molecules of ATP for each molecule of glucose metabolized. Actually four new phosphate links are formed, but one of these merely replaces the one which is used early in the sequence. The numbers on the arrows refer to the discussion of the individual steps which follows. It should be noted that biochemists refer rather loosely to a substance as an acid, even when the pH of the medium is such that it is not an acid but its anion which is actually present. This practice is likely to continue as a matter of convenience particularly as several di- and tribasic acids are involved in metabolism. Phosphoric acid, for example, may be present as any one of three ions, depending on the pH of the solution, and referring to it simply as "phosphate" or as "phosphoric acid" avoids having to be specific in situations in which specificity may be impossible or unimportant.

The individual reactions of glycolysis[2]

Reaction 1. $(C_6H_{10}O_5)_n + n\ H_3PO_4 \underset{Mg^{++}}{\overset{\text{phosphorylase}}{\rightleftharpoons}} n$ Glucose-1-phosphate

The first reaction in the sequence was one of the last to be discovered. In 1936 the Coris, Carl and Gerty, announced the isolation from frog muscle of a new phosphate ester which appeared to be a monophosphate. Up to this time the only known monophosphates were esterified with primary

---

[2] The metal ions which are written below the arrows in certain of the equations which follow are essential to the catalytic action of the enzyme involved. Their position does not indicate that they catalyze the reversal of the reaction.

alcohol groups, but the new compound differed from these in being non-reducing, and in giving rise to reducing power when it was hydrolyzed. It proved to be a derivative of glucose with the phosphate residue at carbon 1. It is formed in muscle as a result of *phosphorolysis* of glycogen. In this reaction phosphoric acid acts as water does in hydrolysis, breaking the 1→4

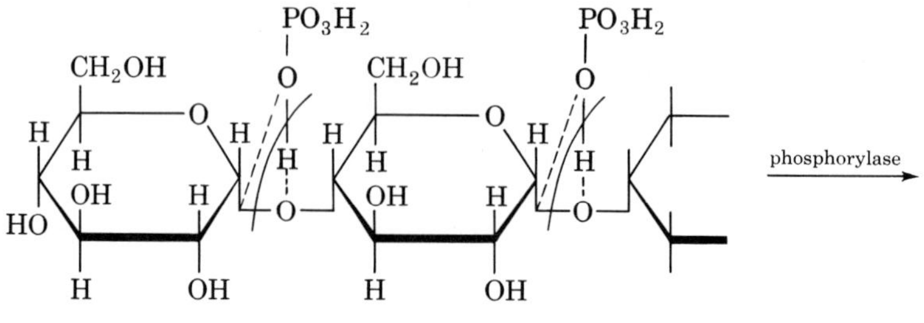

Starch or glycogen

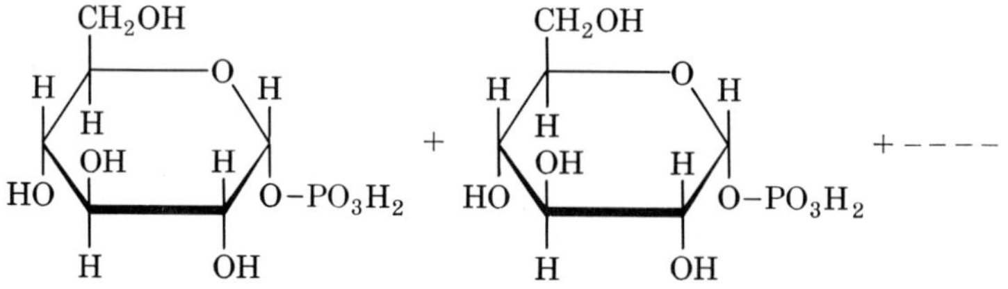

Glucose - 1 - phosphate

bond, contributing a hydrogen to the carbon 4 of one glucose and a phosphate residue to carbon 1 of the other. The *phosphorylase* which catalyzes this degradation has been found in many different animal tissues, while a very similar enzyme from plant tissue brings about phosphorolysis of starch. The enzyme is activated by magnesium ions.

Reaction 2. Glucose-1-phosphate $\underset{\text{glucomutase}}{\overset{\text{phospho-}}{\rightleftarrows}}$ Glucose-6-phosphate

In the presence of *phosphoglucomutase* an equilibrium is established between the two glucose monophosphates. It is strongly in favor of the 6-ester, which makes up nearly 95 per cent of the equilibrium mixture. The mechanism of this shift was clarified when it was discovered that glucose-1,6-diphosphate acts as a coenzyme, by transferring to carbon 6 of the glucose-1-phosphate the phosphate from its own carbon 1. It thus is transformed into glucose-6-phosphate, and the original substrate molecule becomes in its turn a "coenzyme." Thereafter, one by one, each glucose-1-phosphate acts in turn as substrate and as coenzyme, the coenzyme of the moment donating one of its phosphate groups to form whichever of the monoesters is demanded by the equilibrium.

| Coenzyme | Substrate | Product | New coenzyme |

Reaction 3.   Glucose-6-phosphate $\underset{\text{hexomutase}}{\overset{\text{phospho-}}{\rightleftharpoons}}$ Fructose-6-phosphate

The enzyme which catalyzes this shift is also known as *hexose phosphate isomerase*. It is found closely associated with the phosphoglucomutase of Reaction 2, and with a triose phosphate isomerase (see Reaction 6). Nothing is known of the mechanism of this isomerization except that in the presence of the specific enzyme an equilibrium mixture of the two monophosphates is rapidly formed. As indicated on the chart, glucose-6-phosphate is the Robison ester, fructose-6-phosphate is the Neuberg ester, and the equilibrium mixture of the two is known as the Embden ester. It consists of about 70 per cent Robison ester and 30 per cent Neuberg ester.

Reaction 4.   Fructose-6-phosphate + ATP $\xrightarrow[\text{Mg}^{++}]{\text{phosphofructokinase}}$

$$\text{Fructose-1,6-diphosphate + ADP}$$

Those enzymes which catalyze the transfer of a phosphate group from ATP are known collectively as *phosphokinases*. It should be noted that the phosphate ester which forms is not energy-rich, and so this process consists essentially in the squandering of 12,000 cal to produce a 3000-cal linkage. As a result of this great energy difference, this reaction, unlike the previous ones in the sequence, is not directly reversible.

Since it has been necessary at this point to sacrifice a high energy molecule, the present score in terms of ATP synthesis is minus 1.

Reaction 5.   Fructose-1,6-diphosphate $\overset{\text{aldolase}}{\rightleftharpoons}$

$$\text{Dihydroxyacetone phosphate + Glyceraldehyde phosphate}$$

| Fructose - 1, 6 - diphosphate | Dihydroxyacetone phosphate | D - Glyceraldehyde - 3 - phosphate |

Aldolase was first discovered in yeast, but has more recently been crystallized from rabbit muscle. The mechanism of this reaction, in which the carbon chain is split to yield two triose phosphates, is not known. It is not an hydrolysis, but entails migration of two hydrogen atoms and will probably prove to be far more complex than the simple change indicated in the equation.

Reaction 6.　Glyceraldehyde phosphate $\underset{\text{isomerase}}{\overset{\text{phosphotriose}}{\rightleftharpoons}}$

Dihydroxyacetone phosphate

As the triose phosphates form, the attainment of equilibrium is catalyzed by the presence of a specific *isomerase*. As the chart indicates, it is only the glyceraldehyde phosphate which undergoes further reaction in the glycolytic sequence. Consequently if the two triose phosphates were not interconvertible, half of every original glucose molecule would be lost at this point. As a matter of fact the equilibrium between the two three-carbon compounds is very much in favor of the useless ketose phosphate. But in the presence of the isomerase this substance is transformed into the useful aldose derivative as the latter is metabolized, until essentially all the carbon finds its way to the end of the sequence. To indicate this, the latter half of the chart has been written as if two molecules of glyceraldehyde phosphate reacted at this point.

Reaction 7.　3-Phosphoglyceraldehyde $+ H_3PO_4 + DPN^+$ $\underset{\text{hyde dehydrogenase}}{\overset{\text{phosphoglyceralde-}}{\rightleftharpoons}}$

1,3-Diphosphoglyceric acid $+ DPNH + H^+$

Here for the first time the glycolytic sequence is involved in an oxidation. This reaction has now been shown to involve three separate steps. In the first the substrate forms a link with a free sulfhydryl group in the enzyme.

$$
\begin{array}{c}
CH_2O \cdot P \\
| \\
HOCH \\
| \\
CHO
\end{array}
\; + \; HS\!-\!E \; \rightleftharpoons \;
\begin{array}{c}
CH_2O \cdot P \\
| \\
HOCH \\
| \\
CHOH \cdot S\!-\!E
\end{array}
$$

This complex then transfers two hydrogens to DPN^+.

$$
\begin{array}{c}
CH_2O \cdot P \\
| \\
HOCH \\
| \\
CHOH \cdot S\!-\!E
\end{array}
\; + \; DPN^+ \; \rightleftharpoons \;
\begin{array}{c}
CH_2O \cdot P \\
| \\
HOCH \\
| \\
CO \cdot S\!-\!E
\end{array}
\; + \; DPNH + H^+
$$

Finally the oxidized enzyme-substrate compound reacts with phosphate, replacing the enzyme by a phosphate radical and freeing the enzyme. As shown in the formula, the new diphosphate is an energy-rich compound.

$$
\begin{array}{ccc}
CH_2O \cdot P & & CH_2O \cdot P \\
| & & | \\
HOCH & + H_3PO_4 \leftrightharpoons HOCH & + HS{-}E \\
| & & | \\
CO \cdot S{-}E & & CO \cdot O{\sim}P
\end{array}
$$

1,3-Diphosphoglyceric acid

In this seventh step of the glycolytic sequence the reduced DPNH is not immediately reoxidized. At this point then the cell has achieved two newly synthesized high energy molecules in the form of diphosphoglyceric acid, and has on its hands two molecules of DPNH.

Reaction 8.   1,3-Diphosphoglyceric acid + ADP $\underset{\text{kinase}}{\overset{\text{phosphoglycerate}}{\rightleftarrows}}$

ATP + 3-Phosphoglyceric acid

Having now two energy-rich molecules available, the cell is able to transfer phosphate groups to ADP and thus to achieve the synthesis of the first two molecules of ATP. This is one of the two examples in the glycolytic sequence of substrate level phosphate transfer. The cell has now ceased to be a debtor, so to speak, having paid back the energy it borrowed in Reaction 4, and synthesized in addition an extra molecule of ATP.

Reaction 9.   3-Phosphoglyceric acid $\underset{\text{mutase}}{\overset{\text{phosphoglycero-}}{\rightleftarrows}}$ 2-Phosphoglyceric acid

This reaction is exactly analogous to Reaction 2, and the "shift" in the position of the phosphate group is brought about in the same way. The substance which acts as a coenzyme is 2,3-diphosphoglyceric acid, and all the substrate molecules go through a stage in which they act as a coenzyme for others.

$$
\begin{array}{cccc}
COOH & COOH & COOH & COOH \\
| & | & | & | \\
HCO \cdot P & + HCOH & \leftrightharpoons HCO \cdot P & + HCO \cdot P \\
| & | & | & | \\
CH_2O \cdot P & CH_2O \cdot P & CH_2OH & CH_2O \cdot P \\
\textbf{Coenzyme} & \textbf{Substrate} & \textbf{Product} & \textbf{New coenzyme}
\end{array}
$$

Reaction 10.   2-Phosphoglyceric acid $\underset{Mg^{++}}{\overset{\text{enolase}}{\rightarrow}}$

2-Phosphoenolpyruvic acid + H_2O

In the removal of water from 2-phosphoglyceric acid a high energy compound is formed. The enzyme *enolase* achieves maximum activity only in the the presence of magnesium ion.

$$\begin{array}{c} COOH \\ | \\ H\overset{|}{C}O \cdot P \\ | \\ CH_2OH \end{array} \rightleftharpoons \begin{array}{c} COOH \\ | \\ CO{\sim}P \\ \| \\ CH_2 \end{array} + H_2O$$

Phosphoenolpyruvic acid

Reaction 11.   2-Phosphoenolpyruvic acid $+$ ADP $\xrightleftharpoons[\text{kinase, K}^+]{\text{pyruvate phospho-}}$

Enolpyruvic acid $+$ ATP

Again the generation of an energy-rich compound is followed by transfer of phosphate to ADP, thus adding two more molecules of ATP to the one already formed. The phosphokinase which catalyzes this transfer requires the presence of potassium ion.

$$\begin{array}{c} COOH \\ | \\ CO{\sim}P \\ \| \\ CH_2 \end{array} + ADP \rightleftharpoons \begin{array}{c} COOH \\ | \\ C \cdot OH \\ \| \\ CH_2 \end{array} + ATP$$

Enolpyruvic acid

Reaction 12.   Enolpyruvic acid $\rightleftharpoons$ Ketopyruvic acid

This reaction probably takes place spontaneously.

$$\begin{array}{c} COOH \\ | \\ C \cdot OH \\ \| \\ CH_2 \end{array} \rightleftharpoons \begin{array}{c} COOH \\ | \\ CO \\ | \\ CH_3 \end{array}$$

Ketopyruvic acid

Reaction 13.   Pyruvic acid $+$ DPNH $+$ H$^+$ $\xrightleftharpoons[\text{dehydrogenase}]{\text{lactic}}$ Lactic acid $+$ DPN$^+$

The *lactic dehydrogenase* which catalyzes this reversible reaction was discovered many years ago in experiments in which lactic acid as substrate was oxidized to pyruvic acid. Hence at this point, under anaerobic conditions pyruvic acid is able to reoxidize the reduced coenzyme formed in Reaction 7. Thus lactic acid is formed and the coenzyme is again ready to accept hydrogens from another molecule of glyceraldehyde phosphate.

Significance of the glycolytic sequence

Although glycolysis has been presented here in its historical setting as if it were a device to provide energy for muscular contraction, it should be remembered that this same series of reactions takes place in virtually every sort of aerobic cell. It is then the major chemical pathway by which glucose is prepared for complete oxidation, an end which is achieved when, as two molecules of pyruvate, all six carbons of glucose enter the citric acid cycle.

But let us return for a moment to some of the questions raised in connection with muscular contraction. The formation of lactic acid has of course no such significance as the original workers in the field assigned to it. It is simply a by-product which is formed when some of the pyruvate has to be diverted from the oxidative path to reoxidize the reduced coenzyme formed in Reaction 7. Normally the muscles are well supplied with oxygen, both through the agency of the circulating blood, and through their possession of a special store of oxygen in myoglobin, or muscle hemoglobin, found in all red muscle. If muscular contraction is not too violent, this is probably sufficient to keep the coenzyme in the oxidized form through transfer of hydrogen to the cytochromes. Under these conditions the pyruvate enters the citric acid cycle and no lactic acid is formed. On the other hand, blood lactic acid does rise quite spectacularly during violent exercise. This means that under those circumstances part of the pyruvate is requisitioned to reoxidize the rapidly forming DPNH. This gives rise to lactic acid, thus completing the anaerobic cycle for some fraction of the carbohydrate being metabolized. When this happens, the muscle is said to have gone into oxygen debt, since at the end of the contractions oxygen will be needed for direct or indirect reoxidation of the excess lactic acid.

It will be remembered that resting muscle contains both ATP and creatine phosphate, the latter, as a matter of fact, in higher concentration. The sequence of events during contraction may then be outlined as follows:

Preformed ATP furnishes the energy for the initial contractions and is itself split to ADP and inorganic phosphate.

At first this ADP is rephosphorylated at the expense of the stored creatine phosphate.

During moderate activity the glycolytic sequence and the citric acid cycle furnish all the ATP which is needed for contraction.

Following contraction, these two processes continue until both the ADP and the creatine in the muscle have been phosphorylated. Thus at the end of the recovery period they are both ready to deal with the next stimulation of the muscle.

It should be noted that in this, and indeed many other processes which use ATP, it is only the terminal phosphate group which is removed. In other reactions, however, two phosphate residues may be split out as pyrophosphate, leaving AMP. Very occasionally a reaction is encountered in which all three phosphate groups are removed. This means that the structure of ATP makes it possible for the cell to use its energy in many different ways.

Alcoholic Fermentation

Chemical studies of alcoholic fermentation began in 1897 with the classical discovery of Eduard Buchner that cell-free yeast extracts were able to bring about fermentation of sugar. During the next twenty years a long series of papers on fermentation came from Buchner's laboratory, overlapping in time the studies on the same subject by Arthur Harden and his collaborators in London and by Carl Neuberg in Berlin. These three carried out or directed much of the most important early work in the field. The basic reaction may be simplified to

$$C_6H_{12}O_6 \rightarrow 2C_2H_5OH + 2CO_2$$

As the chemical changes in fermentation were slowly elucidated, it began to appear that they involved many of the same substances which take part in the chemical events in muscle. Ultimately it was proved that step for step, in nearly every detail, the chemical reactions leading to ethyl alcohol are identical with those by which lactic acid is formed. At only two points do the two sequences diverge.

If the yeast is acting upon starch, the initial stage is a phosphorolysis of the polysaccharide which yields glucose-1-phosphate exactly as in the analogous breakdown of glycogen. From glucose-1-phosphate, the 6-ester is formed as in muscle. But yeast, like many types of animal cells, can also use glucose as substrate and under these conditions the glycolytic sequence is initiated by a reaction which has no counterpart in muscle metabolism. With glucose as substrate the first step, catalyzed by the enzyme *hexokinase*, brings about transfer of a phosphate group from ATP directly to carbon 6 of glucose.

$$\text{Glucose} + \text{ATP} \xrightarrow{\text{hexokinase}} \text{Glucose-6-phosphate} + \text{ADP}$$

Here a low energy compound is formed at the cost of an energy-rich one. Thus, in terms of triphosphate synthesis, glucose is a less efficient substrate than starch or glycogen.

The intermediate stages between glucose-6-phosphate and pyruvic acid are identical in alcoholic and in lactic acid fermentation. But when pyruvic acid has formed, the two paths of anaerobic metabolism diverge for the second time. The yeast cell contains an enzyme, α-carboxylase, which splits out carbon dioxide from pyruvate, forming acetaldehyde.

$$\text{CH}_3\text{CO} \cdot \text{COOH} \xrightarrow[\text{cocarboxylase, Mg}^{++}]{\text{α-carboxylase}} \text{CH}_3\text{CHO} + \text{CO}_2$$

As the equation indicates, the carboxylase is active only in the presence of a coenzyme. This is the thiamine pyrophosphate which was discussed in connection with the early steps in the citric acid cycle, and which was named cocarboxylase when it was first discovered in work with alcoholic fermentation.

In the series of reactions which lead to the formation of alcohol it is the acetaldehyde formed from pyruvate which is used anaerobically to reoxidize the reduced coenzyme from Reaction 7.

$$\text{CH}_3\text{CHO} + \text{DPNH} + \text{H}^+ \underset{\text{dehydrogenase}}{\overset{\text{alcohol}}{\rightleftharpoons}} \text{CH}_3\text{CH}_2\text{OH} + \text{DPN}^+$$

Since the last two equations must be multiplied by 2 to account for the 2 molecules of pyruvate which were formed, this equation indicates that 2 moles of alcohol are formed and 2 of carbon dioxide freed from each mole of glucose metabolized by the yeast. This is in accord with the known quantitative relations in yeast fermentation.

The fact that the enzyme which brings about reduction of acetaldehyde is labeled "alcohol dehydrogenase" should cause no difficulty. This enzyme, like lactate dehydrogenase, was first discovered in early experiments with the Thunberg technique. It happens that with this particular dehydrogenase the equilibrium point is far to the side of reduction (see page 397). The scheme below outlines the steps which are characteristic of the main fermentation reactions of yeast.

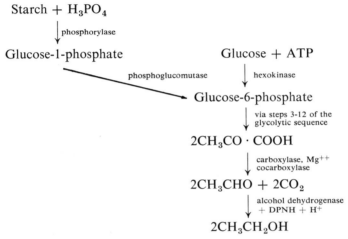

$$\text{Starch} + \text{H}_3\text{PO}_4$$

phosphorylase

$$\text{Glucose-1-phosphate} \qquad \text{Glucose} + \text{ATP}$$

phosphoglucomutase   hexokinase

$$\text{Glucose-6-phosphate}$$

via steps 3-12 of the glycolytic sequence

$$2\text{CH}_3\text{CO} \cdot \text{COOH}$$

carboxylase, Mg^{++} cocarboxylase

$$2\text{CH}_3\text{CHO} + 2\text{CO}_2$$

alcohol dehydrogenase + DPNH + H^+

$$2\text{CH}_3\text{CH}_2\text{OH}$$

By-products of alcoholic fermentation

Although the reactions just outlined describe the main events in alcoholic fermentation, it was recognized very early that other products are always formed in small amounts. The chief of these are glycerol and acetic acid, with smaller amounts of succinic acid and of various alcohols. By controlling the conditions under which fermentation takes place it is sometimes possible to increase the yield of one by-product or another. For example, in an alkaline medium the yield of the trihydric alcohol, glycerol, is greatly increased. This is believed to arise from the fact that in alkaline solution the labile glyceraldehyde phosphate undergoes a *dismutation* in which one molecule of the aldehyde is oxidized at the expense of the other. As shown in the equations, this is brought about as a pair of separate reactions, linked through their use of the same coenzyme. The first of the two reactions is of course Reaction 7 of the glycolytic sequence. The use of DPNH to reduce glyceraldehyde prevents its use in reduction of acetaldehyde and so diverts part of the triose phosphate to the synthesis of glycerol.

$$\begin{matrix} CH_2O \cdot P \\ | \\ CHOH \\ | \\ CHO \end{matrix} + DPN^+ + H_2PO_4^- \rightarrow \begin{matrix} CH_2O \cdot P \\ | \\ CHOH \\ | \\ CO \cdot O \sim P \end{matrix} + DPNH + H^+$$

$$\begin{matrix} CH_2O \cdot P \\ | \\ CHOH \\ | \\ CHO \end{matrix} + DPNH + H^+ \rightarrow \begin{matrix} CH_2O \cdot P \\ | \\ CHOH \\ | \\ CH_2OH \\ + \\ DPN^+ \end{matrix} \xrightarrow[\text{phosphatase}]{+H_2O} \begin{matrix} CH_2OH \\ | \\ CHOH \\ | \\ CH_2OH \\ \textbf{Glycerol} \end{matrix} + P$$

To account for the formation of all the various by-products of fermentation would take us too far afield. In view of the reactivity of acetaldehyde and of pyruvic acid, to mention only two substances in the complex reaction mixture, it should be easy to understand that they alone might well give rise to a number of different products. Furthermore, in the living yeast other reactions than those of carbohydrate metabolism are going forward simultaneously. The cell therefore has available also the products of amino acid and of fatty acid catabolism, and these, too, may interact with each other or with members of the carbohydrate sequence. Thus there are formed a number of substances in trace amounts, including the various alcohols to which are due the special aromas and flavors of different wines.

Glycolytic Sequence in Plants

It is generally believed that utilization of carbohydrates by plant cells follows the pathways just outlined for animal tissues and for yeasts. There have been attempts to find evidence for direct oxidative attack on hexose molecules and indeed the molds *Aspergillus niger* and *Penicillium notatum* have yielded a *glucose oxidase* which catalyzes the direct oxidation of glucose to gluconic acid. But this reaction is probably of limited importance, with the bulk of the carbohydrate in normal healthy plant cells being metabolized by way of the glycolytic sequence followed by oxidation of the pyruvic acid.

The chief reserve substrates of plant respiration are starch and sucrose, both of which are related as indicated below to glucose-1-phosphate. Plant tissues have yielded both a phosphorylase which brings about phosphorolysis of starch and also a specific sucrose phosphorylase.

Starch + H_3PO_4 Sucrose + H_3PO_4

glucosan phosphorylase   sucrose phosphorylase

Glucose-1-phosphate + Fructose

Thus from the two common storage carbohydrates a phosphorylated hexose can be formed without the use of any high energy phosphate compound. There is now a good deal of evidence that plants metabolize this glucose-1-phosphate by the familiar glycolytic pathway. Various phosphorylated intermediates have been isolated, and many of the individual enzymatic reactions have been demonstrated in cell free plant extracts. Pyruvate has been identified as a product of plant enzymes acting on phosphoglycerate. These and many similar facts all point to the probability that the higher plants possess the enzymatic machinery to bring about glycolysis of sugars and polysaccharides with formation of pyruvate.

It has long been known that under anaerobic conditions plants can bring about alcoholic fermentation with evolution of carbon dioxide. This presumably results from decarboxylation of part at least of the pyruvic acid, with subsequent reduction of the acetaldehyde. Whether another part of the pyruvate is reduced to lactic acid under these conditions is not definitely known. However, since lactic dehydrogenase is known to be present in many plant cells, it seems likely that they can also reoxidize reduced coenzyme with pyruvic acid, thus forming small amounts of lactic acid.

THE PENTOSE PHOSPHATE PATHWAY

Although all evidence points to the major importance of the glycolytic pathway in the utilization of glucose, it should not be surprising that alternative metabolic sequences exist. One of these is the series of reactions which has been called the "hexose monophosphate shunt" or the "glucose-6-phosphate oxidation system" or the "pentose phosphate pathway." The enzymes for this sequence have been obtained from a wide variety of plant, animal, and bacterial cells. The sequence is characterized by the use of TPN^+ as hydrogen acceptor, by the fact that carbon dioxide is formed directly from carbon 1 of glucose and by a type of enzymatic reaction which has not been considered before. This type of reaction is catalyzed by enzymes which are known as *transketolases* and *transaldolases*, which bring about transfer from one monose phosphate to another of two or three carbons from the reducing end of a molecule. The reaction of a ketolase may be represented in general terms as follows:

$$
\begin{array}{ccccc}
\text{CH}_2\text{OH} & & & \text{CH}_2\text{OH} \\
| & & & | \\
\text{C}{=}\text{O} & \text{CHO} & \text{CHO} & \text{C}{=}\text{O} \\
| \quad + \, | & \leftrightharpoons & | \quad + \, | \\
\text{CHOH} & \text{R}' & \text{R} & \text{CHOH} \\
| & & & | \\
\text{R} & & & \text{R}'
\end{array}
$$

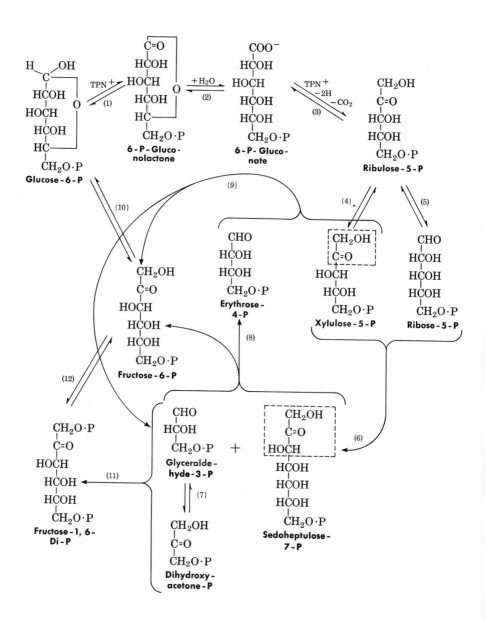

Fig. 15.2. The pentose phosphate pathway.

In Fig. 15.2 an attempt is made to outline this rather confusing set of reactions. It is complicated by the fact that certain of the intermediates react in more than one way. In following the circle around it must be assumed that use of a given molecule for a second time can only be achieved during a second turn of the wheel. The units enclosed in dotted lines are the units which are transferred by the enzyme to the other reactant.

Reactions 1 and 2 achieve the stepwise formation of 6-phosphogluconate from glucose-6-phosphate. The first reaction is catalyzed by a typical dehydrogenase for which TPN$^+$ is the required coenzyme; the second reaction is an hydrolysis catalyzed by a *lactonase*.

Reaction 3 is a decarboxylation and an oxidation, both catalyzed by a single enzyme, *phosphogluconate dehydrogenase*, for which again the required coenzyme is TPN$^+$. The product is the ketose, phosphoribulose or ribulose-5-phosphate.

The two following reactions are isomerizations. Reaction 4 is catalyzed by an *epimerase* and results in formation of the epimeric ketophosphate, xylulose-5-phosphate. Reaction 5 is catalyzed by an *isomerase* and yields ribose-5-phosphate. The sequence of Reactions 1 to 3, followed by Reaction 5 therefore offers a path for the synthesis from glucose of ribose-5-phosphate, which is, as has been noted, an important synthetic substrate. If the sequence as written is not to stop here a molecule of ribose-5-phosphate must be provided from some other source to react with xylulose-5-P.

In Reaction 6, catalyzed by a transketolase, the first two carbons of xylulose phosphate are transferred to ribose phosphate, yielding one molecule of glyceraldehyde phosphate and one of the 7-carbon sedoheptulose phosphate. The glyceraldehyde phosphate will of course establish an equilibrium with dihydroxyacetone phosphate (Reaction 7) under the influence of the same triose isomerase which catalyzes this reaction in the glycolytic sequence.

In Reaction 8 the two products of Reaction 6 undergo another transfer reaction in which carbons 1, 2, and 3 of the heptulose phosphate are transferred to the triose phosphate under the catalytic influence of a transaldolase. This results in formation of fructose-6-phosphate and erythrose-4-phosphate.

Reaction 9 is another transfer catalyzed by a transketolase in which the same two carbons as in Reaction 6 are transferred from another molecule of xylulose-5-phosphate to the 4-carbon erythrose-4-phosphate. This generates a new molecule of glyceraldehyde phosphate and a second one of fructose-6-phosphate.

Reaction 10 is catalyzed by the familiar phosphoglucoisomerase and brings the cycle back again to glucose-6-phosphate.

In Reaction 11 the second molecule of glyceraldehyde phosphate, first equilibrating with its keto isomer, synthesizes fructose diphosphate under the influence of the same aldolase which in Reaction 5 of the glycolytic sequence catalyzed the reverse reaction.

Reaction 12 is a simple hydrolysis, catalyzed by a specific phosphatase, and would be followed by Reaction 10.

The net result, assuming six turns of the cycle, will be complete oxidation of glucose to carbon dioxide and reduction of 12TPN$^+$ molecules to TPNH. This may be summed up:

$$\text{Glucose-6-phosphate} + 12\text{TPN}^+ + 7\text{H}_2\text{O} \rightarrow$$
$$6\text{CO}_2 + 12\text{TPNH} + 12\text{H}^+ + \text{H}_3\text{PO}_4$$

Significance of the Pentose Phosphate Pathway

Many attempts have been made and are being made to determine the quantitative importance of this metabolic pathway. Attempts to do this by determining the distribution of C^{14} when variously labeled glucose molecules are used as substrate involve many technical difficulties. It seems, however, that in most tissues the glycolytic sequence accounts for the major part of the glucose which is used. An exception to this is mammary tissue during lactation, which oxidizes glucose preferentially by way of the pentose phosphate pathway. It should perhaps be emphasized that although its quantitative importance is limited in most tissues, the existence of this pathway has been demonstrated in a wide variety of cells from plants, animals, and bacteria.

THE GLUCURONIC ACID PATHWAY

Studies on the biosynthesis of ascorbic acid, on the one hand, and on the origin of congenital pentosuria, on the other, have led to the recognition of still a third cyclical pathway by which glucose is sometimes metabolized. This cycle is outlined in an abbreviated form in Fig. 15.3. The asterisks mark carbon 1 of the original glucose, which is sometimes written at the top and sometimes at the bottom in the various intermediates. This is necessary because of the shift from the D arrangement in glucose to the L series in gulonic acid.

Reaction 1 on the chart represents the series of reactions referred to in Chapter 13 in connection with the use of glucuronic acid in detoxication. The sequence begins with phosphorylation of glucose by ATP which gives glucose-6-phosphate. This compound then comes to equilibrium with glucose-1-phosphate. In the subsequent reactions the aldehyde group is pro-

$$\text{Glucose} \xrightarrow{\text{ATP}} \text{Glucose-6-P} \rightleftharpoons \text{Glucose-1-P}$$

tected by reaction with uridine triphosphate, so that the primary alcohol group can be oxidized. Removal of the nucleotide and of phosphate yields the D-glucuronic acid which is the second compound on the chart.

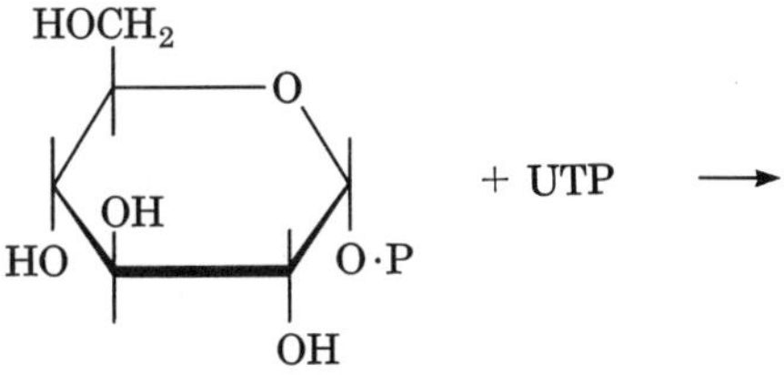

Glucose - 1 - phosphate

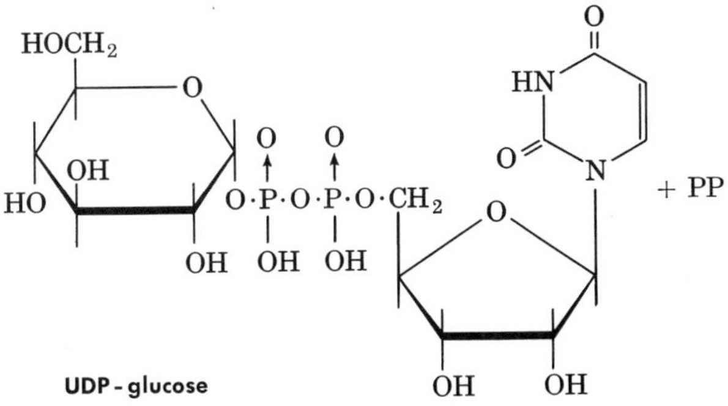

+ UTP ⟶

UDP - glucose   + PP

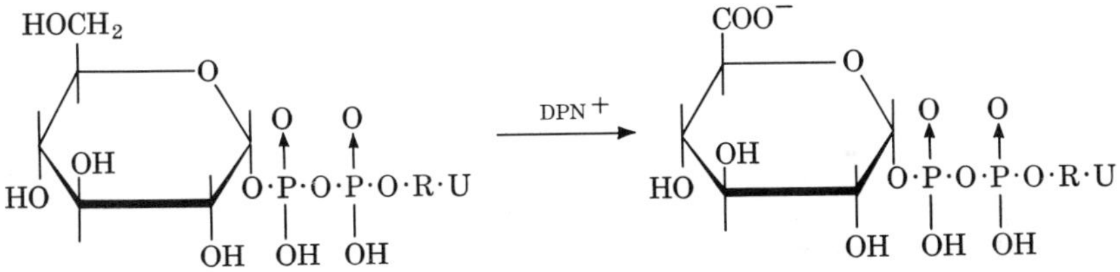

UDP - glucose   DPN⁺ ⟶   UDP - glucuronide

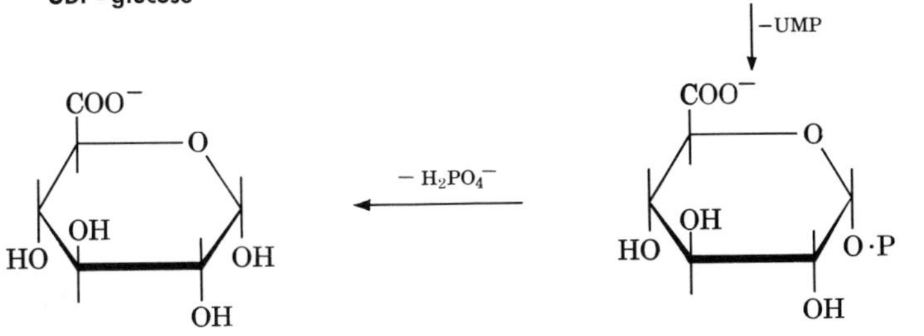

−UMP

D - Glucuronate   − H₂PO₄⁻ ⟵   D - Glucuronate - 1 - phosphate

In Reaction 2 the aldehyde group of glucuronic acid is reduced by transfer of hydrogen from TPNH with formation of L-gulonic acid. This compound as indicated on the chart is the precursor of L-ascorbic acid, which is formed through a lactonization followed by an oxidation. The coenzyme which is used in the oxidative step is not known.

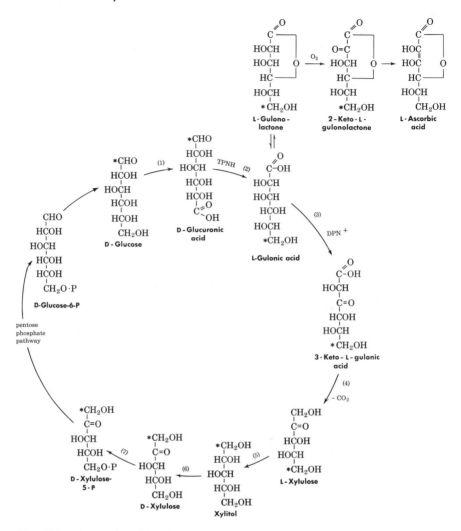

Fig. 15.3. Glucuronic acid pathway. [From J. J. Burns and A. H. Conney, *Ann. Rev. Biochem.*, **29**, 413 (1960).]

Reaction 3, for which DPN$^+$ is required, introduces a keto group on carbon 3, and this is followed, in Reaction 4, by a decarboxylation which yields L-xylulose.

In Reactions 5 and 6 the ketose is first reduced to the symmetrical xylitol, then oxidized with introduction of a keto group in such a position that the resulting ketose is again a member of the D series. The compound formed at this point is the ketopentose, D-xylulose, which is also a reactant in the pentose phosphate pathway, hence in this cycle it is indicated that after being phosphorylated this sugar is metabolized by way of the pentose phosphate pathway, leading back to glucose-6-phosphate and then to glucose.

It is too early to assess the importance of this metabolic sequence. The enzymes leading to synthesis of ascorbic acid have been found in liver of several different animals and in the kidney of birds and reptiles and amphibia. In plants the evidence is conflicting, though some of it does point to this glucuronic acid pathway as a source of ascorbic acid.

The congenital pentosuria referred to earlier is believed to depend upon a genetic block which prevents conversion of L-xylulose to D-xylulose. As a result of this, the L sugar accumulates and is excreted.

BIOSYNTHESIS OF THE CARBOHYDRATES

Biosynthesis of Monoses

Although the supply of glucose from the foodstuffs must usually be more than adequate, it is clear from isotopic studies that many different small molecules lead to glucose synthesis. Although reversal of catabolic reactions has been discredited as an explanation of many different biosyntheses, it still seems to be true that reversal of glycolysis does account for many such syntheses. This has been established, for example, by feeding labeled amino acids or labeled fatty acids and then comparing the labeling in the liver glycogen with that which would result if the precursor had yielded pyruvate and this compound had been acted upon to reverse the glycolytic sequence. It will be remembered that all of the reactions of the sequence are reversible except the one in which hexose diphosphate is formed from fructose mono-phosphate and ATP. However, while this complete reaction cannot be reversed, it is clearly a simple matter of hydrolysis to remove one of the phosphate groups from the diphosphate. Hence, as far as the sugars them-selves are concerned the entire sequence can be reversed to yield glucose-1-phosphate which by hydrolytic removal of its phosphate group would form glucose. The molecules which have been shown to act as precursors of glucose are many. They include any of the amino acids which are degraded by way of pyruvate, the glycerol from fats which, after oxidation and phos-phorylation, enters the sequence at the triose phosphate stage and any compound which is metabolized to form acetyl coenzyme A. This latter compound reaches the glycolytic sequence by a somewhat circuitous path

$$
\begin{array}{ccc}
\text{CH}_2\text{COO}^- & & \text{CH}_2 \\
| & & \| \\
\text{C}\!=\!\text{O} & + \text{GTP} \leftrightarrows & \text{C}\!-\!\text{O}\sim\text{P} + \text{GDP} + \text{CO}_2 \\
| & & | \\
\text{COO}^- & & \text{COO}^- \\
\textbf{Oxaloacetate} & & \textbf{Phosphoenol-} \\
& & \textbf{pyruvate}
\end{array}
$$

which includes the citric acid cycle. In the citric acid cycle it is transformed into oxaloacetate, and this compound, by interaction with the triphosphate of guanosine or inosine and the necessary enzyme, is decarboxylated and phosphorylated with formation of phosphoenolpyruvate.

Synthesis of pentoses has been touched on in connection with the metabolism of glucose. There are three different pathways by which a pentose can be derived from an aldohexose: (1) oxidation of the aldehyde group and subsequent removal of carbon 1 by decarboxylation, (2) reaction between hexose phosphate and triose phosphate involving transketolases and transaldolases as spelled out in the discussion of the pentose phosphate pathway, and (3) oxidative removal of carbon 6 of glucuronic acid. Of these three it would appear from the evidence at present available that the second pathway is the most important. Isotopic labeling shows that the main pathway for synthesis of deoxyribose is reduction of ribose, which probably takes place while the sugars are part of a nucleoside.

The glyoxylate cycle

In the last few years it has been found that isocitric acid, which was discussed in connection with the citric acid cycle, is also the starting point for a reaction sequence which is synthetic rather than oxidative. Since this sequence is most clearly connected with carbohydrate synthesis, it is considered at this point. The reactions known as the *glyoxylate cycle* were first discovered in work with bacteria, and later were shown to take place in various plant tissues. There is no evidence at present that the cycle operates in animals.

The two characteristic enzymes of the cycle are *isocitritase* and *malate synthetase*. Isocitritase catalyzes the splitting of isocitric acid to succinic acid and glyoxylic acid.

$$
\begin{array}{l}
CHOH \cdot COOH \\
|\\
CH \cdot COOH \\
|\\
CH_2COOH
\end{array}
\xrightarrow{\text{isocitritase}}
CHO \cdot COOH +
\begin{array}{l}
CH_2COOH \\
|\\
CH_2COOH
\end{array}
\qquad (1)
$$

Isocitric acid **Glyoxylic acid** **Succinic acid**

This means that isocitrate formed in the course of the citric acid cycle may either react as noted in Chapter 11 and go on, by way of α-ketoglutarate, to complete that cycle, or two of its carbons may be diverted to the glyoxylic acid cycle for synthetic use. This use begins with the condensation of glyoxylic acid with acetyl coenzyme A, under the influence of malate synthetase.

$$
\begin{array}{l}
CHO \\
|\\
COOH
\end{array}
+ CH_3CO \cdot CoA + H_2O \rightarrow
\begin{array}{l}
CHOH \cdot COOH \\
|\\
CH_2COOH
\end{array}
+ HCoA \qquad (2)
$$

Malic acid

This pair of reactions is sometimes referred to as the "glyoxylate shunt," since they lead from one member of the citric acid cycle, isocitrate, to another member, malate, by a second and rather simpler pathway than the one which is followed in the citric acid cycle itself. If the products of Reactions 1 and

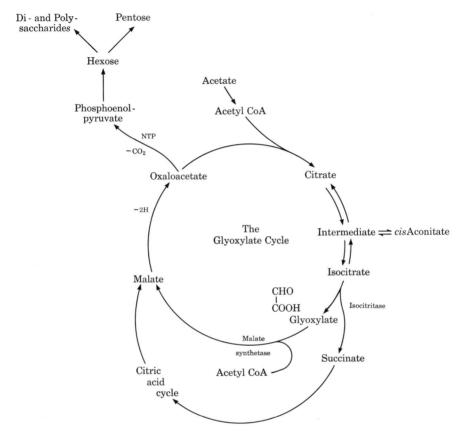

Fig. 15.4. The glyoxylate cycle, showing how it serves to synthesize four-carbon acids for the citric acid cycle, and also to provide phosphoenolpyruvate from acetate for carbohydrate synthesis.

2, succinate and malate, go on in the citric acid cycle, the shunt results in the formation of two molecules of oxaloacetate instead of one, from each molecule of isocitrate, thus allowing acetate to serve as precursor of the four-carbon acids required by the citric acid cycle.

The glyoxylate shunt, through formation of malate, also serves to make acetate carbons available for other syntheses. For example, the bacteria in which the reactions of the shunt were discovered are capable of using acetate as their sole carbon source, and so must be able to build from this simple two-carbon compound all the organic molecules they need. Krebs and Kornberg, who first recognized the possibilities of the glyoxylate cycle, suggest that acetate can, through its operation, be incorporated into carbohydrates and eventually into amino acids and proteins. This results from the transformations referred to above in which malate forms oxaloacetate, and this compound in the presence of nucleoside triphosphate loses carbon dioxide to form phosphoenolpyruvate. Reversal of the glucolytic sequence would yield hexose, while loss of the phosphate group followed by transamination would lead to alanine. Alternatively, as the malate proceeds through the reactions of the citric acid cycle there would be formed two other keto acids, oxaloacetate and α-ketoglutarate, either of which could undergo transamination. Some of these relationships are indicated in Fig. 15.4.

It is becoming increasingly evident that the glyoxylic acid cycle is important in plants, especially in those which are using stored fats and must therefore be using these substances to synthesize carbohydrates. It will be remembered that the primary breakdown product of fatty acids is acetyl CoA, which is therefore present in abundance in those plant tissues which are mobilizing fats for use. Through the glyoxylate cycle this compound is incorporated into malate, after which the reaction sequence outlined above would carry it into both carbohydrates and proteins.

The presence of the enzymes needed to bring about these transformations has been demonstrated in castor bean endosperms and in peanut and sunflower seedlings at the stage in which fat is being rapidly converted to carbohydrate. Furthermore, with these tissues carbon of labeled acetate is incorporated in both malate and the glucose moiety of sucrose. The position of the label when the two acetate carbons are labeled separately proves to be what would be expected if these carbons entered the sequence by way of the glyoxylate cycle. It therefore appears that this cycle plays an important role in bacteria which use acetate as carbon source and in plant tissues which are mobilizing fats for synthesis of carbohydrate.

Biosynthesis of Glycosidic Bonds

Formation of higher saccharides takes place as a result of three different types of transfer reaction.

Transglycosylation

The first type of transfer is catalyzed by enzymes known as *transglycosylases*, and uses the energy of one glycosidic bond to form another. By this type of reaction a glycosyl unit can be transferred to another monose to form a disaccharide, or the process may be repeated many times to form a polysaccharide. This type of synthesis is illustrated by the following equations:

$$n \text{ Maltose} \rightarrow (1\rightarrow4\text{-}\alpha\text{-Glucose})_n + n \text{ Glucose}$$

$$n \text{ Glucose-1-fructose} \rightarrow (1\rightarrow4\text{-}\alpha\text{-Glucose})_n + n \text{ Fructose}$$
(Sucrose)

$$n \text{ Glucose-1-fructose} \rightarrow (1\rightarrow2\text{-fructose})_n + n \text{ Glucose}$$

The enzymes which catalyze the first two reactions come from bacteria and are known respectively as *maltose transglucosylase* and *sucrose transglucosylase*. The first reaction begins with transfer of a glucose unit from one maltose molecule to another and goes on with repeated additions of one glucose from each maltose which reacts. In the second reaction each sucrose contributes its glucose to building up of the polysaccharide and frees the fructose. The third reaction requires an enzyme found in plants which catalyzes formation of the plant polysaccharide, inulin, from sucrose. The enzyme is *sucrose transfructosylase* which brings about formation of 2→1 linkages between fructose molecules. Many bacterial enzymes of these general types have been identified, leading to synthesis of various polysaccharides and a few disaccharides by transfer of a glycosyl residue from combination with one monose residue to form a glycosidic link with a different molecule though not necessarily with a different kind of molecule.

Biosyntheses brought about by phosphorylases

It will be remembered that the first step in the degradation of glycogen is phosphorolysis of the polysaccharide catalyzed by a muscle *phosphorylase*. The first laboratory synthesis of a polysaccharide was achieved when this reaction was reversed by adding either muscle phosphorylase or a similar enzyme from potato tubers to glucose-1-phosphate. This latter enzyme has sometimes been called "P-enzyme," but as at least two entirely different enzymes have been called this, it is better to use the descriptive name *glucosan phosphorylase* for the enzyme from either plant or animal sources. This type of phosphorylase has been isolated from yeast, muscle, liver, heart, and brain and from many different plant tissues. They all act upon glucose-1-phosphate to form 1→4 linked polysaccharides of the amylose type and to free inorganic phosphate. Thus the phosphorylases prepared from muscle and from potato yield similar linear products, though the normal polysaccharide of muscle is the branched glycogen, and starch normally consists largely of the branched amylopectin. This discrepancy is due to the lack in the purified enzymes of a second enzyme or "branching factor" required for formation of 1→6 links at the branching points. The Coris showed that there is such a factor in several crude preparations of animal phosphorylase, and in Haworth's laboratory a similar factor, known as Q enzyme, has been isolated from potato juice. Thus the synthesis of a branched polysaccharide requires the collaboration of two different enzymes, one of which brings about formation of amylose or an amylose-like unbranched polysaccharide. The enzyme required for formation of the 1→6 links is called a *glucosan transglycosylase* because it transfers part of an already formed 1→4 chain from linkage at carbon 4 to linkage at carbon 6 on some intermediate glucose unit.

In view of the similar requirement in nucleic acid biosynthesis, it is of interest that with purified enzymes no synthesis takes place unless the system is primed with a small amount of polysaccharide.

It should be noted also that it is only in the building of the unbranched poly-saccharide chain that the energy of a phosphate link is used. The branching reaction does not involve a phosphate compound at all, so that formation of the 1→6 links is a reaction like those discussed in the previous section, namely transfer of a glycosyl group from linkage with a carbohydrate residue.

Uridine compounds in synthesis

Mention has already been made more than once of the use in carbohydrate biosynthesis of the uridine diphosphate derivatives. In these compounds a hexose or hexose derivative is attached through a pyrophosphate group to uridine. From such a compound the sugar residue may be transferred to various glycosyl acceptors. It was shown on page 492 that uridine diphosphate glucuronide transfers the glucuronic acid residue to aromatic compounds to detoxicate them.

The disaccharide trehalose is synthesized in yeast as a result of transfer of a glucosyl residue from UDP-glucoside (often called UDP-glucose) to glucose-6-phosphate, forming trehalose-6-phosphate.

UDP - glucoside   Glucose - 6 - phosphate

Trehalose - 6 - phosphate

Chitin, which is a polymer of N-acetylglucosamine, results from a similar transfer of an *N*-acetylglucosaminyl group from linkage to UDP to a chain of such groups. Like the formation of a glucose polymer from glucose-1-phosphate, this reaction does not take place except in the presence of a primer. If **R'** stands for an indefinite number of glucosaminyl groups attached to one such terminal group, the biosynthesis of chitin may be represented:

$$\beta(1 \to 4) \text{ Poly - N - acetylglucosamine}$$

Successive repetitions of this type of transfer would eventually build up the $\beta(1{\to}4)$ glycosidic chain of chitin.

It has now begun to appear that glycogen synthesis *in vivo* also makes use of uridine triphosphate to form the active glucose compound from which a glucosyl residue can be transferred. Thus the carbohydrates join the proteins and the fats in having separate catabolic and synthetic pathways. The enzyme phosphorylase is then to be thought of as concerned in the cell with glycogen breakdown. Building up of glycogen is a result of transfer from UDP-glucoside.

PHOTOSYNTHESIS

The most fundamental example of biosynthesis is of course the one which is carried out by green plants. In photosynthesis the energy of sunlight is transformed into the chemical energy of a variety of organic compounds on which all heterotrophic organisms depend for food. This unique achievement is made possible by the presence in the leaves of the catalyst, chlorophyll.

Structure of Chlorophyll

Chlorophyll is a magnesium tetrapyrrole compound very like heme in structure. Willstätter, in whose laboratory it was first purified, separated the green coloring matter into chlorophyll *a* and chlorophyll *b* and proved that these two components are present in fairly constant ratio in the chloroplasts, where they occur in close association with the lipoprotein of the membrane which bounds each granum. Chlorophyll *b* differs from chlorophyll *a* in having in position 3 of the tetrapyrrole ring a formyl group instead of a methyl.

Decomposition of chlorophyll gives rise to substituted pyrroles very like those obtained from heme. Removal of the magnesium by treatment with acid leaves a waxy compound with no acidic groups, thus indicating that the metal is bound to nitrogen and not to an acidic group as a salt. As with heme, elucidation of the structure of the chlorophylls came as a result of work in many different laboratories, notably those of Willstätter and Hans Fischer in Munich and of Conant at Harvard. As the formula below makes clear, chlorophyll *a* proved to differ from heme in the following ways: (1) ring IV has lost the double bond between carbons 7 and 8; (2) one propionic acid side chain has been esterified with the long chain unsaturated alcohol, phytol; (3) the other propionic acid has been esterified with methyl alcohol and is

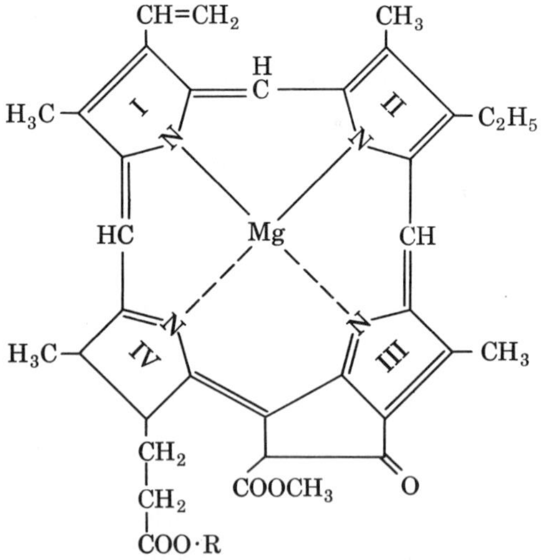

Chlorophyll a

$$R= -CH_2 \cdot CH=C \cdot CH_2 \cdot CH_2 \cdot CH_2 \cdot CH \cdot CH_2 \cdot CH_2 \cdot CH_2 \cdot CH \cdot CH_2 \cdot CH_2 \cdot CH_2 \cdot CH \cdot CH_3$$

with CH_3 groups below.

Phytyl group

involved in formation of a five-membered ring; (4) the vinyl group at carbon 4 has been saturated; and, of course, (5) magnesium is held in the center of the large ring instead of iron. The structure indicated for the phytyl group should make clear why this portion of the molecule was referred to back in Chapter 3 as a lipophilic, hydrocarbon area.

Chlorophyll occurs in the grana in close association with other pigments, the carotenoids; in leaves the main carotenoid constituent is β-carotene. What function, if any, these substances serve in photosynthesis is not known.

Function of Chlorophyll in Photosynthesis

The broad outlines of the photosynthetic process were established in the course of about thirty years, beginning with Priestley's discovery that air which had been "injured" by having a candle burned in it could be restored by vegetation. The importance of light, the participation of water, and the incorporation of carbon dioxide in the plant fabric had all been recognized by the opening years of the nineteenth century. At that time the photosynthetic equation was written:

$$CO_2 + H_2O \xrightarrow{\text{light}} (CH_2O) + O_2$$
$$\textbf{Carbohydrate}$$

On the assumption that the first step in photosynthesis was a direct interaction of water and carbon dioxide, various possible intermediates were suggested from time to time. The one for which there was at least a shadow of proof, and which held the stage longest was the obvious one, formaldehyde. When Emil Fischer succeeded in preparing a dilute glucose solution by allowing formaldehyde to stand in contact with barium hydroxide, it seemed highly probable that a similar reaction took place in plant cells, and that formation of formaldehyde from carbon dioxide and water was followed by an aldol condensation involving six formaldehyde molecules. Largely for lack of any more authoritative guess, formaldehyde continued to be the favored intermediate well into the twentieth century.

It is now known that even as a summary of events the simple formulation above is incorrect. This becomes apparent when the water provided for photosynthesis is labeled with O^{18}. The isotopic concentration of the oxygen evolved proves to be exactly like that of the water, showing that none of it is derived from the unlabeled carbon dioxide. Clearly then two molecules of water are involved for each molecule of carbon dioxide reduced and all the free oxygen comes from the water.

$$CO_2 + 2H_2O^{18} \rightarrow (CH_2O) + O_2^{18} + H_2O$$

That the photosynthetic process, here expressed as a single equation, actually involves two separate types of reaction has been known for many years. Of the two only one requires sunlight; the subsequent reactions proceed equally well in light or darkness. Thus the green cells which are illuminated in the absence of carbon dioxide must undergo some undefined photochemical change, for when they are later brought into contact with carbon dioxide, even in the dark, they are able to bring about its fixation. Further examination of photosynthesis therefore requires separate examination of the light reaction and of those reactions which take place in the dark.

It will be recalled that the chlorophyll is concentrated within the chloroplast in small bodies known as grana in which the chlorophyll is spread in a monomolecular layer closely associated with the lipoprotein membrane. If green leaves are finely ground, it is possible to separate from the tissue debris a fluid which contains whole and broken chloroplasts. This green fluid as prepared in the early experiments was not able to fix carbon dioxide, but if it was illuminated, it was still capable of setting free oxygen provided a hydrogen acceptor was available. This reaction in which chlorophyll catalyzes the evolution of oxygen from water and the reduction of a hydrogen acceptor is known as the *Hill reaction*. In the expressed cell juices there may be natural acceptors, or artificial ones such as quinone or potassium ferric oxalate may be added to the medium. Thus it has been shown that broken grana will reduce quinone to hydroquinone or the ferric oxalate to the ferrous level, with a concomitant evolution of oxygen. This is believed to indicate that the light-induced step in photosynthesis, for which chlorophyll acts as a catalyst, is a splitting of water. In this process oxygen is set free, though not necessarily directly and in a single step, and the hydrogen reduces some compound which will later be used to reduce carbon dioxide. When cells or grana are illuminated in the absence of carbon dioxide, the reducing compound accumulates and can later act upon added carbon dioxide in the dark. In these terms the essential photochemical reaction is the generation of reducing power.

Warburg has recently reported that, contrary to our previous belief, the photoevolution of oxygen does not take place if carbon dioxide is rigidly excluded, and it has been confirmed in Vennesland's laboratory that in the complete absence of carbon dioxide the Hill reaction is partially abolished. Warburg interprets these results to mean that the carbon dioxide provides a precursor for the photoevolution of oxygen. If this proves to be true, it may entail a revision of present theories about the primary step in photosynthesis, and it is impossible at the moment to say how this new fact will be fitted into the picture.

Meantime, all evidence still points to water as the ultimate source both of the oxygen evolved and of the reducing power which is used later in reduction of carbon dioxide to the carbohydrate level.

The form in which this reducing power is stored was indicated in experiments reported a few years ago by Ochoa. He found that suspensions of green grana from spinach leaves catalyze the photochemical reduction of both pyridine coenzymes, and that the reaction requires both chlorophyll and light.

He was further able to couple these reductions with other reactions in which the reduced coenzymes acted as reducing agents, thus using the trapped reducing power from water as it is presumably used in the photosynthesizing cell. The equations indicate such a coupled reaction.

$$2H_2O + 2TPN^+ \xrightarrow[\text{light}]{\text{grana}} 2TPNH + 2H^+ + O_2$$

$$TPNH + H^+ + CH_3CO \cdot COOH + CO_2 \xrightarrow[\text{enzyme}]{\text{``malic''}}$$

$$HOOC \cdot CHOH \cdot CH_2 \cdot COOH + TPN^+$$

Malic acid

The "malic" enzyme is not malate dehydrogenase, but a single enzyme which catalyzes the two reactions involved in the equation shown, the carboxylation of pyruvate and reduction of the resulting keto acid to the malic acid shown as the final product.

The Path of Carbon in Photosynthesis

While one group of investigators has focused attention upon the photochemical generation of reducing power, others have concerned themselves with the chemical reactions in which carbon-to-carbon bonds are formed in green plants. This second type of experiment became possible only with the advent of isotopic carbon and of effective analytical procedures for the separation and identification of small amounts of very similar compounds. The first studies were carried out when the only available carbon isotope was the short-lived C^{11}, but since 1948 the carbon dioxide used for this type of photosynthetic investigation has been labeled with the long-lived radioactive C^{14}.

The outstanding early contributions to the elucidation of the path of carbon in photosynthesis came from Calvin's[3] group in California and Gaffron's[4] group in Chicago. In both laboratories the experiments were designed to allow identification of the earliest product of photosynthesis.

---

[3] Professor Melvin Calvin (1911–) is Director of the Biochemical Division of the Radiation Laboratory at the University of California in Berkeley. His interest in the mechanism of organic reactions is being applied specifically to the mechanism of photosynthesis. In 1961 he was awarded the Nobel Prize in Chemistry.

[4] Hans Gaffron (1902–) was born in Peru and educated in Berlin where he carried on his early biochemical research. Between 1939 and 1960 he was a Professor at the University of Chicago. In 1960 he became a Professor in the Department of Biological Science at Florida State University. He has been chiefly interested in plant physiology, in the metabolism of the purple bacteria, and in photochemistry in general.

For this purpose green algae are allowed to assimilate labeled carbon dioxide for brief periods and are then killed and extracted. In the Calvin experiments, for example, the algae undergo a brief period of "pre-illumination" and are then allowed to fix $C^{14}O_2$ in the dark. The soluble compounds are extracted from the plants at the end of the fixation period, separated by two-dimensional paper chromatography, and allowed to identify themselves by forming a radioautograph on a photographic film.

It was found that after ninety seconds of dark fixation fifteen different compounds had acquired the radioactive label. In thirty seconds C^{14} was incorporated in eight different substances, among them the five acids, glycolic, malic, aspartic, phosphopyruvic, and phosphoglyceric acids. The other three substances which were identified were a triose phosphate, hexose monophosphate, and hexose diphosphate. Most of these compounds are familar intermediates in glycolysis or in the citric acid cycle, and they therefore suggest that photosynthesis may turn out to be in detail as well as in general, a reversal of respiration.

Shortening the period of dark fixation to five seconds resulted in confining the isotope to four or five compounds, with 65 per cent of it in the carboxyl group of phosphoglyceric acid.

$$CH_2O \cdot PO_3H_2$$
$$|$$
$$CHOH$$
$$|$$
$$*COOH$$

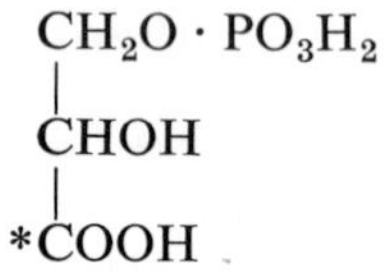

**Phosphoglyceric
acid**

The establishment of this compound as the first recognizable labeled compound formed in photosynthesis made it possible to pose two related questions: (1) by what chemical reaction is carbon dioxide incorporated in the carboxyl group of phosphoglyceric acid and (2) what chemical reactions

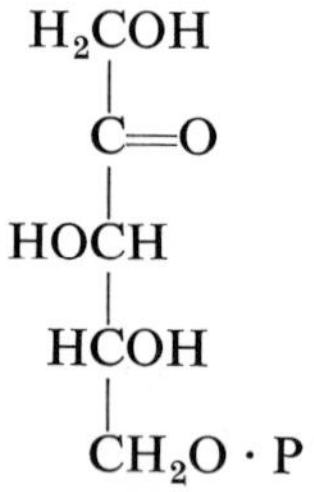

H_2COH	CHO	CH_2OH
$C{=}O$	HCOH	$C{=}O$
HOCH	HCOH	HOCH
HCOH	HCOH	HCOH
$CH_2O \cdot P$	$CH_2O \cdot P$	HCOH
Xylulose-5-phosphate	**Ribose-5-phosphate**	HCOH
		$CH_2O \cdot P$
		Sedoheptulose-7-phosphate

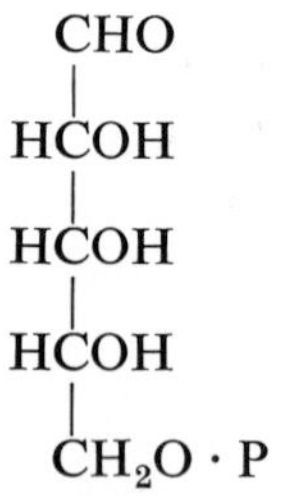

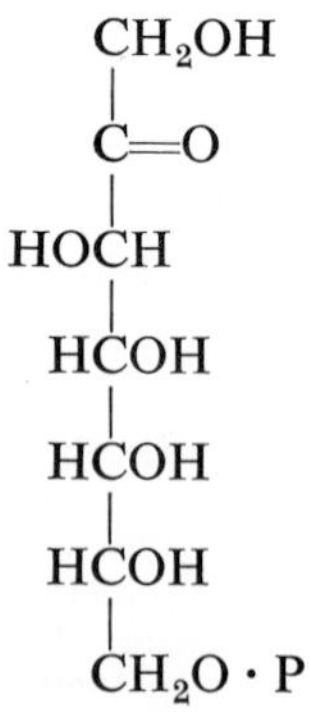

lead from this compound to glucose? To these questions the group in Calvin's laboratory addressed themselves, and eventually found answers. They found among the products of photosynthesis, separated by paper chromatography, various phosphorylated derivatives of keto- and aldo-pentoses and of the 7-carbon sedoheptulose, in addition to the expected hexoses and trioses.

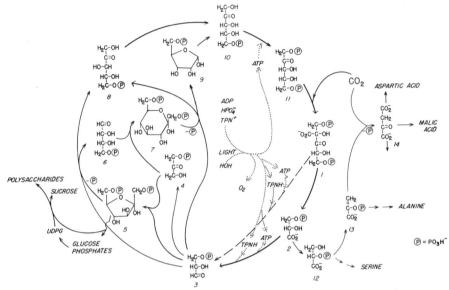

Fig. 15.5. The path of carbon in photosynthesis. (Courtesy of Dr. M. Calvin.)

As a result of studies in which the distribution of C^{14} in these various compounds was determined, it became possible to trace the order in which the known components must form. This led to the formulation of the reactions indicated in Fig. 15.5, now generally accepted as representing the path of carbon in photosynthesis.

In this most recent formulation Calvin has represented in the center, using dotted arrows, the formation of ATP, TPNH, and free oxygen by interaction between water, ADP, inorganic phosphate, TPN^+, and light. The ATP and TPNH are required for the reactions of the cycle, and the method of their formation will be considered in more detail in a later section. For the moment we need only realize that they are available for use when they are needed.

As shown in the scheme, the primary acceptor of carbon dioxide is ribulose diphosphate, numbered 11, and represented in the upper right-hand quadrant. Interaction of this compound with carbon dioxide forms the α-hydroxy-β-keto acid which is compound No. 1 on the chart. This substance has been represented in all earlier formulations as splitting to yield two molecules of the phosphoglyceric acid (compound No. 2) which had been identified as a very early product of photosynthesis. Reduction of this acid by TPNH, which is the obligatory coenzyme for this particular reaction, yields compound No. 3 or phosphoglyceraldehyde. It will be noted that ATP is needed at this point as an energy source. A new feature of this formulation is the broken arrow leading from the β-keto acid to phosphoglyceraldehyde, indicating that there is some evidence that part of the triose phosphate arises in this more direct transformation.

From this point on the reactions connected directly with the cycle are very like those of the pentose phosphate pathway. Compound No. 4, dihydroxyacetone phosphate, arises through the equilibration, catalyzed by triose phosphate isomerase, which was first described in the glucolytic sequence. The two triose phosphates then unite to form compound No. 5 which is fructose diphosphate. The reaction which follows involves one molecule of fructose diphosphate and one of glyceraldehyde phosphate (No. 3) and is catalyzed by a transketolase. It frees one phosphate group, and yields one molecule of xylulose-5-phosphate (No. 8) and one of erythrose-4-phosphate (No. 6). This latter compound then reacts with dihydroxyacetone phosphate under the catalytic influence of aldolase to form sedoheptulose-1,7-diphosphate (No. 7), here shown in the pyranose ring form. Interaction of this diphosphate with glyceraldehyde phosphate is catalyzed by a transketolase and gives rise to a second molecule of xylulose-5-phosphate (No. 8) and one of ribose-5-phosphate (No. 9). Epimerization of the xylulose phosphate and isomerization of the ribose phosphate both yield ribulose-5-phosphate (No. 10), and phosphorylation of this compound by ATP ends the cycle by reconstituting the ribulose diphosphate (No. 11) with which it began.

Outside the main circle various other pathways are indicated. Shift of the phosphate group in compound No. 2 yields 2-phosphoglyceric acid (No. 12), which is a precursor of serine and can also be dehydrated to yield phosphoenolpyruvate (No. 13). This reactive compound may then after losing its phosphate group be carboxylated to form oxaloacetate (No. 14) or be used in a transamination reaction to synthesize alanine.

The reactions outside the circle in the lower left-hand quadrant indicate the formation of glucose phosphates from fructose diphosphate, and use of the glucose, in the form of uridine diphosphate glucoside, in synthesis of higher carbohydrates.

It is of interest to note here that with improved techniques for isolating the chloroplasts it has been possible to show that this entire reaction sequence takes place in these small particles.

Photosynthetic Phosphorylation

It is clear that the reactions just outlined depend upon an adequate supply of ATP and TPNH. Within the last few years a series of reports from

Arnon's[5] laboratory at Berkeley has shown that these two compounds are also synthesized in the chloroplasts. This results in the formation, in close association with the enzymes of the Calvin sequence, of what Arnon calls "assimilatory power," represented by the two compounds, ATP and TPNH, and brings us one step nearer an understanding of the point at which light energy and chlorophyll intervene to make the carbon sequence possible.

It will be remembered that the Hill reaction is brought about by broken chloroplasts and consists in evolution of oxygen accompanying a transfer of hydrogen to some artificial acceptor. Since the source of the hydrogen and the oxygen is believed to be water, this reaction may be expressed in a hypothetical equation in which A stands for an unidentified hydrogen acceptor. The substance AH_2 then represents photosynthetically produced reducing power.

$$A + H_2O \xrightarrow[\text{chlorophyll}]{\text{light}} AH_2 + \tfrac{1}{2}O_2$$

In a study of the Hill reaction in absence of CO_2 Arnon noted that if chloroplast preparations were fortified with ADP and inorganic phosphate as well as a hydrogen acceptor, the rate of the reaction was more than doubled, ATP was formed and there was a stoichiometric relation between the moles of oxygen evolved and the moles of ATP formed. The need to add various substances to the chloroplasts arises from the fact that many of them are ruptured when the leaves are macerated, and while in recent preparations the enzymes remain attached to the membranes, soluble substrates are lost. Among the hydrogen acceptors used in these experiments was the natural one, TPN^+ which was reduced to TPNH. It therefore appeared that one reaction catalyzed by chloroplasts could be summed up in the equation:

$$2TPN^+ + 2H_2O + 2ADP + 2P \xrightarrow[\text{Mg}^{++}]{\text{light}} 2TPNH + 2H^+ + 2ATP + O_2$$

This means that "AH_2," generated in the photolysis of water, has a reduction potential low enough so that it can transfer hydrogen to TPN^+, freeing energy in the process to synthesize ATP. This process, for a reason which will become apparent in a moment, Arnon calls *noncyclic photophosphorylation*. It forms, as the equation shows, equimolar amounts of ATP and TPNH.

The reactions which constitute *cyclic photophosphorylation* were discovered as a result of the observation that several different substances added to chloroplasts in catalytic amounts abolished the evolution of oxygen and the reduction of TPN^+, but increased sharply the esterification of ADP to ATP. The compounds which were active in effecting this change were vitamin K,

---

[5] Daniel Arnon (1910–   ) was born in Poland but has pursued his scientific career in California. He is now Professor in the Department of Plant Physiology at Berkeley.

ascorbic acid, and flavin mononucleotide. Ascorbic acid and FMN have already been described as hydrogen carriers. Vitamin K, as its formula shows, is a quinone and is therefore also capable of transferring hydrogens. It was found further that the extent to which oxygen evolution was repressed

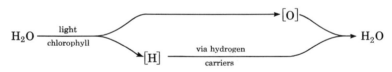

$$O$$
$$-CH_3$$
$$-CH_2CH{=}C(CH_2)_3CH(CH_2)_3CH(CH_2)_3CH \cdot CH_3$$
$$CH_3 \quad CH_3 \quad CH_3 \quad CH_3$$
$$O$$

Vitamin K₁

by the added substances depended upon their concentration. With minute amounts, some TPNH and oxygen were formed, and less ADP was esterified. With increasing concentrations of added carrier less and less TPNH formed and there was a concomitant rise in ATP formation. It is therefore clear that two separate phosphorylating processes go on in the chloroplast following the photolysis of water. In one TPN⁺ is reduced and oxygen is evolved, with a simultaneous formation of ATP. In the other, the hydrogen carriers, FMN, vitamin K and ascorbic acid, singly or in sequence transfer hydrogen from "AH₂" to an eventual reunion with oxygen, and the energy which is freed in these transfers is used to synthesize ATP. The cyclic character of this process

$$H_2O \xrightarrow[\text{chlorophyll}]{\text{light}} [H] \xrightarrow[\text{carriers}]{\text{via hydrogen}} [O] \rightarrow H_2O$$

is obvious in the diagram. [H] and [O] represent two substances the actual chemical nature of which is unknown. By analogy with oxidative phosphorylation it seems likely that there is more than one hydrogen transfer involved, but there is as yet no clear indication what hydrogen carriers occur in the chloroplast. However the transfer is managed, this cyclic process results in formation of ATP without any concomitant synthesis of TPNH. Since fixation of carbon dioxide requires both substances, there must be in the chloroplast some mechanism for maintaining a proper balance between the two light-catalyzed processes.

The dependence of carbon dioxide fixation upon these two processes is shown in such experiments as the following. Broken chloroplasts which are entirely dependent upon noncyclic phosphorylation because no hydrogen carriers have been added, fix carbon dioxide in phosphoglyceric acid, but fail to go on to the following reductive step and to form phosphorylated sugars.

Here evidently the supply of ATP is inadequate. Similarly, if the concentration of added carrier is so high that all the reducing power is used in cyclic phosphorylation, the reaction sequence stops again at the phosphoglycerate stage. In experiments of this type the supply of TPNH is the limiting factor. It is only when the carrier concentration is low enough so that both processes are proceeding simultaneously that fixation of carbon dioxide leads into the complete reaction sequence and phosphorylated sugars are formed.

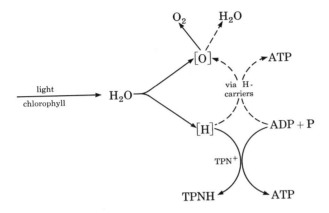

Fig. 15.6. The cyclic and the noncyclic pathways of photophosphorylation. In each pathway the reaction shown on the left provides energy for the esterification shown on the right. Solid arrows, noncyclic pathway; broken arrows, cyclic pathway.

One other experiment inexorably links carbon dioxide fixation with photophosphorylation in the chloroplast. Carbon dioxide fixation has long been known to go on in the dark in intact cells after a period of preillumination. But with broken chloroplasts, fortified with only catalytic amounts of ADP and TPN^+, fixation goes on only in the light. This is clearly referable to the fact that there is no reserve supply of ATP or TPNH; hence, when the few molecules present have been used, they must be reconstituted before photosynthesis can proceed. In Fig. 15.6 an attempt is made to show the relation of the two phosphorylating processes to each other and to that still unknown photochemical event which splits water. The solid arrows show the reactions of the noncyclic process, and the broken arrows those of the cyclic one.

In the experiments with the added hydrogen carriers, it was possible to swing all the reducing power into the cyclic phosphorylation by raising the concentration of the carrier and to allow both processes to go forward simultaneously by limiting the amount of carrier available. There is no present indication of the way in which the flow of material into these processes is controlled in the chloroplast. It is interesting, however, that in recent years it has been shown that control of enzyme synthesis is frequently achieved by what is known as a "feedback mechanism." This means that when the concentration of the product of an enzymic reaction passes a certain critical level, the synthesis of the enzyme which catalyzes formation of that substance is sharply curtailed. It is possible that such a control could operate in the chloroplast, and that a piling up of ATP might shut off the further synthesis of enzymes used in the cyclic process, and so shunt the reducing power into the TPNH-generating sequence.

Summary

All the reactions by which carbon dioxide is transformed into sugars are localized in the chloroplasts. There the energy of sunlight is used, under the catalytic influence of chlorophyll, to generate from water oxidizing and reducing power. These fragments, or units, then react by way of two possible reaction sequences to form ATP and TPNH in the proper ratio to assure carbon dioxide fixation. When fixation takes place as a dark reaction this is made possible by supplies of these two essential reactants previously built up in the light. There is at present no indication how many reactions beyond those shown in Figs. 15.5 and 15.6 take place in the chloroplast. Within five minutes after intact cells have been exposed to labeled carbon dioxide, the label has found its way into lipids, and in a remarkably short time amino acids are also labeled. It is probable that these transformations involve familiar biosynthetic substrates such as acetyl coenzyme A, pyruvate, and one-carbon units whether at the level of formate or of carbon dioxide. Wherever the reactions take place, it is clear that the catalytic machinery of the cell allows them to proceed with extraordinary efficiency.

SUGGESTIONS FOR FURTHER READING

The bibliography in the field of carbohydrate metabolism is now so long, and includes so much detail about individual enzymes, that it is almost impossible to choose a meaningful list of moderate length. The references given are therefore either to papers of historical interest which might otherwise be missed, or to books which broadly survey the field, or part of it, and will provide detailed references, or to a few quite recent papers.

Papers of Historical Interest

Bernard, Claude, *Leçons de Physiologie*, Paris, 1855. This is a charming report on some of the earliest observations.

Fletcher, W. M., and F. G. Hopkins, Lactic acid in amphibian muscle, *J. Physiol.*, *35*, 247 (1906–1907).

Lundsgaard, E., Muscular contraction without lactic acid formation, *Biochem. Z.*, *217*, 162 (1930).

Meyerhof, O., Carbohydrate and lactic acid exchange in frog muscle, *Arch. ges. Physiol.*, *185*, 11 (1920).

Meyerhof, O., On the separation of the lactic acid forming enzymes from muscle, *Naturwiss.*, *14*, 196 (1926).

Books and Review Articles

Ann. Rev. Biochem., Annual Reviews, Palo Alto, Calif.

Ann. Rev. Plant Physiol., Annual Reviews, Palo Alto, Calif.
> These carry articles on carbohydrate metabolism each year with references to hundreds of papers published in each reviewed period.

Dixon, M., and E. C. Webb, *Enzymes*, Longmans, Green, London, 1958.
> In this book is an exhaustive list of enzymes and a staggering list of references from which to begin a study of any specific enzyme.

Pigman, W. W. (ed.), *The Carbohydrates*, 2nd ed., Academic, New York, 1957.
> This book was referred to in the chapter concerned with chemistry of carbohydrates, but it also carries a section dealing with their biochemistry and another with their physiology.

Edelman, J., Formation of oligosaccharides by enzymic transglycosylation, *Advances in Enzymol.*, *17*, 189 (1956).

Kalckar, H. M., Uridinediphospho galactose, *Advances in Enzymol.*, *20*, 111 (1958).

Papers on Several Different Subjects

Butt, V. S., and H. Beevers, Regulation of pathways of glucose catabolism in maize roots, *Biochem. J.*, *80*, 21 (1961).

Canvin, D. T., and H. Beevers, Sucrose synthesis from acetate in the germinating castor bean, *J. Biol. Chem.*, *236*, 988 (1961).

Chakravorty, M., and D. P. Burma, Enzymes of the pentose phosphate pathway in the Mung-bean seedling, *Biochem. J.*, *73*, 48 (1959).

Charalampous, F. C., Mechanism of cleavage of inositol to D-glucuronic acid, *J. Biol. Chem.*, *235*, 1286 (1960).

Eisenberg, F., *et al.*, Studies on the glucuronic acid pathway of glucose metabolism, *J. Biol. Chem.*, *234*, 250 (1959).

Feingold, D. S., *et al.*, Xylosyl transfer catalyzed by an asparagus extract, *J. Biol. Chem.*, *234*, 488 (1959).

Katz, J., *et al.*, The occurrence and mechanism of the hexose monophosphate shunt (another name for the pentose phosphate pathway) in rat liver slices, *J. Biol. Chem.*, *214*, 853 (1955).

Kornberg, H. L., and J. R. Sadler, Microbial oxidation of glycollate via a dicarboxylic acid cycle, *Nature*, *185*, 153 (1960).

Kornberg, H. L., and H. A. Krebs, Synthesis of cell constituents from C_2 units by a modified tricarboxylic acid cycle, *Nature*, *179*, 988 (1957).

Leloir, L. F., and S. H. Goldemberg, Synthesis of glycogen from uridine diphosphate glucose in liver, *J. Biol. Chem.*, *235*, 919 (1960).

Leloir, L. F., *et al.*, Starch and oligosaccharide synthesis from uridine diphosphate glucose, *J. Biol. Chem.*, *236*, 636 (1961).

Marcus, A., and J. Velasco, Enzymes of the glyoxylate cycle in germinating peanuts and castor beans, *J. Biol. Chem.*, *235*, 563 (1960).

Nadkarni, G. B., *et al.*, Gluconeogenesis from glycine and serine, *J. Biol. Chem.*, *235*, 420 (1960).

Pontremoli, S., *et al.*, A coupled reaction catalyzed by . . . transketolase and transaldolase, *J. Biol. Chem.*, *235*, 1881 (1960).

Reichard, P., *et al.*, Formation of deoxycytidine phosphates from cytidine phosphates in extracts from *E. Coli*, *J. Biol. Chem.*, *236*, 1150 (1961).

Tonomura, Y., *et al.*, On the active site of myosin A-adenosine triphosphatase, *J. Biol. Chem.*, *236*, 1968 (1961).

Venkataraman, R., and E. Racker, Mechanism of action of transaldolase, I, *J. Biol. Chem.*, *236*, 1875 (1961); II, *ibid.*, *236*, 1883 (1961).

Villar-Palasi, C., Enzymes of the uridine linked pathway of glycogen synthesis in muscle, *Federation Proc.*, *18*, 344 (1959).

Yamamoto, Y., and H. Beevers, Malate synthetase in higher plants, *Plant Physiol.*, *35*, 102 (1960).

Photosynthesis

Arnon, D. I., Localization of photosynthesis in chloroplasts, p. 279 in *Enzymes; Units of Biological Structure and Function*, O. H. Gaebler (ed.), Academic, New York, 1956.

Arnon, D. I., The chloroplast as a complete photosynthetic unit, *Science*, *122*, 9 (1955).

Calvin, M., Energy reception and transfer in photosynthesis, in *Biophysical Science*, J. L. Oncley (ed.-in-chief), Wiley, New York, 1959.

Davenport, H. E., Relationship between photophosphorylation and the Hill reaction, *Nature*, *184*, 524 (1959).

Losada, M., *et al.*, Photosynthesis by isolated chloroplasts, XI, *J. Biol. Chem.*, *235*, 832 (1960).

Trebst, A. V., *et al.*, Photosynthesis by isolated chloroplasts, X, *J. Biol. Chem.*, *234*, 3055 (1959); XII, *ibid.*, *235*, 840 (1960).

Vishniac, W., *et al.*, Enzymic aspects of photosynthesis, *Advances in Enzymol.*, *19*, 1 (1957).

Index

Index

Note: Acids are listed both as acids and as ions, i.e., acetic acid appears both as such and as acetate. Many substances are listed both in the singular and the plural.

Abderhalden, E., polypeptide synthesis, 205
Abel, J. J., vividiffusion, 383
Absorbance, 36
 ultraviolet, by purine and pyrimidine bases, 241
Absorption, of foodstuffs, *see* Carbohydrate absorption; Fats, absorption of; Proteins, absorption of
 of light, 32–43
Absorption coefficients, 18
Absorption spectra, 37–43
 infrared, 40–43
Absorptivity, 36
Acetal, formation of, 126
 link in phospholipids, 268
Acetaldehyde, catalytic oxidation, 388–389
 formation from threonine, 494
Acetate, conversion, to acetyl CoA, 448–449
 to amino acids, 606
 to carbohydrates, 605–606
 to cholesterol, 569–574
 to fatty acids, 450, 565–566
 to heme, 353, 515–517
 to β-hydroxy-β-methylglutaryl CoA, 572
 to mevalonic acid, 572
 to squalene, 569–570
 in detoxication, 492

Acetate (*Continued*)
 metabolism, via the citric acid cycle 424, 428–431
 via the glyoxylate cycle, 605
Acetic acid, ionization constant, 51
 titration curve, 50
Acetoacetate, formation, from fatty acids, 541–542, 550–553
 from leucine, 497
 from phenylalanine, 507
 from tyrosine, 507
Acetoacetyl CoA, conversion, to acetoacetate in muscle, 551
 to acetoacetate in liver, 552
 to β-hydroxy-β-methylglutaryl CoA, 552, 572
 in formation of succinyl CoA, 551
Acetone, 146, 451, 541
 reaction with glucose, 146
Acetyl CoA, 443–450
 biosynthesis, from acetyldihydrolipoate, 427
 from amino acids, 449–450
 from fatty acids, 449, 450, 549–550
 from pyruvate, 424–427
 conversion, to butyryl CoA, 566
 to citrate, 428
 to β-hydroxy-β-methylglutaryl CoA, 572
 to malonyl CoA, 565
 to squalene, 572–574
 mechanism of synthesis, 444, 448–449

Acetyl CoA *(Continued)*
  metabolic relationships, 450
  reaction, with acetoacetyl CoA, 572
    with oxaloacetate, 428
  use, in acetylation, 449
    in detoxication, 492
    in mercapturic acid formation, 492
    in synthesis of acyl CoA, 493
Acetyl donors, 450
N-Acetyl neuraminic acid, 159, 271
Acetyl phosphate, 435
Acetylcholine, 481
6-S-Acetyldihydrolipoate, conversion to
    acetyl CoA, 427
N-Acetylglucosaminyl transfer, 609
Acid, definition, 48
α₁-Acid glycoprotein, 180
cis-Aconitic acid, 420, 428–429
Acree-Rosenheim reaction, 198–199
α-Acrose, 154
Actin, 581
Activation of one-carbon unit, 452–453
Active acetate, see Acetyl CoA
Active carbon dioxide, 453–454
Active formaldehyde, see One-carbon unit
Active hydroxymethyl, 453, 494
Active methionine, see S-Adenosylmeth-
    ionine
Active site, see Enzymes, active site in
Active sulfate, see 3'-Phosphoadenosine-
    5'-phosphosulfate
Active transport, 23
  of carbohydrates, 385–386
  of cations, 344–345
Activity coefficient, 45
Actomyosin, 581
Acyl CoA, mechanism of formation, 448
Adamkiewicz reaction, 198–199
Adenine, 239, 240, 514
Adenosine, 241
Adenosine-5'-diphosphate, 244
  phosphorylation of, 436–441, 591–592,
    616–620
Adenosine monophosphate, see Adenylic
    acid
Adenosine-5'-phosphosulfate (APS), 491
Adenosine triphosphatase (ATP-ase),
    291, 585
Adenosine-5'-triphosphate, 244, 435, 583
  in activation of amino acids, 443, 518
  in bioluminescence, 441
  free energy of hydrolysis, 243, 436
  in muscular contraction, 441, 584–585
  in phosphorylation of arginine, 442
    of choline, 442
    of creatine, 440–441
    of galactose, 442

Adenosine-5'-triphosphate *(Continued)*
  in synthesis of S-Adenosylmethionine,
    442
    of glutathione, 520
    of proteins, 518–519
  photosynthetic formation of, 616–620
S-Adenosylmethionine, 483
  in creatine synthesis, 486
  synthesis of, 442
Adenylic acid, 241, 244
ADP, see Adenosine-5'-diphosphate
Aglycone, 151
Agmatine, 488
AICA, see 5-Amino-4-imidazolecarbox-
    amide
AICAR, see 5-Amino-4-imidazolecar-
    boxamide ribotide
AIR, see 5-Aminoimidazole ribotide
β-Alanine, 488
D-Alanine, 188
L-Alanine, formation from pyruvate, 475,
    477
  formula, 186
  ionization constant, 186
  oxidation of, 308
  stereochemical configuration, 188
L-Alanine dehydrogenase, 474–475
Albuminoids, 213
Albumins, 213
Alcaptonuria, 322
Alcohol dehydrogenase, 395–397, 594
  active site, 314
  function of metal, 314
Alcoholic fermentation, 593–595
  by-products, 595–596
Aldol condensation, 140, 599, 616
Aldolase, 589, 599, 616
Aldonic acids, 137
Aldoses, quantitative estimation, 137
Aldosterone, 559, 562
Alkoxydiglyceride, 261
Allantoic acid, 513
Allantoin, 513
Allopregnane, 559
Allose, 124
Altrose, 124
Amidine group, 485
D-Amino acid oxidase, 297, 306–308, 410
  mechanism of action, 472–473
L-Amino acid oxidases, 410
  distribution, 473
  dual specificity, 294
  substrates for, 473
D-Amino acids, occurrence, 188
L-Amino Acids, 188–203
  amino group reactions, 196–198
  ammine salts of, 194

L-Amino Acids (*Continued*)
ampholyte properties, 191
bioassay, 215, 459
carbobenzoxy derivatives, 203–205
carboxyl group reactions, 194–196
chemical properties, 191–203
chromatography, 28, 30, 216–219
conversion, to acetyl CoA, 449, 506–507
to pyruvate, 506–507
deamination, 471–476
oxidative, 472–475
reductive, 476
decarboxylation, 196, 486–487, 488–489
as dipolar ions, 190
electrophoresis, 191–192, 214
formol titration, 196–197, 295
glycogenic, 504–505
indispensable, for animals, 459–462
for bacteria, 459
ionization constants, 192–194
isoelectric points, 192
ketogenic, 504–505
metabolism, 470–507
peptide formation from, 203–207
phthalyl derivatives, 205
physical properties, 190–191
quantitative estimation, 195
reaction, with 1-fluoro-2,4-dinitrobenzene, 197
with phenylisothiocyanate, 198
residue symbols, 186–187, 189, 219
stereochemical configuration, 188–189
transamination reactions, 477–480
2-Amino-4-hydroxy-6-methyltetrahydropteridine, 499
5-Amino-4-imidazolecarboxamide (AICA), 524
5-Amino-4-imidazolecarboxamide ribotide (AICAR), 501, 527
α-Amino-β-ketoadipic acid, 516
Amino sugars, 157–159
Aminoacyladenylate, 443, 518
L-α-Aminoadipic acid, 504
γ-Aminobutyrate, from L-glutamate, 488
5-Aminoimidazole ribotide (AIR), 526
Aminolevulinate dehydrase, 516
δ-Aminolevulinic acid, 516
in heme biosynthesis, 516–517
Aminopeptidases, 380
Ammonia excretion, 508–509
Amoeba, 97
AMP, *see* Adenylic acid
Ampholyte, definition, 192
Amygdalin, 153
Amylase, 297, 373

α-Amylase, 385
β-Amylase, 176–177, 385
Amylopectin, 174–177
Amylose, 174–177
helix in, 176
iodine complex, 176
Androgens, 558, 561
Δ⁴-Androstene-3,17-dione, 562
Δ⁴-Androstene-19-ol-3,17-dione, 562
Ångstrom, A. J., 33
Angstrom unit, definition, 33
5,10-Anhydroformyltetrahydrofolic acid, *see* N^5,N^{10}-Methenyltetrahydrofolic acid
Anhydroleucovorin, *see* N^5,N^{10}-Methenyltetrahydrofolic acid
Animal structures, 103–111
Anode, definition, 63
Anomers, 128
projection formulas, 129
Anthranilic acid, 501
Antibodies, 181, 212
Antigens, 181, 212
Antiparallel chain pleated sheet, 225, 227
Apoenzyme, 306
APS, *see* Adenosine-5'-phosphosulfate
APS-kinase, 491
Arabinose, 124
Arachidic acid, 259
Arachidonic acid, 259, 555
Arginase, 293, 509–510
L-Arginine, in biosynthesis, of creatine, 485–486
of urea, 509–512
chemistry, 202–203
conversion, to agmatine, 488
to arginine phosphate, 442
to ornithine, 485, 495, 509–510
formation from glutamate, 495
formula, 187
indispensability, 461, 462
ionization constant, 187
oxidation, 495
Sakaguchi test, 202
L-Arginine decarboxylase, 488
Arginine phosphate, 435, 442, 585
transfer of phosphate to ADP, 441–442
Arginosuccinase, 512
Arginosuccinate, in urea synthesis, 511–512
Arginosuccinate synthetase, 511
Armstrong, E. F., 128
Arnon, D., 617–620
Ascorbate oxidase, 413, 417
in plant respiration, 413
Ascorbate reductase, in plant respiration, 413

L-Ascorbic acid, 159–160, 414
  biosynthesis, 600–602
  in photosynthesis, 618–620
Asparagine, 187, 467, 475–476
L-Aspartate, conversion, to β-alanine, 488
    to L-alanine, 488
  in purine biosynthesis, 526–527
  in pyrimidine biosynthesis, 521
  in urea biosynthesis, 510–512
L-Aspartate α-decarboxylase, 488
L-Aspartate β-decarboxylase, 488
L-Aspartate transcarbamylase, 521
L-Aspartic acid, conversion to fumaric
    acid, 476
  formula, 187
  ionization constant, 187
Astbury, W. T., 227, 229
ATP, *see* Adenosine-5′-triphosphate
ATP-sulfurylase, 491
Autolysis, 287
Auxin, *see* Indolyl-3-acetic acid
Axial bonds, 135
Azelaic acid, 280
Azelao-glycerides, 279

B vitamins, table, 445–447
Barbituric acid, 236
Base, conjugate, definition, 48
Base pairing in nucleic acids, 246–247
Batyl alcohol, 262
Benzoic acid, 51
Benzoyl CoA, conversion to hippuric
    acid, 450
1-O-Benzoyl-D-glucuronic acid, 139
Benzyl alcohol, conversion to benzoxycar-
    bonyl chloride, 204
Bergmann, M., 203, 379
Best, C. H., 540
Betaine, biosynthesis from choline, 482
  conversion, to dimethylglycine, 482
    to glycine, 558
Bicarbonate-Ringer solution, 326
Bile, 373, 374–376
Bile acids, 563–564
  steroid components of, 374, 376–377
Bile pigments, 354
Bile salts, role in fat absorption, 384–385
Bilirubin, 354, 355
Biliverdin, 354
Biotin, 446, 453–454, 511
  carbon dioxide compound of, 454
Biuret test, 207
Bloch, K., 556
Blood, 340–363
Blood buffers, 359–360
Boat conformations, 134
Bollman, J. L., 471

Branching factor in carbohydrate syn-
    thesis, 607–608
Braunstein, A. E., 477
p-Bromophenylmercapturic acid, 492
Brønsted, J. N., 48
Buchanan, J. M., 524
Buchner, E., 285, 593
Buffers, 52–56
  preparation, 53–56
Butyric acid, 259
Butyryl CoA, biosynthesis from acetyl
    CoA, 566
  incorporation in fatty acids, 566

Cadaverine, from L-lysine, 489
Caffeine, 240, 481
Calvin, M., 613–616
Camphor, 574
Capric acid, 259
Caproic acid, 259
Caprylic acid, 259
Carbamate phosphokinase, 511, 521
Carbamino compound, 357, 361–362
Carbamyl phosphate, in urea synthesis,
    511
  in pyrimidine synthesis, 521
Carbamylaspartate, 521
Carbohydrate absorption, active transport
    in, 385–386
Carbohydrate metabolism, anaerobic,
    579–597
Carbohydrates, chemistry, 115–181
  classification, 116
Carbon, path in photosynthesis, 613–616
Carbon dioxide, activation, 453–454
  effect on Hill reaction, 612
  in purine biosynthesis, 526–527
  transport in blood, 357–359
  in urea biosynthesis, 511
Carbon monoxide hemoglobin, absorp-
    tion spectrum, 400
Carbonic acid, 51
  titration curve, 360
Carbonic anhydrase, 291, 359
Carboxyhemoglobin, 350
α-Carboxylase, 488, 594
Carboxylases, *see* Decarboxylases
Carboxypeptidases, 222, 380
Cardiolipin, 263
Carotene, biosynthesis from leucine, 497
β-Carotene, 575
Catalase, 297, 411, 416
Cathepsins, 287, 469
Cathode, definition, 63
Cell, concentration, 65
  electrophoresis, 85, 211
  voltaic, 59

Cellobiose, 167, 173
Cells, animal, 90–94
  autotrophic, 99
  fractionation of, 91
  heterotrophic, 99
  plant, 90, 98
Cellular oxidation, 387-432
  localization in mitochondria, 431–432
Cellulose, 172–174, 176
  hydrogen bonds in, 174
Cephalin, *see* Phosphatidyl ethanolamine
Cerebrosides, 269–270
Cerotic acid, 259
Chair conformations, 134–136, 161
Chaulmoogric acid, 259, 279
Chenodeoxycholic acid, 377, 564
Chimyl alcohol, 262
Chitin, 178–179
  biosynthesis, 609
Chitosamine, 158, 609
Chloride shift, 362, 363
Chlorocruorins, 104, 364–365
Chlorophyll, 95
  function in photosynthesis, 611–613, 617–620
  localization, 94–95
  structure, 610–611
Chloroplasts, 91, 94, 95
  function in photosynthesis, 616–620
Δ^5-Cholesten-3β-ol, 273
Cholesterol, 272
  biosynthesis, 569–574
  as biosynthetic substrate, 562
  excretion, 563–564
Cholic acid, 376–377, 563–564
Choline, conversion, to acetyl choline, 449
  to betaine, 482
  to glycine, 558
  in phospholipids, 264, 267–269
Choline dehydrogenase, 396
Chondroitin sulfates, 158, 180
  sulfate transfer to, 491
Chondrosamine, 158
Chromatography, column, 26, 217–219
  gas, 29
  paper, 27, 614
Chromoproteins, 213
  See also Hemoglobins; Respiratory pigments
Chromosomes, 250
Chylomicrons, 384, 539
Chyme, 371
Chymotrypsin, 375, 380–381
Chymotrypsinogen, 373
Circulatory system, 104, 378
cis-enediol, 140

Citric acid, 419–421, 428–429
Citric acid cycle, 418–431
  localization of enzymes, 431–432
  reactions of, 423–431
Citrulline, 203
  conversion to arginine, 510–512
  in urea synthesis, 510–511
Clupanodonic acid, 259
Coacervation, 76
Cocarboxylase, *see* Thiamine pyrophosphate
Coenzyme I, *see* Diphosphopyridine nucleotide
Coenzyme II, *see* Triphosphopyridine nucleotide
Coenzyme A, 444
  in citric acid cycle, 425, 427, 429–430
Coenzyme Q, 415
Coenzyme-linked dismutation, 595–596
Coenzyme-linked oxidoreduction, 414
Coenzymes, 290, 306–308
  at active site, 314
  oxidative, 391–412
Cohen, P. P., 475
Cohn, E. J., 344
Collagen, precursors of, 495
  turnover of, 467
Colloidal dimensions, 71–72
Colloids, 70–88
  analysis, 81–88
  protective, 75
  sensitization by, 76
Colorimetry, 34–36
Conformation, 134–136
Coproporphyrin I, 349, 350
Coproporphyrin III, 349, 350
Coprostanol, 563–564
Corey, R. B., 226–227, 229
Cori, C., 145
Cori, Gerty, 145
Cori ester, synthesis, 146
Corticosteroids, 558–559
Corticosterone, 559, 562
Cortisol, 559, 562
Cortisone, 559
Countercurrent distribution, 275
Creatine, 236
  biosynthesis, 484–486
  conversion to creatine phosphate, 441–442
  decomposition by Ba(OH)$_2$, 485
Creatine phosphate, 236–237, 435, 441, 481
  in muscle, 584
  transfer of phosphate to ADP, 441–442
Creatinine, 236, 484
Cristae mitochondriales, 92

Crotonase, dual specificity of, 550
Crotonic acid, 549–550
Cyanocobalamine, 447
Cyanohydrin reaction, 118–119
Cyclohexanols, 160–162
Cymarose, 152
Cystathionine, 503
L-Cysteic acid, 503
  conversion to taurine, 488
Cysteic acid decarboxylase, 488, 503
L-Cysteine, 187
  biosynthesis, 503
  chemistry, 199–200
  conversion, to hypotaurine, 503
    to sulfate, 493, 503
    to taurine, 376, 488, 503
  in detoxication, 492
  in glutathione biosynthesis, 520
  ionization constant, 187
L-Cysteine sulfinate decarboxylase, 488
Cysteine sulfinic acid, 503
  conversion to hypotaurine, 488
L-Cystine, 186
Cytidine, 241
Cytidine-5'-diphosphate choline, 569
Cytidine-5'-diphosphate diglyceride, 568
Cytidine-5'-diphosphate ethanolamine, 569
Cytidine-5'-phosphate, 242
Cytidine-5'-triphosphate, biosynthesis
    from uridylic acid, 522
  in lipid biosynthesis, 568–569
Cytidylic acid, 241
Cytochrome a, in oxidative phosphoryla-
    tion, 437–439
  reduction potential, 406, 413
Cytochrome a_1, 406, 412
Cytochrome a_2, 406
  structure, 405
Cytochrome a_3, 406, 412
  copper in, 407
    See also Respiratory enzyme
Cytochrome a_4, 406
Cytochrome b, 406, 412, 413
Cytochrome b_1, 406
  in oxidative phosphorylation, 437–439
Cytochrome b_2, 406, 410
    See also Lactate dehydrogenase
Cytochrome b_3, 406
Cytochrome b_4, 406
Cytochrome b_5, 406
Cytochrome b_6, 406
Cytochrome b_7, 406
Cytochrome c, cysteine bridges in, 404
  imidazole link in, 404
  molecular weight, 406
  reduction, active site for, 411
  reduction potential, 406, 413

Cytochrome c (*Continued*)
  structure, 403–404
Cytochrome c_1 406, 412
Cytochrome c_2, 406
Cytochrome c_3, 406
Cytochrome c_4, 406
Cytochrome c_5, 406
Cytochrome c reductases, 410
Cytochrome e, *see* Cytochrome c_1
Cytochrome f, 406, 413
Cytochrome h, 406
Cytochrome m, *see* Cytochrome b_5
Cytochrome x, *see* Cytochrome b_5
Cytochrome oxidase, 405–407, 412
    See also Respiratory enzyme
Cytochromes, 400–407
Cytoplasm, 91
Cytosine, 239, 240

Deamination, oxidative, of amino acids,
    472–475
  reductive, of amino acids, 476
Decarboxylases, table, 488–489
Decarboxylation, of amino acids, 486–
    489
Dehydroascorbic acid, 160, 414
Dehydrogenases, table, 396
5-Dehydroquinic acid, 498
5-Dehydroshikimic acid, 498
Denaturation, of nucleoproteins, 238
  of proteins, 232–233
Denitrification, 458
Deoxy sugars, 156
Deoxycholic acid, 377, 563–564
Deoxyribofuranose, 238
Deoxyribose nucleic acid, biosynthesis,
    520–530
  as coding device, in genes, 251
    for protein synthesis, 517–518
  helical structure, 246–249
  hydrogen bonding in, 246–247
  hydrolytic products, 238
  localization in the cell, 244
  molecular weight, 245
  structure, 245–249
Deoxyribose nucleotides, biosynthesis
    from uridylic acid, 523
Desmosterol, 571
Detoxication, by acetylation, 492
  by cysteine, 492
  by glucuronic acid, 491–492
  by glycine, 493
  by oxidation, 487
  by sulfate transfer, 487–491
Deuteroporphyrin, 348, 349
Diabetes, in metabolic experiments, 322,
    539–541

Diacetylurea, 236
Diamino-dideoxyglucose, 158
Diaphorase, 430
    See also Dihydrolipoate dehydrogenase
Diazobenzenesulfonic acid, reaction with histidine, 201
Dietary lipids, influence on body lipids, 542–543
Digestive system, 107–108, 370–379
Digitalose, 152
Digitoxose, 152
α, β-Diglyceride, 567
Dihydrolipoate, oxidation by DPN$^+$, 396, 427, 430
Dihydrolipoate dehydrogenase, 396
Dihydrolipoic acid, 425
Dihydroorotase, 521
Dihydroorotic acid, in pyrimidine biosynthesis, 521–522
Dihydroxyacetone, biosynthesis from glyceraldehyde, 156
    conversion to fructose and sorbose, 140
Dihydroxyacetone phosphate, 587, 589–590, 598–599
    in photosynthesis, 615–616
Diiodotyrosine, 201
Diisopropylfluorophosphate, 312
Diisopropylidene-D-glucose, 146
    reaction with POCl$_3$, 147
Dimethyl sulfate, 150
γ, γ-Dimethylallyl pyrophosphate, 573
Dimethylglycine, formation from betaine, 482
Dimethylpropiothetin, 483
Dimethylthetin, 483
1, 3-Diphosphoglyceric acid, 435
    conversion to 3-Phosphoglyceric acid, 591
    transfer of phosphate to ADP, 591
Diphosphopyridine nucleotide, absorption spectra, 394
    chemistry, 392–394
    mechanism of reduction, 394–395
    in oxidative phosphorylation, 437–439
    reduction potential, 398, 413
    stereospecific reduction, 397
Disulfide bonds, in keratin, 228
    in ribonuclease, 222–223
Dixon, M., 290, 325
DNA, *see* Deoxyribose nucleic acid
Donnan equilibrium, 79–81
DOPA decarboxylase, 489
DPN, *see* Diphosphopyridine nucleotide
Dual specificity, of digestive proteinases, 294
    of L-amino acid oxidase, 294

Dual specificity (*Continued*)
    of xanthine oxidase, 294
    of crotonase, 550

E_0, definition, 62
E_0', definition, 67
Ectoplasm, 91
Edman degradation, 221
Electrophoresis, 84
    zone, 88
Electrophoresis cells, 85, 211
Eleostearic acid, 259
Embden, G., 583–584
Embden ester, 589
Embden-Meyerhof sequence, *see* Glycolytic sequence
Emulsifying agents, 78, 535
Emulsin, 129, 293
Emulsions, 78
End group analysis, 170–171, 173–176, 178
Endocrine glands, 109, 110
Endogenous metabolism, 464
Endopeptidases, 380–381
Endoplasm, 91
Endoplasmic reticulum, 93
Enediols, cis and trans, 140
Energy-rich compounds, 236–237, 434–436
Energy sources for cells, 99–100
Enolase, 591
Enterokinase, 373
Enzyme, definition, 286
Enzyme specificity, 292–294
    dual, 294, 550
    stereochemical, 293–294, 397
Enzyme-substrate compounds, 301–304, 308, 313, 428, 448, 502, 516, 518, 590
Enzyme synthesis, control by nucleic acids, 250–251, 517–519
Enzymes, 283–315
    activation, 304–306
        by inorganic ions, 305–306
    active site in, 290, 313, 314, 411, 448
        role of inorganic ions, 306, 314
    catalytic constant, 291
    competitive inhibition, 310
    copper protein, 417–418
    flavoprotein, 407–412
    history, 283–286
    imidazole groups in, 311, 404
    inhibition of, 309–310
    iron porphyrin, 399–407, 416–417
    isolation, 286–290
    properties, 292–315
    protein-splitting, 379–382

Enzymes (*Continued*)
  pyridinoproteins, 392–399
  secondary structure, importance, 311
  sulfhydryl groups in, 311, 314, 590
  tertiary structure, importance, 311
  turnover number, 290–291
Enzymic reaction rates, influence of activity, 296
  of enzyme concentration, 299
  of pH, 296–298
  of substrate concentration, 300
  of temperature, 298–299
Enzymic reactions, coupled, 332, 414, 613
  integrated, 315
  kinetics, 294–304
  mechanism, 310–315
  Michaelis constant, 301
  Michaelis theory, 301–304
  role of coenzymes, 306–308
  stereospecificities, 293–294, 397
Epimerization, 137–138
Equatorial bonds, 135
Erucic acid, 259
Erythrose, 124
D-Erythrose-4-phosphate, conversion to shikimic acid, 498
  in pentose phosphate pathway, 598
  in photosynthesis, 615–616
Ethanolamine, 264, 267–268, 494, 557, 567, 569
  conversion to choline, 568–569
Ethyl alcohol, caloric value, 580
  formation by fermentation, 593–595
Etioporphyrin, 348, 349
Estradiol, 560, 562
Estrane, 560
Estriol, 560, 562
Estrogens, 558, 560
Estrone, 560, 562
Even distribution, principle of, 281
Excretory system, 109
Exogenous metabolism, 464
Exopeptidases, 380
Extinction coefficient, 36

F, definition, 44
F$_s$, definition, 24
FAD, *see* Flavin adenine dinucleotide
FAICAR, *see* Formyl AICAR
Farnesyl pyrophosphate, 573–574
Fats, absorption of, 384
  caloric value, 536
  component acids, 277–279
  component triglycerides, 279–281
  conversion to carbohydrates, 543–544
  depot, 536

Fats (*Continued*)
  digestion of, 383–384
Fatty acid spiral, enzymes of, 549–550
Fatty acids, biosynthesis, in liver, 565–566
  in mitochondria, 566
  conversion, to acetyl CoA, 449
    to ketone bodies, 541–542, 550–553
  desaturation, 554–556
  essential, 554–555
  nomenclature, 260
  occurrence in fats, 277–279
  oxidation in plants, 553
  β-oxidation, 547–550
Fatty acyl CoA dehydrogenase, 549
Fatty acyl CoA synthetase, 549, 567–568
Fatty liver, 540–541
Feedback control of enzyme synthesis, 620
FGAM, *see* Formylglycinamidine ribotide
FGAR, *see* Formylglycinamide ribotide
Fibroin, 225–226
Fischer, E., 117, 121–123, 126–131, 141, 154, 203, 205, 310, 611
  separation of amino acids, 214
Fischer, H., 346, 347, 610
Flavin adenine dinucleotide, 408–409
  in D-amino acid oxidase, 306–308, 473
  oxidation-reduction, 408
  reduction potential, 413
Flavin mononucleotide, in L-amino acid oxidase, 473
  in photosynthesis, 618
Flavoproteins, 407–412
Flotation, in isolation of lipoproteins, 538
Fluorescence, 43
  quenching of, 45
1-Fluoro-2,4-dinitrobenzene, reaction with amino acids, 197
  in study of protein structure, 219, 221
Folic acid, 446
Folin, O., 464
Folin and Looney test for tyrosine, 201
Folinic acid, *see* 5-Formyl-5, 6, 7, 8-tetrahydrofolic acid
Formaldehyde, in photosynthetic theory, 611
  reaction with the amino group, 196
  in tryptophan test, 198–199
Formol titration, 196–197
Formyl AICAR, in purine biosynthesis, 527
5-Formyl-5,6,7,8-tetrahydrofolic acid, 452

Formylglycinamide ribotide (FGAR), in purine biosynthesis, 525
Formylglycinamidine ribotide (FGAM), in purine biosynthesis, 526
N^{10}-formyltetrahydrofolic acid, 452
   in purine biosynthesis, 527
Free energy, 68–70
Free energy change, standard, $\Delta F°$, 69
Frequency, definition, 32
β-D-Fructofuranose, 132
Fructose, 140
   formula, 125
   optical rotation, 164
   structure, 118, 120
Fructose cyanohydrins, 120
Fructose diphosphate, 148
   biosynthesis from triose phosphate, 598–599, 615–616
   conversion to triose phosphates, 589
Fructose oxime, 120
Fructose-6-phosphate, 148, 598–599
   conversion to fructose diphosphate, 589
Fucose, 152
Fumarase, 430
Fumarate, conversion to malate, 421–422, 423, 430
Fumaric acid, 420, 421
   from aspartic acid, 476
Furan, 130
Furanose, 131
Furanoside, 131

Galactaric acids, 123
Galactokinase, 293, 442
Galactosamine, 158
D-Galactose, 123, 124
   in sphingolipids, 270
D-Galactose-1-phosphate, 442
Gangliosides, 270
GAR, *see* Glycinamide ribotide
Gas electrode, 61
Gases, solubility, 17–20
   effect of salts, 19–20
Gastric juice, 371
Gels, 77
Genes, 250
Geranyl pyrophosphate, conversion to farnesyl pyrophosphate, 573
Globular proteins, 229–232
Globulins, 213
   serum, dimensions, 229–230
Glucaric acid, 119
α-D-Glucofuranose, projection formula, 131
Gluconic acid, 119
   γ- and σ-lactones, 138

α-D-Glucopyranose, projection formula, 131
Glucosamine, 125, 158
Glucosan phosphorylase, 607–608
Glucosan transglycosylase, 608
Glucosazone, 141
   mechanism of formation, 142
D-Glucose, caloric value, 580
   chemistry, 117–120, 136–151
   conversion, to acetone derivative, 146–147
      to fructose, 142
      to glucosazone, 141–142
      to glucose-6-phosphate, 594
      to glucosides, 126–128
      to glucuronic acid, 491–492, 600–601
      to pentoses, 603–604
      to ribose-5-phosphate, 598–599
   equilibrium in alkali, 140
   in water, 132–133
   formula, 122, 130
   optical rotation, 128, 164
   reaction with Fehling's solution, 141
   reduction, 136–137
   in sphingolipids, 270
Glucose cyanohydrins, 119
Glucose dehydrogenase, 396
Glucose hemiacetal, 127
Glucose oxime, 119
Glucose pentaacetate, 126, 133–134
   conversion, to glucose-1-phosphate 145–146
      to tetracetylglucosyl bromide, 145
Glucose-1-phosphate, conversion, to glucose-6-phosphate, 588–589
   to glucuronic acid, 492
   synthesis from glucose pentaacetate, 146
Glucose-3-phosphate, synthesis, 147
Glucose-6-phosphate, 148
   conversion, to fructose-6-phosphate, 589
      to 6-phosphogluconate, 598–599
Glucose-6-phosphate dehydrogenase, 396
α-Glucosidases, 176–177, 297, 385
Glucosides, reaction with periodic acid (HIO_4), 143–144
Glucosone, 142
Glucosylamine, 157
D-Glucuronic acid, 139
   biosynthesis from glucose, 491–492, 600–601
   conversion to L-gulonic acid, 601–602
   in detoxication, 491–492, 563
Glucuronic acid pathway, 600–603
β-Glucuronidase, 563

634   Index

L-Glutamate decarboxylase, 488
L-Glutamate dehydrogenase, 396, 474, 478
L-Glutamic acid, 187, 466, 467, 474, 478
  conversion, to γ-aminobutyrate, 488
    to arginine, 495
    to ornithine, 495
    to proline, 495
  formation from α-ketoglutarate, 474
  in glutathione synthesis, 520
  oxidation, 495
  oxidative deamination, 474
Glutamic semialdehyde, 495
Glutamine, 187, 475–476
  in histidine biosynthesis, 500
  in purine biosynthesis, 523–524, 525
  in transamination, 475–476, 478
Glutaric acid, 504
Glutathione, 234–235
  biosynthesis, 519–520
  function, 234
  in mercapturic acid formation, 492
Glutathione dehydrogenase, 410, 413
Glutathione reductase, see Glutathione dehydrogenase
Glutelins, 213
D-Glyceraldehyde, 140
  conversion, to dihydroxyacetone by bacteria, 156
    to sorbose and fructose, 140
  projection formula, 121
  stereoisomers, 121
D-Glyceraldehyde-3-phosphate, 598–599
  dismutation, 595–596
  equilibrium with dihydroxyacetone phosphate, 590, 598
Glyceraldehyde phosphate dehydrogenase, 590
β-Glycerophosphatase, 297
L-α-Glycerophosphate, 567
  See also Phosphoglycerol
Glycerophosphatides, 262–269
α-Glycerophosphoric acid, 263
Glycerose, see Glyceraldehyde
Glyceryl ethers, 261–262
Glycinamide ribotide (GAR), in purine biosynthesis, 525
Glycine, conversion, to acetylglycine, 449
    to active hydroxymethyl, 453
    to active one-carbon unit, 451, 507
    to ethanolamine, 494
    to serine, 494
  in creatine biosynthesis, 485–486
  in detoxication, 493
  in glutathione biosynthesis, 520
  in heme biosynthesis, 516
  ionization constant, 51, 186

Glycine (Continued)
  metabolic use, 465
  titration curves, 193–194
Glycine dehydrogenase, 474
Glycocholic acid, 374, 376
Glycocyamine, see Guanidoacetic acid
Glycogen, 178
  conversion to glucose-1-phosphate, 587–588
Glycolic acid, 118
α-Glycols, oxidation by periodate, 142
Glycolytic sequence, 585–597
  in plants, 596–597
  reversal of, 603
Glycoprotein, α₁-acid, 180
Glycoproteins, 213
Glycosides, natural, 151
Glyoxylate, biosynthesis from allantoin, 514
  conversion to malate, 604–605
Glyoxylate cycle, 604–606
  in plants, 606
Glyoxylic acid, in tryptophan test, 198–199
Graham, T., 70
Grana, 94–95, 613
Green, D. E., 473, 549–550
Greenberg, G. R., 524
GSH, see Glutathione
Guanidine, 190, 235
Guanidoacetic acid, 485–486
Guanine, 239, 240
Guanosine, 241
Guanosine diphosphate, reaction with succinyl CoA, 440
Guanosine-3′-phosphate, 242
Guanosine-5′-triphosphate, 440, 506, 519
Guanylic acid, 241
D-Gulonic acid γ-lactone, 138
L-Gulonic acid, 601–602
L-Gulonolactone, 602
Gulose, 124
  conversion to idose, 138
Gums, 178
Gynaminic acid, 159

Harden, A., 147, 594
Harden-Young ester, 148
Haworth, W. N., 130, 150
Heat of fusion, 16–17
Heat of vaporization, 16–17
Heavy water, preparation, 333
  use with carboxypeptidase, 222
α-Helix, hydrogen bonds in, 230
  in myoglobin, 231
  in proteins, 229
Hematoporphyrin, 349, 350

Heme, biosynthesis, 353, 515–517
  conversion to bile pigments, 354
    to stercobilin, 354–355
    to urobilin, 354–355
  destruction, 352–356
  structure, 345–351
Hemerythrins, 364, 365
Hemiacetal, 126
Hemicelluloses, 177
Hemiglobin, *see* Methemoglobin
Hemin, 345, 346
Hemocyanins, 104, 364, 365
Hemoglobin, 345–356
  in carbon dioxide transport, 357–359
  in oxygen transport, 356–357
  plant, 347
  structure, 351–352
  turnover, 467
Hemoglobins, 363–365
  oxygen affinities of, 364
Henry's law, 18
Heparin, 180
  as emulsifying agent, 535
  sulfate transfer to, 491
Hepatectomy, 323, 471
  effect on nitrogen metabolism, 471
Heteroxanthine, 240
Hexokinase, 293
Hexose phosphate isomerase, 589
High energy compounds, 236–237, 434–436
Hilditch, T. P., 278
Hill reaction, 612, 617
Histamine, formation from L-histidine, 489
L-Histidine, 187
  biosynthesis, 497, 500
  conversion, to active one-carbon unit, 451, 507
    to histamine, 489
  indispensability, 461, 462
  Pauly test, 201
  precipitation, 215
L-Histidine decarboxylase, 489
L-Histidinol, 500
Histones, 213
Hoagland, M. B., 518
Holoenzyme, 306
Homo-γ-linolenic acid, 555
Homocysteine, conversion to methionine, 482
Homogentisic acid, 322
Hopkins, F. G., 234, 581–582
Hopkins-Cole reaction, 198–199, 208
Hormones, 109, 110, 558–563
Hudson, C. S., 129
Hyaluronic acid, 179

Hydnocarpic acid, 259, 279
Hydra, 100
Hydrogen, activation of, 388–391
Hydrogen bonds, in cellulose, 174
  in deoxyribose nucleic acid, 246–247
  in α-helix, 229
  in water, 15
Hydrogen ion concentration, 45–68
Hydrogen peroxide, enzymic formation, 306–308, 398, 410, 416
Hydrolipoic acid, *see* Dihydrolipoic acid
β-Hydroxy-β-methylglutaryl CoA, conversion to mevalonic acid, 572
  from acetoacetyl CoA, 552
  from leucine, 497
β-Hydroxyacyl CoA dehydrogenase, 550
β-Hydroxybutyrate, 541
  oxidation in mitochondria, 437
β-Hydroxybutyrate dehydrogenase, 396, 437
Hydroxylysine, 187
Hydroxyphenylalanine decarboxylase, 489
17α-Hydroxyprogesterone, 562
Hydroxyproline, 187, 198
  in collagen synthesis, 495
  oxidation, 495
  from proline, 495
Hyodeoxycholic acid, 377
Hypoiodite, in estimation of aldoses, 137
Hypotaurine, 488, 503
Hypoxanthine, 239, 240, 514

Identity period, definition, 225
Idonic acid lactone, 138
Idose, 124
  synthesis from gulose, 138
Imidazole ring, biosynthesis, 500
Imidazoleglycerol phosphate, in histidine biosynthesis, 500, 528–529
Imino acids, from amino acids, 308, 472
Inborn errors of metabolism, 322–323
Indican, 152–153, 490
Indicators, table, 57
Indole, 190, 490
Indole group, biosynthesis, 501
Indolyl-3-acetic acid, 502
Indolyl-3-glycerol phosphate, 501
Indoxyl, 152, 490
Indoxyl sulfuric acid, 490
Infrared absorption, curves, 40,42
  of functional groups, 43
Inosine-5'-triphosphate, 506
Inosinic acid, 523
  conversion, to adenylic acid, 528–529
    to guanylic acid, 528–529
Inositides, 265–267

Inositol, 446
  See also Myo-inositol
Inositol triphosphate, 266
Inositols, 161–162
Insulin, amino acid sequence in, 219–221
  molecular weight, 220
Interfacial tensions, table, 25
Intestinal juice, 371, 373
Invert sugar, 164
Iodic acid, HIO₃, 142
Iodine number, 275
Iodoacetate poisoning of muscle, 584
Ionization constants, of acids, 51
  of amino acids, 186–187
Irvine, J. C., 130, 149
Isoalloxazine, 408
Isobutylamine, from L-valine, 489
Isocitrate, conversion, to glyoxylate, 604–605
  to α-ketoglutarate, 429
  to succinate, 604–605
Isocitrate dehydrogenase, 429
Isocitric acid, 420, 428–429
Isocitritase, 604
L-Isoleucine, 186
  biosynthesis, 496
  degradation, 506–507
  indispensability, 461
Δ³-Isopentenyl pyrophosphate, isomerization, 573
Isoprene, 570
Isotonic saline, 23, 326
Isotopes, table, 334
  use in metabolic studies, 332–339
Isovaleric acid, 259

K_a, definition, 49
  values, table, 51
Kassell and Brand estimation of cysteine
  and cystine, 200
Keilin, D., 401
Kendrew, J. C., 224, 231
Keratins, 227–229
Keto acids, oxidative decarboxylation,
  424–427, 429
  transaminations, 477–478, 496, 499,
  500
2-Keto-3-deoxyaraboheptonic acid-7-
  phosphate, 498
3-Keto-L-gulonic acid, 602
α-Keto-β-methylvalerate, formation from
  α-ketobutyrate, 496
α-Ketobutyrate, conversion to α-keto-β-
  methylvalerate, 496
Ketogenesis, 541–542
α-Ketoglutarate, conversion to 6-S-
  succinylhydrolipoate, 429

α-Ketoglutarate dehydrogenase, 429
α-Ketoglutaric acid, 420, 421, 429
α-Ketoisocaproic acid, conversion to
  leucine, 478
α-Ketoisovalerate, formation from pyruvate, 496
  conversion, to leucine, 496
  to valine, 496
Ketone bodies, 541
β-Ketothiolase, 551
Kiliani, H., 118
Kiliani synthesis, 118–119
K-m-e-f group, 227
Knoop, F., 323, 547–549
Kornberg, A., 529–530
Krebs, H., 326, 472
Krebs cycle, *see* Citric acid cycle, Krebs
  urea cycle
Krebs-Henseleit solution, 326
Krebs urea cycle, 509–512
Kritzmann, M. G., 477
Kuhn, R., 27
Kühne, W., 284
Küster, W., 345

Laccase, 417
Lactaminic acid, 159
Lactase, 297, 373
Lactate dehydrogenase, 293, 410, 412
  See also Cytochrome b_2
D-Lactate dehydrogenase, 396
L-Lactate dehydrogenase, 396
Lacteals, 377, 379
Lactic acid, 51
  stereochemical configuration, 188
Lactose, 165–166
Lambert-Beer law, 34–36
Lanosterol, 571
Lauric acid, 259, 545, 565
Leaf structure, 102–103
Leaves, as experimental material, 325,
  467–469
Lecithin, *see* Phosphatidyl choline
Legumes, hemoglobin in, 458
  nitrogen fixation by, 458
Lehninger, A. L., 437–439
L-Leucine, biosynthesis, 478, 496
  conversion, to carotene, 497
  to mevalonic acid, 496–497
  degradation, 497, 506
  formula, 186
  indispensability, 46¨
  ionization constant, 186
  metabolic use of, 465–467
Leucine equivalent, definition, 222–223
Leucovorin, *see* 5-Formyl-5,6,7,8-tetra-
  hydrofolic acid
Leucoplasts, 91

Liebig, J., controversy with Pasteur, 284–285
  theory of enzyme action, 285
Lignin, methyl groups in, 481, 484
Limit dextrins, 174
Linoleic acid, 259, 278
  conversion to arachidonic acid, 555
Linolenic acid, 259
γ-Linolenic acid, 555
Lipases, 292
Lipid analysis, 274–281
Lipid equilibrium, 539–547
Lipids, classification, 257
  compound, 262–271
  fatty acids from, 259
  half life, 546–547
  lability in tissue, 544–547
  occurrence, 536–539
  serum, 537
  storage, 536
  structural, 536–537
  turnover times, 546–547
Lipmann, F., 435
Lipoic acid, 425
  conversion to 6-*S*-Acetylhydrolipoate, 426
Lipoproteins, 274
  in cell membranes, 90, 94, 95, 537
  composition, 538–539
  isolation from serum, 538
  in plasma, 537–538
Lipotropic factors, 540–541
Lithocholic acid, 377
Liver, role, in fat metabolism, 540–541
  in nitrogen metabolism, 470–471
Longsworth scanning method, 86
Lundsgaard, E., 584
Lymphatic system, 105
Lynen, F., 453–454, 552, 572–574
L-Lysine, 187
  conversion, to cadaverine, 489
    to glutamate, 504
    to pipecolic acid, 504
  degradation, 504
  indispensability, 460, 461
L-Lysine decarboxylase, 489
Lysophosphatides, 267, 557
Lyxose, 124

Malate, conversion to oxaloacetate, 421–422, 423, 430
L-Malate dehydrogenase, 396, 430
Malate synthetase, 604
Maleic acid, reaction with cysteine, 200
Malic acid, 420–423, 430
"Malic" enzyme, 613
Maltase, 129, 293, 297, 373

Maltose, 166–167
Maltose transglucosylase, 607
Mann, F. C., 471
Mannitol, 120
Mannose, 124
Manometric methods, 326–331
Martin, A. J. P., 28, 30, 216
Melibiose, 167
Melizitos, 165
Membrane phenomena, 20–24
Menthol, 574
Mesobilirubin, 355
Mesoporphyrin, 348, 349
Metal carbonyls, 399
Methemoglobin, 350
N^5, N^{10}-Methenyltetrahydrofolic acid, 452, 525
L-Methionine, 186
  activation by ATP, 442, 483
  biosynthesis from homocysteine, 482
  chemistry, 200–201
  conversion, to active one-carbon unit, 451, 507
    to *S*-Adenosylmethionine, 442, 483
    to cysteine, 503
  in creatine synthesis, 486
  indispensability, 461
  sulfonium derivative, 201, 483
  in transmethylation, 480
Methostenol, 273
Methyl donors, table, 483
4α-Methyl-Δ^7-cholesten-3β-ol, 273
Methyl β-D-glucopyranoside, 132, 136
Methyl glucoside, 144
  conversion to methyl (2,3,4-trimethyl)glucoside, 151
  Fischer formulation, 127
  optical rotation, 128
Methyl α-D-mannopyranoside, 132
Methyl tetramethylglucose, 150
Methyl (2,3,4-trimethyl)glucopyranoside, 151
Methylation, of sugars, 149–150, 151, 164, 166, 169, 173, 174
β-Methylcrotonyl CoA, 497
5-Methylcytosine, 240
Methylene blue, 389–391
Methylmalonyl CoA, conversion to succinyl CoA, 554
S-Methylmethionine, 201, 483
N^1-Methylnicotinamide, 480–481
10-Methylstearic acid, 261
Mevalonic acid, 496–497, 552, 572
Mevalonic acid-5-pyrophosphate, 573
Meyer, K., 176, 178
Meyerhof, O., 582–583
Michaelis, L., 301
Michaelis constant, 301, 303

Microliters (μl), definition, 329
Microsomes, 91, 93, 96
    in protein biosynthesis, 519
Million's test, 208
Mitochondria, 91–92
    localization, of oxidizing enzymes in, 331, 431–432
        of oxidative phosphorylation in, 437–439
Monosaccharides, *see* Monoses
Monoses, 117–162
    bacterial synthesis, 155–156
    biosyntheses, 603–606
    chain lengthening, 155
    chain shortening, 155
    chemistry, 136–151
    classification, 122–125
    Fischer synthesis of, 153–154
    methyl ethers, 149–150
    phosphate esters, 145–148
    projection formulas, 120–122, 129, 130–132, 134–136
    ring structure, 125–130
    stereochemistry, 120–136
    tosyl esters, 149
    trityl ethers, 150–151
Moore, S., chromatographic separation of amino acids, 217–219
Mucopolysaccharides, 179–181
    sulfate transfer to, 491
Muscle extracts, 583–584
Muscular contraction, early experiments, 581–583
Mutarotation, 126
Mycolic acid, 261
Myo-inositol, conformation, 161
Myoglobin, structure, 231
    X-ray analysis, 231–232
    X-ray diagram, 224
Myosin, 581
    as ATP-ase, 585
Myristic acid, 259, 278, 545, 565–566

NAD, definition, 393
    See also Diphosphopyridine nucleotide
NADP, definition, 393
    See also Triphosphopyridine nucleotide
α-Naphthol, reaction with arginine, 202
Naphthoquinone reductase, 410
Neuberg, C., 148, 331, 587, 594
Neuberg ester, 148, 586, 589
Neuraminic acid, 159
    in gangliosides, 270
Nicotinamide, 393, 394, 480–481

Nicotinamide coenzymes, mechanism of reduction, 395
    See also Diphosphopyridine nucleotide; Pyridinoproteins; Triphosphopyridine nucleotide
Nicotine, 481
Nicotinic acid, 445
Ninhydrin polychromatic reagent, 217
Ninhydrin reaction, 208
    color formation in, 216–217
Nitrate reductase, 410
Nitrification, 458
Nitrite reductase, 291, 410
Nitrogen equilibrium, 462–463
    in animals, 464–467
    in plants, 467–469
    role of the liver, 470–471
    theories of, 463–464, 467–470
Nitrogen excretion, 462–463, 507–515
Nitrogen fixation, by bacteria, 457–458
    by legumes, 458
Nitrogen sources, 456–459
Nitroprusside test, 200
Nitrous acid, reaction with the amino group, 196
Nucleases, 512
Nucleic acids, 237–253
    biosynthesis, 529–530
    deoxyribofuranose in, 238
    formation of cyclic phosphate esters, 242
    hydrolytic products, 238–241
    isolation, 237–238
    localization, 244
    ribofuranose in, 238
Nucleoprotein particles, 237
Nucleoproteins, 213, 238
Nucleoside diphosphate kinase, 492
Nucleotide structure, 241–242

Ochoa, S., 529, 612–613
Octadecanoic acid, 260
9-Octadecenoic acid, 260
Oleic acid, 259, 277
Oligosaccharides, 162–168
One-carbon unit, 450–453
    metabolic relationships, 451
    in purine biosynthesis, 525, 527
Optical density, 36, 38
L-Ornithine, 203
    biosynthesis, from glutamate, 495
        from arginine, 485
    conversion, to citrulline, 510–511
        to putrescine, 489
    in urea synthesis, 509–511
L-Ornithine decarboxylase, 489
L-Ornithine transcarbamylase, 511

Orotidine-5'-phosphate, in pyrimidine biosynthesis, 522
Osmotic pressure, 21–22
Oxalic acid, 118
Oxaloacetate, conversion, to citrate, 428
  to phosphoenolpyruvate, 506, 603–604
Oxaloacetic acid, 420, 421–422
α-Oxidation, of fatty acids in plants, 553
β-Oxidation, of fatty acids, 547–550
β-Oxidation-condensation, in fatty acid metabolism, 551–552
Oxidative phosphorylation, 436–441
  efficiency of, 439–441
  localization, 437
  mechanism, 437–439
Oxygen, activation, 388
Oxygen transport in blood, 356–357

Palmitic acid, 259, 278, 545, 565–566
  conversion to other fatty acids, 545
  desaturation, 545
Palmitoleic acid, 259, 278, 545
Pancreatic juice, 373
Pantothenic acid, 445
PAPS, see 3'-Phosphoadenosine-5'-phosphosulfate
Parallel chain pleated sheet, 228
Pasteur, controversy with Liebig, 284–285
  theory of enzyme action, 285
Pasteur effect, 580
Pauling, L., 226–227
  α-helix, 229
Pauly test for histidine, 201
Pectic substances, 177
Pentaacetyl glucose, see Glucose pentaacetate
Pentose phosphate pathway, 597–600
Pentoses, biosynthesis from glucose, 603–604
Pentosuria, congenital, 600, 603
Pepsin, 297, 371–372, 380–381
  amino acid composition, 219
Pepsinogen, 372
  activation, 305, 371
Peptide bonds, 189
  synthesis of, 203–205
Peptide chain, fully extended, 225–226
Peptones, 214
Perfusion, 324
Periodic acid (HIO₄), 142–144
  oxidation, of glucosides, 143–144
  of serine, 199
  of threonine, 199
Peroxidases, 416–417
Pfeffer, W., 21

pH, definition, 46
  measurement of, 57–68
pH optima of enzymes, 297
pH5 enzymes of protein biosynthesis, 518
Phenaceturic acid, 493
Phenanthrene, 271
Phenol reagent, 201
Phenolase, 417
Phenyl group, as metabolic label, 323, 547–548
L-Phenylalanine, 186
  biosynthesis, 497–499
  conversion to tyrosine, 338, 499
  degradation, 506–507
  indispensability, 461
γ-Phenylbutyric acid, excretion of, 548
Phenylisothiocyanate, 198, 221
Phenylketonuria, 322
Phenyllactate, 322
Phenylpyruvate, 322
Phenylthiohydantoin, 198, 221
δ-Phenylvaleric acid, excretion of, 548
Phloem, 101
Phloretin, 152
Phlorizin, 152
Phosgene, 204
Phosphate group, migration, 148, 242
  symbols for, 148
Phosphate Ringer solution, 326
Phosphatidic acid, 263, 567
Phosphatidyl choline, 264
  biosynthesis, 567–569
  degradation, 556–558
Phosphatidyl ethanolamine, 264
  biosynthesis, 567–569
  degradation, 556–558
Phosphatidyl inositol, 265
  biosynthesis, 567–569
Phosphatidyl serine, 264–265
3'-Phosphoadenosine-5'-phosphosulfate (PAPS), 490, 563
  biosynthesis, 491
  use in sulfate transfer, 490–491
Phosphocreatine, see Creatine phosphate
Phosphoenolpyruvate, 435
  absorbance, 288
  conversion to pyruvate, 592
  in shikimic acid synthesis, 498
  transfer of phosphate to ADP, 592
Phosphofructokinase, 589
Phosphoglucoisomerase, 599
  See also Phosphohexomutase
Phosphoglucomutase, 588
6-Phosphogluconate, conversion to ribulose-5-phosphate, 598–599
Phosphogluconate dehydrogenase, 599

3-Phosphoglyceraldehyde, conversion to 1,3-Diphosphoglycerate, 590–591
Phosphoglyceraldehyde dehydrogenase, 396
Phosphoglycerate kinase, 591
2-Phosphoglyceric acid, 288
conversion to phosphoenolpyruvate, 591
3-Phosphoglyceric acid, in glycolysis, 586, 590–591
in photosynthesis, 614–615
L-α-Phosphoglycerol, 294
Phosphoglycerol dehydrogenase, 396
Phosphoglyceromutase, 591
Phosphohexomutase, 589
Phosphoinositides, 265–267
from brain, 266
Phosphokinase, 293
Phospholipases, 557–558
Phospholipids, biosynthesis, 566–569
degradation, 556–558
Phosphoproteins, 213
5-Phosphoribosyl-1-pyrophosphate (PRPP), in histidine biosynthesis, 500
in purine biosynthesis, 524
in pyrimidine biosynthesis, 522
in tryptophan biosynthesis, 501
Phosphoribosyladenylic acid, in histidine biosynthesis, 500, 528
in purine biosynthesis, 528
5-Phosphoribosylamine (PRA), 524
Phosphoric acid, 50–51
titration curve, 50, 360
Phosphorolysis, of glycogen, 588
of nucleosides, 513
Phosphorylases, in biosynthesis, 607–608
in degradation, 513, 588
Phosphoserine, 199
Phosphotriose isomerase, 590
Phosphotungstate reduction, 200, 201
Photophosphorylation, cyclic, 617–620
noncyclic, 617–620
Photosynthesis, 609–620
Photosynthetic phosphorylation, 616–620
Physiological saline solutions, 326
Phytic acid, 161
Phytoglycolipid, 267
Pigments, bile, *see* Bile pigments
Pigments, respiratory, *see* Respiratory pigments
Pipecolic acid, 504
Plant structures, 101–103
Plants, digestion in, 369–370
transport, of photosynthetic products, 367–368
of water, 366–367

Plasma, composition, 341–345
lipids in, 537
proteins in, 343
Plasmalogens, 267–268
Plasmolysis, 22
Plastids, 91
Polypeptides, hydrolysis of, 206
synthesis of, 203–205
Polysaccharides, 168–181
immune bacterial, 181
molecular weights of, 171–172
periodate oxidation, 169, 170
structure of, 168–171
Pope and Stevens method for amino acid estimation, 195
Porphin, 348
Porphobilinogen, in heme biosynthesis, 516–517
Porphyrin enzymes, 399–407, 416–417
Porphyrins, nomenclature, 347–351
PRA, *see* 5-Phosphoribosylamine
Pregnane, 559, 560
Δ⁵-Pregnenolone, 562
Prephenic acid, biosynthesis, 498
conversion, to phenylalanine, 499
to tyrosine, 499
Primary alcohol groups, identification, 149
Procarboxypeptidase, 305, 373
Proenzymes, activation, 304–305
Progesterone, 560, 561
Projection formulas, 120–122, 129, 130–132, 134–136
Prolamines, 213
Proline, 186, 198
biosynthesis from glutamate, 495
in collagen synthesis, 495
conversion to hydroxyproline, 495
ninhydrin color, 217
oxidation, 495
Propionic acid, conversion, to methylmalonyl CoA, 553–554
to propionyl CoA, 553
to succinate, 506, 554
Propionyl CoA, reaction with methylmalonyl CoA, 554
Prorennin, 371
Protamines, 213, 237
Protein precipitants, 185, 188
Protein structure, 219–232
Proteinases, dual specificity, 294
in microorganisms, 459
Proteins, 207–233
absorption of, 381–383
amino acid sequence in, 219–223
as antigens, 212
antiparallel chain structure, 225, 227

Proteins (*Continued*)
  biosynthesis, 517–520
  classification, 212–214
  color tests, 207–208
  degradation by carboxypeptidase, 222
  denatured, 214, 232–233
  digestion of, 379–381
  disulfide bonds in, 222–223
  electrophoresis of, 210–211
  elementary composition, 185
  fibrous, 225–229
  formol titration, 295
  globular, *see* Globular proteins
  half life in liver, 467
  α-helix in, 229–230
  hydrogen bonds in, 225, 228, 229, 230
  isoelectric points, 209
  isolation, 208–209
  parallel chain structure, 228
  quantitative analysis, 214–219
  reaction with 1-fluoro-2,4-dinitroben-
    zene, 219–220
  reaction with phenylisothiocyanate, 221
  shapes, 72
  specificity, 185
Proteoses, 214
Protoporphyrin, 348, 349
PRPP, *see* 5-Phosphoribosyl-1-pyrophos-
    phate
Purdie, T., 130, 149
Purine, 239
Purine bases, 239, 240
  absorbances, 241
  conversion to uric acid, 513–514
Purine ring, precursors, 523
Purines, biosynthesis, 523–529
Putrescine, from L-ornithine, 489
Pyran, 130
Pyranose, 131
Pyranose ring, conformation, 134–136
Pyranoside, 131
Pyridinoproteins, 391–399
Pyridoxal, 479
Pyridoxal phosphate, absorption spec-
    trum, 39
  coenzyme, of decarboxylases, 487
    of transaminases, 479–480
  formula, 480
Pyridoxamine, 479
Pyridoxamine phosphate, 480
  absorption spectrum, 39
  coenzyme of transaminases, 479–480
Pyridoxine, 445, 479
Pyrimidine, 239
Pyrimidine bases, 239, 240
  absorbances, 241
  biosynthesis, 521–523

Pyrimidine bases (*Continued*)
  degradation, 513
Pyrrole, 346
Pyruvate, conversion, to acetaldehyde,
    594
  to acetyl CoA, 449
  to α-ketoisovalerate, 496
  to lactate, 592
  oxidation, 418–431
  reaction with thiamine pyrophosphate,
    426
Pyruvic acid, 387, 420, 422
Pythocholic acid, 377

Q enzyme, 607

R_f, definition, 29
Radioautograph, 338
Raffinose, 165
Ratner, S., 510
Reduction potentials, at physiological pH,
    66–68
  standard, 62
Reichert-Meissl number, 276
Reinecke salt, 198
Rennin, 371
Resacetophenone glucuronide, 492
Residue symbols for amino acids, 186–
    187, 189, 219
Respiration, inhibition by carbon monox-
    ide, 399–400
Respiratory enzyme, 388, 399–400, 407
    See also Cytochrome a_3; Cyto-
      chrome oxidase
Respiratory organs, 106
Respiratory pathway, in animals, 412–
    413
  in plants, 413–414
  relation to oxidative phosphorylation,
    438–440
Respiratory pigments, 104, 363–365
Respiratory quotient, 543–544
Retrogradation of starch, 175
Rhamnose, 157
Rhodanilic acid, 198
Ribitol, 161
Riboflavin, 445
Riboflavin monophosphate, *see* Flavin
    mononucleotide
Ribofuranose, 238
Ribonic acid, 137
Ribonuclease, catalytic action, 242, 512
  structure, 221–224
Ribose, 124
Ribose nucleic acids, hydrolytic products,
    238
    localization of, 244

Ribose nucleic acids (*Continued*)
  molecular weights, 249
  in protein biosynthesis, 518–519
  ribosomal, relation to DNA, 519
  soluble, *see* Soluble RNA
  structure, 249
  synthetic, 529
Ribose-1-phosphate, 513
Ribose-5-phosphate, in biosynthesis of his-
    tidine, 500
  in photosynthesis, 614–616
Ribosomes, 96, 519
D-Ribulose, 125
Ribulose-5-phosphate, conversion, to
    xylulose-5-phosphate, 598–599
  to ribose-5-phosphate, 598–599
Ribulose phosphates, in photosynthesis,
    615–616
Ricinine, 481
Ricinoleic acid, 259
Ringer, S., 324
Ringer solutions, modified, 326
Rittenberg, D., 353, 545
RNA, *see* Ribose nucleic acid
Robison, R., 148
Robison ester, 148, 586, 589
Rosanoff classification of monoses, 123–
    124
Rose, W. S., 460
Ruhemann's purple, 216

s, sedimentation coefficient, definition, 83
S, svedberg unit, definition, 83
S_f°, standardized flotation rate, definition,
  538
SAICAR, *see* Succino-5-amino-4-imida-
    zolecarboxamide ribotide
Sakaguchi test for arginine, 202
Saliva, 370
Sanger, F., 219–221
Saponification number, 275–276
Sarcosine, 485
Schiff's base, 479, 487
Schoenheimer, R., 465–469, 545
Scleroproteins, 213
Sedimentation coefficient, 83
Sedoheptulose-7-phosphate, in pentose
    phosphate pathway, 598–599
  in photosynthesis, 614–616
  ring structure, 616
Selachyl alcohol, 262
L-Serine, 186
  conversion, to active hydroxy methyl,
    494
    to active one-carbon unit, 451, 507
    to cysteine, 503
    to ethanolamine, 494

L-Serine (*Continued*)
  conversion (*Continued*)
    to glycine, 337, 494
    to pyruvate, 494–495
  deamination of, 494–495
  periodic acid oxidation, 199
Serine dehydrase, 494
Shemin, D., 353, 516
Shikimic acid, 497
  biosynthesis from glucose, 498
Shikimic acid-5-phosphate, conversion, to
    anthranilic acid, 501
    to indolyl-3-glycerol phosphate, 501
    to prephenic acid, 498
Sialic acid, 159
  in gangliosides, 270
Skatole, 490
Sols, hydrophilic, 74
  hydrophobic, 73
Soluble RNA, 249
  in glutathione biosynthesis, 519–520
  in protein biosynthesis, 518–519
  terminal nucleotides in, 519
Sorbitol, 137
Sorbose, 140, 156
Sørensen, S. P. L., 46, 197
Specific heats, 16
Specific rotation, 126
Spectrum, electromagnetic, 33
Sphingomyelins, 269
Sphingosine, 269, 270
Squalene, biosynthesis, 572–574
  conversion to cholesterol, 570–571
SRNA, *see* Soluble RNA
Stachyose, 165
Starch, 174–177
  retrogradation of, 175
Stearic acid, 259, 278, 545, 566
  conversion to oleyl CoA, 556
Stein, W. H., chromatographic separation
    of amino acids, 217–219
Stercobilin, 355
Stercobilinogen, 355
Steroid hormones, 558–563
  biosynthetic paths, 562
  excretion, 561–563
Steroid sulfatase, 563
Steroids, 271–274, 558–564, 569–574
  biosynthesis, 569–574
  cis-trans isomerism, 273
  excretion, 561–564
  metabolism, 558–564
  nomenclature, 273, 559–560
  separation by gas chromatography, 31
  stereochemistry, 272–273
  sulfate transfer to, 491, 563
Streptomycin, 158

Substrate, 284
Substrate level phosphorylation, 551–552, 586, 591–592
Succinate, 420–421, 423
in citric acid cycle, 429–430
Succinate dehydrogenase, 410, 411, 430
Succino-5-amino-4-imidazolecarboxamide ribotide (SAICAR), 527
Succinyl CoA, conversion to succinate, 430
formation from acetoacetyl CoA, 551
in heme biosynthesis, 515–517
reaction with guanosine diphosphate, 440
Succinyl CoA deacylase, 430
Succinyl CoA synthetase, 551
6-*S*-Succinyldihydrolipoate, 424
in photosynthesis, 614–616
Sucrase, 293, 373
Sucrose, 163–164
inversion of, 164
periodate oxidation, 164–165
Sucrose transfructosylase, 607
Sucrose transglucosylase, 607
Sulfanilamide, acetylation, 449
Sulfate activation, 487–491
Sulfhydryl group, in enzymes, 234, 311, 314, 404, 590
nitroprusside test for, 200
Sulfokinase, 491
Sulfone of methionine, 201
Sulfoxide of methionine, 201
Sumner, J. B., 289
Surface tension, 24–25
Svedberg, T., 82
Svedberg unit, 83
Symbiosis, in alder, 458
in digestion, 376
in nitrogen fixation, 458
Szent-Györgyi, A., 159
dicarboxylic acid cycle of, 422–423

Talose, 124
Tanret, C., 127
Tariric acid, 259
meso-Tartaric acid, 120
Taurine, 374
biosynthesis, 376, 488, 503
Taurocholic acid, 374, 376
Testosterone, 561, 562
Tetraacetylglucopyranosyl bromide, 145
Tetrahydropteroylglutamic acid, 494
Tetratosylglucopyranosyl chloride, 149
Theobromine, 240
Theophylline, 240
Theorell, H., 394, 403, 404
Thiamine hydrochloride, 445

Thiamine pyrophosphate, 425, 429
in alcoholic fermentation, 594
reaction with α-ketoglutarate, 429
reaction with pyruvate, 426
Thiolkinase, 448
Thioltransacylase, 429
L-Threonine, 186
conversion, to acetaldehyde, 494
to glycine, 494
to α-ketobutyrate, 494–495
deamination of, 494–495
indispensability, 461
periodic acid oxidation, 199
Threonine dehydrase, 494
Threose, 124
Thudicum, J. L. W., 262
Thunberg technique, 389–392
Thymine, 239, 240
Tiselius, A., 85
Tissue slice technique, 325–331
Tosyl esters, 149
TPN, *see* Triphosphopyridine nucleotide
Trans-enediol, 140
Transacetylase, 551
Transacylase, 550
Transaldolases, 597, 599
Transamination, 447–480
coenzyme for, 479–480
mechanism of reaction, 479–480
Transglycosylation, 606–607
in synthesis of branched poly-saccharides, 608
Transketolases, 597, 599, 616
Transmethylation, 480–484
Transmittance, 36
Transpiration, 101
Trehalose, biosynthesis, 608
Tricarboxylic acid cycle, *see* Citric acid cycle
Triglycerides, analysis, 277–279
biosynthesis, 566–567
replacement by waxes, 260
structure, 257–260
Triketohydrindene hydrate, *see* Ninhydrin
Triose phosphate isomerase, in glycolysis, 590
in photosynthesis, 616
Triphenylmethyl ethers, 150–151
Triphosphopyridine nucleotide, absorption spectra, 394
chemistry, 393–394
mechanism of reduction, 394–395
photosynthetic reduction, 613, 616–620
reduction potential, 398, 413
stereospecificity of reduction, 397
Tris, *see* Tris(hydroxymethyl)amino-methane

Tris(hydroxymethyl)aminomethane, 51
Trypsin, 297, 375, 380–381
  active site in, 313
Trypsinogen, activation, 313, 373
Typtamine, 502
L-Tryptophan, 186
  biosynthesis, 497, 501–502
  color test for, 198–199
  conversion, to indolyl-3-acetic acid, 502
    to nicotinic acid, 502
  indispensability, 460, 461
Tryptophan synthetase, 501–502
Tyramine, formation from L-tyrosine, 489
L-Tyrosine, 187
  bioysnthesis, 497–499
  conversion to tyramine, 489
  Folin and Looney test for, 201
L-Tyrosine decarboxylase, 489

UDP glucoside dehydrogenase, 492
UDP glucoside pyrophosphorylase, 492
UDPG, *see* Uridine-5'-diphosphate glucoside
Ultracentrifuge, 82
  in protein isolation, 209
Uracil, 239, 240
Urea, 235
  biosynthesis, 470–471, 509–512
Urease, 297, 284
  crystallization, 289
Ureidosuccinate, *see* Carbamylaspartate
Ureotelic, 509
Urey, H. C., 332
Uric acid, 239, 240
  conversion to allantoic acid, 513
  excretion, 508, 513–514
Uricotelic, 509
Uridine, 241
Uridine diphosphate glucose, *see* Uridine-5'-diphosphate glucoside
Uridine-5'-diphosphate glucoside, biosynthesis, 492, 600–601
  conversion to glucuronide, 492
  in glucuronic acid pathway, 600–601
  in glycogen biosynthesis, 609
  in trehalose biosynthesis, 608
Uridine-5'-diphosphate glucuronide, 601
  glucuronate transfer by, 492
Uridine-5'-triphosphate, in carbohydrate synthesis, 608–609
  conversion to cytidine triphosphate, 522
Uridylic acid, 241, 522
  conversion to other nucleotides, 522–523

Urobilin, 355
Urobilinogen IX, 355
Uronic acids, 139
Uroporphyrin I, 349, 350
Uroporphyrinogen I, 517

L-Valine, 186
  biosynthesis, 496
  conversion to isobutylamine, 489
  degradation, 506–507
  indispensability, 461
L-Valine decarboxylase, 489
van Eckenstein, A., 127
Van Slyke, D. D., 196
Van Slyke reaction, 196
Vanillin, 484
van't Hoff, H., 22
Verbascose, 165
Vickery, H. B., 467
Vigneaud, V. du, 482
Vinylglycine, 503
Virus nucleoproteins, 251–253
Vitamin A₁, 575
Vitamin B₁, 445
Vitamin B₂, 408, 445
Vitamin B₆, 445, 479
Vitamin B₁₂, 447
  in isomerization of methylmalonyl CoA, 554
Vitamin K₁, 415
  in photosynthesis, 617–618

Waldschmidt-Leitz, E., 286
Warburg, O., 325, 388, 392, 612
Warburg apparatus, 326–329
Water, biosynthesis in oxidation, 387–418
  heavy, *see* Heavy water
  hydrogen bonds in, 14
  physical properties, 14–17
  structure, 15
Water transport in plants, 366–367
Watson and Crick, DNA structure, 246
Wave number, 32
Wavelength, 32
Waxes, 260–261
  as storage lipids, 260
Wieland, H., 388
Willstätter, R., 346

X-ray analysis, of polysaccharides, 171
  of proteins, 223–229, 231–232
X-ray diagram of myoglobin, 224
Xanthine, 239, 240
Xanthine oxidase, 410, 514
  dual specificity, 294

Xanthoproteic acid test, 208
Xylem, 101
Xylitol, 602
Xylose, 124
D-Xylulose, 602
L-Xylulose, 125, 602

D-Xylulose-5-phosphate, 602
  in photosynthesis, 614–616

Young, W. J., 147

Zymogen activation, 304